Study Guide

for use with

NELSON

BIOLOGY
EXPLORING THE DIVERSITY OF LIFE

SECOND CANADIAN EDITION

RUSSELL   HERTZ   MCMILLAN
FENTON   ADDY   MAXWELL   HAFFIE   MILSOM

Prepared by WENDY KEENLEYSIDE
UNIVERSITY OF GUELPH

JULIE SMIT
UNIVERSITY OF WINDSOR

COLIN MONTPETIT
UNIVERSITY OF OTTAWA

NELSON / EDUCATION

NELSON / EDUCATION

Study Guide for use with Biology: Exploring the Diversity of Life, Second Canadian Edition

Peter J. Russell, Paul E. Hertz, Beverly McMillan, Brock Fenton, Heather Addy, Denis Maxwell, Tom Haffie, and Bill Milsom

Study Guide prepared by Wendy Keenleyside, Julie Smit, and Colin Montpetit

Vice President, Editorial Higher Education:
Anne Williams

Publisher:
Paul Fam

Executive Marketing Manager:
Sean Chamberland

Senior Developmental Editor:
Mark Grzeskowiak

Content Production Manager:
Christine Gilbert

Proofreader:
Wendy Yano

Production Coordinator:
Ferial Suleman

Design Director:
Ken Phipps

Managing Designer:
Franca Amore

Cover Design:
Jennifer Stimson

Cover Image:
Sea slug: Dr. Mary Tyler & Dr. Mary Rumpho, University of Maine, (2008). "Horizontal gene transfer of the algal nuclear gene psbO to the photosynthetic sea slug Elysia chlorotica," *PNAS*, 105 (46), 17868, Copyright 2008 National Academy of Sciences, U.S.A. Generic DNA code: kentoh/Shutterstock

Printer:
RR Donnelley

Contents

Using This Study Guide

Welcome to the Study Guide for use with *Biology: Exploring the Diversity of Life*, Second Canadian Edition. This study resource has been dramatically adapted to meet the needs of Introductory Biology students to better prepare you for the content of your course and to help you make connections to the textbook's content and beyond. The Study Guide is organized into two distinct parts: study resources by chapter, and an answers section that will allow you to check your work.

Study Resources by Chapter

Each chapter of this section corresponds to the chapter in your textbook. Within these chapters you will find the following:

- *Topic Map:* Each chapter contains one of these maps to provide you with a visual understanding of how the content within the chapter fits together.

- *Learning Outcomes and Study Strategies:* The learning outcomes address what you should know having completed your review of the chapter, while the study strategies are designed to provide insight into how best to approach the chapter content and study effectively.

- *Self-Test Questions:* These multiple-choice questions toward the end of the chapter are designed to test you on the content of the entire chapter. Answers to these questions are provided within the Answers section at the end of the Study Guide.

- *Integrating and Applying Key Concepts:* These represent "big-picture" or "real-life" applications of the concepts presented in the chapter. Some guidance as to how to approach these concepts is provided within the Answers section.

Within the body of these chapters you will find various exercises designed to help familiarize yourself with the material such as: Section Review (fill-in-the-blank style questions), Labelling, True/False Questions, Matching, Complete the Table, Short Answer Questions, and Building Vocabulary. The answers to all questions within these chapters are available in the Answers section at the back of the Study Guide.

Answer Section

At the very end of the Study Guide the answers to the questions noted above are contained and are organized as they appear within the chapter.

For more study aids and materials related to your text visit www.biologyedl2e.nelson.com. Here you will find flashcards, weblinks, and crosswords.

 CourseMate

The more you study, the better the results. Make the most of your study time by accessing everything you need to succeed in one place. Your Biology CourseMate includes the following components:

- An interactive eBook with highlighting, note taking, and an interactive glossary
- Interactive learning tools, including:
  - Quizzes
  - Design an Experiment, Interpret the Data, and Apply Evolutionary Concepts exercises
  - Flashcards
  - Videos
  - BioExperience 3D Animations

The CourseMate for *Biology: Exploring the Diversity of Life*, Second Canadian Edition, was prepared by Dora Cavallo-Medved, University of Windsor and Reehan Mirza, Nipissing University.

aplia™

Founded in 2000 by economist and Stanford Professor Paul Romer, Aplia™ is an educational technology company dedicated to improving learning by increasing student effort and engagement. Currently, Aplia™ products have been used by more than 650 000 students at over 750 institutions. For students, Aplia™ offers a way to stay on top of coursework with regularly scheduled homework assignments. Interactive tools and additional content are provided to further increase engagement and understanding.

1 Light and Life

TOPIC MAP

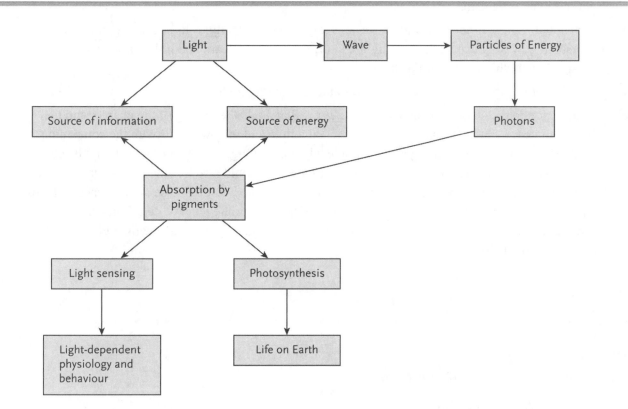

LEARNING OUTCOMES AND STUDY STRATEGIES

By the end of this chapter, you should be able to

- Describe the physical nature of light and the relationship between wavelength and energy, and identify the wavelength range of the visible region of the spectrum, including which colours are at the two ends and which of these are closer to the ultraviolet and infrared regions of the spectrum

- Describe the relationship between photosynthesis and the growth of various life forms: plants as well as life forms that perform cellular respiration

- Describe the various non-photosynthetic light-absorbing pigments—those used for information. Be aware of the various levels of complexity of light-sensing units: the more basic the unit, the more basic the information and response.

- Describe the various roles light sensing plays in the biology of Earth

Study strategies for this chapter:

- Remember that the goal of this chapter is to understand the nature of light and to appreciate how it impacts all life on Earth—i.e., the big picture. You should first focus on the nature of light and the relationship between wavelength and energy.

- Make sure you understand how light interacts with matter. What happens when a photon is absorbed or when light of a particular wavelength is transmitted? These processes underlie all of the effects of light on living organisms.

- Learn about retinal, rhodopsin, and the various levels of complexity of light-sensing units. Once you understand how organisms can *sense* light/colour, then you can learn about the various roles light sensing plays in the biology of Earth.

- Don't forget to carefully examine the figures and read the figure legends.

- Pay attention to the chapter breakdown in the Study Plan at the beginning of the chapter and the questions in each Study Break. Take one section at a time and then work through the companion section in the study guide. After you've completed going through the chapter you should be able to go back and expand on the points within the Study Plan. You should also be able to answer the various questions in the chapter and the Self-Test questions in the study guide. These are designed to focus your attention on the principles and help you gauge the appropriate level of detail. In general, the answers to these questions should not be memorized but come to you because you understand the underlying principles.

INTERACTIVE EXERCISES

Why It Matters [pp. 1–2]
1.1 The Physical Nature of Light [pp. 2–4]

Section Review (Fill-in-the-Blanks)

The sun's energy is given off as (1) _____ _____, which can be described as

a(n) (2) _____ of energy-containing particles called (3) _____. The (4) _____

spectrum contains, at its two extremes, gamma rays and radio waves. Within the spectrum, shorter

wavelengths have (5) _____ energy, and visible light is the narrow portion that humans can

(6) _____.When light hits matter, the particles within that light may be (7) _____ by the

matter, (8) _____ through the matter, or (9) _____ by the matter. It is the latter process

that underlies the ability of life forms to use light as a source of (10) _____ or (11) _____

about the environment. The molecules responsible for these abilities are collectively called

(12) _____.

Sequence

13. Arrange the following components of the electromagnetic spectrum in the correct sequence, from short wavelength to long wavelength: ____ ____ ____ ____

   A.   infrared

   B.   blue

   C.   UV

   D.   red

Labelling

14. Label the following diagram of light absorption by an excitable electron of a pigment molecule.

   A.   _____

   B.   _____

   C.   _____

   D.   _____

   E.   _____

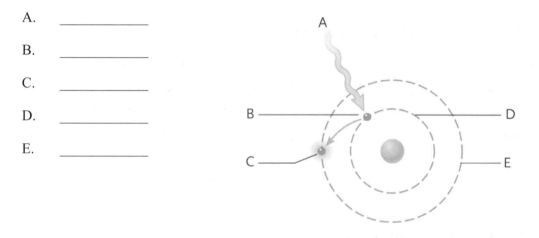

True/False

Mark if the statement is true (T) or false (F). If the statement is false, justify your answer in the lines below each statement.

15. _____ The energy of light is directly proportional to its wavelength.

   _____

   _____

16. _____ Sunlight results from the fusion of helium nuclei.

   _____

   _____

17. _____ Plants appear green because of the inability of chlorophyll to absorb the green region of the visible spectrum.

   _____

   _____

18. _____ The differences between the ground state and excited states of chlorophyll's light-absorbing electrons equal the energy of the red and green wavelengths.

_____

_____

19. _____ Pigments possess a conjugated system of bonds and the electrons within these bonds are held firmly in place.

_____

_____

Matching

Match each of the following terms with its correct definition or descriptor.

20. ____ Retinal

21. ____ Absorption

22. ____ Pigment

23. ____ Chlorophyll

A. Mechanism of light capture by molecules

B. Molecules possessing alternating double and single carbon-carbon bonds

C. Absorbs light of blue and red wavelengths for photosynthesis

D. Pigment involved in vision

1.2 Light as a Source of Energy [pp. 4–6]
1.3 Light as a Source of Information [pp. 6–10]

Section Review (Fill-in-the-Blanks)

The energy from sunlight enters the biosphere through the process of (24) _____. Upon absorption of

light energy by pigments such as (25) _____, electron transport results in the synthesis of energy-rich

molecules such as ATP and (26) _____. These molecules provide the energy for synthesizing

(27) _____ from CO_2 and water. Completing the process, cellular (28) _____ releases the

energy in these photosynthetic products, producing (29) _____ which provides the energy for cellular

metabolism and growth. In contrast to classical photosynthetic organisms, the (30) _____ use a light-

dependent proton pump called (31) _____ to generate a proton gradient across the plasma membrane.

The energy from this gradient can be harnessed to make (32) _____. In light-sensing organisms,

(33) _____ is the most common photoreceptor. Absorption of light energy by the photoreceptor

pigment (34) _____ ultimately triggers signalling events such as changes in intracellular

(35) _____ concentrations. The alga *C. reinhardtii* senses light through its (36) _____

_____, which controls a(n) (37) _____ response. (38) _____ in the plant cell cytosol triggers the developmental process of (39) _____ when seedlings are exposed to light. The image-forming eyes include the (40) _____ eyes of insects and crustaceans and the (41) _____-_____ eyes of most vertebrates.

Matching

Match each of the following terms with its correct definition or descriptor.

42. ____	Bacteriorhodopsin	A.	Pigment molecule in rhodopsin
43. ____	Phototaxis	B.	Light-sensing unit in compound eyes
44. ____	Photomorphogenesis	C.	Swimming in a light-dependent direction
45. ____	Photoreceptor	D.	Light-activated proton pump
46. ____	Phytochrome	E.	Simple eye containing around 100 photo-receptor cells lining a cup or pit
47. ____	Retinal	F.	Back of single-lens eye containing photoreceptors
48. ____	Rhodopsin	G.	Light-sensing system
49. ____	Retina	H.	Protein associated with retinal in rhodopsin
50. ____	Ommatidium	I.	Most common photoreceptor
51. ____	Ocellus	J.	Photoreceptor in the cytosol of all plants
52. ____	Opsin	K.	Development of seedlings triggered by exposure to light

Complete the Table

53. Complete the following table.

Type of Eye	Type of Organism	Characteristic Property
Ocellus	Planaria	A.
B.	Some invertebrates/most vertebrates	Image-forming "camera" eye contains cornea, lens, and retina
Compound	C.	Contains hundreds to thousands of visual units

Short Answer

Provide an explanation of the following:

54. How do eyes differ from eyespots?

_____

_____

55. How do eyespots differ from the ocelli of planaria?

_____

_____

56. What is the advantage of a compound eye over a single-lens eye?

_____

_____

57. What are the two initial effects of light absorption by retinal?

_____

_____

True/False

Mark if the statement is true (T) or false (F). If the statement is false, justify your answer in the lines below each statement.

58. _____ The halobacteria use light energy for photosynthesis.

_____

_____

59. _____ Charles Darwin explained the rapid evolution of the human eye by proposing gradual improvements that provided a strong selective advantage.

_____

_____

1.4 The Uniqueness of Light [pp. 10–12]
1.5 Light Can Damage Biological Molecules [pp. 12–14]

Section Review (Fill-in-the-Blanks)

One reason that life on Earth has evolved to use the (60) _____ portion of the electromagnetic

spectrum is that most of the wavelengths outside this range are (61) _____ by molecules in Earth's atmosphere or by the (62) _____ on Earth's surface. In addition, radiation with wavelengths

(63) _____ than the visible region possesses enough energy to break the chemical bonds of

molecules, while wavelengths that are (64) _____ do not have enough energy to (65) _____

electrons. While critical to life, visible light can also cause (66) _____. To compensate for this,

photosynthetic organisms have highly efficient repair mechanisms for their (67) _____. In animals,

absorption of UV light energy damages DNA, creating (68) _____ between neighbouring

(69) _____; these may ultimately lead to (70) _____ and cancer. (71) _____ is a

protective pigment in the skin of humans that absorbs these wavelengths and dissipates the energy as

(72) _____.

True/False

Mark if the statement is true (T) or false (F). If the statement is false, justify your answer in the lines below each statement.

73. _____ Wavelengths shorter than 400 nm do not contain enough energy to excite pigment electrons.

_____

_____

74. _____ The ozone layer of Earth's atmosphere absorbs the majority of UV radiation from the sun.

_____

_____

75. _____ Dark-skinned people living in northern climates may suffer vitamin D deficiencies.

_____

_____

1.6 Using Light to Tell Time [pp. 14–16]

Section Review (Fill-in-the-Blanks)

The Earth takes (76) _____ _____ to rotate around its axis and (77) _____ to circle

around the sun. All life has evolved to respond to the resulting fluctuations in (78) _____ and

temperature on Earth's surface. Phenomena that exhibit a daily or (79) _____ cycle but do not require

daily changes in light are said to display a (80) _____ rhythm. This rhythm is controlled by the so-called (81) _____ clock. The physical basis for this phenomenon is a small set of

(82) _____ genes and proteins that are self-regulating and (83) _____ in abundance and

activity over a 24-hour period. Because these genes are self-regulating, the clock is (84) _____-

_____. This is the explanation for (85) _____ _____, where the internal clock is

out of (86) _____ with the external light environment. In some organisms, the clock keeps track of

the changing seasons, responding to the changes in day length or (87) _____ and causing seasonal

behaviours such as the (88) _____ of angiosperm plants in the spring and leaf-drop of trees in the

fall.

Complete the Table

89. Complete the following table.

Type of Organism	Type of Circadian Behaviour	Selective Advantage of Behaviour
Insects	Emergence from pupal case at dawn	A.
Many organisms	Synthesis of proteins for DNA replication at dusk	B.
C.	Fur colour changes between brown and white	Season-appropriate camouflage

True/False

Mark if the statement is true (T) or false (F). If the statement is false, justify your answer in the lines below each statement.

90. _____ Organisms from all phyla display circadian rhythm.

_____

_____

91. _____ The pineal gland releases melatonin at night.

_____

_____

92. _____ Hibernation and migration in animals and dormancy in plants are triggered by a desire to avoid cold temperatures.

_____

_____

1.7 Role of Light in Behaviour and Ecology [pp. 17–20]

Section Review (Fill-in-the-Blanks)

In animals, colour may be used to attract (93) _____ or to provide camouflage from potential

(94) _____. Research on the biochemistry of the carotenoid pigments in the King penguin's

(95) _____ shows the pigments are obtained from the diet and first circulate in the blood where they

protect against reactive (96) _____ species. For these animals then, the degree of colour provides

information on an individual's age, (97) _____, and ability to raise chicks. In flowers, the colours,

shapes, and smells have (98) _____ with their animal pollinators. Differently coloured flowers reflect

the different (99) _____ systems of the pollinators. In contrast to these natural roles of light in

physiology and behaviour, artificial light can give rise to the phenomenon of ecological (100) _____

_____, which can have devastating impacts on (101) _____ animals such as newly hatched

sea turtles.

Short Answer

102. What aspect(s) of a flowering shrubs would attract hummingbirds to certain species and bees to others?

_____

_____

103. Explain how, in the past, natural selection selected for the rare dark-coloured variants of the peppered moth.

_____

_____

1.8 Life in the Dark [pp. 20–21]
1.9 Organisms Making Their Own Light: Bioluminescence [pp. 21–23]

Section Review (Fill-in-the-Blanks)

The giant squid and some other animals have evolved extremely large eyes that collect more

(104) _____ and allow them to see in the dark. In contrast, the blind (105) _____

_____ lives underground, has extremely small tissue-covered eyes but functional

(106) _____. This probably allows for the maintenance of the animal's (107) _____

_____, an idea supported by the animal's functional suprachiasmatic nucleus. The phenomenon of

(108) _____ is based on the ability of certain life forms to produce light. The reaction is initiated by

ATP which promotes a(n) (109) _____ of a substrate molecule from ground state to a(n)

(110) _____ state. Its potential energy is released as a(n) (111) _____ of light when it falls

back down to ground state. This light is used for a variety of purposes; some marine bacteria use it to

communicate in a phenomenon called (112) _____-sensing. Dinoflagellates use it as a(n)

(113) _____ mechanism, illuminating nearby fish to their own (114) _____.

True/False

Mark if the statement is true (T) or false (F). If the statement is false, justify your answer in the lines below each statement.

115. _____ Many of the animals living in the ocean's depths are unable to see.

_____

_____

116. _____ Bioluminescence in the night sea is a newly discovered phenomenon.

_____

_____

SELF-TEST

1. Which statement is NOT true of light with a wavelength of 400 nm? [p. 3]
   a. Its energy is higher than light of 700 nm wavelength.
   b. It is near the blue region of the spectrum.
   c. It is closer to the infrared region than the UV region of the spectrum.
   d. It contains photons of energy.

2. Which statement is NOT true of pigments? [p. 4]
   a. They possess alternating single and double bonds.
   b. Their colour corresponds to the wavelength(s) of absorbed light.
   c. They possess delocalized electrons that absorb light energy and move to an excited state.
   d. They are characterized by a conjugated system.

3. What determines whether a photon of light will be absorbed by a molecule? [p. 4]
   a. a match between photon energy and the energy difference between ground and excited states
   b. whether the molecule has a carbon bond system
   c. the colour of the pigment
   d. the angle at which the photon hits the molecule

4. Which of the following is characteristic of chlorophyll? [p. 4]
   a. It absorbs light in the green region of the spectrum.
   b. It is involved in vision.
   c. It transmits light in the blue and red regions of the spectrum.
   d. It is used in photosynthetic electron transport.

5. Which statement is true? [pp. 4–6]
   a. Phototrophs, but not photosynthetic organisms, use light energy to create ATP.
   b. Only photosynthetic organisms perform cellular respiration.
   c. Light energy enters the biosphere through the photosynthetic organisms.
   d. Phototrophs are a type of photosynthetic organism.

6. Which is NOT characteristic of bacteriorhodopsin? [pp. 4–6]
   a. It is found in *Halobacterium*.
   b. It uses light energy to make ATP.
   c. It is a light-dependent proton pump.
   d. It is involved in certain types of photosynthesis.

7. Which is NOT true of retinal? [pp. 6–8]
   a. It forms complexes with bacteriorhodopsin and rhodopsin.
   b. It changes shape when it absorbs light energy.
   c. It contains a conjugated system.
   d. It is only found in organisms capable of vision.

8. Which is NOT associated with vision? [pp. 7–9]
   a. the ocellus
   b. a nervous system
   c. *C. reinhardtii* eyespot
   d. an ommatidium

9. Which is associated with photomorphogenesis? [pp. 8–9]
   a. phytochrome
   b. phototaxis
   c. flagella
   d. the retina

10. Which is associated with the human eye? [p. 10]

    a. a single lens
    b. accessory pigments
    c. ommatidia
    d. ocelli

11. Which statement is true? [pp. 11–13]

    a. Ultraviolet light is absorbed by water and water vapour.
    b. Infrared light is absorbed by the Earth's ozone layer.
    c. Long wavelength light damages DNA, leading to mutations.
    d. Longer wavelengths of UV light are not absorbed by Earth's atmosphere.

12. With which of the following is ionizing radiation associated? [p. 13]

    a. infrared light
    b. wavelengths of 700 nm or more
    c. absorption by atmospheric water vapour
    d. wavelengths in the UV region of the spectrum

13. Which statement about light absorption by DNA is false? [pp. 13–14]

    a. Melanin is protective and also plays a role in synthesis of vitamin D.
    b. It can cause a distortion of the double-helical shape.
    c. It can result in the formation of dimers between neighbouring bases.
    d. Fur and feathers provide protection.

14. Which statement about the circadian rhythm is false? [pp. 14–15]

    a. It is a daily response to sunlight.
    b. It is associated with hormonal fluctuations.
    c. It is found in all types of organisms.
    d. It is provides a selective advantage.

15. Which is characteristic of biological clocks? [pp. 14–16]

    a. They only exist in organisms capable of vision.
    b. They regulate diurnal and seasonal behaviours.
    c. The key regulatory component is a light-absorbing pigment.
    d. They require a nervous system.

16. Which structure is NOT involved in the human circadian rhythm? [pp. 14–16]

    a. the retina
    b. melanin
    c. the suprachiasmatic nucleus
    d. the pineal gland

17. Which statement about plants and their pollinators is true? [pp. 17–18]

    a. The specificity of the flower-pollinator is a recently recognized phenomenon.
    b. Flowers that are more brightly coloured are more likely to be successfully pollinated.
    c. The plant-pollinator association has undergone co-evolution.
    d. Flower colours have evolved to provide camouflage for their pollinators.

18. Which statement about peppered moths is true? [p. 19]

    a. The common form is light-coloured.
    b. It uses camouflage to avoid predation.
    c. It almost became extinct during the Industrial Revolution.
    d. It uses its bright colour to warn off predators.

19. Which statement about mole rats is false? [p. 21]

    a. They are nocturnal, so can see best under low light conditions.

    b. They live most of their lives in the dark.

    c. They have a well-developed suprachiasmatic nucleus.

    d. They have eyes but cannot see.

20. Which of the following statements about bioluminescence is false? [pp. 21–23]

    a. It describes the excess nighttime light of urban environments.

    b. It is an energy-requiring biological process.

    c. It can be used to attract mates.

    d. It is a form of communication among bacteria.

INTEGRATING AND APPLYING KEY CONCEPTS

1. Explain why Darwin had difficulties in explaining the evolution of the eye and how the evolution of the eye can, in fact, be explained based on natural selection. How, then, would you explain the "backwards" evolution of the mole rat's eyes?

2. Why are chlorophyll, rhodopsin, and phytochrome all critical to life on Earth?

3. a) Explain how fusion of hydrogen nuclei in the sun results in the cycle of life on Earth:

        energy to matter $\Leftrightarrow$ matter to energy

    b) Why is there a difference between the electromagnetic radiation reaching Earth's outer atmosphere and Earth's surface?

2 The Cell: An Overview

TOPIC MAP

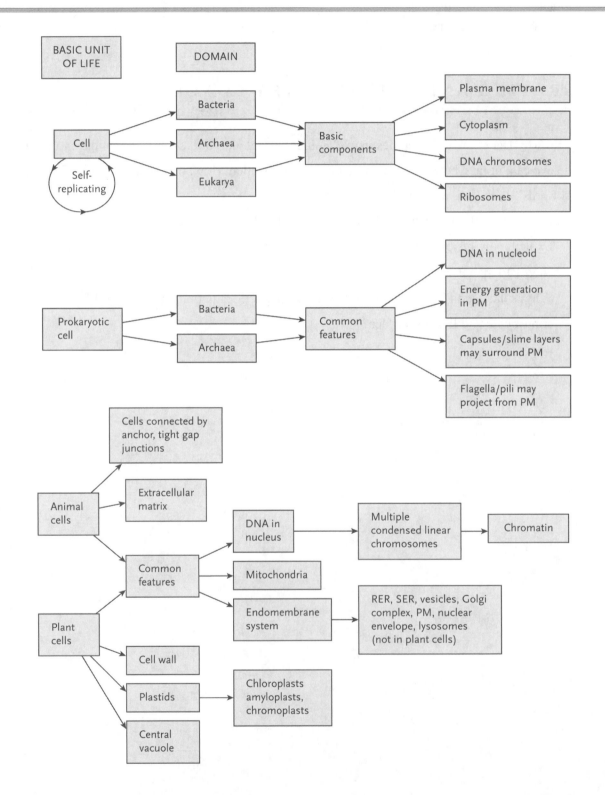

LEARNING OUTCOMES AND STUDY STRATEGIES

By the end of this chapter, you should be able to

- Describe the cell theory, identify the three domains of life, and explain the basic structural features of all cells

- Understand why cells are so small and the concepts of magnification and resolution as they pertain to light and electron microscopy, and name the units of measurement, in order of size, used to describe microscopic specimens

- Understand the basic similarities and essential differences between prokaryotic and eukaryotic cells

- Draw a typical prokaryotic cell identifying the basic cellular structures, their composition where described, as well as the functions of each

- Draw a typical eukaryotic cell identifying the basic cellular structures, their composition where described, as well as the functions of each

- Draw a typical animal and plant cell, identifying the basic cellular structures as well as the structure and function of each

Study strategies for this chapter:

- This chapter primarily requires the ability to visualize the three types of cell: prokaryotic, animal, and plant. Therefore, as you go through the chapter, make sure you can draw the basic structural features.

- From there, you should be able to fill in more details: what is the function of each and what is the primary structural component of each?

- As you read the textbook, don't forget to carefully examine the figures and read the figure legends.

- Take one section of the textbook at a time and then work through the companion section of the study guide. If you focus on understanding the concepts and principles instead of memorizing, the details will "come along for the ride"!

- After you have finished the chapter, go back to the chapter breakdown in the Study Plan at the beginning of the chapter and the questions in each Study Break. You should be able to go back and expand on the points within the Study Plan, and answer the various questions in the chapter. Finish by doing the Self-Test questions in the study guide and see if you can fill in specific details on the structures in the topic map shown above, or even devise your own topic map.

INTERACTIVE EXERCISES

Why It Matters [pp. 25–26]
2.1 Basic Features of Cell Structure and Function [pp. 26–30]

Section Review (Fill-in-the-Blanks)

The word (1) _____ derives from a word meaning "small rooms". It arose following the early light

(2) _____ studies of Robert Hooke in the 1600s. The cell theory, which was not described until the

middle of the 19th century has three tenets: all (3) _____ _____ are composed of cells, cells are the (4) _____ _____ of all living organisms, and cells arise only from the division of

(5) _____-_____ cells. Most cells are smaller than 0.1 (6) _____, the minimum

diameter that can be seen with the human eye, so they must be visualized with microscopes. Of the two basic

types of microscope, the (7) _____ microscope has higher magnification and resolution. The two

basic types of cellular architecture are the (8) _____ and the more complex (9) _____ cells.

However, both types share certain features: they contain a central (10) _____-containing region and

this is surrounded by the (11) _____. Eukaryotic cells, unlike prokaryotic cells, are distinguished by

the presence of a central (12) _____ and extensive (13) _____ system.

Matching

Match each of the following structures with its correct definition or descriptor.

14. ____	Yeasts	A.	The structure that separates the external environment from a cell's cytoplasm
15. ____	Prokaryotic	B.	Unicellular protists
16. ____	Organelles	C.	Unicellular fungi
17. ____	Cytoskeleton	D.	Bacteria and archaea
18. ____	Amoebas	E.	The organization of lipids in biological membranes
19. ____	Nucleoid	F.	Cellular protein framework important for chromosome segregation
20. ____	Plasma membrane	G.	Small organized cellular structures with discrete functions
21. ____	Bilayer	H.	The DNA-containing region in prokaryotic cells

Sequence

22. Arrange the following units of measurement from smallest to biggest: ____ ____ ____ ____

    A. nanometre

    B. millimetre

    C. micrometre

    D. centimetre

True/False

Mark if the statement is true (T) or false (F). If the statement is false, justify your answer in the lines below each statement.

23. _____ One of the tenets of the cell theory is that when cells are broken open, they lose the properties of life.

_____

_____

24. _____ The cellular cytoskeleton is unique to eukaryotes.

_____

_____

25. _____ The cytoplasm is where most proteins and other molecules are made and where energy from the environment is converted to usable energy for cellular processes.

_____

_____

26. _____ A light microscope is capable of higher magnification than electron microscopes but its resolution is lower.

_____

_____

Short Answer

27. What is the difference between the cytoplasm and the cytosol?

_____

_____

28. Why is the hydrophobic nature of the plasma membrane so important to the cell structure?

_____

_____

29. Why are cells generally so small?

_____

_____

2.2 Prokaryotic Cells [pp. 30–31]
2.3 Eukaryotic Cells [pp. 31–43]

Section Review (Fill-in-the-Blanks)

Mosr prokaryotic cells are (30) _____ and simpler than eukaryotic cells. The prokaryotic

chromosome is generally (31) _____ in shape and located in the central (32) _____. Most

have a rigid (33) _____ _____ surrounding the plasma membrane. The features that

characterize eukaryotic cells include possessing a true membrane-enclosed (34) _____ and an

endomembrane system in the cytoplasm that minimally consists of both rough and smooth

(35) _____ _____ and the (36) _____ complex. Most eukaryotes also possess

(37) _____ for cellular respiration. In contrast to the prokaryotic chromosome, eukaryotes generally

possess more than (38) _____ chromosome(s) and they are (39) _____ instead of circular.

Compared to prokaryotic ribosomes, eukaryotic ribosomes are (40) _____ and although they may be

suspended in the (41) _____, they may also be found on the outer membrane of the

(42) _____ envelope or on the (43) _____ endoplasmic reticulum. Within the cytoplasm of

most cells is a protein-based filamentous framework called the (44) _____. This serves many roles in

the cell including (45) _____ segregation and cell (46) _____. It is most highly developed in

(47) _____ cells. Finally, both prokaryotes and eukaryotic cells may possess external structures

called (48) _____ for movement. Also extending from the surface of cells may be the shorter

(49) _____ on prokaryotic cells and the (50) _____ on eukaryotic cells.

Matching

Match each of the following structures with its correct definition or descriptor.

51. ____	Nucleolus	A.	A system of two concentric membranes containing hundreds of large protein complexes
52. ____	Smooth ER	B.	Membrane-bound compartment containing hydrolytic enzymes for digestion
53. ____	Ribosome	C.	Chromosomal region where rRNA is formed and assembled into ribosomes
54. ____	Nuclear envelope	D.	Non-membrane-bound organelle that assemble amino acids into proteins

55. ____	Nucleoporin	E.	Site of lipid synthesis and breakdown of toxins
56. ____	Flagella	F.	Site of synthesis and transport of proteins
57. ____	Cilia	G.	Internal membrane folds in mitochondria
58. ____	Lysosome	H.	Key distribution site for membranes and proteins
59. ____	Cristae	I.	Octagonally symmetrical protein complex containing a central channel for independent or assisted flow of materials
60. ____	Rough ER	J.	Long, hairlike structures on the cell that function in movement
61. ____	Golgi complex	K.	Structures on animal cells that move by beating

Labelling

Identify each numbered part of the following illustration.

62. _____

63. _____

64. _____

65. _____

66. _____

67. _____

68. _____

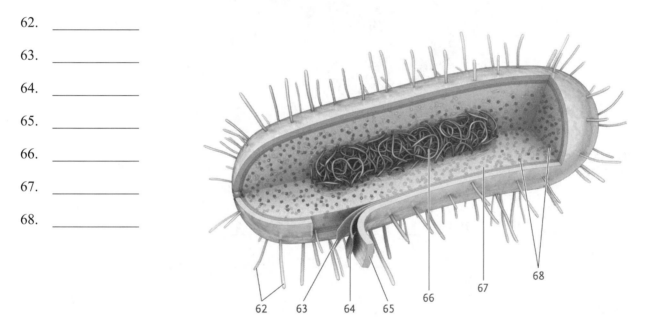

Labelling

Identify each numbered part of the following illustration.

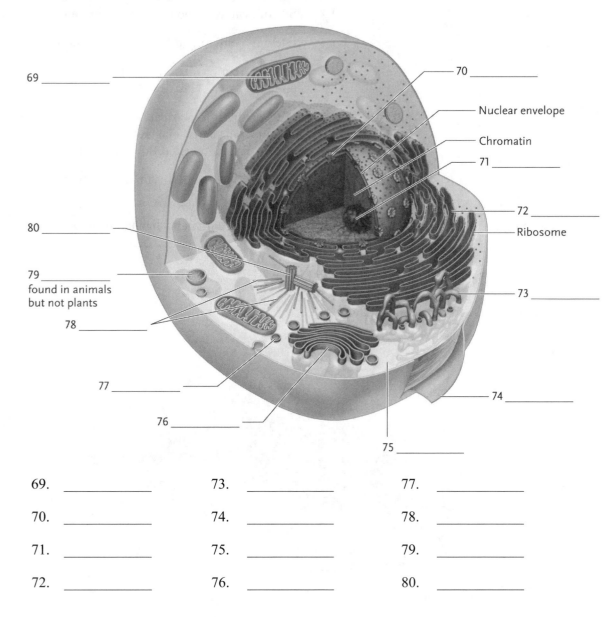

69 _____

80 _____

79 _____
found in animals
but not plants

78 _____

77 _____

76 _____

70 _____

Nuclear envelope

Chromatin

71 _____

72 _____

Ribosome

73 _____

74 _____

75 _____

69. _____	73. _____	77. _____
70. _____	74. _____	78. _____
71. _____	75. _____	79. _____
72. _____	76. _____	80. _____

Sequence

81. Arrange the following in order of occurence, leading to the secretion of a protein hormone:

_____ _____ _____ _____ _____ _____

    A.   budding from ER

    B.   modification within Golgi

    C.   translation on RER

    D.   exocytosis

    E.   fusion with *cis* face of Golgi

    F.   budding from *cis* face of Golgi

Complete the Table

82. Complete the following table.

Structure or Process	Description
Exocytosis	A.
B.	Method used to import food materials
C.	A cytoskeleton component only found in multicellular organisms
Microfilaments	D.
E.	Biggest cytoskeleton element, made of tubulin dimers, important for chromosome segregation, movement of flagella and cilia
Phagocytosis	F.
Motor proteins	G.
Centrioles	H.

True/False

Mark if the statement is true (T) or false (F). If the statement is false, justify your answer in the lines below each statement.

83. _____ Cells of all types of organism may possess a cell wall outside of the plasma membrane.

_____

_____

84. _____ The ribosome is a non-membrane-enclosed organelle.

_____

_____

85. _____ The flagella of eukaryotes are related to those of bacteria and archaea.

_____

_____

86. _____ The mitochondrial matrix contains a chromosome and ribosomes.

_____

_____

87. _____ The nucleolus forms part of the chromatin not the chromosome.

_____

_____

88. _____ Lysosomes digest cellular organelles.

_____

_____

Short Answer

89. Compare and contrast eukaryotic cilia and flagella.

_____

_____

90. Identify some key differences in function of the plasma membrane of prokaryotes and eukaryotes.

_____

_____

91. Identify some key differences between the plasma membrane and the nuclear envelope.

_____

_____

92. What is the distinction between chromosomes and chromatin?

_____

_____

2.4 Specialized Structures of Plant Cells [pp. 43–45]
2.5 The Animal Cell Surface [pp. 45–47]

Section Review (Fill-in-the-Blanks)

Plants cells differ structurally from animal cells in the absence of the (93) _____ and the presence of

the energy-generating (94) _____, a central (95) _____, and the cellulose-containing

(96) _____ _____. The latter structure also occurs in algal protists and (97) _____

although it may contain chitin instead of cellulose. The chloroplast is also found in (98) _____

protists, and is the site where (99) _____ are made using the chemical energy generated from

sunlight. In mature plant cells, the (100) _____ _____ may occupy greater than 90% of the

cell volume. This structure serves three critical functions: it develops (101) _____ to support the cell,

it enlarges to facilitate cell (102) _____, and it serves as a (103) _____ site. In animals, the

binding of cell (104) _____ molecules holds together cells of the same type, such as in body

(105) _____. These are reinforced by various (106) _____ including tight

(107) _____ which seal together the plasma membrane of adjacent cells. The ECM or

(108) _____ _____ functions primarily in (109) _____ and support.

Matching

Match each of the following structures with its correct definition or descriptor.

110. _____	Stroma	A.	Family of plant organelles that contain chlorophyll, other coloured pigments, or starch
111. _____	Thylakoids	B.	Primarily made of glycoproteins, may connect bone to muscle
112. _____	Plastids	C.	Membrane enclosing the central vacuole
113. _____	Grana	D.	Binds cells together
114. _____	Chlorophyll	E.	The predominant glycoprotein in the ECM
115. _____	Tonoplast	F.	A protein-based pipeline between adjacent animal cells
116. _____	Plasmodesmata	G.	The fluid interior of the chloroplast
117. _____	Extracellular matrix	H.	Pigment found in thylakoid membranes
118. _____	Cell adhesion molecules	I.	Common in tissues subject to stretching or that cover organs/line body cavities
119. _____	Anchoring junctions	J.	Membrane system within the stroma
120. _____	Gap junctions	K.	Cytosol-filled channels perforating cell walls of adjacent plant cells
121. _____	Collagen	L.	Stacked thylakoids found in higher plants

Complete the Table

122. Complete the following table.

Structure	Description
A.	Openings connecting the cytoplasm of adjacent plant cells
Tight junction	B.
Gap junctions	C.
D.	Weld adjacent animal cells together

True/False

Mark if the statement is true (T) or false (F). If the statement is false, justify your answer in the lines below each statement.

123. _____ The plastids of plant cells contain a chromosome and ribosomes.

_____

_____

124. _____ The central vacuole in plants may serve the same function as the lysosome in animals.

_____

_____

125. _____ The consistency of the extracellular matrix depends upon whether collagen is present.

_____

_____

Short Answer

126. What are some of the diverse functions of the central vacuole?

_____

_____

127. Compare and contrast plasmodesmata and gap junctions.

_____

_____

128. What are some of the diverse functions of the extracellular matrix?

_____

_____

SELF-TEST

1. Which of the following is NOT a component of the cell theory? [p. 26]
   a. New cells arise from preexisting cells.
   b. Cells contain genetic material.
   c. The cell is the smallest unit of life.
   d. Living things are composed of cells.

2. Which of the following is NOT a domain of life? [p. 26]
   a. the Prokaryotes
   b. the Eukarya
   c. the Bacteria
   d. the Archaea

3. Which statement is true? [p. 27]
   a. Viruses can be seen with a light microscope.
   b. Resolution is the ratio of the size of the object as viewed to its real size.
   c. Magnification is the minimum distance between two visually distinct points in a specimen.
   d. Bacteria can only be seen with a microscope.

4. Which statement explains why cells are small? [p. 27]
   a. As cells grow, the surface area to volume ratio increases.
   b. As cells grow, the surface area to volume ratio doubles.
   c. As cells grow, the surface area to volume ratio decreases.
   d. As cells grow, the surface area to volume ratio does not change.

5. Which statement is false? [pp. 28–29]
   a. The cytosol is the aqueous part of the cytoplasm.
   b. DNA contains genes that code for individual proteins.
   c. Organelles are membrane-enclosed.
   d. The cytoskeleton is present in all types of cells.

6. Which statement about prokaryotic and eukaryotic cells is true? [pp. 28–29]
   a. Prokaryotic cells have a plasma membrane but eukaryotic cells do not.
   b. Eukaryotic cells have DNA, but prokaryotic cells do not.
   c. Eukaryotic cells have a nucleus, but prokaryotic cells do not.
   d. Prokaryotic cells have ribosomes but eukaryotic cells do not.

7. Which of the following is NOT a property of the nucleoid? [p. 30]
   a. It can be seen with the light microscope.
   b. It contains a highly condensed prokaryotic chromosome.
   c. It is located in the cytoplasm of prokaryotic cells.
   d. It contains the genes necessary for life in bacteria and achaea.

8. Which of the following functions is performed by both bacterial pili and capsule? [pp. 30–31]
   a. attachment to surfaces and other cells
   b. providing rigidity to the cell
   c. protection against dessication
   d. connecting mating cells

9. Which of the following structures propels prokaryotic cells through liquid? [p. 31]

   a. the pili
   b. the slime layer
   c. the flagella
   d. membrane proteins

10. Which of the following is NOT a characteristic of the nuclear envelope? [pp. 33–34]

    a. It is a typical phospholipid bilayer.
    b. It contains hundreds of protein complexes containing nucleoporins.
    c. It allows the material to move back and forth between the nucleus and the cytoplasm.
    d. It maintains a liquid interior that differs in composition from the cytoplasm.

11. Which of the following sets of structures is typical of eukaryotic cells but not prokaryotic cells? [pp. 30–34]

    a. circular chromosome(s), chromatin, nucleolus
    b. nucleoid, chromatin, nucleolus
    c. chromosome(s), nucleoid
    d. nuclear envelope, chromatin, nucleolus

12. Which of the following is NOT part of the endomembrane system? [p. 34]

    a. the RER
    b. the nuclear envelope
    c. cristae
    d. the Golgi complex

13. Which of the following occurs in the Golgi complex? [p. 36]

    a. autophagy
    b. lipid synthesis
    c. chemical modification of proteins
    d. assembly of proteins using an mRNA template

14. Which of the following statements about lysosomes is false? [p. 37]

    a. They are important in the process of exocytosis.
    b. They are important in the process of autophagy.
    c. They fuse with phagocytic vesicles.
    d. They may be associated with human disease.

15. Which statement regarding cellular respiration is false? [pp. 38–39]

    a. It involves the oxidation of food molecules for energy generation.
    b. It generates approximately half of the ATP in the animal cell.
    c. It occurs in plant and animal cells.
    d. It involves an organelle that may have a bacterial ancestor.

16. Which of the following is NOT associated with the cytoskeleton? [pp. 39–42]

    a. cilia
    b. collagen
    c. microtubules
    d. motor proteins

17. Which of the following would NOT be found in a unicellular eukaryote such as yeast? [p. 41]

    a. microtubules
    b. actin
    c. microfilaments
    d. intermediate filaments

18. Which structure is responsible for storage of starch in plant cells? [pp. 43–44]

    a. amyloplasts
    b. chloroplasts
    c. tonoplasts
    d. chromoplasts

19. Which of the following would NOT be stored in a plastid and in the central vacuole? [pp. 43–44]

    a. red and yellow pigments

    b. starch

    c. DNA

    d. water molecules

20. Which of the following is NOT associated with the plant cell wall? [pp. 44–45]

    a. protection against pathogens

    b. cell shape

    c. cellulose fibres

    d. gap junctions

21. Which of the following pairs of structures serve the same function? [pp. 45–46]

    a. plasmodesmata and gap junctions

    b. tight junction and plasmodesmata

    c. anchoring junctions and tight junctions

22. Which of the following junctions and body structure go together? [pp. 45–46]

    a. anchoring junctions and heart muscle tissue

    b. gap junctions and kidney cells

    c. tight junctions and the stomach lining

23. Which of the following structures is NOT associated with an extracellular matrix? [p. 47]

    a. hair

    b. bones

    c. cartilage

    d. tendons

INTEGRATING AND APPLYING KEY CONCEPTS

1. As you will learn in the next chapter, a widely held theory is that all life on Earth is descended from a single common ancestor. Similarly, all bacteria, believed to have appeared first, are thought to have evolved from a single common ancestor, as are all archaea and eukaryotes. There are certain predictions one can make from this hypothesis and certain observations one should therefore be able to make. Based on the information in this chapter, identify those predictions and the observations that support the theory of a single common ancestor of all life on Earth.

3 Defining Life and Its Origins

TOPIC MAP

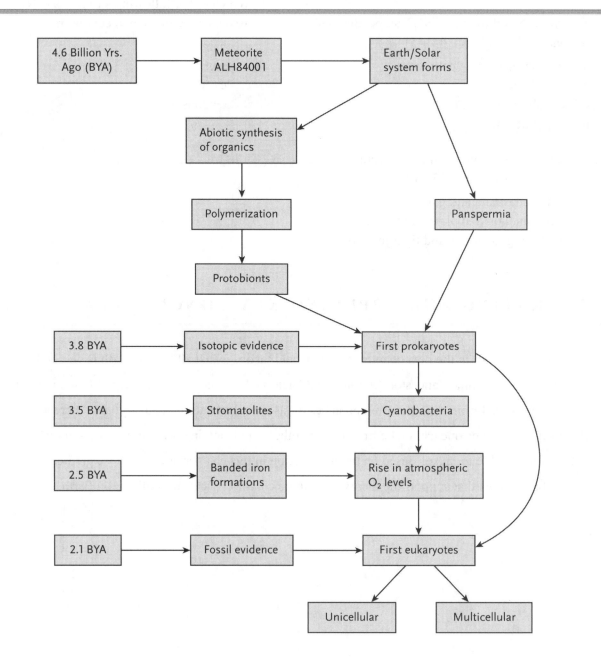

LEARNING OUTCOMES AND STUDY STRATEGIES

By the end of this chapter, you should be able to

- Name the seven characteristics of life and understand why it is called "emergent"
- Describe the prevailing conditions on abiotic Earth and the three theories on how organic chemicals may have emerged, as well as how the first cell may have arisen on Earth; you should know what the theory of panspermia proposes as an alternative explanation for the appearance of life on Earth
- Describe how the metabolism of prokaryotes evolved, leading to the oxygenation of Earth's atmosphere
- Describe the endosymbiosis theory and supporting evidence
- Describe how the evolution of the mitochondrion was critical to the subsequent evolution of the complex traits typical of the modern eukaryotic organisms
- Identify the dates and sources of evidence for the various evolutionary transitions and the names of the people who contributed theories or experimental evidence for the evolution of life on Earth

Study strategies for this chapter:

- This chapter is relatively simple and mainly requires imagination to picture the prevailing conditions and evolutionary transitions believed to have led to modern-day life on Earth. Remember that the goal of this chapter is to understand the conditions on abiotic Earth and how these may have allowed for the spontaneous evolution of organic molecules, the polymerization of these monomers to yield the critical macromolecules of cells, and the assembly of membrane-bound vesicles leading ultimately to the first prokaryotic cell. From here, you need to understand how the metabolism of prokaryotes evolved, leading to the predecessor of the mitochondrion and chloroplast and the evolution of the first eukaryotic cells.
- Make sure you can describe the key roles of the following: reducing atmosphere, liposomes, clay, autotrophs, oxygenic photosynthesis, aerobic heterotrophs, and overcoming the energy barrier.
- Try drawing a timeline from 4.6 billion years ago, including prevailing atmospheric conditions, abiotic events, and key evolutionary transitions.
- Don't forget to carefully examine the figures and read the figure legends—these provide a visual means of understanding, and remembering, the concepts described in the textbook.
- Pay attention to the chapter breakdown in the Study Plan at the beginning of the chapter and the questions in each Study Break. Take one section at a time and then work through the companion section in the study guide. After you've completed going through the chapter you should be able to go back and expand on the points within the Study Plan. You should also be able to answer the various questions in the chapter and the Self-Test questions in the study guide.
- As always, focus on understanding concepts and principles instead of memorizing them. If you do, the details will form part of your understanding!

INTERACTIVE EXERCISES

Why It Matters [pp. 50–51]
3.1 What Is Life? [pp. 51–52]
3.2 The Chemical Origins of Life [pp. 52–57]

Section Review (Fill-in-the-Blanks)

At the molecular level, living and non-living things are made of the same elements and (1) _____. In

addition, they both follow the same laws of physics and (2) _____. Living things are distinguished

from non-living things by seven characteristics: they display (3) _____, harness and utilize

(4) _____, reproduce, respond to (5) _____, exhibit homeostasis as well as growth and

(6) _____, and (7) _____ to become better adapted to their environment. Earth formed

(8) _____ billion years ago and took approximately (9) _____ million years to cool

sufficiently to support life. The conditions on abiotic Earth were very different from those of the present day

and included large quantities of water vapour and four other gases: (10) _____, _____,

_____, and _____. In addition, there was virtually no (11) _____ in the atmosphere.

The (12) _____–_____ hypothesis proposed that organic molecules could have formed

spontaneously in the reducing (13) _____ of early Earth. The (14) _____–_____

experiments provided support for this hypothesis. The (15) _____ hypothesis provides an explanation

for the subsequent polymerization of organic monomers.

True/False

Mark if the statement is true (T) or false (F). If the statement is false, justify your answer in the lines
below each statement.

16. _____ Meteorite ALH84001 is the subject of much interest because it may have brought life to
Earth.

_____

_____

17. _____ Ozone was present on primordial Earth and was a critical component of the Miller–Urey experiment.

_____

_____

18. _____ The term "emergent" refers to the point in Earth's history where life emerged from the primordial soup.

_____

_____

19. _____ Alternatives to the theory that organics originated in the atmopshere include their evoution around deep-sea vents or their delivery from outer space via meteorites.

_____

_____

Matching

Match each of the following terms with its correct descriptor or relevance to the origins of life on Earth.

20. _____ Polymers

A. Containing primarily electron-rich molecules

21. _____ Oparin–Haldane

B. The name for the experiment that replicated conditions on early Earth and demonstrated the abiotic synthesis of organic molecules

22. _____ Miller–Urey

C. The name for the hypothesis that organic molecules were synthesized abiotically on primordial Earth

23. _____ Clay

D. Macromolecules formed by the bonding together of monomers through dehydration

24. _____ Reducing environment

E. A solid that can store potential energy and provide a substrate for the abiotic polymerization of organic monomers

Sequence

25. Arrange the following proposed steps for the origin of life on Earth: ____ ____ ____ ____

A. cooling of Earth's surface

B. accumulation of organic molecules

C. polymerization of complex macromolecules

D. condensation of interstellar gases

Complete the Table

26. Complete the following table.

Characteristic of Life	Explanation
A.	Manner of organization with the cell as the fundamental unit
Harness and utilize energy	B.
C.	Generation of more of the same kind
D.	Changes in external conditions trigger adjustments in structure, function, and behaviour
Homeostasis	E.
Growth and development	F.
G.	Changes over generations to become better adapted to the environment

Short Answer

27. How is a primordial reducing atmosphere critical to one theory of the formation of organics on Earth?

_____

_____

28. Describe the features that viruses share with living things.

_____

_____

29. Describe how the original Miller–Urey experiment was designed.

_____

_____

3.3 From Macromolecules to Life [pp. 57–60]

Section Review (Fill-in-the-Blanks)

A key advancement toward the evolution of life was the formation of a(n) (30) _____-enclosed

compartment. The first such structures are referred to as (31) _____ and laboratory experiments

confirm these may form spontaneously, without an input of (32) _____. The discovery of

(33) _____ by Thomas Cech has led to the idea that early life used (34) _____ as a carrier of

(35) _____ and as a biological (36) _____. It is then hypothesized that some cells evolved

the ability to synthesize simple (37) _____ from the information in RNA. These molecules are far

stronger (38) _____ than ribozymes and have a far greater structural (39) _____, giving such

cells a tremendous (40) _____ advantage. Similarly, those cells that evolved to synthesize and use

(41) _____ for information storage would have had an advantage. Energy transduction and

(42) _____ probably evolved from simple oxidation– (43) _____ reactions. The subsequent

development of more complex multistep (44) _____ would allow for more efficient stepwise energy

release.

Short Answer

45. What is the "central dogma" and how do ribosomes provide a hint at how it might have evolved?

_____

_____

46. What are the three reasons why proteins are better molecules for catalyzing chemical reactions than ribozymes?

_____

_____

47. Compare the structures of DNA and RNA.

_____

_____

48. What are protobionts and what is their connection to clay and liposomes?

_____

_____

True/False

Mark if the statement is true (T) or false (F). If the statement is false, justify your answer in the lines below each statement.

49. _____ The catalyst for the polymerization of modern-day proteins is a ribozyme.

_____

_____

50. _____ If RNA molecules were normally double-stranded, they would not be able to function as ribozymes.

_____

_____

51. _____ Cellular respiration was probably one of the earliest methods of energy generation.

_____

_____

52. _____ Thomas Cech is famous for discovering how the first protobionts formed.

_____

_____

3.4 The Earliest Forms of Life [pp. 60–64]

Section Review (Fill-in-the-Blanks)

The earliest conclusive evidence of life on Earth comes from fossils in the form of (53) _____. The

oldest of these formed about (54) _____ billion years ago. Indirect isotopic evidence based on the

(55) _____ composition of ancient rocks dates the first life forms to even earlier, around

(56) _____ billion years ago. Because this represents a relatively short time-span since the formation

of (57) _____, some scientists believe that life has its origins from outer space, a theory called

(58) _____. The earliest life forms were likely (59) _____ heterotrophs, since there were

initially only trace levels of (60) _____ in the atmosphere. This changed with the evolution of

(61) _____ photosynthesis. Evidence for the resulting change in Earth's atmosphere comes from

banded (62) _____ formations, the oldest of which have been dated to around (63) _____

billion years ago.

Matching

Match each of the following terms with its correct descriptor or relevance to the origins of life on Earth.

64. _____ Stromatolites   A. Lacking oxygen

65. _____ Autotrophs   B. Bacteria that perform oxygenic photosynthesis

66. _____ Anoxygenic phototrophs   C. A process of energy generation that oxidizes
                                               water for electrons

67. _____ Cyanobacteria   D. The earliest photosynthetic organisms

68. _____ Oxygenic photosynthesis   E. Layered rock structures created by
                                               cyanobacteria

69. _____ Anaerobic   F. Organisms that obtain their carbon from
                                               carbon dioxide

Short Answer

70. Discuss how scientists can determine whether carbon deposits are of biological origin.

_____

_____

71. Compare and contrast the stromatolites of Western Australia's Shark Bay with those from primordial Earth.

_____

_____

72. How does the theory of panspermia relate to astrobiology?

_____

_____

73. What is LUCA and what evidence supports the concept?

_____

_____

True/False

Mark if the statement is true (T) or false (F). If the statement is false, justify your answer in the lines below each statement.

74. _____ Cyanobacteria were likely the first life forms.

_____

_____

75. _____ Modern bacterial spores can survive exposure to radiation, desiccation, freezing, and extreme heat and could theoretically survive space travel.

_____

_____

76. _____ Although life is believed descended from a single ancestor, life itself may have arisen many times on primordial Earth.

_____

_____

3.5 The Eukaryotic Cell and the Rise of Multicellularity [pp. 64–67]
3.6 The Search for Extraterrestrial Life [pp. 68–69]

Section Review (Fill-in-the-Blanks)

Unlike bacteria and archaea, modern-day eukaryotes possess a(n) (77) _____ and

(78) _____-_____ compartments in the cytoplasm. These include the energy-transforming

(79) _____ and (80) _____. According to the theory of (81) _____, these two

organelles evolved from free-living (82) _____ cells engulfed by larger host cells. Eventually the

host and (83) _____ became inseparable parts of a single organism. The (84) _____ is

thought to have evolved first since it is found in virtually every eukaryotic cell. This would have been

followed by the endosymbiosis of oxygenic (85) _____ bacteria, eventually giving rise to the

(86) _____. It is speculated that the endomembrane system developed following the

(87) _____ of the (88) _____ membrane. The evolution of the mitochondrion allowed the

ancestral eukaryotes to overcome a(n) (89) _____ barrier which then allowed for the evolution of

(90) _____ eukaryotes. Scientists continue to search for evidence of (91) _____ life. As of

2011, the NASA Keppler mission had identified 1200 (92) _____ planets. Theoretically, the most

important requirement for life is that the planet exist in the (93) _____ zone.

Matching

Match each of the following terms with their correct relevance to theories on the evolution of eukaryotes.

94. ____	Binary fission	A.	Genetic reorganization critical to the metabolic integration of the cell and the evolution of the nucleus
95. ____	Mitochondrial predecessor	B.	A group of algae that serve as a model for studying multicellularity
96. ____	Circular chromosomes	C.	Method of division of bacterial, archaea, mitochondria, and chloroplasts
97. ____	Horizontal gene transfer	D.	Aerobic, heterotrophic bacteria
98. ____	Volvocine	E.	Bacterial, archaeal, mitochondrial, and chloroplast genomes

Short Answer

99. What kind of evidence is used to support the endosymbiont theory?

_____

_____

100. What process(es) resulted in the endosymbiotic protomitochondria and protochloroplasts evolving to become organelles within the eukaryotic cell?

_____

_____

101. What group of organisms are believed to have given rise to eukaryotic cells?

_____

_____

True/False

Mark if the statement is true (T) or false (F). If the statement is false, justify your answer in the lines below each statement.

102. _____ All multicellular eukaryotes developed from the same unicellular organism.

_____

_____

103. _____ Mitochondria and chloroplasts contain ribosomes that resemble those of prokaryotes.

_____

_____

104. _____ Mitochondria and chloroplasts have chromosomes and follow the central dogma so are considered endosymbiotic life forms.

_____

_____

105. _____ The evolution of life on Earth is the result of such highly improbable events that there is little evidence that similar events may have taken place elsewhere in the universe.

_____

_____

Labelling

Identify the structure or evolutionary step for each numbered part of the following illustration.

106. _____

107. _____

108. _____

109. _____

110. _____

111. _____

112. _____

113. _____

114. _____

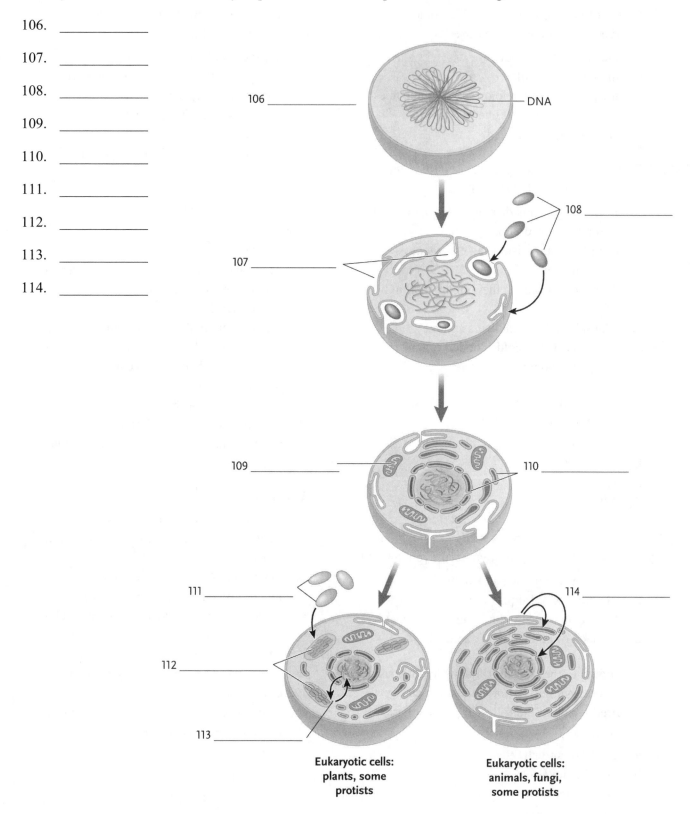

106 _____ ——— DNA

108 _____

107 _____

109 _____   110 _____

111 _____   114 _____

112 _____

113 _____

Eukaryotic cells: plants, some protists

Eukaryotic cells: animals, fungi, some protists

1. Which of the following is NOT common between living things and viruses? [p. 51]

    a. the ability to reproduce
    b. the ability to evolve
    c. the presence of nucleic acid chromosomes
    d. the ability to extract energy from the environment

2. Which of the following is true regarding the characteristics of life? [pp. 51–52]

    a. Living organisms display order but non-living systems do not.
    b. Cellular metabolism is an emergent phenomenon.
    c. The chromosome is the fundamental unit of life.
    d. Warm blooded organisms exhibit homeostasis but cold-blooded organisms and plants do not.

3. How many billions of years ago was Earth estimated to have formed? [p. 53]

    a. 6.4
    b. 4.6
    c. 3.5
    d. 2.0

4. Which of the following was NOT critical to the evolution of life on primitive Earth? [pp. 54–55]

    a. existing within the sun's habitable zone
    b. the presence of liquid water
    c. having an oxygen-containing atmosphere
    d. the lack of atmospheric ozone

5. According to the Oparin–Haldane hypothesis, the abiotic synthesis of organic chemicals required which of the following atmospheric gases? [p. 55]

    a. H_2, CH_4, and NH_3
    b. O_2, H_2, and H_2O
    c. O_2, N_2, and CO_2
    d. CH_4, NH_3, and O_2

6. Which of the following describes the experiments of Miller and Urey? [pp. 55–56]

    a. They did not require water.
    b. Organic chemicals were formed in the presence of oxygen.
    c. They observed the spontaneous formation of cells.
    d. Organic chemicals formed using a reducing environment and electricity.

7. Which of the following statements about the first organic molecules on primitive Earth is false? [pp. 56–57]

    a. The organic building blocks necessary for life may have formed in Earth's atmosphere.
    b. The organic building blocks necessary for life may have formed in the superheated waters around deep-sea vents.
    c. Meteorites may have carried organic molecules to Earth.
    d. Polymerization of the first organic macromolecules required abiotic formation of primitive enzymes.

8. Which statement is true? [pp. 57–58]

    a. An oxidizing atmosphere was critical to the evolution of organic molecules on abiotic Earth.
    b. On abiotic Earth, polymerization of organic macromolecules and formation of protobionts may have both involved clay particles.
    c. The first cells on abiotic Earth were likely synthesized from abiotically formed enzymes.
    d. The first enzymes on abiotic Earth may have formed on clay surfaces.

9. Which is believed to have been responsible for catalyzing the formation of proteins on primitive Earth? [pp. 58–59]

    a. DNA

    b. RNA

    c. enzymes

    d. ribosomes

10. Which statement about the advantage of enzymes vs. ribozymes is false? [pp. 58–59]

    a. Enzymes are better catalysts because they do not have to serve the dual roles of structure/function and information storage.

    b. Ribozymes catalyze reactions much more slowly than enzymes.

    c. Enzymes are formed from many more building blocks making them more diverse.

    d. The three-dimensional structure of ribozymes is restricted by the limited intramolecular bonding arrangements.

11. Which statement relating to the evolution of the central dogma is true? [pp. 59–60]

    a. The last step would have been the evolution of enzymes to synthesize DNA.

    b. The evolution of DNA would have reduced the rate of chemical and mutational damage to the genetic material.

    c. Its selective advantage results from the fact DNA is simpler to synthesize vs. RNA.

    d. In modern cells it is universal, including in viruses.

12. What is the earliest fossil evidence of life on Earth? [p. 61]

    a. 4.6 billion year-old stromatolites

    b. 2.2 billion year-old fossilized cyanobacteria

    c. 3.5 billion year-old stromatolites

    d. 1.0 billion year-old fossilized cyanobacteria

13. Which type of life form is thought to have evolved first on primitive Earth? [p. 61]

    a. aerobic heterotrophic organisms

    b. oxygenic photosynthetic organisms

    c. anaerobic heterotrophic organisms

    d. anaerobic autotrophic organisms

14. Which provides early evidence of the rising oxygen levels in Earth's atmosphere? [pp. 61–62]

    a. 2.5 billion year old banded iron formations

    b. 2.5 billion year old fossils of cyanobacteria

    c. 2.5 billion year old fossils of anoxygenic photosynthetic bacteria

    d. 2.5 billion year old fossils of small algae

15. Which statement is true? [pp. 62–64]

    a. The discovery of extremophiles on a Mars meteorite supports the theory of panspermia.

    b. Fossil evidence of ~ 4.0 billion year old spores supports the theory of panspermia.

    c. The presence of a nucleus in archaea suggests that eukaryotes arose from an archaeal ancestor.

    d. LUCA may not have been the first life form on Earth.

16. Approximately how many billion years old is the oldest fossil of a eukaryote? [p. 64]

    a. 4.6

    b. 3.5

    c. 2.5

    d. 2.1

17. Which statement about mitochondria and chloroplasts is false? [pp. 64–65]

    a. They are both found in plant cells.

    b. They are both found in animal cells.

    c. They both contain circular DNA chromosomes.

    d. Sequence analysis places both on the bacterial branch of the tree of life.

18. Which set of structures is part of the theory of endosymbiosis? [pp. 64–65]

    a. the mitochondrial membrane and ER

    b. the ER and nuclear membrane

    c. the mitochondria and chloroplasts

    d. the nucleus, mitochondria, and chloroplasts

19. Which is thought to explain the much higher complexity of eukaryotes vs. prokaryotes? [p. 67]

    a. Eukaryotes can synthesize much higher levels of cellular ATP.
    b. Eukaryotes have much larger genomes.
    c. Eukaryotes are biochemically more flexible than prokaryotes.

20. Which of the following is a key trait of multicellular organisms? [p. 67]

    a. The individual cells are much bigger compared to unicellular organisms.
    b. The individual cells exhibit division of labour.
    c. They are all found on the same evolutionary lineage.

INTEGRATING AND APPLYING KEY CONCEPTS

1. Discuss why the evolution of oxygenic photosynthetic bacteria was a critical and essential transition leading ultimately to the evolution of eukaryotic cells.

2. Discuss the connection(s) between the new field of astrobiology, the concept of a habitable zone, and NASA's Kepler Mission.

4 Energy and Enzymes

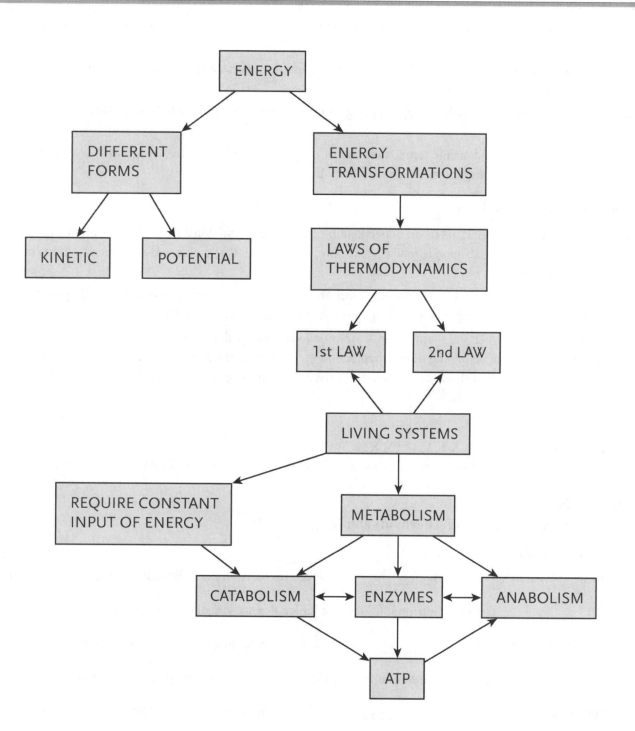

LEARNING OUTCOMES AND STUDY STRATEGIES

By the end of this chapter, you should be able to

- Describe first and second laws of thermodynamics and the three types of thermodynamic systems, giving an example of each
- Identify how living organisms obey the first and second laws of thermodynamics
- Define a spontaneous reaction and explain, using thermodynamic terms, how one predicts whether a reaction will be spontaneous
- Describe, using the components of metabolism as examples, the factors that determine whether a reaction will be spontaneous
- Describe the phenomenon of energy coupling using ATP and explain why this is not strictly a hydrolysis reaction
- Explain, using thermodynamic terms, the roles of enzymes as biological catalysts and how they are regulated in order to respond to the cell's metabolic needs

Study strategies for this chapter:

- As you read the textbook, focus on understanding the concepts and don't forget to carefully examine the figures and read the figure legends. Make sure, as you read, that you can answer the questions in each Study Break.
- Take one section of the text at a time then work through the companion section of the study guide. Try devising your own topic map, adding to it with each major section of the chapter.
- After you have finished the chapter, test your knowledge (rather than how much you've memorized) by going back to the beginning of the chapter and seeing if you can expand on the points within the Study Plan. Do the Self-Test questions and see if you can fill in specific details on the structures in the topic map shown above.

INTERACTIVE EXERCISES

Why It Matters [pp. 71–72]
4.1 Energy and the Laws of Thermodynamics [pp. 72–75]

Section Review (Fill-in-the-Blanks)

Life forms use catalysts called (1) _____ to speed up reaction rates. Because they can harness and

use (2) _____ from their surroundings, these molecules are key players in the (3) _____

pathways of living organisms. (4) _____ is the capacity to do work and is classified as either

(5) _____ energy, the energy of motion, or (6) _____ energy, the energy arising from

location or chemical structure. (7) _____ is the study of energy flow between a system and its

(8) _____. There are three types of systems: a(n) (9) _____ system exchanges neither

(10) _____ nor matter with its surroundings, a(n) (11) _____ system exchanges

(12) _____ but not matter with its surroundings, and a(n) (13) _____ system exchanges both

with its surroundings. The first law of thermodynamics states that energy can be transformed or transferred,

but cannot be (14) _____ nor (15) _____. The result is that the total energy of a(n)

(16) _____ and its surroundings remains unchanged. The second law of thermodynamics states that

each energy transformation causes a net increase in (17) _____ or disorder of the system and its

surroundings. Although life is highly ordered, it requires (18) _____ to maintain this order. Life

forms are examples of (19) _____ systems and they obey the (20) _____ law of thermo-

dynamics, absorbing energy from their surroundings and increasing the (21) _____ of the universe.

Matching

Match each of the following terms with its correct definition or descriptor.

22. ____	Energy	A.	A measure of disorder
23. ____	Thermodynamics	B.	Stored energy
24. ____	Earth	C.	Open system(s)
25. ____	Heat	D.	The ability to do work
26. ____	Kinetic energy	E.	The energy of movement
27. ____	Entropy	F.	Closed system(s)
28. ____	Potential energy	G.	The study of energy and its transformations
29. ____	Organisms	H.	The energy of random molecular motion

Short Answer

Explain how each of the following represents a source of potential energy.

30. A hamburger:

_____

_____

31. A skier at the top of a ski run:

_____

_____

32. Water at the top of a dam or waterfall:

_____

_____

Complete the Table

33. Complete the following table.

Type of System	Definition	Example
Isolated	A.	A Thermos
B.	C.	The ocean, living organisms
D.	Exchanges energy but not matter with its environment	E.

Identification

For each of the following forms of kinetic energy, identify what it is that is moving.

34. Electricity:

_____

_____

35. Heat:

_____

_____

36. Light:

_____

_____

37. Ultraviolet radiation:

_____

_____

4.2 Free Energy and Spontaneous Reactions [pp. 75–78]

Section Review (Fill-in-the-Blanks)

Spontaneous chemical or physical reactions do not require an input of (38) _____ from their

surroundings but instead release (39) _____ _____ (G), defined as the ability to do

(40) _____. The ΔG of a reaction is dependent on the change in (41) _____ (ΔH) or energy

content of the system and the change in disorder or (42) _____ (S) of the system. The formula

(43) _____ is used to determine whether a reaction will occur (44) _____. If the ΔG is

(45) _____ then the reaction is said to be (46) _____ and it will proceed spontaneously. If

the ΔG is (47) _____ then the reaction is said to be (48) _____ and requires free energy to

proceed. As spontaneous reactions proceed, the free energy of the system becomes progressively

(49) _____ until they reach a state of (50) _____ where $\Delta G = 0$ and the rates of the forward

and reverse reactions are (51) _____. The sum of all reactions taking place in living systems is

defined as (52) _____. These reactions are of two major types: (53) _____ pathways are

generally exergonic and (54) _____ pathways are generally endergonic.

Matching

Match each of the following terms with its correct definition.

55.	_____	Free energy		A.	Reactions that break down larger molecules into smaller chemicals
56.	_____	Metabolism		B.	$\Delta G = 0$
57.	_____	Endergonic		C.	Reactions that build larger molecules
58.	_____	Catabolism		D.	Potential energy of a system
59.	_____	ΔG		E.	Reactions that release energy
60.	_____	Anabolism		F.	Exergonic
61.	_____	Exergonic		G.	All chemical reactions in a living organism
62.	_____	Spontaneous reaction		H.	Reactions that require energy
63.	_____	Equilibrium		I.	Energy available to do work
64.	_____	Enthalpy		J.	Change in free energy

True/False

Mark if the statement is true (T) or false (F). If the statement is false, justify your answer in the lines below each statement.

65. _____ Cellular respiration is an anabolic pathway.

_____

_____

66. _____ Photosynthesis is an exergonic process.

_____

_____

67. _____ The melting of ice at room temperature is an endergonic process.

_____

_____

68. _____ Diffusion is a process with a negative ΔG.

_____

_____

Short Answer

69. Using thermodynamic terms, explain how one would predict whether a chemical reaction is going to be spontaneous.

_____

_____

70. Using thermodynamic terms, explain why catabolic pathways are exergonic and anabolic pathways are endergonic.

_____

_____

71. Explain why equilibrium is attained for chemical reactions in closed systems but not in living organisms.

_____

_____

4.3 Adenosine Triphosphate Is the Energy Currency of the Cell [pp. 79–81]

Section Review (Fill-in-the-Blanks)

ATP used to drive the majority of energy-requiring or (72) _____ reactions in the cell. These

reactions form the majority of biosynthetic or (73) _____ reactions in the cell. The breakdown of

ATP to (74) _____ + _____ releases free energy and this can be used by enzymes to drive

(75) _____ reactions. The combining of these two reactions is called (76) _____

_____, and it gives an overall negative ΔG. Regeneration of ATP from ADP has a(n)

(77) _____ ΔG and requires an input of energy. This comes from the coupling of ATP synthesis with

exergonic reactions such as those involved in the (78) _____ of food molecules.

Matching

Match each of the following terms with its correct definition or descriptor.

79. _____	Phosphorylation	A.	Exergonic reaction
80. _____	ATP	B.	Couples endergonic and exergonic metabolic reactions
81. _____	ATP cycle	C.	Endergonic reaction
82. _____	ATP hydrolysis	D.	Addition of a phosphate group to a molecule
83. _____	Glutamine synthesis	E.	Primary coupling agent in all living things

Short Answer

84. Name the three reasons why ATP breakdown releases energy.

   _____

   _____

85. Why are coupled reactions so important for life?

   _____

   _____

86. If ATP hydrolysis is exergonic, why does the cell use enzymes to catalyze this breakdown?

   _____

   _____

4.4 The Role of Enzymes in Biological Reactions [pp. 81–85]

Section Review (Fill-in-the-Blanks)

Exergonic reactions usually have to overcome an energy barrier called the (86) _____ energy (E_a) in

order to proceed spontaneously. The E_a is the energy required to attain the (87) _____ state where

bonds are (88) _____ and ready to be broken. (89) _____ increase the speed of a reaction by

(90) _____ the activation energy of the reaction. They do not provide (91) _____

_____ (G) to the reaction and do not alter the change in (92) _____ _____ of the

reaction. Enzymes function as biological (93) _____ because they increase the rate of chemical

reactions but do not take part in the reactions themselves. Reactions occur in the (94) _____ site of

the enzyme; this site is specific for a single type of (95) _____, and this specificity is currently

explained by the (96) _____ _____ hypothesis. Three mechanisms explain the catalytic

ability of enzymes: they use their (97) _____ _____ to bring the (98) _____ closer

together; they expose substrates to altered (99) _____ environments that promote catalysis; and they

change the (100) _____ of the substrate(s) to help distort them toward the (101) _____ state.

Matching

Match each of the following terms with its correct definition or descriptor.

102.	_____	Cofactor	A.	An organic molecule essential for catalytic activity
103.	_____	Catalyst	B.	Basis for enzyme specificity
104.	_____	Activation energy	C.	Reacting molecules after attaining E_a
105.	_____	Enzyme cycle	D.	Increases the kinetic instability of a reaction without taking part in the reaction
106.	_____	Coenzyme	E.	These are often metals and are required by some enzymes
107.	_____	Induced fit	F.	Kinetic barrier for exergonic reactions
108.	_____	Transition state	G.	Results from fact enzymes are unchanged by their catalytic reactions

Complete the Table

109. There are three mechanisms that contribute to the catalytic function of enzymes. Complete the following table with specific information about these mechanisms.

Mechanism	Information
A.	
B.	
C.	

True/False

Mark if the statement is true (T) or false (F). If the statement is false, justify your answer in the lines below each statement.

110. _____ A spark used to initiate combustion of propane provides the E_a for the reaction.

_____

_____

111. _____ Enzymes provide the activation energy required for exergonic and endergonic biological reactions.

_____

_____

112. _____ The activation energy of chemical but not biological reactions can be provided by heat.

_____

_____

Short Answer

113. Compare kinetic instability with thermodynamic instability.

_____

_____

4.5 Conditions and Factors that Affect Enzyme Activity [pp. 85–90]

Section Review (Fill-in-the-Blanks)

When a substrate is in excess, the catalytic rate (114) _____ as enzyme concentration increases. In

contrast, at a fixed concentration of enzyme, catalytic rate (115) _____ with increasing substrate but

peaks when the active sites are (116) _____. Non-substrate molecules that slow or stop enzymatic

reactions are called (117) _____. (118) _____ inhibitors have shapes similar to the natural

substrate and act by binding the (119) _____ _____. (120) _____ inhibitors are

molecules that bind elsewhere on the enzyme, causing a change in (121) _____ of the enzyme.

Regulation of the enzymes of metabolic pathways may occur through (122) _____ regulation. This

resembles non-competitive inhibition except that activity may be (123) _____ or

(124) _____. An example of the former is feedback inhibition, where the (125) _____

_____ of the pathway is the allosteric regulator. Alternatively, enzymes may be activated or

inactivated by (126) _____ modification—for example, through the addition or removal of a

phosphate group.

Identification

Identify the mechanism of regulation.

127. Competitive inhibition:

_____

_____

128. Allosteric regulation:

_____

_____

129. Feedback inhibition:

_____

_____

130. Phosphorylation:

_____

_____

131. Proteolytic cleavage:

_____

_____

Identify how each of the following types of physical or chemical factors affects enzyme function.

132. Increasing temperature:

_____

_____

133. pH:

_____

_____

True/False

Mark if the statement is true (T) or false (F). If the statement is false, justify your answer in the lines below each statement.

134. _____ Irreversible inhibition can be overcome by making more enzyme.

_____

_____

135. _____ Protein kinases are common allosteric regulators that remove a phosphate group from the allosteric site.

_____

_____

136. _____ An allosteric inhibitor converts an enzyme to the high-affinity conformation.

_____

_____

1. Which of the following represents a form of potential energy? [p. 72]
   a. light
   b. electricity
   c. glucose
   d. heat

2. Which statement is true? [pp. 72–73]
   a. A hydroelectric plant is an example of an open system.
   b. A hydroelectric plant converts the potential energy of water to the kinetic energy of electricity.
   c. Earth is an open system.
   d. A greenhouse is an isolated system.

3. Which term refers to the disorder in a system? [pp. 73–74]
   a. enthalpy
   b. anabolism
   c. free energy
   d. entropy

4. Which statement is false? [pp. 74–75]
   a. A living cell has low entropy but its surroundings have high entropy.
   b. A living cell obeys the second law of thermodynamics.
   c. After a cell dies, its entropy increases.
   d. A living cell is a closed system.

5. Which statement is false? [p. 76]
   a. Methane has high enthalpy.
   b. Ice has low enthalpy.
   c. Ice has high entropy.
   d. Steam has higher entropy than liquid water.

6. Which statement would NOT be true for a chemical reaction that has a negative ΔG? [pp. 76–77]
   a. The reaction would be spontaneous.
   b. The reaction would release free energy.
   c. The reaction would be endergonic.
   d. In an isolated system, the reaction would run to equilibrium.

7. Which statement is true regarding spontaneous reactions? [pp. 76–77]
   a. They have a positive ΔG.
   b. They tend to happen if the reaction increases disorder.
   c. They tend to happen if the reaction increases enthalpy.
   d. They are endergonic.

8. Which statement about cellular metabolism is NOT true? [pp. 77–78]
   a. Anabolism refers to the breakdown of organic (food) molecules.
   b. Catabolic pathways may have endergonic reactions.
   c. The sum of the free energy changes arising from cellular metabolism has a negative ΔG.
   d. When an organism dies, ΔG of the system eventually reaches 0.

9. Which of the following is NOT true of ATP? [p. 79]
   a. Its hydrolysis reduces intramolecular repulsion.
   b. Its hydrolysis requires a large amount of free energy.
   c. Its hydrolysis in aqueous solution is kinetically slow.
   d. Release of the P_i upon hydrolysis increases the entropy of the system.

10. Which statement is NOT true of a coupled reaction? [pp. 79–80]

    a. It has an overall positive ΔG.

    b. It links exergonic and endergonic reactions.

    c. It is spontaneous.

    d. It releases free energy.

11. Which of the following statements about activation energy is true? [pp. 81–82]

    a. It is a kinetic barrier to spontaneous reactions.

    b. It is provided by enzymes.

    c. It is provided by hydrolysis of ATP.

    d. It increases as a system becomes more thermodynamically stable.

12. Which statement correctly describes a catalyst? [p. 82]

    a. It increases the change in free energy of a reaction.

    b. It undergoes a chemical change during a reaction.

    c. It is always an inorganic molecule.

    d. It speeds up a chemical reaction.

13. Which statement is NOT true for enzymes? [pp. 82–83]

    a. They catalyze a specific reaction.

    b. They are unchanged by the reaction.

    c. They temporarily combine with the substrate.

    d. They make an endergonic reaction proceed spontaneously.

14. Which is an inorganic enzyme helper? [p. 84]

    a. a coenzyme

    b. an activator

    c. a cofactor

    d. an allosteric activator

15. Which is an organic enzyme helper? [p. 84]

    a. a coenzyme

    b. an inhibitor

    c. a cofactor

    d. an allosteric activator

16. Which of the following statements describes the enzyme cycle? [p. 84]

    a. Enzymes cycle between one conformation and another.

    b. After catalysis, enzymes are released unchanged to bind another substrate.

    c. Enzymes are continuously cycling energy between exergonic and endergonic reactions.

    d. Enzyme active sites cycle between high affinity and low affinity.

17. Which statement is NOT true of an enzyme-catalyzed reaction? [pp. 84–85]

    a. The enzyme helps the reactant(s) reach the transition state.

    b. An enzyme catalyst is necessary because the reaction is not spontaneous.

    c. Its efficiency may be affected by a vitamin deficiency.

    d. At transition state the reactant(s) has high enthalpy.

18. Which has a shape similar to an enzyme's substrate? [pp. 85–86]

    a. a competitive inhibitor

    b. an allosteric inhibitor

    c. a non-competitive inhibitor

    d. a coenzyme inhibitor

19. Which factor does NOT affect enzyme activity? [pp. 85–90]

    a. temperature

    b. pH

    c. substrate concentration

    d. free energy

20. Which statement about feedback inhibition is true? [p. 88]

a. The inhibitor induces a conformational change from the low-affinity to the high-affinity state.

b. It involves allosteric binding of pathway end products to early enzymes of a pathway.

c. It occurs when the binding site of an enzyme is saturated.

d. It results from competition for the active site.

21. Which statement about enzyme activity is NOT true? [pp. 88–90]

a. Increasing the temperature of an enzyme reaction will destroy the enzyme structure.

b. Enzyme activity is maximal at a characteristic pH.

c. Enzyme activity can be reversibly altered by phosphorylation.

d. An example of enzyme activation through covalent modification is proteolytic cleavage.

INTEGRATING AND APPLYING KEY CONCEPTS

1. Explain why ATP is called the primary coupling agent. Consider why ADP might not provide as much energy as a coupling agent compared to ATP.

2. Explain how phosphorylation of a reactant in a reaction allows an endergonic reaction to proceed. Make sure you distinguish between the *enzyme-catalyzed* reaction and the *net* reaction and that you understand why this is not *hydrolysis* of ATP.

5 Cell Membranes and Signalling

TOPIC MAP

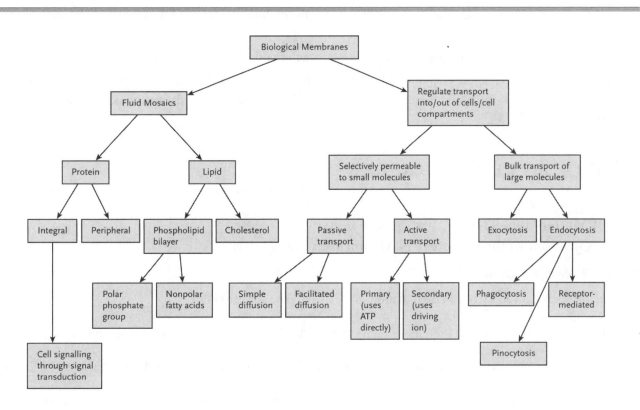

LEARNING OUTCOMES AND STUDY STRATEGIES

By the end of this chapter, you should be able to

■ Describe the fluid mosaic model and how it relates to membrane transport and membrane structure

■ Explain what makes the plasma membrane so important and how its structure can be altered in response to changes in temperature

■ Clearly distinguish between all of the various forms of passive and active transport and give examples of molecules transported by the various types of processes

■ Explain the differences between endocytosis, exocytosis, and phagocytosis, giving examples of uses for each

■ Describe the process of signal transduction using surface receptors and understand how it relates to one of the seven characteristics of life

Study strategies for this chapter:

- Review the topic map above to get an overview of the chapter.

- As you read the textbook, focus on understanding the concepts and don't forget to carefully examine the figures and read the figure legends. Make sure, as you read, that you can answer the questions in each Study Break.

- Do not try to work through all of this material in one setting. Do one section at a time, paying attention to new terms and processes, and then work through the corresponding section of the study guide.

- Try devising your own topic map, adding to it with each major section of the chapter.

- After you have finished the chapter, go back to the beginning of the chapter and see if you can expand on the points within the Study Plan. Finally, do the Self-Test questions in the textbook and study guide.

INTERACTIVE EXERCISES

Why It Matters [pp. 92–93]
5.1 An Overview of the Structure of Membranes [pp. 93–94]

Section Review (Fill-in-the-Blanks)

Cystic fibrosis is caused by a genetic mutation in CFTR, a gene for a(n) (1) _____ _____

protein. This plasma membrane protein normally transports (2) _____ out of lung and intestinal

mucosal epithelial cells, establishing a high ion concentration outside the cells. Key to maintaining this is the

fact that the plasma membrane is a (3) _____ permeable barrier. Our view of cellular membranes is

described by the (4) _____ _____ model. This model states that membranes consist of a(n)

(5) _____ bilayer in which (6) _____ float freely, and that membranes contain an assortment

of (7) _____ that are asymmetrically distributed between the two (8) _____ of the membrane

bilayers.

Short Answer

9. Describe the experimental evidence for the asymmetrical organization of membranes.

   _____

   _____

10. Describe the Frye–Edidin experiment.

_____

_____

True/False

Mark if the statement is true (T) or false (F). If the statement is false, justify your answer in the lines below each statement.

11. _____ Lipid bilayers are less than 10 nm thick.

_____

_____

12. _____ Lipid molecules within a bilayer can vibrate, spin, move sideways, and flip-flop between the two layers.

_____

_____

5.2 The Lipid Fabric of a Membrane [pp. 94–97]

Section Review (Fill-in-the-Blanks)

(13) _____ are the dominant lipids in membranes. Critical to their barrier function is their

(14) _____ polar head groups and their (15) _____ fatty acid tails. Molecules with both

qualities are said to be (16) _____. In aqueous solution, these molecules form bilayers with the

(17) _____ regions facing out and the (18) _____ tails associated together in the interior.

Membrane fluidity is affected by temperature and the (19) _____ _____ composition of the

membrane lipids. Fully (20) _____ fatty acids are linear, whereas (21) _____ fatty acids

contain one or more (22) _____-_____ double bonds and are bent. The more

(23) _____ fatty acids in the membrane lipids, the lower the gelling temperature. Organisms that

cannot regulate their body temperature are called (24) _____. They maintain membrane fluidity using

(25) _____, enzymes that catalyze the formation of (26) _____ bonds in the fatty acid tails.

Matching

Match each of the following terms with its correct descriptor or definition.

27. _____ Unsaturated fatty acid   A.   Develops spontaneously in aqueous solution

28. _____ Hydrophilic   B.   Molecule that possesses polar and non-polar regions

29. _____ Hydrophobic   C.   Contains linear carbon chain with one or more carbon-carbon double bonds

30. _____ Amphipathic   D.   Molecules found in the membranes of animals but not plants

31. _____ Desaturases   E.   Unable to regulate body temperature

32. _____ Lipid bilayer   F.   Non-polar

33. _____ Cholesterol   G.   Enzymes that create double bonds in fatty acids

34. _____ Ectotherm   H.   Polar

True/False

Mark if the statement is true (T) or false (F). If the statement is false, justify your answer in the lines below each statement.

35. _____ Membranes with higher amounts of saturated fatty acids will remain fluid and functional at higher temperatures.

_____

_____

36. _____ Desaturases remove hydrogen atoms from the phosphate groups of phospholipids.

_____

_____

37. _____ At low temperatures, sterols help restrain the movement of membrane lipids.

_____

_____

Short Answer

38. Explain how the presence of double bonds in the fatty acids of phospholipids influences membrane fluidity.

_____

_____

39. Explain why sterols are important membrane components.

_____

_____

40. Explain how extreme temperature adversely affects cell membrane structures.

_____

_____

5.3 Membrane Proteins [pp. 97–100]

Section Review (Fill-in-the-Blanks)

The unique set of (41) _____ embedded in a membrane determines its function. (42) _____

proteins are responsible for controlling the movement of hydrophilic molecules into and out of the cell. Those

with (43) _____ activity are critical for such processes as respiratory and photosynthetic

(44) _____ transport. Receptor proteins are responsible for (45) _____ _____,

which, upon binding of signal molecules elicits an intracellular response. Finally, proteins on either side of

the membrane can function in (46) _____ or cell–cell (47) _____. Proteins embedded in the

lipid bilayer are called (48) _____ _____ proteins. They are characterized by

(49) _____ domains that interact with the membrane's hydrophobic core. In contrast,

(50) _____ membranes associate with the membrane surfaces through non-covalent

(51) _____ and (52) _____ bonds.

Complete the Table

53. Complete the following table.

Membrane Protein	Structural Characteristics	Example Function
Peripheral	A.	B.
Integral	C.	D.

Short Answer

54. Explain how an integral membrane protein can be recognized based on analysis of its amino acid sequence.

_____

_____

Labelling

55. Identify each labelled part in the following illustration of an animal cell plasma membrane.

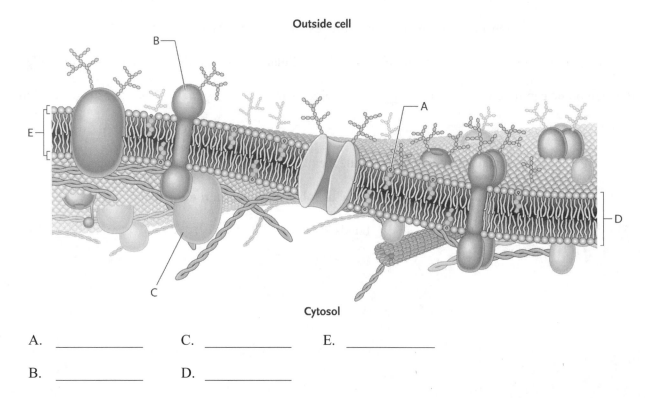

Outside cell

Cytosol

A. _____   C. _____   E. _____

B. _____   D. _____

5.4 Passive Membrane Transport [pp. 100–104]

Section Review (Fill-in-the-Blanks)

Membranes control what enters and exits the cell because of their (56) _____ nature. However

certain small molecules cross the membrane from a region of (57) _____ concentration to one of

(58) _____ concentration, without the expenditure of energy: this process is referred to as

(59) _____. A molecule's (60) _____ and (61) _____ determines how quickly this

happens. Simple diffusion occurs with molecules that are small and (62) _____ or amphipathic, so

that they can move through the (63) _____ interior of the membrane. The process of

(64) _____ diffusion is faster because of the involvement of transport proteins. Two types of integral

membrane protein carry out this process: (65) _____ proteins and (66) _____ proteins. The

former create hydrophilic (67) _____ in the membrane through which water and (68) _____

pass, whereas the latter (69) _____ a single specific solute and undergoes a (70) _____

change that moves the (71) _____-binding site from one side of the membrane to the other. Diffusion

of water molecules across a selectively permeable membrane is specifically referred to as (72) _____.

This process occurs constantly in living cells and can occur by passive diffusion or through the help of

channel proteins called (73) _____.

Matching

Match each of the following terms with its correct descriptor or definition.

74. ____	Hypotonic environment	A.	Containing dissolved substances at concentrations equal to that of the cytoplasm
75. ____	Hypertonic environment	B.	A protein channel critical to the transport of most ions
76. ____	Isotonic environment	C.	A membrane protein that forms a hydrophilic channel through which water and ions can pass
77. ____	Gated channel	D.	Containing dissolved substances at concentrations greater than the cytoplasm
78. ____	Channel protein	E.	Channel protein that facilitates the diffusion of water

79. _____ Carrier protein

F. A transport protein that binds to a single solute particle to move it across the plasma membrane

80. _____ Aquaporin

G. Containing dissolved substances at concentrations less than that of the cytoplasm

True/False

Mark if the statement is true (T) or false (F). If the statement is false, justify your answer in the lines below each statement.

81. _____ During diffusion or osmosis, minimum entropy is reached at equilibrium.

_____

_____

82. _____ Membranes are relatively impermeable to ions because of the charge and hydration shell of the ions.

_____

_____

Short Answer

83. Compare and contrast simple diffusion with facilitated diffusion.

_____

_____

84. Discuss the basis for the specificity of aquaporins for water molecules.

_____

_____

85. What would happen if isolated animal cells were placed in a hypotonic solution?

_____

_____

Labelling

86. Identify each labelled part in the following figure.

A. _____

B. _____

C. _____

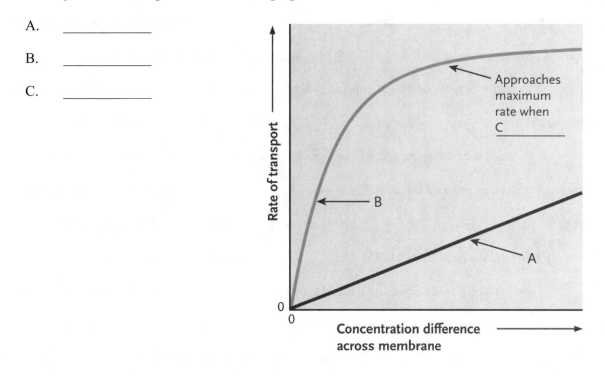

87. Label the following figures of cells undergoing osmosis.

A. _____

B. _____

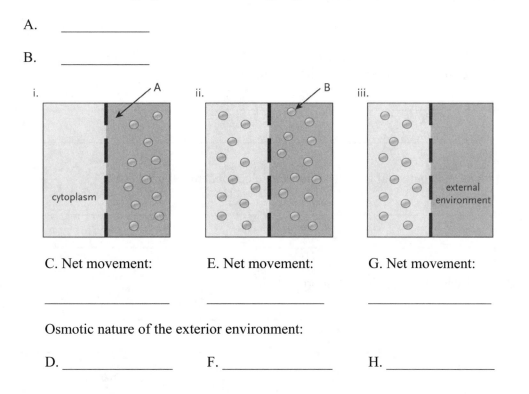

C. Net movement: E. Net movement: G. Net movement:

_____   _____   _____

Osmotic nature of the exterior environment:

D. _____   F. _____   H. _____

5.5 Active Membrane Transport [pp. 104–107]

Section Review (Fill-in-the-Blanks)

Active transport is (88) _____-dependent and moves ions or molecules against their concentration

gradient. Transport proteins contain (89) _____ sites for specific substances, undergo

(90) _____ changes to move bound substrates across the membrane and become saturated at high

concentrations of (91) _____ . In (92) _____ active transport, energy comes from

(93) _____ and this may represent as much as 25% to the cell's requirements for this molecule. This

type of transport is used to generate concentration (94) _____ of positively charged ions and these, in

turn, can be used to power (95) _____ active transport. For example, the Na^+/K^+ primary transporter

simultaneously pumps three molecules of (96) _____ out of the cell and two molecules of

(97) _____ into the cell, establishing a membrane (98) _____ that can be used for secondary

transport. This may occur through two processes, depending upon the relative directions of the solute and the

driving (99) _____ . If they move in the same direction, the process is called (100) _____ and

if they move in opposite directions, it is called (101) _____ .

Short Answer

102. Identify the similarities of active transport and facilitated transport.

_____

_____

103. Explain why the membrane potential is referred to as an electrochemical gradient.

_____

_____

104. Name the three main functions of active transport.

_____

_____

Complete the Table

105. Complete the following table by filling in the appropriate description of a listed transport process or by naming the transport process based on the listed description.

Process	Description/Function
Active transport	A.
B.	Cotransported solute moves in same direction as driving ion
C.	Exchange diffusion

5.6 Exocytosis and Endocytosis [pp. 107–109]

Section Review (Fill-in-the-Blanks)

Molecules larger than amino acids or monosaccharides are transported into and out of eukaryotic cells by

(106) _____ and (107) _____, respectively. In the latter, a(n) (108) _____ carrying

secreted materials travel to, and fuses with, the (109) _____ _____. In

(110) _____, materials outside the cell become enclosed in a segment of plasma membrane, which

bulges inward and pinches off to form a(n) (111) _____ _____ inside the cell. There are two

distinct pathways by which this happens: (112) _____-_____ endocytosis, sometimes called

pinocytosis, and (113) _____-_____ endocytosis, which involves formation of vesicles at

clathrin-coated pits. Endocytic vesicles generally fuse with (114) _____, leading to digestion of the

contents and (115) _____ of the resulting small molecules across the vesicle (116) _____.

Some cells, such as certain white blood cells and protists, take in much larger substrates, including whole

cells, in a process called (117) _____.

Matching

Match each of the following substrates with its correct method of entry or exit from the cell.

118. ____	Amoeba prey	A.	Exocytosis
119. ____	Waste material	B.	Endocytosis
120. ____	Extracellular dissolved solutes	C.	Phagocytosis
121. ____	Plant cell wall carbohydrates		
122. ____	Bacterial pathogens in the bloodstream of an infected person		

Short Answer

123. What do endocytosis, exocytosis, and active transport have in common?

_____

_____

124. Explain the process of receptor-mediated endocytosis.

_____

_____

5.7 Role of Membranes in Cell Signalling [pp. 109–112]

Section Review (Fill-in-the-Blanks)

Cells sense and respond to environmental changes through the perception of chemical or physical

(125) _____. These lead to cellular responses through a (126) _____ _____

cascade. These cascades usually consist of three steps: reception, followed by (127) _____

_____, finally triggering a cellular (128) _____. Reception often involves the binding of an

extracellular signal (129) _____ by an integral (130) _____ protein. This binding is specific,

similar to enzyme substrate binding, and results in a molecular change that (131) _____ the

cytoplasmic activity of the protein. Quite often the result is a (132) _____ cascade involving a series

of phosphorylation events catalyzed by protein (133) _____. Because each step in these pathways

involves enzyme activation, the signal is (134) _____ so that only a few signal molecules generate a

full cellular response. This response is balanced or reversed by protein (135) _____, which, unlike

the protein kinases, are continuously (136) _____ in the cell.

Labelling

137. Identify each labelled part in the following figure.

A. _____

B. _____

C. _____

D. _____

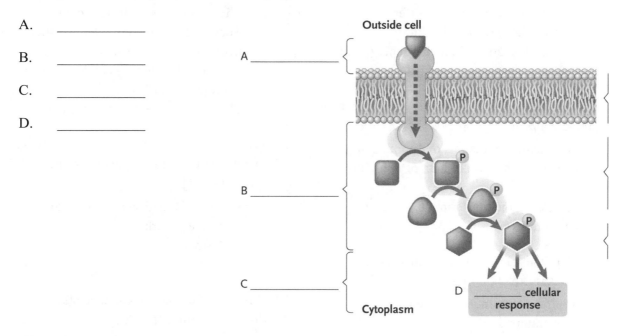

Short Answer

138. Describe the molecular events in a phosphorylation cascade.

_____

_____

139. Explain, using a phosphorylation cascade as an example, how signal transduction can result in a cellular response.

_____

_____

SELF-TEST

1. Which of the following statements about the fluid mosaic model is false? [pp. 93–94]

   a. The lipids within the membrane form a continuously moving mosaic.
   b. The proteins are asymmetrically distributed.
   c. The lipids can spin, vibrate, and move laterally but rarely move from one side to the other.
   d. The proteins can move within the membrane.

2. Which of the following is NOT a structural component of plant membranes? [pp. 95–96]

   a. phospholipids
   b. fatty acids
   c. cholesterol
   d. varying levels of saturation and unsaturation

3. Why do phospholipids spontaneously assemble into bilayers in aqueous environments? [p. 96]

   a. because of the hydrophilic effect
   b. because they are amphipathic
   c. because this gives the highest energy state
   d. because they contain fatty acids

4. Which of the following would cause a reduced gelling temperature? [pp. 96–97]

   a. increasing the amounts of saturated lipids
   b. increasing the unsaturation of lipid fatty acids
   c. decreasing the transcription levels of desaturases

5. Which of the following statements about desaturases is NOT correct? [pp. 96–97]

   a. Their expression is increased at higher temperatures.
   b. They remove two hydrogen atoms from adjacent carbon atoms in fatty acids.
   c. They create double bonds in the fatty acids of lipids.
   d. They are enzymes that help maintain a fluid membrane.

6. Which of the following is NOT a function of membrane proteins? [pp. 97–98]

   a. transport
   b. recognition/adhesion
   c. receptor
   d. diffusion barrier

7. Which is NOT a shared feature of peripheral and integral membrane proteins? [pp. 97–100]

   a. multiple stretches of 17–20 hydrophohic amino acids in the primary sequence
   b. may function in recognition
   c. may function in attachment
   d. hydrophilic surface domains

8. Which of the following statements about integral membrane proteins is false? [pp. 98–99]

   a. They contain polar head groups.
   b. They often have more than one stretch of hydrophobic amino acids.
   c. The folded protein has hydrophobic and hydrophilic surface regions.
   d. They can have enzymatic activity.

9. Which of the following would likely cross the membrane through simple diffusion? [pp. 100–101]

   a. small uncharged sugars such as glucose
   b. oxygen and carbon dioxide
   c. very small ions
   d. hormones

10. Which of the following statements about diffusion is true? [p. 100]

   a. Minimum entropy is reached at equilibrium
   b. The movement of solutes stops when equilibrium is reached
   c. The process is driven by entropy
   d. There is an indirect expenditure of energy

11. Which is least likely to cross a plasma membrane by simple diffusion? [pp. 100–101]

   a. O_2
   b. H_2O
   c. CO_2
   d. Na^+

12. Which describes aquaporins? [pp. 101–104]

   a. They bind a molecule of water and transport it after undergoing a conformational change.
   b. They use Na^+ as a driving ion in symport.
   c. They are voltage-gated channels.
   d. They form a substrate-specific hydrophilic channel.

13. Which of the following is NOT energy-dependent? [pp. 102–107]

   a. K^+-gated channel
   b. Na^+/K^+ pump
   c. receptor-mediated endocytosis
   d. symport

In a two-compartment system separated by cellophane, compartment A is filled with a 0.5 M sucrose solution and compartment B is filled with a 1 M sucrose solution. Given that cellophane is only permeable to the water, characterize the following aspects of the system in questions 14 to 16. [pp. 100–104]

14. Which term describes compartment B relative to compartment A?

    a. B is hypotonic
    b. B is isotonic
    c. B is hypertonic

15. Given that compartment A is contained in a cellophane bag, which of the following describes what happens when the bag is suspended in a beaker of solution B?

    a. There would be no net movement of sucrose.
    b. There would be net movement of water from A to B.
    c. There would be net movement of sucrose from B to A.

16. Which is false?

    a. Water would move from B to A until the bag could not swell any further.
    b. Movement across the cellophane barrier is through osmosis.
    c. Movement would stop once equilibrium was reached.
    d. At equilibrium there would be maximum entropy.

17. Which would NOT be transported through primary active transport? [p. 105]

    a. H^+
    b. Ca^{2+}
    c. K^+
    d. H_2O

18. Which of the following statements about calcium pumps is false? [pp. 104–106]

    a. They use ATP for energy.
    b. They push calcium out of the cytoplasm.
    c. They are rare in animal cells.
    d. Their activity generates an electrochemical gradient.

19. Which is NOT true of secondary active transport? [p. 107]

    a. They may simultaneously transport two solutes in the same direction.
    b. The transporter relies on ion gradients to drive transport.
    c. ATP provides the energy to drive transport.
    d. Antiporters are secondary active transporters.

20. Which of the following is NOT associated with receptor-mediated endocytosis? [pp. 108–109]

    a. It involves binding of the substrate by clathrin.
    b. The endocytic vesicle fuses with a lysosome.
    c. The solute binds to a specific cell surface receptor.
    d. The process requires the production of ATP by the cell.

21. Which statement about exocytosis is false? [pp. 107–109]

    a. It is often called pinocytosis.
    b. It occurs between the various components of the endomembrane system.
    c. It is prevalent in glandular/secretory cells.
    d. It is essential to cell wall growth in plants.

22. Which is NOT associated with cell signalling using surface receptors? [pp. 109–112]

    a. it is the basis for adaptation in living organisms
    b. diffusion
    c. ATP
    d. a fluid membrane

INTEGRATING AND APPLYING KEY CONCEPTS

1. Although people are susceptible to hypothermia when exposed to freezing temperatures for any length of time without the proper clothing, it is estimated that the majority of biomass in the Southern Ocean of Antarctica are archaea. These prokaryotes thrive at sub-zero temperatures. Discuss one or more of the likely differences between humans and archaea that allow only the latter to thrive.

2. Cholesterol is transported in the blood in large complexes known as lipoproteins; a major cholesterol-containing lipoprotein is low-density lipoprotein (LDL). Some individuals have a genetic defect that results in chronic elevated levels of cholesterol in their blood. What defect might explain this condition?

3. In this chapter, you learned about the discovery of the CF gene and the results of a defect in this gene. Explain, at the molecular level, why such a defect would have some of the effects it does, and describe the molecular events that happen with a normal CFTR gene.

6 Cellular Respiration

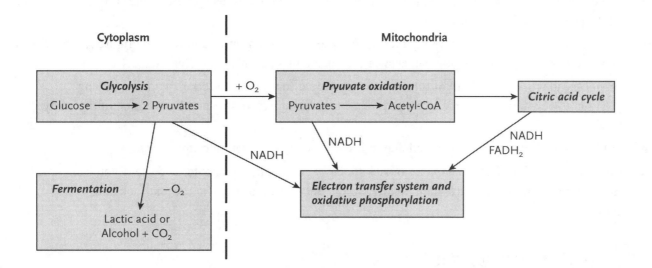

LEARNING OUTCOMES AND STUDY STRATEGIES

By the end of this chapter, you should be able to

- Identify how chemicals can be sources of energy and how redox reactions are central to respiration

- Describe the purpose and basic components of cellular respiration, identifying the cellular location for each

- Describe what an electron transport chain is, where the respiratory chain is found, how it functions, and how its function is coupled to the production of energy

- Define chemiosmosis, proton-motive force, and oxidative phosphorylation, and distinguish between the catabolic and anabolic roles of these pathways and products

- Calculate the energy yield from the various components of eukaryotic aerobic respiration and understand why this is less than 100% efficient

- Describe the role of oxygen in cellular respiration and the alternatives to the use of oxygen

- Describe the similarities and differences between eukaryotes and the prokaryotes

Study strategies for this chapter:

- Review the topic map above to get an overview of the chapter.

- This chapter has extensive chemical pathways. Do not try to memorize all of the chemical reactions but focus instead on understanding how the process works to generate energy for the cell.

- Concentrate on the key concepts: how does each stage relate to the other two, what are the substrates and products of each.

- Make sure you understand any regulatory or environmental conditions that affect the flow of electrons through these pathways.

- As you read the textbook, don't forget to carefully examine the figures and read the figure legends. Make sure, as you read, that you can answer the questions in each Study Break.

- Do not try to work through all of this material in one setting. Do one section at a time, paying attention to new terms and processes, and then work through the corresponding section of the study guide.

- Try devising your own topic map, adding to it with each major section of the chapter.

- After you have finished the chapter, go back to the beginning of the chapter and see if you can expand on the points within the Study Plan. Finally, do the Self-Test questions in the textbook and study guide.

INTERACTIVE EXERCISES

Why It Matters [pp. 115–116]
6.1 The Chemical Basis of Cellular Respiration [pp. 116–118]

Section Review (Fill-in-the-Blanks)

The eukaryotic mitochondrion is the site of key reactions of cellular (1) _____, the process by which

the energy of (2) _____ molecules is extracted and converted to a form usable by the cell. The vast

majority of energy in the biosphere enters through the trapping of solar energy in the process of

(3) _____. The energy is used to convert carbon dioxide and water to high-energy (4) _____

molecules that are, in turn, used almost universally as energy sources for cellular activities. The energy in

molecules such as glucose results from the fact that (5) _____ can be easily removed and used to do

(6) _____. The (7) _____ of chemicals to obtain energy is a process that involves the

(8) _____ of electrons and because these reactions are always coupled with (9) _____

reactions, where electrons are transferred to another molecule, the term (10) _____ is used for short.

The energy liberated through respiration is converted to (11) _____, which can be used for many

energy-requiring cellular reactions.

Matching

Match each of the following terms with its correct definition.

12. ____ Oxidation

    A. A chemical from which electrons have been removed

13. ____ Oxidized

    B. A group of enzymes that remove protons and electrons from molecules being oxidized

14. ____ Reduction

    C. A chemical to which electrons have been added

15. ____ Reduced

    D. A coenzyme that carries electrons and protons

16. ____ Redox reactions

    E. Coupled reactions where electrons released from one chemical are added to another chemical

17. ____ Dehydrogenases

    F. Process of removing electrons from a chemical

18. ____ NAD^+

    G. Process of adding electrons to a chemical

Complete the Table

19. Choose the most appropriate descriptor from the pairs in the first column to describe photosynthesis and cellular respiration.

Descriptor	Photosynthesis	Cellular Respiration	Chemical or Result
makes/breaks	A.	B.	Sugars
uses/releases	C.	D.	O_2
uses/releases	E.	F.	CO_2
stores/releases	G.	H.	Net energy

True/False

Mark if the statement is true (T) or false (F). If the statement is false, justify your answer in the lines below each statement.

20. _____ CO_2 is highly oxidized, so is not a good energy source.

_____

_____

21. _____ Electrons that move closer to the atom's nucleus gain energy.

_____

_____

22. _____ Oxidation reactions involve the transfer of electrons to oxygen.

_____

_____

Short Answer

23. For the combustion of methane, $CH_4 + O_2 \rightarrow CO_2 + H_2O$, identify which molecule(s) is(are) oxidized and reduced and why, without the obvious transfer of electrons, this is still a redox reaction.

_____

_____

6.2 Cellular Respiration: An Overview [pp. 118–119]
6.3 Glycolysis: The Splitting of Glucose [pp. 120–122]
6.4 Pyruvate Oxidation and the Citric Acid Cycle [pp. 122–123]

Section Review (Fill-in-the-Blanks)

Cellular respiration occurs in (24) _____ stages, beginning with (25) _____, where glucose

is converted to two molecules of (26) _____. These are oxidized and the products enter the

(27) _____ _____ cycle for complete oxidation to (28) _____. These first two

stages produce ATP through (29) _____-_____ phosphorylation, and also produce the high-

energy reduced coenzymes (30) _____ and _____. It is through these reduced coenzymes

that high-energy electrons enter the respiratory (31) _____ _____ _____. This is a

critical component of the last stage of cellular respiration: (32) _____ phosphorylation. The energy in the electrons is used to establish a(n) (33) _____ gradient across the membrane that, in turn, is used

to synthesize more (34) _____. Respiration occurs in both prokaryotes and eukaryotes; however, in

eukaryotes the second and third stages occur in the (35) _____.

Matching

Match each of the following terms with its correct definition or descriptor.

36. ____ Substrate-level phosphorylation

    A. Involves an enzyme complex that catalyzes the production of CO_2, NADH, and acetyl coA

37. ____ Decarboxylation

    B. Glycolysis

38. ____ Pyruvate oxidation

    C. Transfer of phosphate from a phosphorylated molecule to ADP

39. ____ Occurs in cytoplasm

    D. Produced in citric acid cycle

40. ____ Occurs in inner mitochondrial membrane

    E. Produces CO_2

41. ____ $DAFH_2$

    F. Electron transport chain

True/False

Mark if the statement is true (T) or false (F). If the statement is false, justify your answer in the lines below each statement.

42. _____ Glycolysis is a typically eukaryotic process.

_____

_____

43. _____ In animal cells, glycolysis and formation of acetyl coA both occur in the cytoplasm.

_____

_____

44. _____ Pyruvate enters the mitochondrion by diffusion.

_____

_____

Short Answer

45. What is the evidence that glycolysis is one of the most ancient of all metabolic pathways?

_____

_____

46. Explain why four molecules of ATP are made during glycolysis but the ATP *yield is only two molecules.*

_____

_____

47. Since there are six carbons in two molecules of pyruvate, just as there are six carbons in glucose, why is there less free energy in two molecules of pyruvate?

_____

_____

Complete the Table

48. The following represents a "balance sheet" for the first two stages of cellular respiration.

Stage	Pathway or Reactions	Substrate	Net Products
First stage	A.	B.	C.
	Pyruvate oxidation	D.	E.
Second stage	F.	G.	H.

6.5 Oxidative Phosphorylation: Electron Transport and Chemiosmosis [pp. 123–129]

Section Review (Fill-in-the-Blanks)

In the third stage of cellular respiration, electrons from the reduced coenzymes (49) _____ and

(50) _____ are transferred through an electron transport chain. The chain consists of four major

multi-protein (51) _____ and two smaller (52) _____ carriers. The chain is located within

the mitochondrial (53) _____ _____. Each electron transfer is (54) _____, meaning that free energy is released, so movement through the chain is (55) _____. The free energy that is

released is used to generate a(n) (56) _____ gradient across the membrane, the so-called proton

(57) _____ _____. Through the process of (58) _____, the force can be used to

drive nutrient (59) _____ or to generate ATP through the action of the membrane-bound ATP

(60) _____. This is a multi-enzyme complex that couples the flow of protons (61) _____

their gradient with the synthesis of ATP from (62) _____ and (63) _____. In most cases,

ATP synthesis is coupled with (64) _____ _____; however, they can be uncoupled by

chemical uncouplers called (65) _____ or by uncoupling proteins. The result is the energy released

by electron flow in the form of (66) _____.

Matching

Match each of the following terms with its correct definition or descriptor.

67. _____	ATP synthase	A.	Fe-containing prosthetic group that accepts and donates electrons
68. _____	Heme	B.	The use of a proton motive force to do work
69. _____	Oxidative phosphorylation	C.	Region with high concentration of protons
70. _____	Proton-motive force	D.	An uncoupler of oxidative phosphorylation
71. _____	Chemiosmosis	E.	A proton and voltage gradient that is a source of potential energy
72. _____	Intermembrane compartment	F.	The synthesis of ATP using the energy from chemical oxidation
73. _____	Ionophore	G.	An enzyme that uses a H^+ gradient to generate ATP

Short Answer

74. Differentiate between oxidative phosphorylation and substrate-level phosphorylation.

_____

_____

75. Explain the role of reduced coenzymes in generating ATP.

_____

_____

76. Compare the location of ATP synthase in the mitochondrion and prokaryotes.

_____

_____

77. Explain the connection between the electron transport chain, oxidative phosphorylation, and the mechanism used by hibernating mammals and newborn infants to generate body heat.

_____

_____

Labelling

78. Identify each part of the mitochondrion.

A.   _____

B.   _____

C.   _____

D.   _____

E.   _____

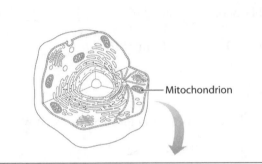

Locate the following structures or processes in the figure:

79. _____   Glycolysis

80. _____   Pyruvate oxidation

81. _____   Citric acid cycle

82. _____   Electron transport chain

83. _____   ATP synthase

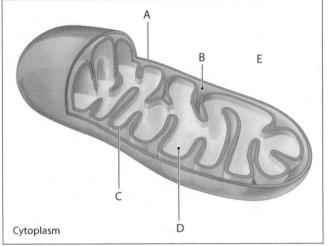

Sequence

84. Arrange the following steps of cellular respiration in the correct sequence: _____ _____ _____ _____

A.   citric acid cycle

B.   electron transport chain

C.   glycolysis

D.   pyruvate oxidation

6.6 The Efficiency and Regulation of Cellular Respiration [pp. 129–132]

Section Review (Fill-in-the-Blanks)

Biochemists have calculated that (85) _____ protons are pumped across the mitochondrial inner

membrane for each molecule of NADH oxidized and that 1 ATP is synthesized for every (86) _____

that flow(s) back into the matrix. Therefore, the oxidation of 1 NADH yields approximately

(87) _____ ATP. This is in contrast to the reduced coenzyme (88) _____, which only yields

2 ATP. So theoretically, the maximum net yield of ATP from the complete oxidation of glucose would be

(89) _____ ATP. Considering the caloric content of glucose, this represents an efficiency of

approximately (90) _____ percent. Organics such as (91) _____, _____, and

_____ are also oxidized by cellular respiration. The intermediates of cellular respiration are also used

for (92) _____ reactions, and as a result, the pathways are controlled by (93) _____ and

(94) _____. The glycolytic pathway is controlled through the activation of the early enzyme

(95) _____ by (96) _____. It is inhibited by (97) _____ and (98) _____

from the citric acid cycle.

True/False

Mark if the statement is true (T) or false (F). If the statement is false, justify your answer in the lines
below each statement.

99. _____   In cellular respiration, the ATP is produced in the mitochondrion.

_____

_____

100. _____   Cellular respiration converts only 38% of the energy in glucose to ATP.

_____

_____

101. _____   Respiratory organisms do not produce the maximum theoretical yield of ATP from
cellular respiration.

_____

_____

102. _____ Phosphofructokinase is competitively inhibited by ATP and citrate.

_____

_____

Labelling

103. For this figure depicting the complete oxidation of glucose, identify the correct values for each label.

A. _____

B. _____

C. _____

D. _____

E. _____

F. _____

G. _____

H. _____

I. _____

J. _____

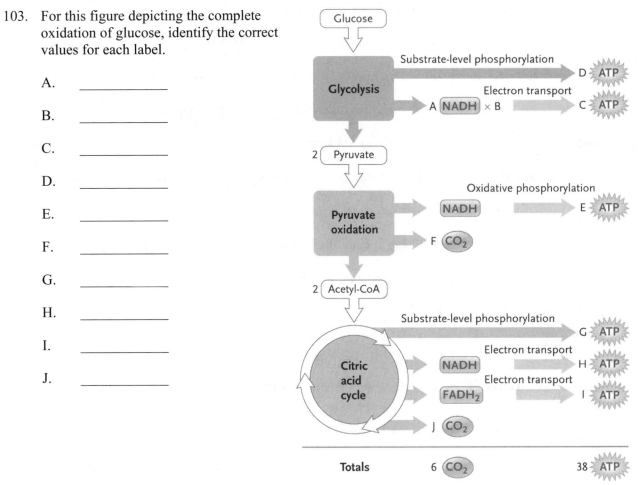

Short Answer

104. Explain why eukaryotes do not produce the theoretical maximum yield of ATP from respiration.

_____

_____

105. Explain why ATP is not a product of electron transport.

_____

_____

6.7 Oxygen and Cellular Respiration [pp. 132–136]

Section Review (Fill-in-the-Blanks)

There are two general mechanisms by which organisms may continue to oxidize fuel molecules and produce

(106) _____ in the absence of oxygen. Eukaryotic cells such as yeast and muscle cells, as well as

some bacteria and archaea, use the process of (107) _____, This process does not utilize electron

transport and (108) _____ phosphorylation but instead reduces (109) _____ in the

cytoplasm. The important result of this reduction is that (110) _____ is regenerated so that glycolysis

may continue to produce ATP by (111) _____-_____ phosphorylation. The second

mechanism, (112) _____ _____, is seen only in some bacteria and archaea. This process

uses molecules such as (113) _____ as terminal electron acceptors. Organisms vary in their ability to

use oxygen: the strict (114) _____ have an absolute requirement, whereas (115) _____

_____ can use oxygen when it is present and adapt when it isn't. Strict (116) _____ cannot

grow in its presence. Underlying this inability is what is called the "paradox of aerobic life," a result of the

production of toxic (117) _____ _____ _____ through partial reduction of oxygen.

Matching

Match each of the following terms with its correct definition or descriptor.

118.	____	Fermentation	A.	Superoxide and peroxide
119.	____	Lactate	B.	Absent in strict anaerobes
120.	____	Alcohol fermentation	C.	Pyruvate + NADH $\rightarrow$ lactate + NAD$^+$
121.	____	ROI	D.	Reducing agent
122.	____	Superoxide dismutase	E.	Present in yogurt
123.	____	Vitamin E	F.	Occurs in baker's yeast

Short Answer

124. Explain in general how ROS are detoxified.

_____

_____

125. Explain how the reduction of oxygen in aerobic respiration is controlled to prevent ROS generation.

_____

_____

Complete the Table

126. Complete the following table describing anaerobic metabolism in muscle cells.

Steps of Anaerobic Metabolism	Location in the Cell	Number of ATP Produced	Number of NADH Produced	O$_2$ Used	End Product
A. Glycolysis					
B. Fermentation					

True/False

Mark if the statement is true (T) or false (F). If the statement is false, justify your answer in the lines below each statement.

127. _____ Fermentation produces less energy than anaerobic respiration, which, in turn, produces less than in aerobic respiration.

_____

_____

128. _____ Anaerobic respiration is seen in yeast cells.

_____

_____

129. _____ The rate of cellular respiration in heart cells can be measured through the rate of oxygen consumption.

_____

_____

1. Which statement about fats is NOT true?
   [p. 116]

   a. They can provide energy through oxidation reactions.

   b. They contain a lot of oxygen molecules.

   c. They contain more potential energy per unit weight than carbohydrates.

   d. They contain a higher proportion of high-energy C-H bonds than carbohydrates.

2. Which of the following is true regarding redox reactions? [p. 117]

   a. Reduction is the loss of electrons.

   b. Oxidation is the combining of electrons with oxygen.

   c. Photosynthesis involves reduction reactions and respiration involves oxidation reactions.

   d. The gain or loss of an electron is not always complete.

3. Which molecule would be produced by a dehydrogenase? [p. 118]

   a. FAD^+

   b. ATP

   c. NADH

   d. H_2O

4. Which of the following is NOT true? [p. 118]

   a. Burning and the respiratory oxidation of glucose both result in the complete oxidation of the molecule.

   b. Cellular respiration is the enzyme-controlled combustion of glucose.

   c. The combustion and the respiratory oxidation of glucose are both energy-liberating processes.

   d. The energy released by combustion of glucose is in the form of CO_2.

5. Which statement about nicotinamide adenine dinucleotide is correct? [p. 118]

   a. It is a coenzyme.

   b. When reduced, it carries an additional two electrons and two protons.

   c. When reduced, it carries an additional two electrons and one proton.

   d. In cellular respiration, it is reduced by hydrogenase enzymes.

6. How many ATP molecules are invested in glycolysis? [p. 120]

   a. 2

   b. 4

   c. 36

   d. 38

7. What is the end product of glycolysis? [p. 120]

   a. lactic acid

   b. pyruvate

   c. citric acid

   d. acetyl-CoA

8. Where in the cell does glycolysis take place? [p. 120]

   a. in the cytoplasm

   b. in the mitochondrial matrix

   c. in the intermembrane compartment

   d. in the inner membrane of mitochondria

9. Which of the following steps of cellular respiration does NOT give rise to ATP? [p. 122]

   a. the citric acid cycle

   b. pyruvate oxidation

   c. glycolysis

   d. the electron transport chain

10. Which of the following explains why two molecules of pyruvate have less potential energy than glucose? [pp. 120–122]

    a. They have fewer bonds than glucose.

    b. They have been oxidized so have less high-energy electrons compared to glucose.

    c. Their carbon atoms are less energetic compared to glucose.

    d. They have more oxygen atoms compared to glucose.

11. Which is NOT associated with the citric acid cycle? [p. 123]

    a. NADH

    b. $FADH_2$

    c. pyruvate

    d. CO_2

12. Which statement regarding electron transport chains is NOT true? [pp. 125–127]

    a. They are found in the plasma membranes of bacteria and archaea.

    b. They convert the energy in NADH and $FADH_2$ to a concentration and voltage gradient across the mitochondrial membrane.

    c. They contain proteins with prosthetic groups.

    d. They produce ATP.

13. Which statement about phosphorylation by the ATP synthase is true? [pp. 126–128]

    a. The substrates are ADP and a high-energy phosphorylated molecule.

    b. It only occurs in eukaryotic cells.

    c. It is associated with both respiratory and photosynthetic electron transport chains.

    d. It occurs in the outer mitochondrial membrane.

14. Why is Peter Mitchell famous? [p. 128]

    a. He proposed the chemiosmotic theory.

    b. He was the first to determine that certain diseases are caused by defects in mitochondrial function.

    c. He first described the process of fermentation.

    d. He identified the ATP synthase.

15. Which of the following statements about the ATP synthase is false? [pp. 127–128]

    a. It is not present in prokaryotic cells.

    b. It is a molecular motor.

    c. Its movement is related to its catalytic activity .

    d. It is fully reversible.

16. Which of the following statements about uncouplers is false? [pp. 128–129]

    a. They destroy the proton gradient across the membrane.

    b. They prevent electron transport chains from generating a proton motive force.

    c. They inhibit the movement of electrons through electron transport chains.

    d. They can be formed naturally in some eukaryotic cells.

17. Which of the following processes does NOT explain why cellular respiration in eukaryotes does not give the maximum yield of 38 ATP? [pp. 129–130]

    a. ATP is used to transport NADH into the mitochondrion.

    b. The mitochondrial membrane is leaky.

    c. Proton motive force is used to transport pyruvate into the mitochondrion.

    d. The use of enzymes to control the combustion of glucose is not as efficient as using fire to burn it.

18. Why is phosphofructokinase allosterically regulated? [pp. 131–132]

    a. so that the cell always has a store of glucose

    b. because the respiratory pathways are used for anabolism as well

    c. so that NADH is always available in the cell

    d. because feedback inhibition is important in avoiding wasted energy

19. Which of the following supplies ATP in muscle cells during exercise, when oxygen is limited? [p. 132]

    a. aerobic respiration

    b. glycolysis

    c. the citric acid cycle

    d. the electron transport chain

20. Where in the cell does the fermentation step take place? [p. 132]

    a. in the cytoplasm

    b. in the mitochondrial matrix

    c. in the intermembrane compartment

    d. in the inner membrane of mitochondria

21. Which of the following produces the sour flavour of yogurt? [p. 132]

    a. glycolysis

    b. the citric acid cycle

    c. the electron transport chain

    d. fermentation

22. Which process is exploited when using *Saccharomyces cerevisiae* to make bread? [p. 133]

    a. glycolysis

    b. the citric acid cycle

    c. the electron transport chain

    d. alcoholic fermentation

23. Which of the following occurs in prokaryotes only? [pp. 133–134]

    a. cytochrome oxidase

    b. anaerobic respiration

    c. facultative anaerobes

    d. alcoholic fermentation

24. Which of the following statements about the cytochrome oxidase of aerobic electron transport chain is false? [pp. 135–136]

    a. It has four prosthetic groups that must be reduced before it will transfer them to oxygen.

    b. It is a universal component of aerobic organisms.

    c. It may be present in facultatively anaerobic organisms or cells.

    d. It probably evolved early.

INTEGRATING AND APPLYING KEY CONCEPTS

1. Draw a diagram of a eukaryotic cell with a mitochondrion and, next to it, a diagram of an aerobic bacterial cell. Using these two diagrams, compare the location and direction of electron flow of the three stages of respiration. Now consider if the process would differ in the (a) bacteria that perform anaerobic respiration and (b) the bacteria used to make yogurt.

2. Explain how the 1930s diet drugs that contained uncouplers would have led to weight loss.

3. What is the explanation for the burning feeling of overexercised muscles? Given this explanation, why is cyanide such a deadly toxin?

7 Photosynthesis

TOPIC MAP

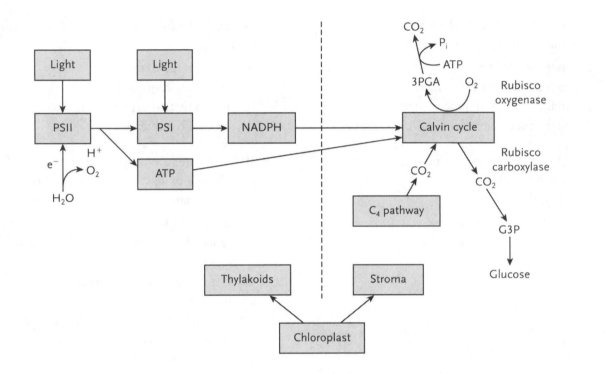

LEARNING OUTCOMES AND STUDY STRATEGIES

By the end of this chapter, you should be able to

- Describe what happens when photons are absorbed by pigments and understand the differences between the light absorption by an accessory pigment, an antenna chlorophyll, and a reaction centre chlorophyll

- Explain the function of the molecules in the antennae and how they accomplish this

- Distinguish between linear and cyclic electron transport and explain the need for both

- Explain how photosynthetic electron transport is used to make ATP, where this occurs, in which direction proton flow occurs, and what processes contribute to the development of proton motive force

- Describe the basic process of the Calvin cycle, where it happens, and provide the name of the critical enzyme and intermediate

- Understand what photorespiration is, why it happens, why it is a problem, and the various ways that have evolved to compensate for the process

Study strategies for this chapter:

- This chapter has a substantial amount of detail on electron transport and enzymatic pathways. Do not get lost in the details of each pathway and the names of any but the more central names.

- Remember that the goal of this chapter is to understand how phototrophs trap light energy in the form of ATP and NADPH and how these molecules are used to make the organic chemicals required by the cell.

- Concentrate on the key concepts and pay attention to the figures—they will help you visualize the processes and see the bigger picture.

- Work through one section at a time and then the corresponding section of the study guide.

- Make sure, as you read, that you can answer the questions in each Study Break.

- After you have gone through the chapter, see how much you can expand on the Study Plan at the beginning of the chapter, and see if you can come up with alternative topic maps to the one above.

INTERACTIVE EXERCISES

Why It Matters [pp. 139–140]
7.1 Photosynthesis: An Overview [pp. 140–142]

Section Review (Fill-in-the-Blanks)

Life on Earth is entirely dependent on (1) _____ organisms in both terrestrial and (2) _____

habitats. Because these organisms use the energy they derive to convert inorganic carbon, (3) _____,

to complex organic molecules, they are referred to as (4) _____. Ultimately, the organic molecules

they produce serve as fuel for all the (5) _____, so photoautotrophs are the primary

(6) _____ of this planet. In the first of the two phases of photosynthesis, the (7) _____

reactions, solar energy is captured by (8) _____ molecules and used to synthesize the high-energy

molecules (9) _____ and (10) _____. In the second phase, the (11) _____ cycle uses

the products of the first phase to convert CO_2 into a(n) (12) _____. This reduced carbon product is

then used to make all of the other (13) _____ molecules they require for growth. In eukaryotic

organisms, both photosynthetic stages occur in (14) _____, whereas in photosynthetic prokaryotes,

they take place in the cytosol and (15) _____ _____.

Labelling

16. Identify each part of the chloroplast.

A. _____

B. _____

C. _____

D. _____

Locate the following reactions in the chloroplast:

17. _____ Light-dependent reactions

18. _____ Light-independent reactions/Calvin cycle

True/False

Mark if the statement is true (T) or false (F). If the statement is false, justify your answer in the lines below each statement.

19. _____ Cells lacking chloroplasts may be photosynthetic.

_____

_____

20. _____ Photoautotrophs fix carbon dioxide, but phototrophs do not.

_____

_____

21. _____ Phototrophs are only found in the Bacteria and Eukarya, not in the Archaea.

_____

_____

Matching

Match each of the following terms with its correct definition.

22. ____	Photosynthesis	A.	Electrons and protons are used to reduce CO_2
23. ____	Primary producers	B.	Organelles in eukaryotic cells where photosynthesis takes place
24. ____	Consumers	C.	Process by which organisms harness light energy to convert CO_2 to organics
25. ____	Decomposers	D.	Results from splitting water molecules
26. ____	Carbon fixation	E.	Generic designation for carbohydrate units
27. ____	Chloroplasts	F.	Fluid inside the chloroplast
28. ____	Thylakoids	G.	Organisms that produce organics from inorganic CO_2 and form the base of most food chains
29. ____	Stroma	H.	Organisms that break down dead plants and animals to obtain organic chemicals
30. ____	$(CH_2O)_n$	I.	Organisms that live by eating plants and animals
31. ____	Oxygenic photosynthesis	J.	A stack of membrane sacs inside the chloroplast

Complete the Table

32. Electron flow connects two processes: photosynthesis and cellular respiration. Complete the following table by selecting your answer from the parentheses, giving specific information about each process.

Events	Photosynthesis	Cellular Respiration
Sugars (makes/breaks)	A.	B.
O_2 (uses/releases)	C.	D.
CO_2 (uses/releases)	E.	F.
Net energy (stores/releases)	G.	H.

Short Answer

33. Provide the balanced equation for both stages of photosynthesis and identify where the two stages occur in the chloroplast.

_____

_____

34. Compare and contrast the terms: photosynthesis, phototrophs, and chemoautotrophs.

_____

_____

7.2 The Photosynthetic Apparatus [pp. 142–146]

Section Review (Fill-in-the-Blanks)

Photosynthesis begins when (35) _____ molecules absorb light of specific wavelengths. Upon

absorption of a photon of light, electrons move from their (36) _____ state to a(n)

(37) _____ state. From this state, there are three possible outcomes: the absorbed energy may be

released as heat or as (38) _____; it may be transferred directly to a neighbouring molecule, a process

called inductive (39) _____; or the (40) _____ state electron may be transferred to another

molecule—in the case of photosynthesis, the (41) _____ acceptor. (42) _____ and

carotenoids are the photon-absorbing pigments in eukaryotes and cyanobacteria. Photosynthetic pigments and

proteins are organized as clusters called (43) _____, which, in the chloroplast, are embedded in the

(44) _____ membranes. These contain a(n) (45) _____ centre chlorophyll surrounded by an

aggregate of accessory pigments and proteins called the (46) _____ complex. This complex traps

light energy and funnels it to the (47) _____ centre. This is then oxidized, donating its electrons to

the (48) _____ acceptor. In PSII the reaction centre chlorophyll is P680 which, when excited, is

denoted as (49) _____ and when this is oxidized, it is denoted as (50) _____. Reduction of

this molecule by an electron obtained from (51) _____ regenerates P680 and releases

(52) _____ to the atmosphere.

Matching

Match each of the following terms with its correct definition.

53. _____ Chlorophylls

54. _____ Carotenoids

55. _____ Ground state electrons

56. _____ Excited state electrons

57. _____ Fluorescence

58. _____ Primary acceptor

59. _____ Absorption spectrum

60. _____ Action spectrum

61. _____ Photosystem

62. _____ Antenna complex

63. _____ Reaction centre

64. _____ Inductive resonance

65. _____ Oxygen-evolving complex

A. Electrons closest to nucleus

B. Direct transfer of energy to a neighbouring molecule

C. Reduced by reaction centre molecule

D. Photosynthetic pigments that donate to the primary acceptors

E. The amount of energy absorbed at different wavelengths of light

F. Green pigments present in plants, algae, and cyanobacteria

G. Accessory photosynthetic pigments

H. Light energy released by excited electrons returning to ground state

I. Reflects the combined effects of chlorophyll and carotenoids and measured by the rate of O_2 release

J. Responsible for oxygenic phtosynthesis

K. Electrons promoted to outer orbital

L. Cluster of light-absorbing pigments and proteins located in the thylakoid membranes

M. An aggregate of chlorophyll and carotenoid molecules in a photosystem

Short Answer

66. Explain the major role of the light-dependent reaction in photosynthesis.

_____

_____

67. What is the difference between a chlorophyll molecule in the antenna and a reaction centre chlorophyll?

_____

_____

68. Explain the difference(s) between P680, P680*, and P680⁺.

_____

_____

True/False

Mark if the statement is true (T) or false (F). If the statement is false, justify your answer in the lines below each statement.

69. _____ One can determine the absorption spectrum for chlorophyll by measuring oxygen production as a function of wavelength.

_____

_____

70. _____ P700 and P680 are different types of chlorophyll.

_____

_____

71. _____ PSII is called the "engine of life" because of its associated oxygen-evolving complex.

_____

_____

7.3 The Light Reactions [pp. 146–149]

Section Review (Fill-in-the-Blanks)

Through the oxidation of the light-activated (72) _____ _____ chlorophylls of PSI and II,

electrons enter the associated (73) _____ electron transport chains. In (74) _____ electron

transport, after losing their energy, the electrons from PSII are passed to P700⁺, which has undergone a(n)

(75) _____ as a result of light absorption. Absorbing light, the electrons in this molecule are excited

again, and a similar process of oxidation and (76) _____ transfer ensues before the electrons are

finally transferred to NADP⁺ by the enzyme (77) _____ _____. The electrons lost by the

oxidized chlorophyll (78) _____ are replenished by splitting (79) _____, catalyzed by the

(80) _____-_____ complex of PSII. As with the respiratory electron transport chain, the

energy of electrons flowing through the chain generates a(n) (81) _____ _____

_____ across the thylakoid membrane. Through chemiosmosis, this is coupled with the synthesis of

ATP by the membrane-bound (82) _____ _____ in a process referred to as

(83) _____. PSI can also work independently of PSII in a process of (84) _____ electron

transport. This process makes additional (85) _____ but no (86) _____.

Matching

Match each of the following terms with its correct definition or descriptor.

87. ____	ATP synthase	A.	Requires the enzymatic activity of the oxygen-evolving complex
88. ____	Proton motive force	B.	The use of the potential energy of proton motive force to do work
89. ____	Chemiosmosis	C.	The reaction centre pigment of PSII after absorption of a photon of light
90. ____	Linear electron flow	D.	The reaction centre pigment of PSII after oxidation by primary acceptor
91. ____	Cyclic electron flow	E.	Enzyme activity dependent on proton motive force
92. ____	NADP$^+$ reductase	F.	A mobile electron carrier that reduces P700
93. ____	Cytochromes	G.	Potential energy associated with the thylakoid membrane
94. ____	Plastoquinone	H.	Generates proton motive force and ATP only
95. ____	P680*	I.	An enzyme associated with non-cyclic electron flow and the PSI electron transport chain
96. ____	P680$^+$	J.	A protein complex in electron transport chains with bound cofactors that undergo redox reactions

Sequence

97. Arrange the following steps of linear electron flow in their correct sequence. One or more of these terms may be used twice: ____ ____ ____ ____ ____

   A. Photosystem I

   B. Photosystem II

   C. NADPH

   D. Electron transport chain

True/False

Mark if the statement is true (T) or false (F). If the statement is false, justify your answer in the lines below each statement.

98. _____ The purpose of cyclic electron flow is to make extra NADPH.

_____

_____

99. _____ ATP synthesis in photosynthetic processes happens by the chemiosmotic flow of electrons through the ATP synthase.

_____

_____

100. _____ Photosynthetic electron flow results in a higher concentration of protons in the thylakoid lumen.

_____

_____

101. _____ The oxygen-evolving complex is located on the stromal side of the thylakoid membrane.

_____

_____

Complete the Table

102. Complete the following table.

Process/Structure	Role in Light-dependent Reaction
A. Linear electron flow	
B. P680*	
C. Thylakoid membrane	
D. P680$^+$	

Short Answer

103. Explain the reason for, and the process by which, water is split in the light-dependent phase of photosynthesis.

_____

_____

_____

104. Explain how cyclic photosynthesis relates to the subsequent needs of the Calvin cycle.

_____

_____

_____

105. How many photons must be absorbed to generate 1 molecule of O_2? Explain how this is determined.

_____

_____

_____

106. Three process contribute to the development of photosynthetic proton motive force. What are they?

_____

_____

_____

7.4 The Calvin Cycle [pp. 149–152]

Section Review (Fill-in-the-Blanks)

In the Calvin cycle, CO_2 is reduced by (107) _____ from the light reaction, producing

(108) _____. ATP is also needed as this is an energy-requiring, or (109) _____, process. The

key enzyme in this light-independent cycle is (110) _____ (RuBP carboxylase/oxygenase) which

combines CO_2 with (111) _____ (RuBP), a five-carbon molecule. After phosphorylation and

reduction reactions, two molecules of (112) _____ are produced. It takes (113) _____ cycles

to produce one surplus (114) _____, which is used as a building block for the subsequent synthesis of

many other (115) _____ molecules.

Matching

Match each of the following terms with its correct definition or descriptor.

116. _____ rubisco

117. _____ G3P

118. _____ Rubisco large subunits

119. _____ Rubisco small subunits

A. Encoded by nuclear genome

B. Encoded by chloroplast genome

C. Product is two molecules of 3-phosphoglycerate

D. Product of an endergonic reduction reaction

True/False

Mark if the statement is true (T) or false (F). If the statement is false, justify your answer in the lines below each statement.

120. _____ The Calvin cycle produces one molecule of glucose per cycle.

_____

_____

121. _____ Sucrose is a glucose-containing disaccharide that circulates between plant cells.

_____

_____

122. _____ Rubisco consists of such a large percentage of plant leaf protein because carbon fixation is so important to the biosphere.

_____

_____

123. _____ The Calvin cycle is unique to eukaryotic photoautotrophs.

_____

_____

Short Answer

124. What are the three distinct phases of the Calvin cycle?

_____

_____

_____

Complete the Table

125. Complete the following table.

Chemicals/Structure	Role in Calvin Cycle
RuBP	A.
G3P	B.
3-phosphglycerate	C.
Rubisco	D.
Stroma	E.

126. Complete the following table with specific information on each step of photosynthesis.

Stage	Location in Chloroplast	ATP Used or Produced	NADPH Used or Produced	O_2 Used or Produced or NA	CO_2 Used or Produced or NA	G3P Produced or NA
A. Light dependent						
B. Calvin cycle						

7.5 Photorespiration and CO2-Concentrating Mechanisms [pp. 152–157]
7.6 Photosynthesis and Cellular Respiration Compared [p. 157]

Section Review (Fill-in-the-Blanks)

Rubisco is inefficient because (127) _____ competes with CO_2 for its (128) _____ site.

When this happens, the enzyme acts as a(n) (129) _____ in a process referred to as

(130) _____. The products of this reaction are (131) _____ to the cell, and elimination of

these molecules results in a loss of carbon, in the form of (132) _____. To avoid this loss, many

photoautotrophs have evolved mechanisms for concentrating (133) _____. Aquatic photoautotrophs

expend ATP to pump (134) _____ anions into the cell, where the enzyme (135) _____ anhydrase converts it CO_2. Some plants have evolved an additional carboxylase, (136) _____ carboxylase, which does not react with oxygen, and fixes CO_2 into (137) _____, which is, in turn, converted to malate. The latter contributes (138) _____ to the Calvin cycle. In C_4 plants, this supplemental enzyme is used in (139) _____ cells, and hydrolysis of its four-carbon product happens in the chloroplasts of (140) _____ _____ cells. In contrast, both processes occur in the (141) _____ cells of CAM plants. Instead, carbon fixation using (142) _____ carboxylase occurs at night when the (143) _____ are open, and the (144) _____ _____ occurs during the day when they are closed.

Matching

Match each of the following terms with its correct definition or descriptor.

145. _____	Photorespiration	A.	Regulated openings on leaves for the diffusion of gases and water
146. _____	Oxaloacetate	B.	Plants that make oxaloacetate and release CO_2 for Calvin cycle
147. _____	Malate	C.	Plants that fix CO_2 to make G3P and cellular organic structures
148. _____	C_3 plants	D.	Plants that make malate at night and release CO_2 in chloroplasts during the day
149. _____	C_4 plants	E.	Light-stimulated use of oxygen and release of CO_2 in chloroplasts
150. _____	CAM plants	F.	Enzyme used by some aquatic photoautotrophs for CO_2 concentration
151. _____	Oxygenase	G.	Generates CO_2 for the Calvin cycle
152. _____	Stomata	H.	Four-carbon chemical used by some plants for CO_2 storage
153. _____	PEP carboxylase	I.	Leads to generations of toxic compound glycolate
154. _____	ATP-dependent	J.	Enzyme used by C_4 and CAM plants for CO_2 bicarbonate pump fixation
155. _____	Malate dehydrogenase	K.	Immediate product of CO_2 fixation in C_4 cycle

True/False

Mark if the statement is true (T) or false (F). If the statement is false, justify your answer in the lines below each statement.

156. _____ Oxygen solubility increases with increasing temperature but CO_2 does not.

_____

_____

157. _____ C_4 plants tend to predominate in hot, dry climates.

_____

_____

158. _____ Although the PEP carboxylase is more efficient than rubisco, the C_4 cycle requires more energy than the Calvin cycle.

_____

_____

Short Answer

159. Discuss the hypothesis for why rubisco is so widespread among photoautotrophic life forms despite its obvious inefficiency.

_____

_____

_____

160. Compare the CO_2-concentrating mechanism in algae with that used by C_4 plants.

_____

_____

_____

161. Compare carbon dioxide fixation in corn to that in cacti.

_____

_____

_____

Labelling

162. Identify each aspect of this comparison between photosynthesis and respiration.

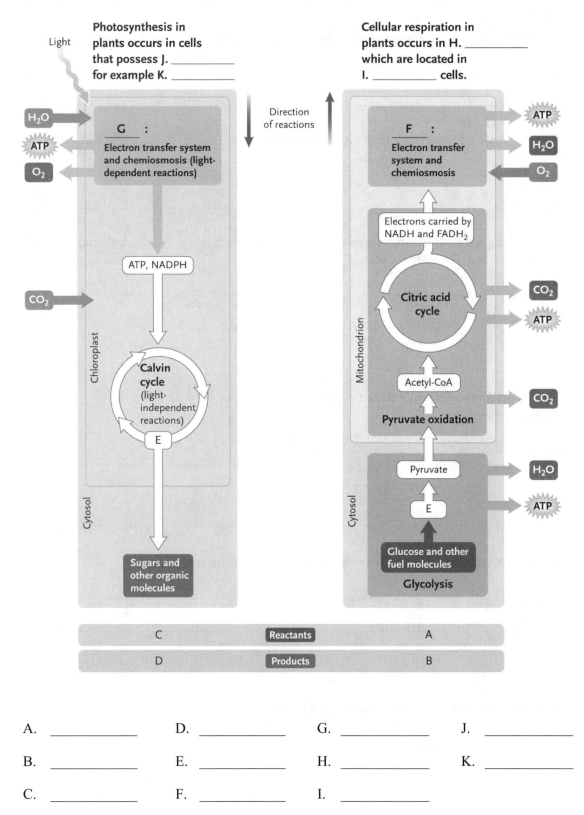

A. _____   D. _____   G. _____   J. _____

B. _____   E. _____   H. _____   K. _____

C. _____   F. _____   I. _____

1. Why is the abundance of phytoplankton higher near the Artic than at the temperate regions of the Atlantic and Pacific? [pp. 139–140]

   a. The water is too hot in the temperate regions.
   b. The UV radiation is too strong in the temperate regions.
   c. Many nutrients are limited in the temperate regions.
   d. CO_2 is poorly soluble in the warmer waters of the temperate regions.

2. Which is the most accurate term to describe plants and algae? [p. 140]

   a. photoautotrophs
   b. phototrophs
   c. heterotrophs
   d. autotrophs

3. Which is the most accurate term to describe halobacteria? [p. 140]

   a. photoautotrophs
   b. phototrophs
   c. heterotrophs
   d. autotrophs

4. Which of the following is NOT produced by the light-dependent reactions? [pp. 140–141]

   a. NADPH
   b. ATP
   c. O_2
   d. G3P

5. In cyanobacteria, which of the following provides the electrons used for CO_2 fixation? [pp. 141–142]

   a. water
   b. chlorophyll
   c. ATP
   d. NADPH

6. Where are photosynthetic pigments present in plant cells? [pp. 141–142]

   a. in the cytoplasm
   b. in the stroma of the chloroplast
   c. in the inner chloroplast membrane
   d. in the thylakoid membranes

7. Which of the following would NOT occur as a result of absorption of a photon of light by a pigment molecule? [pp. 142–143]

   a. An electron would move from an outer orbital to an inner orbital.
   b. An electron would go from ground state to excited state.
   c. An excited electron might transfer its energy to an adjacent molecule.
   d. The pigment might release light.

8. In which of the following would you NOT find chlorophyll? [pp. 140–143]

   a. cyanobacteria
   b. algae
   c. fungi
   d. plants

9. Which statement is correct? [pp. 143–144]

   a. An absorption spectrum measures the absorption of O_2 by a plant over different wavelengths.
   b. A photosynthetic action spectrum measures the rate of O_2 production vs. wavelength.
   c. One can demonstrate the cooperation of chlorophyll and carotenoid pigments in photosynthesis using an absorption spectrum.
   d. Chlorophyll absorbs light most strongly in the green region of the spectrum.

10. In eukaryotes, which of the following acts as the reaction centre molecule? [pp. 144–145]

    a. carotenoids
    b. chlorophyll b
    c. chlorophyll a

11. How is the energy funnelled through a photosynthetic antenna to the reaction centre chlorophyll? [pp. 144–145]

    a. through the release of heat

    b. through successive oxidation-reduction reactions

    c. through inductive resonance

12. Which is reduced by electrons obtained from water? [pp. 145–146]

    a. $P680^+$

    b. P680

    c. P700*

    d. plastocyanin

13. Which of the following produces ATP and NADPH? [pp. 146–148]

    a. linear electron flow

    b. cyclic electron flow

    c. the Calvin cycle

    d. the oxidation of water

14. Which describes how photoautotrophs make ATP for CO_2 fixation? [pp. 147–149]

    a. Protons flowing from the cytoplasm into the stroma by chemiosmosis give rise to photophosphorylation.

    b. Protons flowing from the thylakoid lumen into the stroma by chemiosmosis give rise to photophosphorylation.

    c. Protons flowing from the stroma into the lumen of the thylakoids by chemiosmosis give rise to photophosphorylation.

    d. Protons flowing from the intermembrane space into the stroma by chemiosmosis give rise to photophosphorylation.

15. How many quanta of light would need to be absorbed to produce one molecule of O_2 through linear photosynthetic electron flow? [p. 149]

    a. 2

    b. 4

    c. 6

    d. 8

16. Which statement about cyclic photosynthesis is true? [p. 149]

    a. It produces ATP and NADPH.

    b. It produces ATP but no NADPH.

    c. It produces oxygen.

    d. It fixes CO_2.

17. Which of the following is NOT part of the Calvin cycle? [pp. 149–151]

    a. phosphoenolpyruvate (PEP)

    b. rubisco

    c. RuBP

    d. 3PG

18. How many times must the Calvin cycle go around to provide enough fixed carbon for the synthesis of glucose? [pp. 150–151]

    a. 1

    b. 2

    c. 3

    d. 6

19. Which of the following is NOT true of G3P? [pp. 150–151]

    a. It is the product of rubisco's oxygenase reaction.

    b. It is the intermediate that links the Calvin cycle with glucose synthesis.

    c. Some of the G3P made in the Calvin cycle is used to regenerate RuBP.

    d. It is also an intermediate in glycolysis.

20. Which statement about rubisco is false? [pp. 151–153]

    a. It is a multiprotein complex.

    b. Genes from the nucleus and the chloroplast are required for its synthesis.

    c. It has a higher affinity for oxygen than for CO_2.

    d. Under normal atmospheric conditions and moderate temperatures, it is only about 75% efficient

21. Which statement about algae is true? [p. 153]
    a. Many produce PEP carboxylase in order to overcome the problem of photorespiration
    b. Many have an active transport protein in their plasma membranes for pumping dissolved oxygen out of the cytosol
    c. Many have an active transport protein in their plasma membranes for pumping bicarbonate into the cytosol
    d. Many use the C4 cycle to overcome the problem of photorespiration

22. Which term refers to structures through which plants exchange oxygen and CO_2? [p. 154]
    a. mesophyll cells
    b. bundle sheath cells
    c. cuticle
    d. stomata

23. Which of the following types of plants undergo photorespiration during hot days? [pp. 153–157]
    a. C_3 plants
    b. C_4 plants
    c. CAM plants

24. How do C_4 and CAM store CO_2? [pp. 154–156]
    a. as PEP in the stroma of mesophyll cells
    b. as oxaloacetate in vesicles
    c. as malate
    d. as G3P in the stroma of bundle sheath cells

25. Which statement is true? [pp. 154–156]
    a. C_4 plants are as prevalent as C_3 plants in temperate regions such as Manitoba.
    b. CAM plants are found predominantly in regions with hot days and cool nights.
    c. C_4 plants use the C_4 pathway in bundle sheath cells and the Calvin cycle in mesophyll cells.
    d. CAM plants make and store malate in vacuoles during the day and use the Calvin cycle at night.

INTEGRATING AND APPLYING KEY CONCEPTS

1. Compare the strategies for carbon fixation in an apple tree in Manitoba versus corn versus pineapple, explaining the reason for the differences and the advantages, where appropriate.

2. Draw a single thylakoid within a larger "stroma" zone. Alongside that, draw a cyanobacterium. Now draw the components of oxygenic photosynthesis, making sure everything is in the correct orientation (do not worry about the names of the electron transporters), including the ATP synthase. Show with arrows the absorption of photons, the movement of electrons and protons, the synthesis of any products, and where some may go for the Calvin cycle reactions.

3. Provide the equation for the conversion of CO_2 by the Calvin cycle to glucose, identifying the total numbers of ATP and NADPH required. Explain how this energy requirement is met by the light-dependent phase of photosynthesis. Why else would cyclic electron flow be more necessary than linear electron flow?

8 Cell Cycles

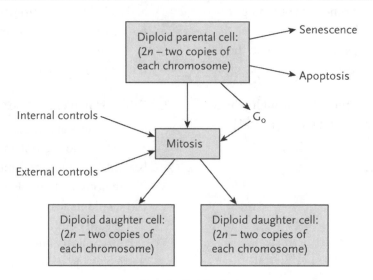

Genetically identical

LEARNING OUTCOMES AND STUDY STRATEGIES

By the end of this chapter, you should be able to

- Describe the stages of the cell cycle and of mitosis and identify how they are regulated
- Understand the components and role of the mitotic spindle and how they, as well as cytokinesis, differ between plant and animal cells
- Define "Hayflick factors," tumour, and metastasis
- Explain how cell growth and division happen in prokaryotes

Study Tips:

- As you are reading, pay attention to the main ideas first: what is the purpose of a step and the main features? Then worry about the various names of the molecules and structures.
- Make sure you understand the components and role of the mitotic spindle and how they, as well as cytokinesis, differ between plant and animal cells.
- Go through each section of the textbook and then work through the companion section of the study guide.
- After reading through all of the chapter sections of the textbook, try drawing a flow chart of the cell cycle, starting with a single diploid parental cell. Identify points at which there may be some control and work these control mechanisms or processes into your flow chart. Finally, indicate with the daughter cell the various possible alternative fates to normal cell cycling.

INTERACTIVE EXERCISES

Why It Matters [pp. 161–162]
8.1 The Cycle of Cell Growth and Division: An Overview [pp. 162–163]
8.2 Cell Division in Prokaryotic Organisms [pp. 163–164]

Section Review (Fill-in-the-Blanks)

Prokaryotes do not undergo mitosis but divide by (1) _____ _____. In most prokaryotes,

there is a single circular DNA (2) _____. Under optimum growth conditions, when cells are growing

quickly, (3) _____ _____ occupies most of the time between cytokinesis events.

Replication begins at a chromosomal sequence called the (4) _____ of replication and is catalyzed by

enzymes located in the centre of the cell. Once this process is complete, the two (5) _____ migrate to

the opposite poles. (6) _____ follows with the infolding of the plasma membrane and synthesis of a

new cell (7) _____ between daughter cells.

True/False

Mark if the statement is true (T) or false (F). If the statement is false, justify your answer in the lines
below each statement.

8. _____   The newly replicated bacterial chromosomes migrate to the opposite poles of the cell
              through the action of bacterial spindles.

_____

_____

Short Answer

9. Define the term "binary fission."

_____

_____

8.3 Mitosis and the Eukaryotic Cell Cycle [pp. 164-171]

Section Review (Fill-in-the-Blanks)

In eukaryotes, the cell cycle consists of (10) _____ interrelated systems. These systems are growth,

ending with (11) _____ _____, followed by the equal segregation of replicated

(12) _____, and finally division of the cytoplasm, or (13) _____. The result of this process is

two (14) _____ cells that are identical to the (15) _____ cell. In eukaryotic cells, organs, and

tissues, where (16) _____ identical copies of the parental cell are required, the process of replication

that is used is (17) _____. The central aspect to this process is the replication and segregation of the

(18) _____, which are linear DNA molecules with associated (19) _____. In most eukaryotic

organisms, the genome is distributed among several (20) _____, and most possess two copies of

each, one from each (21) _____; their genome is therefore described as being $2n$, that is,

(22) _____. There are exceptions to this, however: yeast can switch between $2n$ and $1n$, that is,

(23) _____. Regardless of the number of sets or the so-called (24) _____ of the organism,

replication of each individual chromosome gives two identical copies, and these are referred to as sister

(25) _____.

      There are two major phases of the cell cycle: (26) _____, which is the longest, and

(27) _____. There are three specific stages in the former: (28) _____, the period during

which growth occurs and the one that varies most in duration; (29) _____, when the DNA is

replicated; and (30) _____, when the cell prepares to enter mitosis. Mitosis consists of five stages,

beginning with (31) _____. In this phase, the chromosomes (32) _____, becoming visible in

the microscope as thin threads. Also during this phase, the duplicated (33) _____ start to separate and

generate the (34) _____. In the next stage, (35) _____, the (36) _____ membrane

breaks down, the (37) _____ enters the former nuclear area, and the microtubules of the

(38) _____ attach to each sister chromatid at a structure called a (39) _____. In

(40) _____ or stage 3, the (41) _____ is complete and has moved the chromosomes so that

they are aligned at the (42) _____ plate. Then in (43) _____, the spindle separates the

(44) _____ _____ and moves them to opposite (45) _____ poles, completing

chromosome (46) _____. The chromosomes are now referred to as (47) _____

chromosomes. In (48) _____, the last phase, the chromosomes (49) _____, returning to their

interphase state, the (50) _____ disassembles, and a new (51) _____ envelope forms around the chromosomes. This phase ends with the division of the cytoplasm in (52) _____. This process differs in animal and plant cells, involving (53) _____ in animal cells and cell (54) _____ formation in plant cells.

Matching

Match each of the following terms with its correct definition.

55. ____	Cell cycle	A.	Referring to the number of copies of each type of chromosome
56. ____	Cytokinesis	B.	Having two copies of each type of chromosome
57. ____	Diploid	C.	Newly replicated pairs of identical chromosomes
58. ____	Haploid	D.	The equal distribution of daughter chromosomes to each of two daughter cells
59. ____	Ploidy	E.	Growth followed by nuclear division and cytokinesis
60. ____	Sister chromatids	F.	Division of the cytoplasm
61. ____	Segregation	G.	Having one copy of each type of chromosome

True/False

Mark if the statement is true (T) or false (F). If the statement is false, justify your answer in the lines below each statement.

62. _____ Some plant species may be polyploid.

_____

_____

63 _____ In a multicellular organism, cells of different tissues contain different genetic information.

_____

_____

Matching

Match each of the following phases of the cell cycle with its correct definition.

64. ____	G_1 phase	A.	State of cellular arrest
65. ____	S phase	B.	Sister chromatids are apparent for the first time; spindle begins to develop
66. ____	G_2 phase	C.	Part of cytokinesis in plants; involves formation of a new cell wall from vesicles at the former spindle midpoint
67. ____	G_0 phase	D.	Stage during which DNA is replicated
68. ____	Prophase	E.	Stage preceding mitosis
69. ____	Prometaphase	F.	Spindle midpoint in metaphase
70. ____	Metaphase	G.	After nuclear division, cytoplasm divides and two daughter cells result
71. ____	Anaphase	H.	Stage during which spindles enter the former nuclear area
72. ____	Telophase	I.	Phase of cell growth and DNA replication
73. ____	Cytokinesis	J.	Sister chromatids move to opposite poles
74. ____	Interphase	K.	Spindle disassembles, nuclear envelope reappears, chromosomes become less condensed
75. ____	Mitosis	L.	Sister chromatids are aligned at the midpoint of the spindle
76. ____	Metaphase plate	M.	Phase of cell growth after cytokinesis
77. ____	Cell plate	N.	Nuclear division; consists of 4–5 phases

True/False

Mark if the statement is true (T) or false (F). If the statement is false, justify your answer in the lines below each statement.

78. _____ During G_1, cells are synthesizing RNA, proteins, and DNA.

_____

_____

79. _____ In multicellular organisms, if cells or certain tissues are mature and do not need to increase in numbers or turn over, they enter G_0.

_____

_____

80. _____ During G_2, cells are metabolically inactive.

_____

_____

Identification

81. For each image, identify the phase (top line) and the amount of DNA using the ploidy number (bottom line). For the first cell, A = G_1 phase and B = 2n DNA.

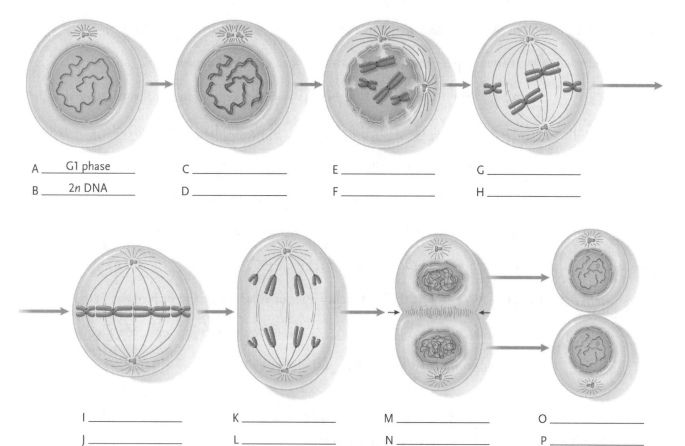

A ____G1 phase____   C _____   E _____   G _____

B ____2n DNA____   D _____   F _____   H _____

I _____   K _____   M _____   O _____

J _____   L _____   N _____   P _____

Short Answer

82. Explain what it is about the G_1/S transition that interests cancer researchers.

_____

_____

83. Explain the difference between chromosomes and sister chromatids.

_____

_____

84.   Compare and contrast cell furrowing with cell plate formation.

_____

_____

8.4 Formation and Action of the Mitotic Spindle [pp. 171–173]

Section Review (Fill-in-the-Blanks)

Mitosis and cytokinesis are both dependent on the formation of the (85) _____. Spindle formation

may develop differently in plants compared with in animals, due to the presence of a(n) (86) _____

in animal cells but not in certain types of plants. This structure is considered the cell's microtubule

(87) _____ centre, or MTOC. During mitosis, this structure divides and the two parts move apart,

with a concomitant formation of the spindle (88) _____. In plant cells, the microtubules assemble

around the (89) _____. Microtubules in the spindle connect to the sister chromotids via

(90) _____. Some microtubules do not connect to these structures, so these two types are referred to

as (91) _____ microtubules and (92) _____ microtubules, respectively. The latter extend

between opposite poles, overlapping with each other at the spindle (93) _____. During anaphase,

chromosomes are believed to "walk" along their stationary microtubules, using motor proteins in the

(94) _____. The microtubule (95) _____ as this structure passes over it. Meanwhile, the

(96) _____ microtubules slide over each other, pushing the (97) _____ further apart.

Matching

Match each of the following terms with its correct definition.

98. ____	Centrosome	A.	The centrosome
99. ____	Mitotic spindle	B.	Two structures within the centrosome, usually arranged at right angles to each other
100. ____	MTOC	C.	The microtubule structures involved in mitosis and cytokinesis
101. ____	Centrioles	D.	The microtubule-organizing centre of the cell

True/False

Mark if the statement is true (T) or false (F). If the statement is false, justify your answer in the lines below each statement.

102. _____ The centrioles are critical to mitosis and cytokinesis.

_____

_____

103. _____ Certain types of plants possess multiple MTOCs.

_____

_____

8.5 Cell Cycle Regulation [pp. 174–178]

Section Review (Fill-in-the-Blanks)

The cell cycle has internal (104) _____, which regulate the division process and prevent the cell from

progressing to the next stage of the cycle unless the (105) _____ of the previous stage are complete.

Internal regulation occurs primarily through the activity of (106) _____ complexes; the

concentrations of these rise and fall with the cell (107) _____, hence the name. When in high enough

concentrations, these complexes activate (108) _____ protein kinases, or CDKs, which, in turn,

activate target proteins through (109) _____. This causes the cell to progress to the next stage of the

cell (110) _____. After this transition, the (111) _____ are enzymatically degraded. The cell

cycle is also regulated externally, primarily through (112) _____ _____ that recognize and

bind signals such as (113) _____ hormones and (114) _____ factors or through

(115) _____ with other cells. These trigger intracellular reactions that can include the addition of

inhibitory or stimulating (116) _____ groups to cyclin/CDK:complexes. Healthy cells in organs and

tissues are normally in contact with other cells and exhibit (117) _____ _____; that is, they

are in G_0 and are prevented from (118) _____. This control, as well as other cell cycle controls, is

absent in cancer cells, which form masses of abnormal cells called (119) _____. Through a process

called (120) _____, cells from the masses break free and spread to other sites within the

(121) _____. In addition to regulating cell division, multicellular organisms regulate cell

(122) _____ through an apparently ancient process called (123) _____. This is often used in

development, when cells are (124) _____, but it is also an important means of eliminating damaged or (125) _____ cells. A key player in this process is a protease from a family of normally inactive proteases called (126) _____.

Matching

Match each of the following terms/concepts with its correct definition.

127. _____ Contact inhibition

A. Cyclin-dependent protein kinase

128. _____ Growth factors

B. Cells are prevented from dividing due to the presence of adjacent cells

129. _____ Oncogene

C. The gradual loss of proliferative ability in cells

130. _____ Tumour

D. The cellular protein critical for regulation of cell cycle transition from G_1 to S

131. _____ Cellular senescence

E. Gene that produces uncontrolled cell division

132. _____ Cyclin E

F. External controls of cyclin:CDK activity

133. _____ CDK

G. Mass of cells as a result of unregulated cell division

True/False

Mark if the statement is true (T) or false (F). If the statement is false, justify your answer in the lines below each statement.

134. _____ Regulation of transitions between the different stages of the cell cycle is accomplished by varying the levels of CDKs.

_____

_____

135. _____ Growth factors can cause a cell to enter G_1 from G_0.

_____

_____

Short Answer

136. Explain the term "cellular senescence" and why it happens.

_____

_____

137. Identify some of the cellular changes that can result in cancer.

_____

_____

_____

SELF-TEST

1. Assuming that no errors occur in DNA replication, which is consistent with the end product of mitosis? [pp. 164–165]
   a. double in chromosomal content
   b. genetically identical to the parental cell
   c. able to grow indefinitely
   d. slightly different from the parental cell

2. Which of the following phases is the most variable with respect to length? [pp. 165–166]
   a. G_1 of interphase
   b. G_2 of interphase
   c. S phase of interphase
   d. mitosis

3. When does the nuclear envelope break down? [p. 167]
   a. during prophase
   b. during G_2 of interphase
   c. during telophase
   d. during prometaphase

4. Mature red blood cells lack a nucleus. In which phase of the cell cycle would you expect to find this cell? [p. 166]
   a. in G_1 of interphase
   b. in G_2 of interphase
   c. in G_0 of interphase
   d. in S phase of interphase

5. Which of the following is false with respect to a pair of sister chromatids? [p. 165]
   a. They are genetically identical.
   b. They will end up in different daughter cells.

   c. They are held together by a single kinetochore.
   d. Once separated, they are called daughter chromosomes.

6. Which of the following is found in animal cells but not in plant cells? [pp. 171–172]
   a. a karyotype
   b. microtubules
   c. a centrosome
   d. a microtubule-organizing centre

7. Which of the following would prevent a cell from progressing to the M phase? [pp. 174–175]
   a. a decrease in the amount of cyclin B
   b. an increase in the amount of phosphate
   c. an increase in the amount of CDK2
   d. a decrease in phosphatase activity

8. What is the likely result of blocking contact inhibition? [pp. 175–176]
   a. Wounds would never heal.
   b. A tumour might develop.
   c. The cell would go into G_0 phase.
   d. The cell would go into S phase.

9. What is a primary difference between mitosis in eukaryotic cells and binary fission in prokaryotes? [pp. 163–164]
   a. Binary fission lacks cytokinesis.
   b. Binary fission is not regulated.
   c. Binary fission does not use centrioles.
   d. DNA replication only occurs in mitosis.

10. Which statement about cells that undergo mitosis is false? [pp. 164–171]

    a. A cell in G_2 has twice as much DNA as in G_1.

    b. DNA replication starts at a specific region.

    c. Chromatids move to opposite poles of the cell.

    d. Checkpoints ensure that one phase is complete before the next phase is initiated.

11. Which statement about apoptosis is incorrect? [pp. 176–177]

    a. It is the explanation for cellular senescence.

    b. It is highly regulated.

    c. It is required for the normal development of multicellular organisms.

    d. It is an ancient mechanism.

12. What is a "Hayflick factor"? [p. 175]

    a. It is a molecule that helps regulate the cell cycle.

    b. It is the MTOC of prokaryotic cells.

    c. It is the critical enzyme that regulates apoptosis.

    d. It is the term used for the as yet unknown cause(s) of cellular senescence.

13. Which statement about cell cultures is NOT true? [p. 166]

    a. They are often used to test the toxicity or carcinogenicity of various chemicals.

    b. They allow scientists to grow clones of an original cell.

    c. They are possible for prokaryotic cells as well as eukaryotic cells.

    d. This technique is restricted only to prokaryotic cells.

14. Which statement about karyotypes is false? [p. 168]

    a. They can allow the identification of a species.

    b. They are made using telophase chromosomes.

    c. They allow the visual characterization of an organism based on the shape and size of sister chromatids.

    d. They can allow the identification of gender.

15. What may cancer be associated with? [p. 176]

    a. a mutation in a plasma membrane nutrient transport protein

    b. yeast cells

    c. loss of contact inhibition

16. What may be included in the external controls of the cell cycle? [pp. 174–175]

    a. CDK2

    b. peptide hormones

    c. cyclins

    d. cyclases

17. Which statement about mitosis is false? [pp. 164–165]

    a. It is believed to have evolved from binary fission.

    b. Because the eukaryotic yeast cells have a mitotic system that more closely resembles the binary fission process of prokaryotes, their process of mitosis is believed to be the ancestor of the more common process in animals and higher plants.

    c. Its evolution was necessary as the genomes of eukaryotic cells became larger and more complex.

    d. Some aspects of this process vary in certain eukaryotic organisms.

18. Which statement is consistent with cell plates? [pp. 163–164]

    a. They are formed by vesicles from the ER and Golgi complex at the site of the spindle midpoint of plant cells.

    b. They are formed by endocytic vesicles at the site of the spindle midpoint of plant cells.

    c. They are formed by microfibres at the site of the spindle midpoint of plant cells.

    d. They are required for segregation of chromosomes in certain types of plant cells.

19. Telomerase is best described by which statement? [p. 176]

    a. an excellent prospect for an anticancer treatment
    b. an enzyme that controls a cell's entry into telophase from anaphase
    c. involved in DNA replication
    d. involved in triggering apoptosis

20. Which statement about HeLa cells is false? [p. 166]

    a. They were the first cancer cell line developed for tissue culture.
    b. They are able to grow indefinitely in tissue culture.
    c. They are a type of cell that has been used in research for over 50 years.
    d. They are a type of cell line that is naturally mortal.

INTEGRATING AND APPLYING KEY CONCEPTS

1. Explain why prokaryotes can successfully divide every 20 minutes and eukaryotic division is significantly longer.

2. In the "Why It Matters" section of this chapter, the process of regeneration of the zebrafish's dorsal fin is described. Having read through the rest of this chapter, go back and discuss the various processes that would be involved in this regeneration. Once regenerated, what would happen to the cell cycle of the new fin?

3. Compare and contrast G_0 with the processes of senescence and apoptosis.

9 Genetic Recombination

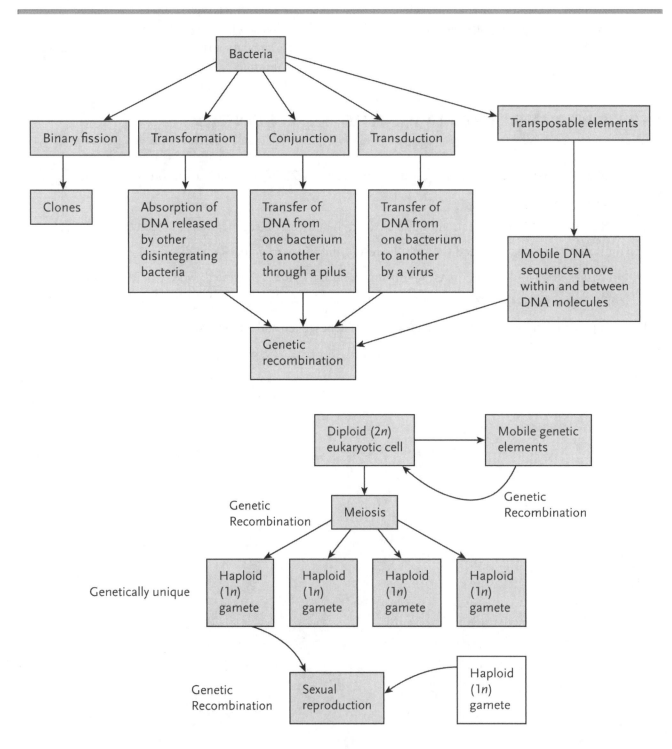

LEARNING OUTCOMES AND STUDY STRATEGIES

By the end of this chapter, you should be able to

- Define and distinguish between conjugation, transformation, and transduction, and explain how each participates in recombination in prokaryotes

- Identify the stages of meiosis and explain how they differ from mitosis, including how the end products differ

- Understand how recombination occurs during meiosis and how sexual reproduction then adds to genetic diversity

- Understand what mobile elements are and identify the differences between those of prokaryotes and those of eukaryotes

Study strategies for thie chapter:

- This is a long chapter with a lot of material, so it is important to go through one section at a time.

- Remember while you are reading that the topic is recombination mechanisms as a means of increasing genetic variability. There are really only two methods of recombination: recombination of nonhomologous sequences, mediated by transposable elements; and recombination of homologous sequences, which is everything else covered in the chapter.

- Focus on the main message, which is generally laid out in the heading for each subsection. Pay attention to the figures; they will make it easier to picture and remember the mechanism of recombination.

- In reading the section on meiosis, focus on the stages of meiosis I and II, paying attention to whether the cells are 2n and 1n and looking for the three places that amplify genetic diversity, and review the similarities and differences with mitosis.

- Finally, as you complete a section in the textbook, work on the accompanying section in the study guide before moving on.

INTERACTIVE EXERCISES

Why It Matters [pp. 181–182]
9.1 Mechanism of Genetic Recombination [pp. 182–183]

Section Review (Fill-in-the-Blanks)

There is a tension in biology between (1) _____, as generated by mitosis in eukaryotes, and

difference. At the level of a multicellular organism, it is important that all of the individual cells are

(2) _____ identical. However, at the level of the (3) _____, evolutionary changes arise from

natural (4) _____ of genetically (5) _____ members of a particular species. In order for

selective advantages to be passed on, differences between individuals must be (6) _____, that is, passed from one generation to the next. In all organisms, the ultimate source of genetic diversity is

(7) _____; however, these occur at very low frequencies. The process of (8) _____ allows

for the amplification of genetic diversity and is at the heart of the eukaryotic process of (9) _____,

which is an essential component of sexual reproduction. Genetic recombination requires two DNA molecules

that (10) _____ from each other in at least two places, a mechanism for bringing the two molecules

into close (11) _____ and enzymes to cut the covalent bonds of the DNA (12) _____,

(13) _____ the ends, and (14) _____ the DNA molecules back together. Most recombination

events occur between (15) _____ regions of DNA, that is, regions that are very similar. This

similarity allows the two molecules to line up and (16) _____ _____ precisely. Enzymes cut

each (17) _____ of both molecules, the free ends are (18) _____, and enzymes then attach

the free ends by making a total of (19) _____ new covalent bonds. Despite the fact that

(20) _____ bonds are cut and reformed, this process leads to a (21) _____ recombination

event. If two (22) _____ DNA molecules were involved in a recombination event, as is the case

between various bacterial DNA molecules, the result would be the (23) _____ into a single larger

molecule.

Matching

Match each of the following scientists with their major contribution.

24. _____	Genetic recombination	A.	A process by which populations undergo change through the natural selection of certain individuals in the population based on heritable traits
25. _____	Asexual reproduction	B.	Identical
26. _____	Evolution	C.	Development of new combinations of genetic information to generate genetic variability
27. _____	Homologous	D.	A reproductive process that generates two identical daughter cells from a parental cell

Short Answer

28. Explain how the product of a single recombination event between two linear molecules would result in a different number of products than if it happened between two circular molecules.

_____

_____

9.2 Genetic Recombination in Bacteria [pp. 183–190]

Section Review (Fill-in-the-Blanks)

Although prokaryotes do not reproduce sexually by meiosis, they do undergo genetic (29) _____.

Through three main processes, these organisms bring DNA from different (30) _____ into their cell,

recombine homologous sequences, and produce (31) _____ that are different from either parent.

Studies with the laboratory workhouse, the bacterial species (32) _____, laid the foundations for our

knowledge of prokaryotic recombination. The first method of acquiring DNA, (33) _____, is

considered a type of sexual reproduction in bacteria. It involves the passage of DNA from a

(34) _____ cell to a recipient cell through a structure called a(n) (35) _____. In the best

characterized example, donor strains are distinguished by the presence of the E. coli (36) _____, an

extrachromosomal DNA molecule. These strains are referred to as being (37) _____; recipients are

designated F⁻. In some donor strains, this molecule becomes (38) _____ into the bacterial

chromosome, and these strains are designated (39) _____ strains. When these particular strains

participate in a "mating," (40) _____ genes of the donor can be transferred to the recipients, along

with a portion of the F (41) _____. By using mating partners that differ in their (42) _____

requirements—that is, their auxotrophies—growth media designed to monitor recombination of these traits,

and determining the time of (43) _____ into recipient cells, researchers were able to use Hfr donors

to (44) _____ genes on the E. coli chromosome. In another type of bacterial recombination, certain

species directly absorb DNA released by (45) _____ cells. This process is called (46) _____,

and studies using one type of bacterium that is capable of being (47) _____, Streptococcus, allowed

researchers to determine that DNA carried the (48) _____ material for pathogenic traits. The third

method of acquiring DNA for recombination, that of (49) _____, involves bacterial viruses, that is,

(50) _____. This transfer is the result of a mistake these agents make when they leave a previous

(51) _____ cell, inserting bacterial DNA instead of, or in addition to, its own in the phage head.

Bacteriophage such as P22 of Salmonella, which undergo a(n) (52) _____ life cycle and

enzymatically break down the host's chromosome during infection, will accidentally package

(53) _____ fragments of host DNA: this is referred to as (54) _____ transduction. In

contrast, (55) _____ transduction results when a bacterial prophage transfers host sequences lying

next to the point of insertion. The best characterized agent of this type of transduction is bacteriophage

(56) _____, and the type of life cycle that allows these phages to integrate into the host chromosome

is referred to as (57) _____.

Matching

Match each of the following scientists with their major contribution.

58. ____	Theodore Escherich	A.	Scientists who used interrupted-mating experiments to map genes on the *E. coli* chromosome
59. ____	Joshua Lederberg and Edward Tatum	B.	Demonstrated transformation in bacteria
60. ____	François Jacob and Elie Wollman	C.	Discovered conjugation in bacteria
61. ____	Oswald Avery	D.	Demonstrated transduction in *Salmonella typhimurium*
62. ____	Fred Griffith	E.	Discoverer of the bacterium that helped lay the foundations for our understanding of recombination
63. ____	Joshua Lederberg and Norton Zinder	F.	Proved that DNA is the transforming factor

Match each of the following terms with its correct definition.

64. _____ Virulent phage

A. An extrachromosomal circular DNA molecule in *E. coli* that is transferred by conjugation

65. _____ Temperate phage

B. Where bacterial cells make a physical connection to pass part of their genetic material from one to another

66. _____ Clone

C. Bacterial cells that have the F plasmid incorporated into their chromosome

67. _____ Sex pilus

D. Bacteriophage that follows the lysogenic cycle

68. _____ Prophage

E. Genetically identical cells

69. _____ Conjugation

F. Bacterial cells that have an F plasmid

70. _____ Hfr cells

G. A tubelike structure that bacteria develop to connect one cell to another

71. _____ F^+ cells

H. Mutant that requires additional nutrients added to the minimal medium

72. _____ F^- cells

I. Refers to determining the location of the genes on a chromosome

73. _____ Genetic map

J. Bacteriophage that follows a lytic life cycle

74. _____ Transformation

K. The form of a temperate phage when it is incorporated into the host chromosome

75. _____ F plasmid

L. The state of bacteria after receiving DNA from another cell but before undergoing genetic recombination

76. _____ Transduction

M. Where a bacterium absorbs DNA released by other dead bacteria

77. _____ Auxotroph

N. Where a virus transfers DNA from one bacterium to another

78. _____ Partial diploid

O. Cells that lack the F plasmid and act as recipients

Complete the Table

79. Bacterial cells divide asexually to produce clones; however, they can achieve genetic recombination through the following three mechanisms.

Mechanism of Recombination	Brief Description
Transformation	A.
Conjugation	B.
Transduction	C.

80. Complete the following table to describe the mechanisms of multiplication in bacteriophages.

Bacteriophage Type	Type of Multiplication	Brief Description
A. Virulent		
B. Temperate		

True/False

Mark if the statement is true (T) or false (F). If the statement is false, justify your answer in the lines below each statement.

81. _____ When bacteria divide, they produce clones.

_____

_____

82. _____ All varieties of bacteria are capable of undergoing transformation.

_____

_____

83. _____ During conjugation, DNA is transferred from the donor to the F⁻ recipient. Eventually, all bacteria in a culture will become F⁺.

_____

_____

84. _____ Temperate viruses follow both the lysogenic and lytic life cycles.

_____

_____

Short Answer

85. Compare and contrast the type of transduction process of bacteriophage P22 with that of bacteriophage λ.

_____

_____

86. Differentiate between a phage and a prophage.

_____

_____

9.3 Genetic Recombination in Eukaryotes: Meiosis [pp. 191–201]

Section Review (Fill-in-the-Blanks)

Sexual reproduction in eukaryotes requires a specialized division process called (87) _____. This

process has two major results: it generates daughter cells with (88) _____ of the number of

chromosomes present in the G_1 nucleus of the species and, just as importantly, it generates diversity through

genetic (89) _____ between homologous sequences. The time and place of this type of cell division

follow one of (90) _____ major pathways in the life cycles of eukaryotes, and these are distinguished

by the proportion of the life cycle spent in the (91) _____, that is, 1n, and (92) _____ or 2n

phases and when the asexual or (93) _____ divisions occur. In animals, the (94) _____

phase dominates and meiosis is not followed by mitosis but leads directly to the formation of

(95) _____. In contrast, plants and most fungi alternate between both phases, either of which can

dominate, and (96) _____ can happen during each phase. The third type of pathway is seen in some

fungi where the diploid phase is limited to a single cell that is produced by (97) _____ and that is

immediately followed by (98) _____. Although there are certain similarities between the phases and

events of meiosis and mitosis, there are essential differences, as evidenced by the final products:

(99) _____ daughter cells instead of two, each of which is (100) _____ if the parent cell was

diploid, and each of which is genetically (101) _____ from the parent cell. The process begins with

DNA replication during the premeiotic (102) _____ and is followed by meiosis (103) _____.

This begins with (104) _____, during which, as with mitosis, the sister (105) _____

condense and the spindle starts to form. A critical difference is that the homologous chromosomes then come

together in a process called (106) _____, to form a tightly associated complex in which

(107) _____ occurs through the exchange of segments of homologous chromosomes. This phase is

followed by the breakdown of the nuclear envelope in (108) _____. Also during this stage, and unlike

prometaphase in mitosis, the kinetochores of each sister chromatid join to a single (109) _____

microtubule, so that when separated, the homologous pairs move to (110) _____ poles of the cell.

During metaphase (111) _____, as in mitosis, the chromosomes line up at the (112) _____

plate, but unlike mitosis, the aligned chromosomes are tetrads, and in the next phase, (113) _____,

the pairs of homologous chromosomes are separated so that each pole has a (114) _____ number of

chromosomes. Meiosis I ends with telophase I and interkinesis, during which there may be (115) _____

of the spindle, may or may not be formation of two new nuclear envelopes, and may or may not be limited

(116) _____ or unfolding of the chromosomes. The two haploid cells from meiosis I then progress to

meiosis II, the phases of which are quite similar to those of mitosis: in (117) _____, the spindles

reform and chromosomes condense; in (118) _____, the spindles enter the former nuclear area and a

kinetochore microtubule attaches to (119) _____ sister chromatid kinetochore; during

(120) _____, the chromosomes line up at the metaphase plate; sister chromatids separate during

(121) _____; and in (122) _____, the spindles disassemble and new nuclear envelopes form.

In animals, all of this happens in the (123) _____ tissue and the cells that are generated, the

(124) _____, remain in G_0 until sexual reproduction happens, giving rise to a diploid

(125) _____. Ultimately, the combined processes of meiosis and fertilization give rise to genetic

variability through four mechanisms: the first is genetic recombination, an inevitable product of prophase

(126) _____; the second is the random segregation of chromosomes during anaphase

(127) _____, giving cells that have a random assortment of (128) _____ and

(129) _____ chromosomes; the third is the random segregation of (130) _____ chromatids

during anaphase II; and, finally, diversity arises with the process of (131) _____, when different

paternal and maternal gametes fuse to give a diploid zygote.

Matching

Match each of the following events with the most appropriate division of meiosis.

132. _____ DNA replication prior to this division

A. Meiosis I

133. _____ Recombination of alleles occurs

B. Meiosis II

134. _____ The product is four daughter cells

135. _____ Homologous pairs line up in synaptonemal complexes

136. _____ Sister chromatids separate

137. _____ Homologous pairs separate

Match each of the following terms or concepts with its correct definition.

138. _____ Chiasmata

A. A protein–DNA structure that is the substrate for crossover events

139. _____ Alleles

B. X and Y in humans

140. _____ Synaptonemal complex

C. The microscopically visible product of crossover events between nonsister chromatids

141. _____ Nondisjunction

D. Genetically distinct versions of the same gene

142. _____ Sex chromosome

E. Occurs when chromosome segregation fails in meiosis I or II

Sequence

143. Arrange the following events of meiosis in the correct hierarchical order and for each identify the phase of meiosis in which it occurs: ____ ____ ____ ____ ____ ____

   A. Homologous pairs undergo synapsis

   B. Four haploid daughter cells result

   C. Sister chromatids separate

   D. Homologous pairs separate

   E. Crossing over

   F. Two haploid daughter cells result

Short Answer

144. Explain the basis of Down syndrome in humans.

_____

_____

_____

145. What is interkinesis?

_____

_____

146. What is the relationship between synapsis and tetrads?

_____

_____

True/False

Mark if the statement is true (T) or false (F). If the statement is false, justify your answer in the lines below each statement.

147. _____ Nondisjunction is a common problem in meiosis.

_____

_____

148. _____ During gamete formation in humans, the X and Y chromosomes behave as homologues.

_____

_____

Labelling

149. For each of the labelled sections, respond to the following:

    A. Number of homologous chromosome pairs: _____. This cell is _____.

    (haploid or diploid)

    B. Assuming this cell is in prophase I, DNA replication has _____. (occurred or not

    occurred)

    C. During this phase, genetic variability is increased by _____.

    D. During this division, the _____ _____ separate. This is done in a(n)

    _____ fashion. Does DNA replication occur again? _____ (Yes or No)

    E. During this division, the _____ _____ separate. Daughter cells are

    _____. (haploid or diploid)

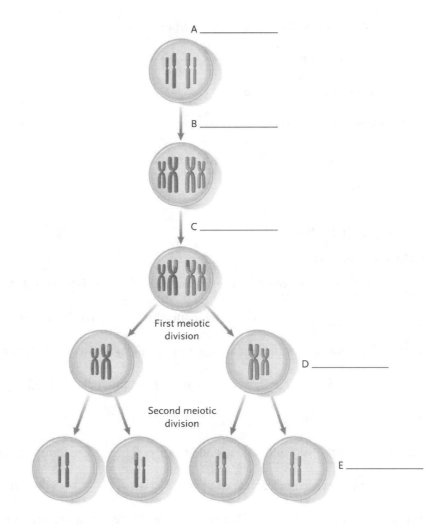

150. For each of the following descriptions, choose the most appropriate label(s) from the diagram.

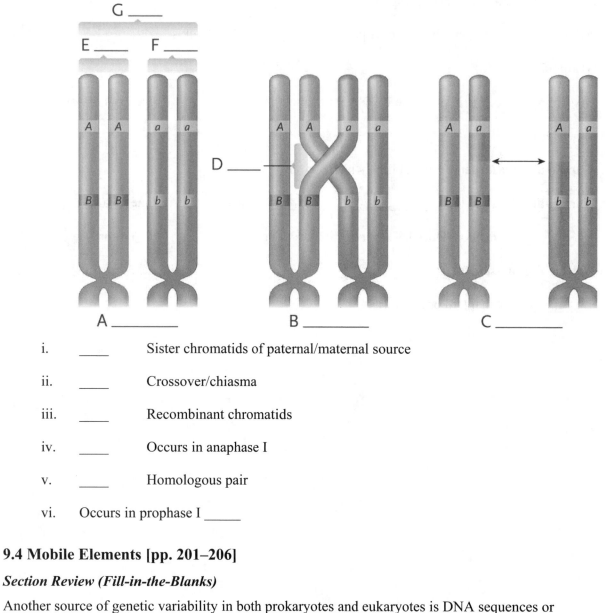

i. _____ Sister chromatids of paternal/maternal source

ii. _____ Crossover/chiasma

iii. _____ Recombinant chromatids

iv. _____ Occurs in anaphase I

v. _____ Homologous pair

vi. Occurs in prophase I _____

9.4 Mobile Elements [pp. 201–206]

Section Review (Fill-in-the-Blanks)

Another source of genetic variability in both prokaryotes and eukaryotes is DNA sequences or

(151) _____ _____ (TEs), which have the ability to move from place to place within DNA

molecules. In contrast to the recombination mechanisms above, this movement involves nonhomologous

sequences and is referred to as (152) _____. Through the action of their (153) _____

enzyme, TEs either move by cutting and (154) _____ or by (155) _____ and inserting the

copy at another location. TEs may insert into a gene and (156) _____ it, or they may insert into

regulatory sequences, causing increased or decreased gene (157) _____. The latter has been

implicated in certain types of (158) _____ in humans and other complex animals. Because of their effects on gene expression, TEs are biological (159) _____ as well as sources of genetic variability.

There are two major types of bacterial TEs: small (160) _____ _____ (IS) and longer

(161) _____. The latter differ from the IS elements by encoding, in addition to the

(162) _____ enzyme, extra genes such as those for antibiotic (163) _____. In *E. coli*,

creation of Hfr strains results from recombination between homologous IS elements in the

(164) _____ and the chromosome. In addition, transposition between the chromosome and

(165) _____ plasmids allows for the spread of genes within and between species. The TEs in

eukaryotes exist as transposons or (166) _____; the latter are similar to a family of viruses called

(167) _____. Both move by transcribing a(n) (168) _____ copy, replicating it, or reverse

(169) _____ it into a DNA copy and inserting it into a new location while leaving the "parent" copy

at the original site. In eukaryotes, TE-mediated change becomes heritable if it occurs in cells that go on to

become (170) _____.

Matching

Match each of the following terms/concepts with its correct definition.

171. _____ Barbara McClintock

A. Eukaryotic viruses that encode reverse transcriptase

172. _____ Target site

B. TE-encoded enzyme that catalyzes cut-and-paste transposition

173. _____ Transposable elements

C. The location where a TE inserts

174. _____ Transposition

D. Eukaryotic TEs that move to different locations via an RNA intermediate

175. _____ Retrovirus

E. Segments of DNA that can move from one place to another

176. _____ Transposase

F. Process of moving segments of DNA from one place to another

177. _____ Retrotransposons

G. Enzyme that copies RNA to make complementary DNA

178. _____ Reverse transcriptase

H. State of virus where its DNA is inserted into eukaryotic genome

179. _____ Provirus

I. Discoverer of transposable elements

True/False

Mark if the statement is true (T) or false (F). If the statement is false, justify your answer in the lines below each statement.

180. _____ Bacterial transposons are small sequences that generally contain a single gene for the transposase enzyme.

_____

_____

181. _____ Approximately 40% of the human genome consists of retrotransposons and retroviruses.

_____

_____

Short Answer

182. Provide an explanation for the multicoloured nature of maize.

_____

_____

183. Discuss the opposing concepts of genome plasticity and stability.

_____

_____

SELF-TEST

1. Which does NOT cause genetic variation in bacterial populations? [p. 190]
   a. Binary fission
   b. transduction
   c. conjugation
   d. transformation

2. Which of the following would describe a type of bacterial variant that may result from exposure to X-rays or UV light? [pp. 183–184]
   a. parental
   b. temperate
   c. virulent
   d. auxotroph

3. Which term refers to the structure that connects two bacterial cells during transfer of DNA? [p. 185]
   a. a plasmid
   b. a nucleoid
   c. a pilus
   d. a flagellum

4. Which strain of bacteria would have the F plasmid integrated into their chromosome? [p. 187]
   a. F^-
   b. Hfr
   c. F^+

5. Which statement about conjugation between an Hfr and an F⁻ recipient is true? [pp. 185–187]

    a. Some of the genes from the Hfr are combined with the DNA of the recipient.
    b. The recipient becomes an Hfr.
    c. The recipient becomes F⁺.
    d. Genes from the F⁻ are transferred to the Hfr.

6. Which term refers to a virus transferring DNA from one bacterium to another? [p. 188]

    a. binary fission
    b. transduction
    c. conjugation
    d. transformation

7. During which cycle does a bacteriophage DNA become incorporated inside the host genome? [pp. 188–190]

    a. during the lytic cycle
    b. during the lysogenic cycle

8. During which cycle does a virus rupture the host cell in order to be released? [pp. 188–190]

    a. during the lytic cycle
    b. during the lysogenic cycle

9. What is a prophage or provirus? [p. 189]

    a. a virus that contains DNA
    b. a virus that has an RNA intermediate
    c. a virus whose DNA is incorporated into the host genome
    d. a virus that is assembled and ready to be released

10. Which statement about bacterial transposable elements is false? [pp. 201–204]

    a. They can move DNA segments from one location in the chromosome to another location in the chromosome.
    b. They can move DNA segments from a plasmid to the main chromosome.
    c. They can move DNA segments from one plasmid to another plasmid.
    d. They can move DNA segments from one bacterial cell to another.

11. If a diploid organism normally has 16 chromosomes in somatic cells, how many chromosomes are from maternal origin and how many are from paternal origin? [p. 193]

    a. 32 from maternal origin; 32 from paternal
    b. 8 from maternal origin; 8 from paternal
    c. 4 from maternal origin; 4 from paternal
    d. 16 from maternal origin; 16 from paternal

12. Which statement is consistent with the alleles on a pair of homologous chromosomes? [p. 193]

    a. They are always the same.
    b. They are always different.
    c. They may or may not be the same.

13. In the process of meiosis, how many times does DNA replication occur? [p. 193]

    a. never
    b. once
    c. twice

14. When do homologous pairs separate? [pp. 194–195]

    a. during anaphase I
    b. during anaphase II
    c. during telophase I
    d. during prophase II

15. Suppose that the diploid number for an organism is six, and one homologous pair underwent nondisjunction during meiosis I. How many chromosomes would be present in the daughter cells at the end of meiosis I? [p. 195]

    a. Both daughter cells would have three chromosomes.
    b. One daughter cell would have two chromosomes and the other would have three.
    c. One daughter cell would have one chromosome and the other would have five.
    d. One daughter cell would have two chromosomes and the other would have four.

16. With respect to the sex chromosomes in humans, females and males will produce gametes with which possible sex chromosomes? [p. 195]

    a. Females will produce only X; males will produce only Y.
    b. Females will produce only X; males will produce both X and Y.
    c. Females will produce both X and Y; males will produce only Y.

17. Suppose that the diploid number for an organism is x, and that a crossover occurred during premetaphase I. What will be the amount of DNA at the end of meiosis I? [p. 195]

    a. $0.5\,x$
    b. $0.75\,x$
    c. x
    d. $2\,x$

18. Which life cycle pattern would not give rise to genetic variability? [pp. 191–192]

    a. diploid dominant
    b. haploid dominant
    c. diploid–haploid alternate
    d. asexual reproduction

19. Regardless of the life cycle pattern, which statement about gametes produced by meiosis is true? [p. 193]

    a. They are different from each other.
    b. They are identical to each other but different from the parental cell.
    c. They are different from each other and from the parental cell.

20. Which statement about retroviruses is false? [pp. 205–206]

    a. They may have been the evolutionary predecessor to retrotransposons.
    b. They synthesize DNA from an RNA sequence.
    c. They are found in bacterial and eukaryotic cells.
    d. They can exist in up to 100 different provirus insertions in the average human chromosome.

1. Discuss the effects of a mutation that prevented synapsis.

2. Discuss the advantages and disadvantages of gametes that are genetically identical versus gametes that are genetically unique.

3. Discuss the effects of a hypothetical process that would allow recombination between nonhomologous chromosomes rather than just homologous pairs.

4. You want to do some chromosomal mapping using an interrupted mating experiment and you have, in your lab, the following strains:

   a) *E. coli* Hfr with the traits his^+ met^- phe^- arg^+

   b) *E. coli* Hfr with the traits his^- met^+ phe^+ arg^-

   c) *E. coli* F⁻ with the traits his^+ met^- phe^- arg^+

   d) *E. coli* F⁻ with the traits his^- met^+ phe^+ arg^-

   where each of the four gene names represents a gene for the biosynthesis of an essential amino acid and the minus sign denotes a mutation, while the plus sign indicates the normally functioning gene. Identify the following:

   i. Which mating pairs would you need to use (in two separate experiments) to map each of the four genes?

   ii. What kind of growth media would you need for each of the two experiments?

   iii. What kind of unit would you be likely to use for the "map" distance between two genes?

   iv. What kind of control(s) would you need?

10 Mendel, Genes, and Inheritance

TOPIC MAP

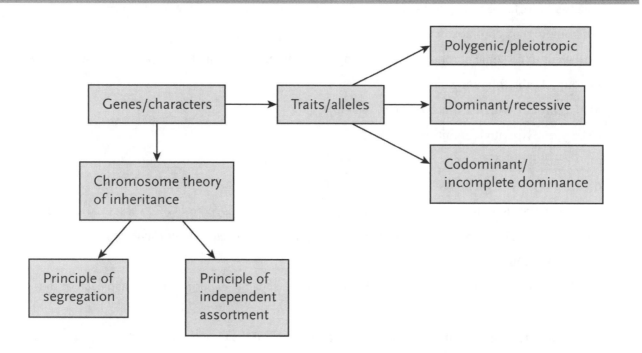

LEARNING OUTCOMES AND STUDY STRATEGIES

By the end of this chapter, you should be able to

- Describe Mendel's three hypotheses and distinguish between an allele and a locus, and a phenotype and a genotype, and relate these to the chromosome theory of inheritance

- Use a Punnett square and define a testcross and a dihybrid cross

- Distinguish between complete dominance, incomplete dominance, codominance, epistasis, pleiotropy, and polygenic inheritance, giving examples of each

Study strategies for this chapter:

- First, focus on the terminology and Mendel's experiments: look at the figures as they make things easier to picture and interpret.

- Next, using testcrosses and Punnett square analysis, predict the probability of gene expression in offspring. There are plenty of problems to work on in the self-test questions at the end of the chapter and in the companion study guide chapter.

- Be able to relate allele and chromosome activities in meiosis to gene expression.

- Finally, focus on the complexity of multiple alleles, gene interactions, and the enormous potential for variation.
- As always, work through the companion section of the study guide after finishing each section of the textbook.

INTERACTIVE EXERCISES

Why It Matters [pp. 211–212]
10.1 The Beginnings of Genetics: Mendel's Garden Peas [pp. 212–223]

Section Review (Fill-in-the-Blanks)

In the 1860s, the monk (1) _____ used careful scientific experimentation combined with quantitative

analyses of the data to disprove the (2) _____ theory of inheritance, proving instead that traits were

passed from one (3) _____ to the next in predictable ratios and combinations. His choice of the

(4) _____ as an experimental organism was a good one for three reasons: they were easy to cultivate,

had easily observed, (5) _____-breeding characters, and allowed him to control the

(6) _____ or sexual reproduction of the plants. This second trait meant that when (7) _____,

parental traits were passed unchanged to the next generation. This allowed him to evaluate the effects of

mating pea plants with varying traits, the term he used for what we now call (8) _____. In his crosses

between two parental plants, that is, the (9) _____ generation, he designated the products as the filial

or (10) _____ generation; when the F_1 plants were allowed to self-pollinate or (11) _____,

the offspring from that cross were designated the (12) _____ generation. After many crosses, he was

able to make conclusions about alleles and chromosome movement during the process of (13) _____,

long before genes (what he called (14) _____), chromosomes, and cell division for gamete formation

were understood. He also provided an explanation for why organisms may look the same but be genetically

different: that is, the relationship between (15) _____ and (16) _____, respectively. Based

on his work with (17) _____ or single-character crosses, Mendel showed that genes that govern traits

in individuals occur in (18) _____; that if different alleles are present in an individual, one allele will

be (19) _____ over the other; and that the two alleles of a gene segregate (20) _____ and

occur in single copy in the gametes, a behaviour known as the principle of (21) _____. To confirm his findings and interpretations, Mendel used (22) _____: he crossed an F_1 heterozygote and a

homozygous recessive or (23) _____-breeding parent. Using this approach, one can determine easily

the (24) _____ of an individual who has a dominant phenotype, that is, homozygous dominant or

heterozygous. The use of (25) _____crosses led Mendel to a fourth hypothesis: the alleles of two

separate characters segregate (26) _____. This is now known as the principle of random

(27) _____. The findings and predictions made by Mendel are the underpinnings of today's science

of genetics and chromosome theory of (28) _____.

Matching

Match each of the following genetics terms and concepts with its correct definition or explanation.

29. ____	Dominance	A.	Testcross to evaluate one gene (character)
30. ____	Dominant trait	B.	The location on a chromosome of a particular gene
31. ____	Recessive trait	C.	The appearance of an organism
32. ____	Homozygote	D.	Trait that is masked unless in the homozygous state
33. ____	Heterozygote	E.	The term used by Mendel for a heritable characteristic; now known as a gene
34. ____	Monohybrid cross	F.	Masking of a allele (trait)
35. ____	Dihybrid cross	G.	Alleles (traits) for a given gene (character) are different
36. ____	Locus	H.	Both alleles (traits) are the same
37. ____	Character	I.	The genetic constitution of an organism
38. ____	Self	J.	A cross between an individual with a dominant trait with one that is homozygous recessive, in order to determine if the individual with the dominant trait is homozygous or heterozygous
39. ____	Genotype	K.	Trait that is expressed when in the heterozygous state
40. ____	Phenotype	L.	Testcross to evaluate two genes (characters)
41. ____	Testcross	M.	In genetics terms, this refers to the process of allowing the F_1 generation to self-pollinate to generate the F_2 generation and thereby determine the genotype of the first generation of offspring

Matching

For each of the following statements, choose the most appropriate genetic term.

42. _____ Expressed alleles

43. _____ When you look in the mirror

44. _____ Purple flowers

45. _____ Plant that is heterozygous for flower colour

46. _____ Alleles that are present

A. Genotype

B. Phenotype

Complete the Table

47. In the following table of garden pea individuals, "T" (Tall) is dominant over "t" (short) for plant height and "R" (red) is dominant over "r" (white) for flower colour. For the genotypes given, identify the number and type of all possible gametes (even if the gametes are identical)—see the example below:

	Number of Potential Gametes	Types of All Possible Gametes			
Tt TT	2 2	T T	t T		
Rr	A.	B.	C.		
TTRr	4	D.	E.	F.	G.
TtRr	H.	I.	J.	K.	L.

48. Given the table above, fill in the blanks in the summary below:

The genotype of the Rr individual is (A) _____, while the flower colour is (B) _____.

The flower colour is not the genotype but the (C) _____. The phenotype of the TTRr individual

is (D) _____ in height and (E) _____ in colour. Another way to indicate the genotype

of the TTRr individual is (F) _____ _____ for the height and (G) _____

_____ for the flower colour. In the case of flower colour, the only way to have a white flower is to have a genotype of (H) _____ _____. The only way to have a short plant is to have a genotype of (I) _____ _____. In both cases, the explanation for the phenotype of the heterozygote is that the T and R alleles are (J) _____, whereas the t and r alleles are (K) _____. In order to determine whether a red flower was due to a homozygous or heterozygous genotype, one would do a (L) _____ and examine the phenotypes of the F_1 generation.

Short Answer

49. Define the principle of segregation.

   _____

   _____

   _____

50. Define the principle of independent assortment.

   _____

   _____

   _____

51. What is a testcross, and why is it used?

   _____

   _____

   _____

52. Describe the chromosome theory of inheritance.

   _____

   _____

   _____

53. In garden pea plants, tall (T) is dominant over dwarf (t). Use the Punnett square method for the monohybrid cross Tt × tt in order to answer the following:

   A.   The genotypes of the possible gametes from both parents

   B.   The genotype probabilities of the offspring

   C.   The phenotype probabilities of the offspring

   D.   Would this be a monohybrid cross or a testcross?

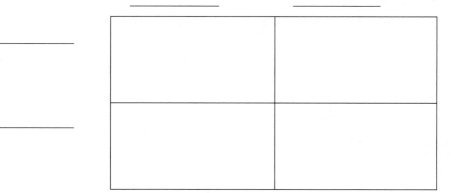

54. The parental or P generation is a cross between two true-breeding plants. One plant is homozygous dominant for both plant height (tall) and stem strength (strong), and the other plant is homozygous recessive for both traits: TTSS × ttss.

   A.   What is the genotype of the possible gametes for the two P generation plants?

   _____

   _____

   B.   What are the genotype probabilities of the F_1 offspring?

   _____

   _____

   C.   What are the phenotype probabilities of the F_1 offspring?

   _____

   _____

Using the Punnett square method for the dihybrid cross in which the F_1 offspring were selfed, answer the following questions:

_____	_____	_____	_____
_____			
_____			
_____			
_____			

D.   The genotype probabilities of the F_2 offspring _____

_____

_____

E.   The phenotype probabilities of the F_2 offspring _____

_____

_____

10.2 Later Modifications and Additions to Mendel's Hypotheses [pp. 223–230]

Section Review (Fill-in-the-Blanks)

Subsequent research has led to some modifications and additions to Mendel's hypotheses. It was determined than some alleles are neither fully (55) _____ nor fully (56) _____ so that the phenotype of the heterozygote is not like that of either homozygote. There are two situations in which this can arise. In (57) _____ dominance, the activity of one allele is insufficient to compensate for the inactivity of another, such as in the case of red, white, and (58) _____ snapdragons or diseases such as the genetic disorder that affects red blood cells, (59) _____ _____ _____. In contrast, in (60) _____ dominance, both alleles in the heterozygote are equally active, as in the example of the (61) _____ blood group. Unlike flower colour in garden peas, many genes within a population have more than one form or (62) _____. The implications of this can have far-reaching effects, as in the situation of trying to find matches for (63) _____ transplants in humans. The coat colour phenotype of Labrador retrievers provides an example of (64) _____, where one gene product has an effect on the expression of genes at other loci. In this breed, the combined effects of two genes determine coat colour: one for production of melanin, a brownish-black pigment, and one for the (65) _____ of the pigment. A homozygous recessive individual for the latter will have virtually no pigment (66) _____, even if the pigment is produced at high levels in a homozygous dominant dog. A (67) _____ trait is one that arises from the combined effects of several genes so that one sees a (68) _____ variation of the trait within a population. Plotting the distribution of height of adult humans is a good example of this variation: with (69) _____ traits, such plots generally yield a (70) _____ curve. In almost the opposite phenomenon, (71) _____ describes the situation where one gene affects more than one character of an organism.

Short Answer

72. Discuss the three types of dominance for the heterozygote Pp.

_____

_____

_____

73. Compare and contrast pleiotropic and polygenic characters.

_____

_____

_____

SELF-TEST

1. Which of the following of Mendel's hypotheses agrees with the events of meiosis? [pp. 212-216]
   a. the principle of segregation
   b. the principle of dependent assortment
   c. the principle of crossovers

2. Suppose that Bob has blood type A, and all his children have blood type O. Bob thinks the mailman might be the father because his wife is also blood type A. Which two terms Bob is getting confused? [pp. 226–227]
   a. phenotype; genotype
   b. dominance; recessive
   c. monohybrid; dihybrid
   d. homozygous; heterozygous

3. An individual genotype is AaBB. What is(are) the type(s) of gametes that can be produced? [p. 216]

   a. Aa and BB
   b. AaB
   c. AB and aB
   d. A and a and B

4. For the cross AA × aa, suppose that the F_1 generation is a different phenotype than either of the parental individuals. Which statement about the alleles A and a best describes the observation? [pp. 223–230]

   a. incomplete dominance
   b. multiple alleles
   c. pleiotropy
   d. lethal

5. Suppose that blue is dominant over white in flowers. Also suppose that a heterozygous blue flower is crossed with a white flower. What would you predict the phenotypic ratio to be? [pp. 216–218]

   a. 100% blue flowers
   b. 75% blue flowers and 25% white (3:1)
   c. 50% blue flowers and 50% white (1:1)
   d. 25% blue flowers and 75% white (1:3)

6. Suppose that blue is dominant over white in flowers. Also suppose that a heterozygous blue flower is crossed with a white flower. What would you predict the genotypic ratio to be? [pp. 216–218]

   a. all Bb
   b. 75% Bb and 25% bb
   c. 50% Bb and 50% bb
   d. 25% BB and 75% bb

7. Suppose that Albert has type A blood and Barbara has type B blood, but you do not know their genotypes? Which of the following lists all the possible blood types of their children? [pp. 226–227]

   a. types A and B
   b. types A, B, AB, and O

   c. types A, B, or AB
   d. types AB and O

8. What is demonstrated by the genetics of the ABO blood types? [p. 226–227]

   a. the phenomenon of codominance
   b. the phenomenon of incomplete dominance
   c. the phenomenon of epistasis
   d. the phenomenon of pleiotropy

9. Suppose that the parents of your yellow Lab puppy are both black Labs. Which statement is consistent with the genotypes of the parents? [p. 228]

   a. *BbEe* or *BBEe*
   b. *BBee* or *Bbee*
   c. *bbEe* or *BBee*

10. What does the genetics of the coat colour for Labrador retrievers demonstrate? [p. 228]

    a. the phenomenon of codominance
    b. the phenomenon of incomplete dominance
    c. the phenomenon of epistasis
    d. the phenomenon of pleiotropy

11. Suppose that Harry, who is 1.88 m tall, knows that he is adopted and that both his parents were less than 1.67 m tall. Harry checked his pedigree for three generations and found that no one was over 1.72 m tall. What would you tell Harry about how the genetics of his family has affected his height? [p. 229]

    a. Harry is correct; he must be adopted.
    b. Height is determined by polygenic inheritance.
    c. Height is a result of the product rule.
    d. Height is pleiotropic.

12. Which is an example of pleiotropy? [p. 230]

    a. human blood types
    b. adult human height
    c. familial hypocholesterolemia
    d. sickle cell anemia

13. What is the distinction between codominance and incomplete dominance? [pp. 223–226]

    a. In codominance, both alleles are equally expressed; in incomplete dominance, one is completely expressed, but the other is not expressed at all.

    b. In codominance, one allele is completely expressed but the other is not expressed at all; in incomplete dominance, both alleles are equally expressed.

    c. In codominance, both alleles are equally expressed; in incomplete dominance, one allele is only partially masked by the other.

    d. In codominance, one allele is only partially masked by the other; in incomplete dominance, both alleles are equally expressed.

14. Suppose you are comparing two matings, i.e., TT × tt and TT × Tt, where you assume T and t are codominant. Which would exhibit the greatest phenotypic diversity in the F_1 generation? [pp. 223–226]

    a. TT × tt

    b. TT × Tt

15. Suppose you are comparing two matings, i.e., TT × tt and TT × Tt, where you assume T is incompletely dominant? Which would exhibit the greatest phenotypic diversity in the F_1 generation? [pp. 224–226]

    a. TT × tt

    b. TT × Tt

16. Which of the following is unlikely to be a polygenic trait? [pp. 229]

    a. skin colour

    b. body weight in humans

    c. cystic fibrosis

    d. eye colour

17. Which human trait does NOT display inheritance patterns that follow Mendelian principles? [p. 223]

    a. sickle cell disease

    b. webbed fingers

    c. albinism

INTEGRATING AND APPLYING KEY CONCEPTS

1. Sometimes recessive alleles are defective or produce an unwanted phenotype and in homozygous individuals can cause health problems. Starting with two healthy, heterozygous mice, design an experiment that would eliminate the recessive allele.

2. After being in a serious traffic accident, Suzie arrives at the hospital and undergoes emergency surgery. She has to have multiple blood transfusions, but the medical staff are worried that they may not be able to get enough from the blood bank, which is running low. If Suzie's blood type is A, her father's is type B, and her mother's is type O, would either of her parents be able to donate blood to Suzie? Who or why not?

3. Joe is accused of fathering a baby with type AB blood. Joe has type O blood, and the mother has type B blood. Does Joe have a case? Defend your response.

11 Genes, Chromosomes, and Human Genetics

TOPIC MAP

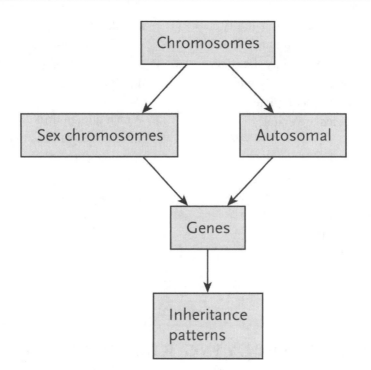

LEARNING OUTCOMES AND STUDY STRATEGIES

By the end of this chapter, you should be able to

- Understand the idea of linkage and sex-linked genes and explain how one would prove one or the other

- Understand how recombination frequencies can be used to map alleles

- Comprehend the differences in the sex chromosomes of mammals and *Drosophila* and explain what determines female versus male and what is done to control the gene dosage of females

- Identify the different kinds of chromosomal alterations and the basic process that generates each (e.g., unequal recombination, nondisjunction)

- Understand the genetics of human diseases, autosomal recessive, autosomal dominant, and X-linked recessive, and know how the inheritance patterns differ between these. Finally, you should understand how they would be identified by a genetic counsellor or physician.

- Define cytoplasmic inheritance and genomic imprinting

Study strategies for this chapter:

- First, focus on the concepts of linkage groups and genetic recombination events. Go through the genetic tests involving the fruit flies, paying particular attention to the method of determining chromosomal maps of specific genes and to the use of reciprocal crosses.

- Be able to relate sex-linked disorders to sex-linked genes; use a Punnett square to go through the various possibilities of X-linked versus autosomal linkage and inheritance patterns.

- Given either genotypes or phenotypes of parents with genetic disorders, predict the probabilities of these genetic disorders in offspring.

- Carefully examine the figures and tables as well as the various subject headings to keep the ideas clearly organized in your mind.

- As always, go through one section of the textbook at a time and then work through the companion section of the study guide.

INTERACTIVE EXERCISES

Why It Matters [pp. 234–235]
11.1 Genetic Linkage and Recombination [pp. 235–240]

Section Review (Fill-in-the-Blanks)

Mendel's principle of independent assortment was based on the concept that different genes were not

(1) _____, that is, located on the same chromosome. We now know that organisms have far more

genes than (2) _____, so that genes that are not located on the same chromosome assort

(3) _____ and display the expected Mendelian inheritance pattern, while (4) _____ genes

assort together, behaving as a single gene during meiosis. However, because prophase I involves

(5) _____ between homologous chromosomes, the inheritance patterns of linked genes generally fails

to match those expected for single genes; the conclusion is that they have undergone a (6) _____

event during prophase I. In most instances, the (7) _____ event leads to the equal exchange of an

allele on one chromosome with its corresponding gene on the (8) _____ chromosome. The amount of

recombination between any two alleles is (9) _____ to the amount of intervening DNA; that is, as

linkage distance between two genes increases, so does the recombination (10) _____. This is the

basis for determining the (11) _____ _____ distance between two alleles whereby genes are

assigned relative locations with respect to (12) _____ _____ and the distance separating

them is described in (13) _____ units. Because recombination (14) _____ vary to some degree from one position to another on chromosomes, this unit of measurement is a (15) _____ one

and does not correlate with the actual bases of intervening DNA. In order to detect linkage and map the

distance between two genes A/a and B/b, dihybrid testcrosses are done: by definition (16) _____

crossed with (17) _____. If all progeny classes are equally frequent, then the genes are determined to

be (18) _____. However, in cases where map distances are extremely long and (19) _____

crossover events occur, the calculated frequency of recombination would suggest that the linked genes are, in

fact, (20) _____ _____.

Matching

Match each of the following genetics terms and concepts with its correct definition or explanation.

21. ____ Locus	A.	The term applied to a genotype or phenotype that is arbitrarily designated as "normal"
22. ____ Linkage	B.	Alternative name for map unit
23. ____ Thomas H. Morgan	C.	Measures distances between adjacent genes using map units
24. ____ Wild-type	D.	The physical location of a gene on a chromosome
25. ____ Linkage map	E.	The phenomenon explained by the inheritance behaviour of genes located on the same chromosome
26. ____ Centimorgan	G.	Discovered the principles of linkage through studies of *Drosophila melanogaster*

Short Answer

27. Explain how the map unit distance between two genes is calculated.

   _____

   _____

28. Provide one type of evidence for linkage groups.

   _____

   _____

True/False

Mark if the statement is true (T) or false (F). If the statement is false, justify your answer in the lines below each statement.

29. _____ Mendel was fortunate in his choice of garden pea characters as they were all unlinked, allowing him to determine his principle of independent assortment.

_____

_____

30. _____ A linkage group would be a collection of genes that are linked on a chromosome.

_____

_____

11.2 Sex-Linked Genes [pp. 240–245]

Section Review (Fill-in-the-Blanks)

In many organisms, males and females have one or more (31) _____ of chromosomes that differ.

These are called the (32) _____ _____; the remaining identical pairs of chromosomes are

called the (33) _____ _____. In humans and (34) _____ _____, females

have two copies of the (35) _____ chromosome, whereas males only have one. In males, the

chromosome that pairs with this during meiosis is the male-specific (36) _____ chromosome. These

sex-based differences are reflected in certain non-Mendelian patterns of (37) _____, and these are

best identified using (38) _____ crosses with true-breeding females. When looking at the expression

of recessive (39) _____-_____ traits, if males inherit the gene, it will be expressed, but

expression in females requires inheritance from both (40) _____. The determination of a human's

(41) _____ is determined by the SRY gene located on the Y chromosome. In mammals, the dosage

of (42) _____-_____ genes is equalized between males and females by (43) _____

of one of the X chromosomes during early embryonic development. This can be seen microscopically since

the method of inactivation is chromosomal (44) _____; the inactivated chromosome is referred to as

the (45) _____ _____.

Matching

Match each of the following with its correct definition or descriptor.

46. _____ Reciprocal cross

A. Describes the non-Mendelian pattern of inheritance of traits carried by the sex chromosomes

47. _____ Autosomal

B. A chart depicting all of the relatives of an individual over many generations, including the sex and presence of a particular trait

48. _____ Sex-linked inheritance

C. The condensed, inactivated X chromosome visible in the nuclei of female cells

49. _____ Sex-linked trait

D. The effective number of genes in a cell; for X-linked genes, this is equalized between males and females by inactivation

50. _____ Pedigree

E. Performing a mating in which the phenotypes of the parental organisms are switched

51. _____ Barr body

F. Chromosomes that are the same between males and females

52. _____ Gene dosage

G. A gene that is linked to a chromosome that is inherited differently in males and females

True/False

Mark if the statement is true (T) or false (F). If the statement is false, justify your answer in the lines below each statement.

53. _____ The gene for hemophilia is located on the Y chromosome.

_____

_____

54. _____ The sex of a child is determined by a gene on the Y chromosome.

_____

_____

55. _____ In a female with different alleles of an X-linked gene, the same chromosome and allele will be inactivated in all cells.

_____

_____

Short Answer

56. Explain how a female can have a sex-linked genetic disorder.

_____

_____

57. An XY individual has a defective SRY gene. Explain the phenotypic sex of the individual.

_____

_____

58. Explain how the two sex chromosomes would be accurately segregated during meiosis.

_____

_____

59. Explain how an X-linked trait "skips" a generation.

_____

_____

Problem

60. Suzie's dad has an X-linked recessive disorder, SQ. Sam, Suzie's husband, has no known genetic disorders in his family. Suzie and Sam want to have children. As their genetic counsellor, you need to determine the answers to the following questions. Hint: the Punnett square method will help.

   A. The genotype and phenotype of Suzie

   _____

   _____

   B. The probability of this couple having a child with the genotype and phenotype of SQ

   _____

   _____

   C. The possible phenotypes and genotypes of this couple's male children

   _____

   _____

   D. The possible phenotypes and genotypes of this couple's female children

   _____

   _____

11.3 Chromosomal Alterations That Affect Inheritance [pp. 245–249]
11.4 Human Genetics and Genetic Counselling [pp. 249–252]

Section Review (Fill-in-the-Blanks)

Changes to the chromosome structure will affect (61) _____ and may affect gene expression. Such

alterations can result from exposure to (62) _____, certain chemicals, or the enzymes of some

(63) _____. The immediate result is breakage of the DNA backbone leading to four common

alterations: (64) _____, _____, _____, and (65) _____. The latter involves

the movement of a chromosomal segment to a non- (66) _____ chromosome. Duplications have been

suggested to play an important role in (67) _____ as the duplicated gene is free to undergo changes in

the DNA sequence without adversely affecting the individual. However, in order for this to happen, the

genetic changes must occur in (68) _____-line cells. Abnormalities in the number of chromosomes

can also arise, most often from (69) _____ during meiosis. This can happen during meiosis I when

(70) _____ chromosomes fail to separate or during meiosis II when (71) _____

_____ fail to separate. In rare cases, a cell will have a whole extra set of chromosomes; these cells

are called (72) _____ and generally arise when the spindle fails to function during

(73) _____ of germ-line cells. There are (74) _____ major types of inheritance patterns in

humans, and determining which governs inheritance of abnormal genes and genetic disorders can be of

critical importance. In (75) _____ recessive inheritance, both male and female heterozygous

individuals are (76) _____, while homozygous recessive individuals exhibit the trait. An indication

of this form of inheritance is the birth of an affected child to (77) _____ parents. In contrast, with

autosomal (78) _____ inheritance, heterozygous and homozygous dominant individuals will both

exhibit the trait, but homozygous (79) _____ individuals will not. In (80) _____-

_____ recessive inheritance, male individuals and homozygous recessive females will exhibit the

trait and (81) _____ females are carriers. Examples of each mode of inheritance are associated with

various genetic disorders, and it often falls to genetic (82) _____ to characterize the mode of

inheritance based on a family (83) _____. Having this information gives prospective parents an idea

of the inherent risks to potential (84) _____.

Matching

Match each of the following terms/concepts with its correct definition.

85. _____ Duplication

A. Segment of a chromosome that is attached to a nonhomologous chromosome

86. _____ Euploids

B. Individual with a 2n that is either −1 or +1 chromosome

87. _____ Translocation

C. The other name for Down syndrome, a disorder resulting from having three copies of chromosome 21

88. _____ Nondisjunction

D. Individual is 2n with no abnormalities

89. _____ Aneuploids

E. Extra set of chromosomes

90. _____ Deletion

F. Segment of a chromosome is present more than once

91. _____ Polyploids

G. Segment of a chromosome that is present, but in the reverse order

92. _____ Inversion

H. Segment of a chromosome is missing

93. _____ Trisomy 21

I. Failure of homologous pairs to separate during meiosis I

True/False

Mark if the statement is true (T) or false (F). If the statement is false, justify your answer in the lines below each statement.

94. _____ Aneuploidy of sex chromosomes is less likely to have lethal effects than autosomal aneuploidy.

_____

_____

95. _____ Polyploidy in eukaryotes is generally fatal during the embryonic stage of development.

_____

_____

Short Answer

96. For a genetic disorder, distinguish between autosomal recessive and autosomal dominant inheritance patterns.

_____

_____

11.5 Nontraditional Patterns of Inheritance [pp. 253–254]

Section Review (Fill-in-the-Blanks)

(97) _____ inheritance and genomic (98) _____ are both modes of inheritance that do not

follow the traditional patterns. In the first type, the inherited trait is encoded by the (99) _____

chromosome, and since these are found in the cytoplasm and the female gamete has far more cytoplasm in the

egg than the sperm, these traits generally exhibit (100) _____ inheritance. Genetic disorders with this

type of inheritance generally result in problems with cellular (101) _____ _____. In the

second type of nontraditional inheritance, the allele inherited from one parent is (102) _____, while the

other is not. This is a form of gene expression control called (103) _____ and depends on

(104) _____ of certain bases within the control region of the gene. This reaction happens in the

(105) _____ and so precedes fertilization. Genetic disorders associated with (106) _____

alleles arise when the homologous allele has suffered a deletion. Certain cancers have also been associated with

these genes; however, in these cases, the problem is from failure to (107) _____ a gene, a phenomenon

called loss of (108) _____, which gives rise to an increased (109) _____ dosage effect.

True/False

Mark if the statement is true (T) or false (F). If the statement is false, justify your answer in the lines
below each statement.

110. _____ Health problems associated with loss of imprinting are due to a methylation of an
essential gene.

_____

_____

Short Answer

111. Define the term "uniparental inheritance."

_____

_____

112. If your genetic counsellor told you that a particular trait is associated with the "egg parent," what
would you conclude about this trait?

_____

_____

SELF-TEST

1. Suppose that all individuals of a group of cats have rounded ears and short whiskers. What is the simplest explanation for this pattern of inheritance? [p. 235]
   a. The two traits are sex-linked.
   b. The two traits are linked.
   c. The traits are pleiotropic.
   d. The traits are independent.

2. Suppose that two moths with short wings have the following offspring: 100 short-winged males, 97 long-winged males, and 205 short-winged females. Which of the following describes the gene that determines wing length? [pp. 240–241]
   a. It is sex-linked and recessive.
   b. It is sex-linked and dominant.
   c. It is autosomal recessive.
   d. It is autosomal dominant.

3. Suppose that the doctor tells Siobhan and James that their new baby is a carrier for red–green colour blindness. What is the sex of the child? [p. 243]
   a. male
   b. female

4. Suppose you are analyzing karyotypes of two patients, a male and a female. The presence of which characteristic would confirm that you are looking at the female karyotype and not the male one? [pp. 244, 247–248]
   a. mitochondria
   b. centrioles
   c. a Barr body
   d. only one Y chromosome

5. Suppose that a normal chromosome sequence is ABCDEFG, but you discover the sequence in your patient is ABGFEDGFEDC. Which genetic alteration(s) most likely occurred? [pp. 245–246]
   a. deletion and duplication
   b. duplication and translocation
   c. inversion
   d. inversion and duplication

6. After conducting six months of experimental crosses with a plant species that has 50 chromosomes, you discover offspring with 150 chromosomes. What must have happened? [pp. 246–248]
   a. nondisjunction
   b. euploidy
   c. tetraploidy
   d. triploidy

7. You need to determine if a patient has trisomy 21 or Down syndrome. Which technique would provide an accurate diagnosis? [p. 247]
   a. pedigree
   b. karyotype
   c. maternal inheritance
   d. mitochondrion

8. Which event most likely leads toTrisomy 21 or Down syndrome? [p. 247]
   a. nondisjunction
   b. polyploidy
   c. translocations
   d. inversions

9. Suppose that 75% of offspring have a genetic condition. What can be concluded about the genetic condition? [p. 250]
   a. It is autosomal recessive.
   b. It is sex-linked autosomal recessive.
   c. It is autosomal dominant.
   d. It is sex-linked autosomal dominant.

10. Suppose you are expecting a child and your doctor wants to test for PKU. Which approach would the doctor take? [pp. 251–252]

    a. chorionic villus sampling
    b. screening test done after birth
    c. amniocentesis
    d. karyotyping

11. Which of the following is NOT an X-linked trait? [p. 249]

    a. hemophilia
    b. *SRY*
    c. red–green colour blindness

12. Julie has a sonogram during her eighth week of pregnancy to confirm that there are no problems with her baby. She and her husband tell the doctor they would like to know the sex of the baby. If you were the doctor, what would you tell them? [pp. 240–241]

    a. The body parts are too small to accurately identify the sex.
    b. It is only possible to tell if the sex is male.
    c. It is not possible to tell the sex because development of the male features does not begin until after 6 to 8 weeks.
    d. Yes, we can identify the gender.

13. Which statement is false? [pp. 244–245]

    a. All calico cats are female.
    b. The father of a calico cat will either be black or orange.
    c. The calico colour in cats is due to imprinting.
    d. The calico coat of some cats is the result of epistasis.

14. Which statement about gene duplication is false? [p. 246]

    a. Gene duplication may have beneficial effects.
    b. Gene duplication is the source of evolutionary changes.

c. Some of the human genes for hemoglobin appear to be the result of gene duplication.
    d. Some of the shark genes for hemoglobin appear to be the result of gene duplication.

15. Which statement about aneuploidy is false? [p. 247]

    a. In humans, aneuploidy of autosomal chromosomes is quite often lethal.
    b. In humans, aneuploidy of autosomal chromosomes quite often has no obvious adverse effects.
    c. Approximately 70% of human miscarriages are the result of aneuploidy.
    d. Aneuploidy results from nondisjunction.

16. Which of the following is autosomal recessive? [p. 250]

    a. cystic fibrosis
    b. trisomy 21
    c. red–green colour blindness
    d. achondroplasia

17. Which of the following would NOT be used for prenatal diagnosis of Down syndrome? [p. 251]

    a. genetic screening
    b. amniocentesis combined with karyotyping
    c. chorionic villus sampling combined with karyotyping

18. How would you know if a trait is cytoplasmically inherited or X-linked recessive? [p. 253]

    a. If only the males exhibit the trait, then it is cytoplasmically inherited.
    b. If only the males exhibit the trait, then it is X-linked.
    c. If males and females show the trait only if their mother also showed it, it is cytoplasmically inherited.

19. In the cross AABB × aabb, suppose you allowed the F_1 generation to breed and you got the ratio expected for unlinked genes. What would you then conclude? [pp. 237–240]

a. A and B are not linked.
b. A and B are linked but widely separated.
c. A and B are either linked but widely separated or unlinked.

20. Suppose you wanted to determine the map unit distance between two widely separated but linked genes in a dihybrid cross. Which of the following would you do? [pp. 239–240]

a. Do a reciprocal cross.
b. Determine the distance to genes close to one or the other.
c. Determine the distance from each gene to one in between.

INTEGRATING AND APPLYING KEY CONCEPTS

1. After completing the chapter in the textbook and the accompanying sections in the study guide, devise your own topic map for this material.

2. Why might polyploidy be advantageous in plants but not in animals?

3. Given the information in your text, predict which is better tolerated, aneuploidy in autosomes or sex chromosomes. Defend your response.

4. Explain how a reciprocal cross can demonstrate that a trait is X-linked.

12 DNA Structure, Replication, and Organization

TOPIC MAP

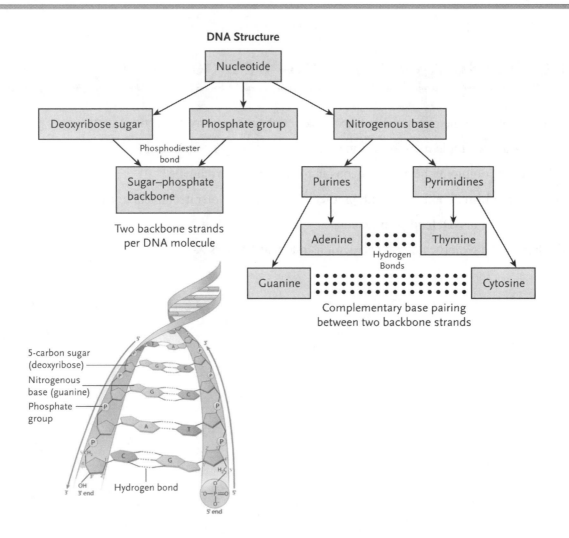

DNA Structure

Nucleotide

Deoxyribose sugar

Phosphate group

Nitrogenous base

Phosphodiester bond

Sugar–phosphate backbone

Two backbone strands per DNA molecule

Purines

Pyrimidines

Adenine

Thymine

Hydrogen Bonds

Guanine

Cytosine

Complementary base pairing between two backbone strands

5-carbon sugar (deoxyribose)

Nitrogenous base (guanine)

Phosphate group

Hydrogen bond

DNA Replication

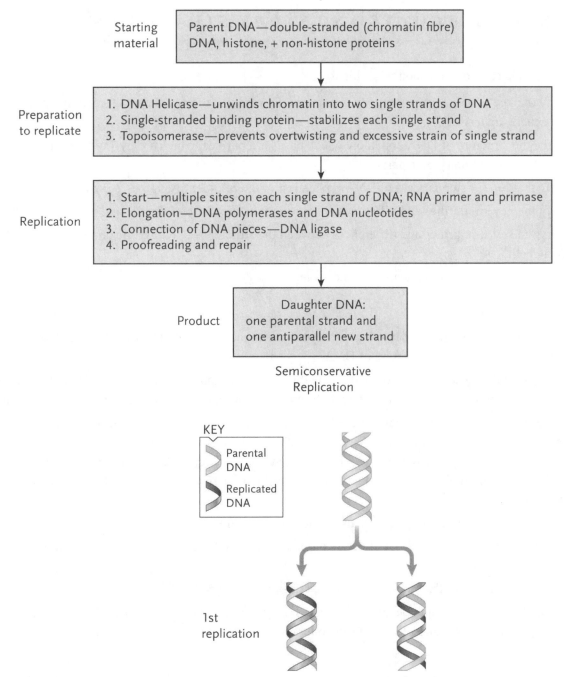

Starting material	**Parent DNA—double-stranded (chromatin fibre)** DNA, histone, + non-histone proteins
Preparation to replicate	1. DNA Helicase—unwinds chromatin into two single strands of DNA 2. Single-stranded binding protein—stabilizes each single strand 3. Topoisomerase—prevents overtwisting and excessive strain of single strand
Replication	1. Start—multiple sites on each single strand of DNA; RNA primer and primase 2. Elongation—DNA polymerases and DNA nucleotides 3. Connection of DNA pieces—DNA ligase 4. Proofreading and repair
Product	Daughter DNA: one parental strand and one antiparallel new strand

Semiconservative
Replication

KEY

Parental DNA

Replicated DNA

1st replication

LEARNING OUTCOMES AND STUDY STRATEGIES

By the end of this chapter, you should be able to

- Identify the key people and experiments that gradually revealed the nature, structure, and replication of the genetic material

- Describe the structure of DNA and know which bases are purines, which are pyrimidines, and the nature of complementary base pairs

- Identify the step-by-step process of DNA replication in *E. coli*, identifying key enzymes and activities

- Identify the key similarities and differences between replication of prokaryotic and eukaryotic DNA

- Identify the key similarities and differences between the structure of prokaryotic and eukaryotic DNA in living cells

- Understand how errors in replication are corrected

Study strategies for this chapter:

- Examine carefully the figures depicting the experiments that lead to the identification of DNA as the hereditary material and the structure of DNA

- Next focus on the basic structure of DNA—the three basic components of a nucleotide, including the two types of nitrogenous bases, and the underlying structural reasons for complementary base pairing.

- Make sure you understand what antiparallel means, what 5′ and 3′ ends mean (carefully examine the figure showing the structure of a nucleotide triphosphate and the numbering system of the carbons in the deoxyribose sugar). Try writing a double-stranded sequence of DNA and figure out, if you were to begin replication in the middle, progressing outward in both directions, where the leading and lagging strands would be.

- DNA replication has multiple steps; focus on one step at a time.

- As always, go through one section of the textbook at a time and then work through the companion section of the study guide.

- Make sure, as you read, that you can answer the questions in each Study Break.

- After you have gone through the chapter, see how much you can expand on the study plan at the beginning of the chapter and see if you can come up with alternative topic maps to the ones above.

INTERACTIVE EXERCISES

Why It Matters [pp. 257–258]
12.1 Establishing DNA as the Hereditary Molecule [pp. 258–261]

Section Review (Fill-in-the-Blanks)

Identification of DNA as the genetic material began with Frederick Griffith's experiments using the bacterial

species (1) _____ _____. He used mice and two strains of the bacterium: a virulent,

(2) _____ strain and a (3) _____ R strain. He found that even when the former was killed, it

was able to pass something to the *R* strain that (4) _____ the *R* strain, making it virulent. He called

the mystery material the (5) _____ principle. Instead of using mice, Avery and colleagues used

(6) _____ _____ of the bacteria, purified the three candidate (7) _____ from the

heat-killed *S* strain and, after selectively degrading each of the three, identified DNA as the (8) _____

principle. Finally, Hershey and Chase used radioactive labelling to show that it is the DNA of

(9) _____ and not its (10) _____ coat that enters bacterial cells and directs the

(11) _____ cycle of the virus. We now know, based on the purification and analysis of ancient, or so-

called (12) _____, that DNA is the genetic material of all current and (13) _____ life forms.

Matching

Match each of the following names or terms with the correct experiment, experimental conclusions, or definition.

14. _____ *S*-type

15. _____ Griffith

16. _____ Hershey and Chase

17. _____ Avery and coworkers

18. _____ Transform

19. _____ T2

A. Using mice, found that nonpathogenic bacteria could be transformed into pathogenic bacteria

B. A type of virus or bacteriophage that infects *E. coli*

C. Term still used to describe process whereby bacteria incorporate extracellular DNA

D. Using bacteriophages and radioactive isotopes of sulphur and phosphate, concluded that DNA is the genetic material rather than proteins

E. Strain of *Streptococcus pneumonia* that produces a capsule and is virulent

F. Found that enzymatically treated material purified from heat-killed bacteria could still transform nonpathogenic bacteria into pathogenic bacteria

True/False

Mark if the statement is true (T) or false (F). If the statement is false, justify your answer in the lines below each statement.

20. _____ ^{32}P can be incorporated into proteins as they are being synthesized and ^{35}S into DNA, providing a way of tracking these molecules.

_____

_____

Short Answer

21. Why would the Hershey and Chase experiments not have worked if, as is the case with animal viruses, the entire bacteriophage infected bacterial cells?

_____

_____

12.2 DNA Structure [pp. 261–264]

Section Review (Fill-in-the-Blanks)

Watson and Crick identified the (22) _____ _____ structure of DNA, using the

(23) _____ diffraction studies of Wilkins and Franklin and (24) _____ rules. The latter

stated that the number of adenines is always equal to the number of (25) _____ and the number of

cytosines is always equal to the number of (26) _____. Watson and Crick specifically described

DNA as having a (27) _____-_____ turn and with one chain being (28) _____ to

the other. The nucleotides of DNA consist of a nitrogenous (29) _____, either a purine or a

(30) _____, covalently attached to a (31) _____ sugar. This is, in turn, covalently attached to

a (32) _____ group. The backbone of each chain consists of alternating (33) _____ and

(34) _____ groups, covalently linked by (35) _____ bonds. The two chains are held together

by non-covalent (36) _____ bonding between the bases, A bonding with (37) _____ and C

bonding with (38) _____. Each full turn of the double helix contains (39) _____ base pairs.

Matching

Match each of the following terms with the correct definition or descriptor.

40. ____	Purines	A.	One full twist of double helix
41. ____	Pyrimidines	B.	Contains a terminal phosphate group
42. ____	5′ end	C.	Containing a terminal hydroxyl group
43. ____	3.4 nm	D.	Hydrogen bonding of purines with pyrimidines
44. ____	Complementary base pairing	E.	Adenine and guanine bases
45. ____	3′ end	F.	Thymine and cytosine bases

True/False

Mark if the statement is true (T) or false (F). If the statement is false, justify your answer in the lines below each statement.

46. _____ A-T base pairs are held together by three covalent bonds.

_____

_____

Short Answer

47. Why is DNA not technically a single molecule?

_____

_____

Labelling

48. Given the backbone of DNA, label the directional ends of the backbone and number the carbons of deoxyribose.

A. _____

B. _____

C. _____

D. _____

E. _____

F. _____

G. _____

H. _____

I. _____

J. _____

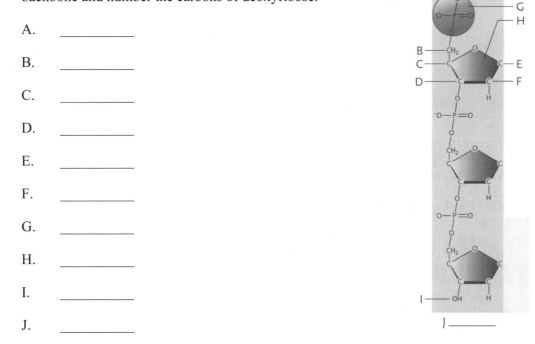

12.3 DNA Replication [pp. 264–276]

Section Review (Fill-in-the-Blanks)

DNA is duplicated in a (49) _____ fashion with each strand acting as a (50) _____ for the

synthesis of a (51) _____ copy. In *E. coli,* when replication begins, the enzyme (52) _____

unwinds the double helix. Replication begins at sites that function as (53) _____ of replication and initiation is primed with short pieces of a(n) (54) _____ _____ , which is produced by the

enzyme (55) _____ . (56) _____ _____ then extends the chain, adding nucleotides

one at a time to the (57) _____ end of the chain. This enzyme moves down the antiparallel template

in the (58) _____ → _____ , polymerizing in the (59) _____ → _____ direction. Replication

progresses outward from the (60) _____ of replication with only one strand, the (61) _____

strand being synthesized in the direction of unwinding. The second DNA strand is synthesized in short

lengths in the opposite direction of unwinding and is called the (62) _____ _____ . Another

DNA polymerase removes the (63) _____ primers and fills in any gaps in the nucleotide strands, then

the enzyme (64) _____ _____ seals all of the single-chain nicks. Because eukaryotic

chromosomes are linear and DNA polymerase only polymerizes in the (65) _____ → _____ direction,

removal of the RNA primer from the (66) _____ end of the chromosome causes a progressive

(67) _____ of the molecule. To protect against deletion of essential genes, eukaryotic chromosomes

have a buffer of noncoding DNA called (68) _____ at each end. With each replication cycle, these

sequences become (69) _____ , eventually leading to cell (70) _____ . Certain non-somatic

cells are protected from these effects by the enzyme (71) _____ .

Matching

For each statement, choose the most appropriate enzyme that DNA replication in *E. coli*.

72. ____	Catalyzes the unwinding of the DNA double helix	A.	DNA polymerase III
73. ____	Produces an RNA strand that acts as a starting point for DNA replication	B.	Helicase
74. ____	Connects Okazaki fragments in the lagging strand	C.	Ligase
75. ____	Reduces twisting in circular chromosomes, working ahead of the replication fork	D.	Topoisomerase
76. ____	Removes RNA primers, replacing them with DNA	E.	Primase
77. ____	Responsible for the bulk of DNA replication	F.	DNA polymerase I

Match each of the following terms with the correct definition or descriptor.

78. _____ Sliding clamp

A. ATP

79. _____ Telomerase

B. Used by Meselson and Stahl to prove semiconservative DNA replication

80. _____ Okazaki fragments

C. Binds template between helicase and DNA polymerase III

81. _____ Nucleoside triphosphate

D. Active in germ cells and cancer cells

82. _____ CsCl density gradient

E. Connects polymerase to template

83. _____ Single stranded binding protein

F. Newly replicated DNA on lagging stand

True/False

Mark if the statement is true (T) or false (F). If the statement is false, justify your answer in the lines below each statement.

84. _____ Because of the semiconservative nature of DNA replication, the oldest part of a DNA molecule is always the 5′ end.

_____

_____

85. _____ Telomerase does not prevent the loss of DNA with removal of RNA primers at the ends of chromosomes.

_____

_____

86. _____ The eukaryotic DNA polymerase is slower than that of E. coli, so chromosomal replication takes much longer in eukaryotes.

_____

_____

87. _____ DNA polymerase I has 5′ → 3′ exonuclease activity.

_____

_____

Short Answer

88. Given the following DNA molecule and assuming the arrow denotes the direction of the helicase, identify which strand is the leading strand and which is the lagging strand:

A. _____   3′ AATCCGTACGGT 5′
             | | | | | | | | | | | | | ⟶
B. _____   5′ TTAGGCATGCCA 3′

89. Refer to the previous question and explain why the lagging strand is synthesized discontinuously.

_____

_____

90. Compare the expected bands in a CsCl density gradient in the case of conservative, semiconservative, and dispersive replication processes, after two replications in ^{14}N-containing media.

_____

_____

12.4 Mechanisms that Correct Replication Errors [pp. 276–277]

Section Review (Fill-in-the-Blanks)

DNA polymerases make very few errors during replication, and most of the errors that are made are base-pair

(91) _____. These can be corrected by the (92) _____ mechanism of DNA polymerase. This

involves the removal of the (93) _____ nucleotide using its (94) _____ ⟶ _____ exonuclease

activity, followed by replacement. Base-pair mismatches remaining after replication cause a(n)

(95) _____ of the double helix, and this is detected by enzymes responsible for (96) _____

repair. The enzymes involved in this process remove a portion of the new chain, including the

(97) _____ nucleotides and the gap filled in by (98) _____ _____. The nicks are

repaired by DNA (99) _____. Errors remaining after proofreading are a primary source of

(100) _____, and these are extremely important for the (101) _____ process.

Short Answer

102. What is the difference between DNA alterations resulting from polymerase errors and mutations?

_____

_____

12.5 DNA Organization in Eukaryotic versus Prokaryotic Cells [pp. 277–280]

Section Review (Fill-in-the-Blanks)

Eukaryotic chromosomes are compacted by a group of proteins called the (103) _____. These

proteins are (104) _____ charged and associated with the oppositely charged (105) _____

groups of the DNA. The (106) _____ represents the first level of compacting, consisting of DNA

wrapped around a complex of two molecules each of histones (107) _____, _____, H3, and

H4. These are separated by a short segment of DNA called the (108) _____. DNA in this structure is

called the (109) _____ _____ _____ fibre. DNA is further condensed by histone

protein (110) _____, giving a more highly coiled structure called the (111) _____

_____ _____ fibre, or solenoid. In interphase cells, the DNA contains regions that are

loosely packed, specifically referred to as (112) _____, and tightly packed regions called the

(113) _____. Genes in the former are transcriptionally active, while those in the latter are

(114) _____ _____. Another group of DNA-associated proteins, the (115) _____

proteins, are involved in regulation of (116) _____ _____. While eukaryotes have multiple

linear chromosomes, prokaryotes generally have a single (117) _____ chromosome. They may have

an additional, independently replicating, DNA molecule called a(n) (118) _____. The chromosome is

folded into (119) _____ by a variety of (120) _____ charged proteins. The resulting

structure resides in the (121) _____ of the cell.

Matching

Match each of the following terms/concepts with its correct definition or descriptor.

122. ____	Euchromatin	A.	The highly condensed and inactivated X chromosome seen in the nucleus of human females
123. ____	Heterochromatin	B.	10 nm in diameter
124. ____	H1	C.	Method of plasmid transfer among bacteria
125. ____	Nucleosome	D.	The method of DNA replication of conjugating plasmids
126. ____	Barr body	E.	30 nm in diameter
127. ____	Conjugation	F.	Helps form solenoid structure
128. ____	Rolling circle replication	G.	The tightly packed regions of the eukaryotic chromosome
129. ____	Solenoid	H.	Loosely packed regions contain transcriptionally active DNA

Labelling

130. Label the various levels of organization of eukaryotic chromatin and chromosomes.

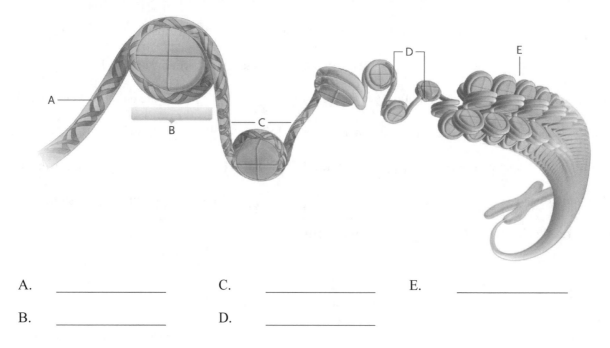

A. _____   C. _____   E. _____

B. _____   D. _____

Short Answer

131. How does replication of bacterial chromosomes differ from the replication of conjugating plasmids?

_____

_____

132. Starting with the most basic, name the various levels of organization of the eukaryotic chromosome and the molecules involved in maintaining each.

_____

_____

SELF-TEST

1. Which statement about Fred Griffith's experiments is true? [p. 259]
   a. The rough *Streptococcus* strains were virulent.
   b. Heat-killed smooth strains caused pneumonia.
   c. Something from the killed *S* strains transformed the *R* strains to smooth.
   d. The *R* strains possessed a transforming principle that enabled them to cause pneumonia.

2. What did Avery and coworkers do? [pp. 259–260]
   a. They proved the semiconservative replication of DNA.
   b. They correctly identified the helical nature of DNA based on X-ray diffraction data.
   c. They purified DNA from test tube–grown, heat-killed S-*Streptococcus* and used it to transform R-*Streptococcus*.
   d. They determined that the number of adenines is equal to the number of thymines and the number of cytosines is equal to the number of guanines.

3. Which statement describes how Hershey and Chase were able to prove that it was the viral DNA that directed the life cycle of bacteriophage T2? [pp. 260–261]
   a. They labelled the DNA with ^{32}P and the proteins with ^{35}S.
   b. They labelled the DNA with ^{35}S and the proteins with ^{15}N.
   c. They labelled the DNA with ^{15}N and the carbohydrates with ^{35}S.
   d. They labelled the DNA with ^{32}P and the lipids with ^{15}N.

4. Which of the following was NOT proposed by Watson and Crick? [pp. 262–264]
   a. They proposed that DNA had a helical structure.
   b. They proposed that DNA was a double-stranded double helix.
   c. They proposed that A base-pairs with T and C base-pairs with G.
   d. They proposed that the two strands of the DNA are antiparallel.

5. Which statement is correct? [pp. 262–264]

   a. A and G are pyrimidines.
   b. C and T are purines.
   c. The double helical DNA has a left-hand turn.
   d. A deoxynucleoside triphosphate has the phosphates attached the to 5′ carbon of deoxyribose.

6. Upon whose X-ray diffraction studies did Watson and Crick rely? [pp. 262–264]

   a. Chargaff's
   b. Wilkins and Franklin's
   c. Avery and colleagues'
   d. their own

7. Which of the following is accurate? [pp. 263–264]

   a. A purine base has to base pair with a pyrimidine to maintain a consistent 2 nm diameter of the helix.
   b. An A-T base pair is held together with three hydrogen bonds.
   c. One full twist of the double helix is 0.34 nm.
   d. Each base is attached to the deoxyribose sugar by a phosphodiester bond.

8. Which of the following was NOT a proposed mechanism for DNA replication proposed by scientists at the time Meselson and Stahl began their collaboration? [pp. 264–266]

   a. semiconservative replication
   b. conservative replication
   c. dispersive replication
   d. rolling circle replication

9. If you were to repeat the experiments of Meselson and Stahl, which of the following would you see in a CsCl density gradient after a single round of replication in ^{14}N-containing media following transfer from the ^{15}N-containing media? [pp. 264–267]

   a. a single band in the density gradient with a density corresponding to DNA that was half ^{14}N and half ^{15}N

   b. two bands in the density gradient, one of a density corresponding to a uniform distribution of ^{15}N and one of a density corresponding to a uniform distribution of ^{14}N
   c. a single band in the density gradient with a density corresponding to a uniform distribution of ^{14}N
   d. two bands in the density gradient, one of a density corresponding to a uniform distribution of ^{15}N and one of a density corresponding to DNA that was half ^{14}N and half ^{15}N

10. Which statement about DNA replication is true? [pp. 268–269]

   a. Hydrolysis of the last phosphate group in the nucleoside triphosphate provides the energy for polymerization.
   b. The polymerase catalyzes the formation of hydrogen bonds between the base pairs.
   c. Hydrolysis of the bond between the inner phosphate group and the terminal pyrophosphate of the nucleoside triphosphate provides the energy for polymerization.
   d. The polymerase hydrolyzes ATP as it replicates in a 5′→ 3′ direction.

11. Which of the following replaces the RNA primers in *E. coli*? [pp. 269–270]

   a. topoisomerase
   b. primase
   c. DNA polymerase I
   d. ligase

12. Which of the following describes replication of the lagging strand? [pp. 270–272]

   a. Its replication is continuous but slower than the leading strand.
   b. It is characterized by Okazaki fragments.
   c. Its replication is dispersive.
   d. It does not use a sliding clamp because the polymerase has to continuously release the template.

13. Which of the following describes the activity of ligase? [pp. 270–272]

    a. It catalyzes formation of phosphodiester bond to seal nicks between lagging strand fragments.
    b. It advances the replication fork.
    c. It relieves twisting of double helix ahead of advancing replication fork.
    d. It replaces RNA primers with DNA.

14. Which statement about chromosomal replication in eukaryotes versus prokaryotes is true? [pp. 277–280]

    a. The eukaryotic DNA polymerase incorporates bases faster than bacterial DNA polymerase.
    b. Similar to prokaryotes, eukaryotic chromosomes only have one origin of replication.
    c. In order to increase the rate of replication of long eukaryotic chromosomes, replication bubbles progress bidirectionally in eukaryotes instead of unidirectionally as in prokaryotes.
    d. Eukaryotic chromosomes can be replicated faster than prokaryotic chromosomes because replication is initiated at multiple spots on each chromosome.

15. Which statement about telomeres is true? [pp. 273–274]

    a. After removal of RNA primers, they allow complementary base pairing between chromosome ends to prime replication of the ends.
    b. They contain the gene for an enzyme that repairs the ends of eukaryotic chromosomes.
    c. They are critical to initiation of replication of eukaryotic chromosomes.
    d. In most eukaryotic cells they eventually get deleted and can lead to cell death.

16. Which statement about telomerase is true? [p. 274]

    a. It is a site-specific eukaryotic DNA polymerase with $5' \to 3'$ activity.
    b. It polymerizes the addition of bases at the ends of eukaryotic chromosomes using $3' \to 5'$ activity.
    c. It is an ancient enzyme, present in all life forms.
    d. It is active in all cells but its activity is unregulated in cancer cells.

17. Upon which of the following activities is the proofreading ability of DNA polymerase based? [p. 276]

    a. on its $3' \to 5'$ polymerase activity
    b. on its $3' \to 5'$ exonuclease activity
    c. on its ability to detect the formation of hydrogen bonds between a newly formed base pair
    d. on its ability to go back and detect distortions in the newly replicated chromosome, after completion of replication

18. Which statement about DNA repair is NOT true? [pp. 276–277]

    a. It reduces errors to one-in-a-thousand.
    b. The mechanism used would not work if the DNA strands were not separated by a constant distance.
    c. It is based on the ability of repair enzymes to recognize distortions in the DNA double helix.
    d. The system functions to repair replication errors as well as chemical and UV damage to DNA.

19. Which statement about eukaryotic chromosomal organization is NOT true? [pp. 277–279]
    a. The nucleosome is the first level of organization and yields 10 nm chromatin fibre.
    b. When a chromosome is associated with proteins, it is referred to as chromatin.
    c. The 30 nm chromatin fibre is formed from the 10 nm chromatin by the binding of nonhistone proteins.
    d. Heterochromatin is the term for the regions of compacted, but transcriptionally active, DNA.

20. Which is common to prokaryotic and eukaryotic chromosomes? [pp. 277, 280]
    a. histone protein H1
    b. positively charged DNA-binding proteins
    c. euchromatin
    d. nucleosomes

21. Which statement is true about rolling circle replication? [pp. 279–280]
    a. It is the method of replication used during conjugative transfer of plasmids.
    b. It is the method of replication of the bacterial chromosome.
    c. It is the method of replication of telomeres.
    d. It is the method of replication used by telomerase enzymes.

INTEGRATING AND APPLYING KEY CONCEPTS

1. Draw a picture of a bacterial chromosome in the process of being replicated. Assuming bidirectional progression of the replication forks, figure out which newly replicated DNA will be the leading and lagging strands. How do these strands relate to each other when comparing one replication fork with the other?

2. Predict the effect(s) of mutations in histone H1 that rendered the protein neutral instead of positively charged.

3. If telomerase activity could be conclusively linked to cancer cell development, predict some of the possible types of treatment or agents to inhibit or stop cancer growth and spread to other tissues.

13 Gene Structure and Expression

TOPIC MAP

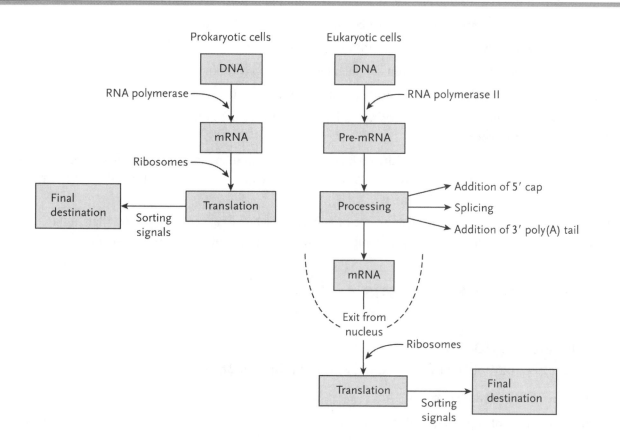

LEARNING OUTCOMES AND STUDY STRATEGIES

By the end of this chapter, you should be able to

- Explain the difference between the one gene–one enzyme hypothesis and the one gene–one polypeptide hypothesis and be able to relate the latter to the central dogma of biology

- Describe the structure of mRNA, the genetic code, and its redundancy, the wobble hypothesis and know the initiation codon and amino acid

- Describe the process of transcription and be able to compare the transcriptional process of prokaryotes with that of eukaryotes

- Explain the molecular process of mRNA splicing

- Describe the basic process of translation, identifying common features in all organisms and those that are distinct between prokaryotes and eukaryotes

- Describe the structure of ribosomes, including the nature of the catalytic component and explain why certain ribosome-targeting antibiotics do not affect the patient's ribosomes
- Explain the process of protein sorting, knowing how a protein is targeted to specific cellular components and why the process is believed to be ancient

Study strategies for this chapter:

- Remember that the goal of this chapter is to understand how cells make proteins.
- There are step-by-step processes that must be understood and followed.
- Concentrate on the key concepts of transcription and translation.
- Once the key ideas are understood, you can then learn the steps within each pathway.
- Keep a list of all of the differences in structures and processes between prokaryotes and eukaryotes.
- Carefully examine the figures and tables as well as the various subject headings to keep the ideas clearly organized in your mind.
- As always, go through one section of the textbook at a time and then work through the companion section of the study guide. Make sure, as you read, that you can answer the questions in each Study Break.
- After you have gone through the chapter, see how much you can expand on the Study Plan at the beginning of the chapter and if you can come up with alternative topic maps to the one above.

INTERACTIVE EXERCISES

Why It Matters [pp. 283–284]
13.1 The Connection between DNA, RNA, and Protein [pp. 284–289]

Section Review (Fill-in-the-Blanks)

The marine mussel Mytilus produces fibres made of (1) _____ that, together with other proteins,

make an exceptionally strong underwater (2) _____ that is of interest for its potential

biotechnological and medical applications. As with all other proteins on Earth, those that collectively make up

this glue are assembled on (3) _____ from instructions encoded by genes in the cell's

(4) _____. Beadle and Tatum determined the correlation between genes and (5) _____ by

studying arg⁻ or so-called (6) _____ mutants of the haploid fungus Neurospora crassa. They proposed

the one gene–one (7) _____ hypothesis, later modified to the one gene–one (8) _____

hypothesis. The path from genes to proteins, called the Central (9) _____ involves two steps:

(10) _____ of the gene sequence in the DNA to a complementary (11) _____ sequence, and

then this sequence is (12) _____ to the amino acid code of the (13) _____. In the latter

process, each amino acid is encoded by a three-base code called a (14) _____. The genetic code is

(15) _____ because most of the 20 amino acids are specified by more than one (16) _____.

Proteins all begin with the amino acid methionine, encoded by the (17) _____ AUG. This determines

the correct (18) _____ frame for the protein.

Matching

Match each of the following terms with its correct definition or descriptor.

19. ____	Auxotroph	A.	Organelle that facilitates conversion of mRNA code to a polypeptide
20. ____	Polypeptide	B.	AUG
21. ____	Transcription	C.	Unable to grow on minimal medium
22. ____	Translation	D.	Code for the termination of the translation process
23. ____	Central dogma	E.	A chain of amino acids
24. ____	tRNA	F.	May consist of one or more polypeptides
25. ____	Ribosome	G.	Product contains the bases A, C, G, and U
26. ____	Codon	H.	Proposed the one gene–one enzyme hypothesis
27. ____	Protein	I.	Most amino acids are encoded by multiple codons
28. ____	Start codon	J.	The conversion of the mRNA code to a polypeptide product
29. ____	Nonsense codons	K.	Molecule that translates a codon into a specific amino acid
30. ____	Degeneracy	L.	Triplet base sequence on mRNA
31. ____	Beadle and Tatum	M.	DNA → RNA → proteins

Labelling

32. Label the major steps of protein synthesis in eukaryotic cells.

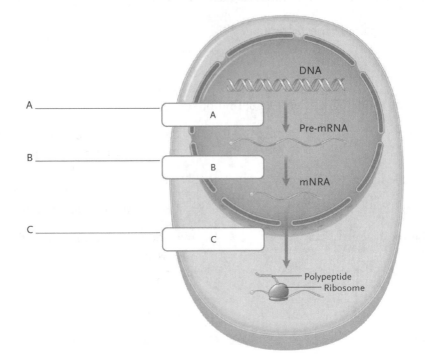

True/False

Mark if the statement is true (T) or false (F). If the statement is false, justify your answer in the lines below each statement.

33. _____ The terms "proteins" and "polypeptides" are synonyms.

_____

_____

34. _____ In transcribing a gene, the polymerase proceeds on the template strand from 3' → 5', synthesizing a mRNA beginning with its 5' end.

_____

_____

Short Answer

35. Explain what is meant by the term "inborn error of metabolism."

_____

_____

36. What is uracil, and where is it found?

_____

_____

37. Explain why transcription and translation occur much more quickly in prokaryotic cells compared to eukaryotic cells.

_____

_____

13.2 Transcription: DNA-Directed RNA Synthesis [pp. 289–291]

Section Review (Fill-in-the-Blanks)

Transcription requires the enzyme (38) _____ _____. Like DNA polymerase, this enzyme

moves along the template sequence (39) _____ → _____, unwinding the DNA double helix and

polymerizing the complementary mRNA in the (40) _____ → _____ direction. In both prokaryotes and

eukaryotes, initiation of transcription begins at the (41) _____ sequence. In eukaryotes, this is

specified by the (42) _____ box, located approximately (43) _____ bases upstream from the

protein-coding sequence. Also in eukaryotes, binding of the polymerase requires (44) _____ factors,

proteins that recruit and facilitate binding of the polymerase. Transcription proceeds to the end of the gene in

eukaryotes and through transcription (45) _____ in prokaryotes. When transcription is complete, both

the enzyme and the (46) _____ release from the (47) _____. In eukaryotes, RNA polymerase

(48) _____ synthesizes mRNA while transcription of non-protein encoding RNA molecules, such as

(49) _____ and (50) _____, is done by RNA polymerases (51) _____ and

_____.

Matching

Match each of the following terms with its correct definition or descriptor.

52. _____ DNA polymerase
53. _____ RNA polymerase
54. _____ RNA polymerase II
55. _____ RNA polymerases I and III
56. _____ Transcription unit
57. _____ Transcription initation complex
58. _____ Non–protein-coding genes
59. _____ Promoter
60. _____ Transcription terminators
61. _____ TATA box
62. _____ Transcription factors

A. DNA sequence that directs the synthesis of a transcript

B. Enzyme(s) for transcription of protein-coding genes in eukaryotic cells

C. Synthesizes nucleic acid containing thymine bases

D. Sequence located before the transcription unit, where RNA polymerase binds

E. Sequences on the 3′ end of prokaryotic mRNA that cause release of the RNA polymerase

F. Transcribes protein-coding and non–protein-coding genes in prokaryotes

G. Recruit and bind eukaryotic RNA polymerases to promoter

H. Enzyme(s) for transcription of non–protein-coding genes in eukaryotic cells

I. Bound by eukaryotic transcription factors

J. Code for RNA molecules such as tRNA and rRNA

K. RNA polymerase bound to promoter

Sequence

63. Arrange the following steps of eukaryotic transcription in the correct sequence:

____ ____ ____ ____ ____ ____ ____ ____

A. Transcription factors bind TATA box .

B. RNA polymerase binds to the promoter region.

C. The enzyme reaches the end of the transcription unit.

D. The enzyme polymerizes complementary sequence to template.

E. The enzyme unwinds the DNA double helix and enters transcriptional unit.

F. mRNA and the enzyme are released from DNA.

G. Complementary nucleotides are added.

H. Initation complex is formed.

Complete the Table

64. Complete the following table comparing DNA replication and transcription of RNA.

Points of Comparison	DNA Replication	Transcription
A. Types of base pairs		
B. Number of DNA strands copied		
C. Unit that is copied to complementary sequence		
D. Replicating enzyme(s)		
E. Enzyme that unwinds double helix		

65. Complete the following table comparing transcription in prokaryotic and eukaryotic cells.

Points of Comparison	Prokaryotic Cells	Eukaryotic Cells
A. Transcription enzyme(s)		
B. Binding of RNA polymerase to promoter region		
C. Termination of transcription		
D. Enzyme(s) for transcribing non-protein coding genes		

Short Answer

66. What are the basic differences between prokaryotic and eukaryotic RNA polymerase(s)?

_____

_____

67. Explain the function of the TATA box.

_____

_____

68. As one RNA polymerase passes over the sequence of the transcription unit, what is happening on the template strand immediately behind the enzyme?

_____

_____

True/False

Mark if the statement is true (T) or false (F). If the statement is false, justify your answer in the lines below each statement.

69. _____ Transcription takes place in the cytoplasm of prokaryotic cells and in the nucleus of eukaryotic cells.

_____

_____

70. _____ In both prokaryotes and eukaryotes, a gene may have multiple RNA polymerase enzymes simultaneously transcribing mRNA molecules.

_____

_____

71. _____ In both prokaryotes and eukaryotes, transcription ends when the polymerase transcribes a transcription terminator sequence.

_____

_____

13.3 Processing of mRNAs in Eukaryotes [pp. 291–294]

Section Review (Fill-in-the-Blanks)

Unlike prokaryotic mRNA, transcription in eukaryotes generally yields pre-mRNAs that must be

(72) _____ prior to leaving the (73) _____. Soon after transcription begins, a(n)

(74) _____ triphosphate is added to the 5′ untranslated region, the so-called 5′ (75) _____,

by a capping enzyme. This protects the transcript against (76) _____ and is the binding site for the

(77) _____ at the beginning of translation. At the 3′ end of the pre-mRNA, a (78) _____

signal is transcribed and cleaved, a process that signals the RNA polymerase to (79) _____ transcription. A chain of adenines is then added to the end of the pre-mRNA by the enzyme

(80) _____ _____ . This is called the (81) _____ tail; it serves to protect the

transcript from (82) _____ and to improve translation efficiency. Eukaryotic pre-mRNA contains

(83) _____, non–protein-coding sequences, which are then removed through the process of mRNA

(84) _____. Small ribonucleoprotein particles called (85) _____ bind the

(86) _____-_____ junction and loop the (87) _____ out of the pre-mRNA. They

then clip the introns at each (88) _____-_____ boundary, joining the adjacent

(89) _____ together. A phenomenon called (90) _____ splicing functions to create a

diversity of proteins from the same (91) _____. Introns may also contribute to the evolution of new

genes and proteins through the phenomenon of (92) _____ _____.

Matching

Match each of the following terms with its correct definition or descriptor.

93.	____	UTR	A.	Added to 3′ end of pre-mRNA by polymerase enzyme that does not require a DNA template
94.	____	Capping enzyme	B.	Base-pair to specific intron-exon sequences to initiate formation of spliceosome
95.	____	poly(A) tail	C.	Untranscribed sequence in gene required for initiation of transcription in prokaryotes and eukaryotes
96.	____	RNA processing	D.	Sequence-specific process catalyzed by snRNPs
97.	____	Introns	E.	Particles containing proteins and small nuclear RNA molecules
98.	____	Exons	F.	Untranslated pre-mRNA sequences recognized by snRNA in snRNPs
99.	____	mRNA splicing	G.	Process required to make mature mRNA only in eukaryotic organisms
100.	____	Spliceosome	H.	Produces different types of mRNA and protein products from same gene
101.	____	Promoter	I.	A process that may facilitate the evolution of new genes and proteins
102.	____	snRNPs	J.	Protein-coding sequence in eukaryotic pre-mRNA

103. _____ Alternative splicing   K.   Untranslated sequences at 3′ and 5′ ends of prokaryotic and eukaryotic mRNAs

104. _____ Exon shuffling   L.   A complex formed by ribonucleoproteins attached to pre-mRNA during editing process

105. _____ snRNA   M.   Adds guanine to 5′ end of UTR without using a DNA template

True/False

Mark if the statement is true (T) or false (F). If the statement is false, justify your answer in the lines below each statement.

106. _____ Not all eukaryotic mRNAs require splicing.

_____

_____

107. _____ Alternative splicing introduces frameshifts that give rise to new mRNA and protein products.

_____

_____

108. _____ The diversity of genes in an organism determines the complexity of functions in that organism.

_____

_____

Short Answer

109. Why is the presence of, and removal of, introns in eukaryotic pre-mRNA not a waste of cellular resources?

_____

_____

110. Identify the similarities or shared structures between protein-encoding prokaryotic and eukaryotic genes and their transcripts.

_____

_____

Labelling

111. The following depicts a protein-encoding eukaryotic gene and a partially-processed mRNA. Label the diagram to identify the appropriate structures and components.

A. _____

B. _____

C. _____

D. _____

E. _____

F. _____

G. _____

H. _____

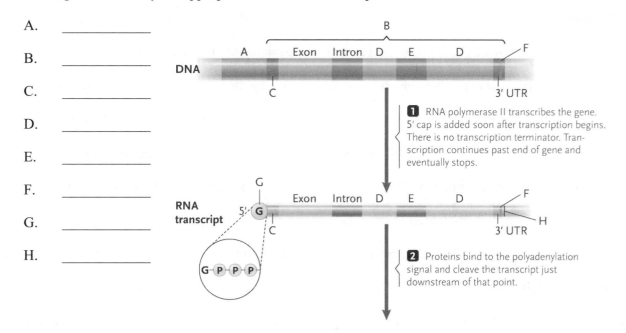

Complete the Table

112. Complete the following table with specific information on the various structures associated with eukaryotic transcripts.

Structure	Associated Enzyme, Catalytic Activity or Structure	Role in Transcription
A. 3′ UTR		
B. 5′ GTP cap		
C. snRNA		
D. Promoter		

13.4 Translation: mRNA-Directed Polypeptide Synthesis [pp. 294–305]

Section Review (Fill-in-the-Blanks)

Ribosomes translate the mRNA sequence or code into the (113) _____ _____ sequence of

the polypeptide. In prokaryotes and eukaryotes, translation occurs in the (114) _____, although some eukaryotic proteins are made in the mitochondrion and (115) _____. (116) _____ molecules carry the amino acids to the ribosome. These molecules are "charged" with their specific amino acids by highly accurate (117) _____-_____ synthetases. At the opposite side of the molecule is the (118) _____, which base-pairs, in an antiparallel fashion, with the mRNA (119) _____. Initiation of translation occurs when the ribosome assembles with the (120) _____ and the initiator tRNA, (112) _____-_____ binds to the (122) _____ site of the ribosome. During the (123) _____ stage, amino acids linked to tRNA in the (124) _____ site are added one at a time to the C-terminal end of the growing (125) _____ chain. The peptide bond is catalyzed by the (126) _____ _____ activity of the ribosome. Hydrolysis of (127) _____ powers the movement of the ribosome to the next codon, shifting the newly uncharged tRNA to the (128) ____ site, and the peptidyl-tRNA to the (129) ____ site. Termination occurs when a(n) (130) _____ codon enters the (131) _____ site and is triggered by binding of a(n) (132) _____ factor. Polypeptides are converted to finished form by (133) _____ reactions, which generally involve removal of (134) _____ _____ from the polypeptide chain, addition of (135) _____ groups, and folding into their final shape with the help of (136) _____. In both prokaryotes and eukaryotes, proteins are targeted to their appropriate cellular destination through amino acid (137) _____ sequences encoded in the (138) _____-terminus of the polypeptide. Mutations in the (139) _____ template can have a variety of effects on the final polypeptide: a(n) (140) _____ mutation changes the codon and the amino acid at that position; a base change giving rise to a stop codon is called a(n) (141) _____ mutation, and the result is premature (142) _____ of the polypeptide; (143) _____ mutations result from the deletion or insertion of a base pair giving rise to a change in the (144) _____ _____ beyond the site of the mutation generally rendering the protein nonfunctional. In contrast, a (145) _____ mutation changes the codon but not the protein sequence, a consequence of the (146) _____ of the genetic code.

Matching

Match each of the following terms with its correct definition or descriptor.

147. _____	Wobble hypothesis	A.	70–90 nucleotides long with modified bases and folded structure
148. _____	Ribosomes	B.	A set of three nucleotides on tRNA that correlates with a particular amino acid
149. _____	tRNA	C.	Explains how 61 amino acids are carried by only 20 different tRNAs
150. _____	Codon	D.	Set of 20 enzymes whose high level of accuracy is responsible for accuracy of translation
151. _____	Anticodon	E.	Site on the ribosome where empty tRNA binds after ribosomal translocation
152. _____	Aminoacylation	F.	Catalytic activity of ribosome, involves ribozyme rather than enzyme
153. _____	Aminoacyl-tRNA synthetases	G.	Prokaryotic and eukaryotic organelles whose structural differences provide the foundation for some antibiotic activities
154. _____	rRNA	H.	Site where charged tRNA binds during elongation phase of translation
155. _____	E site	I.	Site where initiator tRNA and peptidyl tRNA molecules bind
156. _____	Peptidyl transferase	J.	A catalytically inactive protein that is activated by removal of a segment of amino acids following secretion into the stomach
157. _____	A site	K.	A set of three nucleotides on mRNA that codes for a specific amino acid
158. _____	P site	L.	Process specific to proteins synthesized through the rough endoplasmic reticulum
159. _____	Polysome	M.	Proteins that help fold certain polypeptides to achieve a specific three-dimensional shape
160. _____	Pepsinogen	N.	An mRNA molecule containing multiple, regularly spaced ribosomes
161. _____	Chaperones	O.	Energy-requiring process of attaching specific amino acid to a tRNA
162. _____	Cotranslational import	P.	Structural component of ribosomes

True/False

Mark if the statement is true (T) or false (F). If the statement is false, justify your answer in the lines below each statement.

163. _____ Regardless of the protein or the organism, methionine is always the first amino acid in a protein.

_____

_____

164. _____ Release factors are special tRNAs that do not carry amino acids.

_____

_____

165. _____ The gene sequence is read 5′ → 3′ on the mRNA and the corresponding protein sequence is read from the N-terminus to the C-terminus.

_____

_____

166. _____ The wobble position in the anticodon is the 5′ nucleotide and in the codon is the 3′ nucleotide.

_____

_____

Complete the Table

167. Fill in the appropriate mutation or definition.

Type of Mutation	Definition
Silent mutation	A.
B.	Mutation where the change in DNA sequence causes a change in the amino acid sequence and alters the function of the protein
C.	Mutation that results in abrupt termination of the polypeptide, leaving the protein totally dysfunctional
Frameshift mutation	D.

168. Fill in the appropriate sorting components or cellular destination for finished proteins

Final Cellular Destination	Sorting Components
Eukaryotic plasma membrane	A.
B.	None
Nucleus	C.
D.	Transit sequences, posttranslational import, and organelle-specific/transit sequence–specific transporter
ER lumen	E.
Prokaryotic plasma membrane	F.

Short Answer

169. Prokaryotic cells can transcribe and translate simultaneously. What is the advantage and why is this not possible in eukaryotic cells?

_____

_____

170. What is the difference between eukaryotic and prokaryotic polysomes?

_____

_____

171. What is the source of energy for peptide bond formation?

_____

_____

172. Compare and contrast the first steps of translation initiation in prokaryotes versus eukaryotes.

_____

_____

Labelling

173. The following depicts the general process of translation. Label the diagram to identify the appropriate structures and components.

A. _____

B. _____

C. _____

D. _____

E. _____

F. _____

G. _____

H. _____

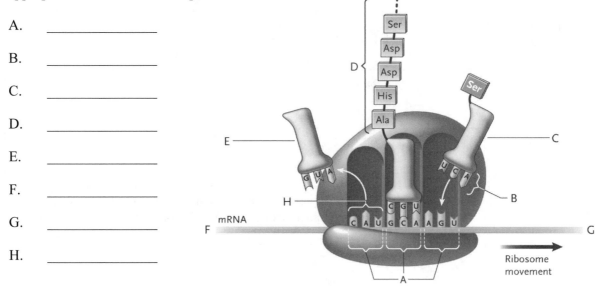

I. Identify any additional required factors not depicted in the above diagram and the specifically labelled components:

_____

SELF-TEST

1. What scientific contribution was made by Beadle and Tatum? [pp. 284–286]

   a. They proposed the Wobble hypothesis.
   b. They proposed the concept of "inborn errors of metabolism."
   c. They proposed the "one gene–one enzyme" hypothesis.
   d. They coined the term "Central Dogma" to describe the flow of information in cells.

2. What is the distinction between a protein and a polypeptide? [p. 286]

   a. A protein is the functional unit and may comprise more than one polypeptide chain.
   b. A polypeptide may contain more than one subunit.
   c. A protein is the polypeptide after it has been properly processed.
   d. A polypeptide has enzymatic function whereas a polypeptide is any product of translation.

3. How many codons are possible using the four types of nitrogenous bases? [p. 287]

   a. 20
   b. 27
   c. 40
   d. 64

4. Which statement about transcription is true? [pp. 289–290]

   a. The substrates for RNA polymerase include deoxyribonucleotide triphopshates.
   b. RNA polymerase reads the template $3' \rightarrow 5'$ and polymerizes mRNA $5' \rightarrow 3'$.
   c. Only messenger RNA molecules contain uracil in place of thymine.
   d. Only one strand of the chromosome contains the genes that are transcribed by RNA polymerase.

5. Which is NOT a shared feature of prokaryotic and eukaryotic transcription? [p. 289]

   a. In both, the RNA polymerase is bound to a TATA box to initiate transcription.
   b. In both, the template usually has multiple RNA polymerases simultaneously transcribing a given gene.
   c. In both, the transcriptional unit includes a promoter sequence upstream of the protein-coding sequence.
   d. Both incorporate the base uracil wherever an adenine occurs in the template strand.

6. Which describes a mechanism of transcription termination in prokaryotic cells? [p. 289]

   a. The 3′ and 5′ ends of the mRNA base pair with each other, preventing the RNA polymerase from progressing further .
   b. The RNA polymerase recognizes a specific sequence, the stop sequence, and releases the completed mRNA .
   c. A 3′ UTR is cleaved by an endonuclease, causing release of the RNA polymerase.
   d. A terminator sequence at the 3′ end of the transcript forms a hairpin structure through internal base pairing, causing release of the RNA polymerase.

7. Which is responsible for transcription of mRNA in eukarotes? [pp. 289–290]

   a. the same RNA polymerase as for other genes, but modified by a specific protein factor
   b. RNA polymerase I
   c. RNA polymerase II
   d. RNA polymerase III

8. Which is formed after completion of transcription in a eukaryotic cell? [p. 291]

   a. the protein precursor
   b. the mRNA
   c. a pre-mRNA
   d. the processed RNA

9. In mature eukaryotic mRNA, which of the following is NOT present? [pp. 291–292]

   a. introns
   b. 5′ GTP cap
   c. 5′ UTR
   d. 3′ poly(A) tail

10. Which statement about mRNA processing is NOT true? [pp. 291–294]

    a. It requires the activity of sequence-specific enzymes.
    b. It is far more common in eukaryotes than prokaryotes.
    c. It means that most eukaryotic genes do not follow the "one gene–one polypeptide" rule.
    d. It happens in approximately 75% of human protein-coding genes.

11. Which of the following is responsible for recognizing the intron-exon boundary? [pp. 292–293]

    a. the spliceosome
    b. snRNA
    c. the lariat ribonucleoprotein
    d. ribonuclease enzymes

12. Which explains the observation that the human genome contains 20 000 genes but encodes over 5× as many proteins? [p. 293]

    a. the Wobble hypothesis
    b. alternate splicing
    c. exon shuffling
    d. alternate protein folding through chaperonin activity

13. Which statement about translation in prokaryotic cells is NOT true? [p. 294]

    a. It occurs in the cytoplasm.
    b. The ribosome reads the mRNA 5′ → 3′ and translates from the N-terminus to the C-terminus.
    c. It begins before transcription is terminated.
    d. It begins with recognition of a 5′ cap on the mRNA.

14. Which is a property of tRNA? [pp. 294–296]

    a. There are more tRNA molecules than the number of different amino acids.
    b. It contains a codon that is read $5' \rightarrow 3'$.
    c. It contains more than four kinds of bases.
    d. It binds in the ribosome through complementary tRNA-rRNA base pairing.

15. Which of the following has the anticodon? [p. 295]

    a. the mRNA
    b. the gene
    c. the tRNA
    d. the rRNA

16. Which statement regarding the Wobble hypothesis is NOT true? [pp. 295–296]

    a. It explains how 20 different tRNAs can translate 61 different codons.
    b. It explains how tRNAs can base-pair with more than one codon on the mRNA.
    c. It states that the third base in the anticodon has relaxed hydrogen-bonding properties.
    d. It explains how the introns in eukaryotic pre-mRNA may be spliced at alternate positions .

17. Which is involved in "charging" of the tRNA? [pp. 296–297]

    a. ATP hydrolysis provides the energy for formation of the tRNA-amino acid bond.
    b. Attachment of alternate amino acids provides variation in proteins without requiring additional gene sequences.
    c. It requires the participation of elongation factors.
    d. This process helps explain the redundancy in the genetic code.

18. Which statement about eukaryotic and prokaryotic ribosomes is correct? [pp. 296–298]

    a. They have different molecular structures.
    b. The prokaryotic ribosomes bind at the start codon, whereas the eukaryotic ribosome binds to the 5′ cap.

    c. Prokaryotic ribosomes have two subunits of identical size , whereas eukaryotic ribosomes have a large and a small subunit.
    d. Prokaryotic ribosomes recognize a different initatiator codon than eukaryotic ribosomes.

19. Which codon encodes the first methionine? [p. 298]

    a. UUA
    b. UAA
    c. AUG
    d. ATG

20. Which of the following sites in the ribosome binds the initiator tRNA? [pp. 298-299]

    a. the P site
    b. the A site
    c. the E site
    d. the peptidyl transferase site

21. Which is NOT involved in initiation of translation in eukaryotes? [pp. 298–299]

    a. scanning of the ribosome
    b. assembly of the ribosome
    c. hydrolysis of ATP
    d. determination of the reading frame

22. Which statement about peptidyl transferase is true? [p. 300]

    a. It uses the energy from GTP hydrolysis to drive bond formation.
    b. It adds the amino acid on the aminoacyl tRNA in the A site to the growing peptide chain on the tRNA in the P site.
    c. It is associated with the small ribosomal subunit.
    d. It is a catalytic rRNA.

23. Which is involved in termination of translation in eukaryotes? [p. 300]

    a. GTP hydrolysis
    b. peptidyl transferase-catalyzed cleavage of the peptide–tRNA bond
    c. binding of an uncharged tRNA to the stop codon
    d. the poly (A) tail

24. Which is NOT involved in trafficking proteins to the nucleus? [pp. 303–304]

   a. an N-terminal localization signal

   b. hydrolysis by a signal peptidase

   c. a specific transport complex

   d. post-translational import

25. Which type of mutation is usually considered most devastating? [pp. 304–305]

   a. base substitution

   b. silent

   c. frameshift

   d missense

INTEGRATING AND APPLYING KEY CONCEPTS

1. Discuss the impact of a splicing error where the spliceosome moved the splice site by four bases relative to the intron–exon boundary.

2. Explain the relationship between gene and protein as referred to by each of the three terms/descriptions:

   (a)   One gene–one protein

   (b)   One gene–one polypeptide

   (c)   One gene–one particular polypeptide under particular conditions

3. Compare the process of translation of a protein destined for the rough ER with that of a nuclear protein and a bacterial membrane protein.

14 Control of Gene Expression

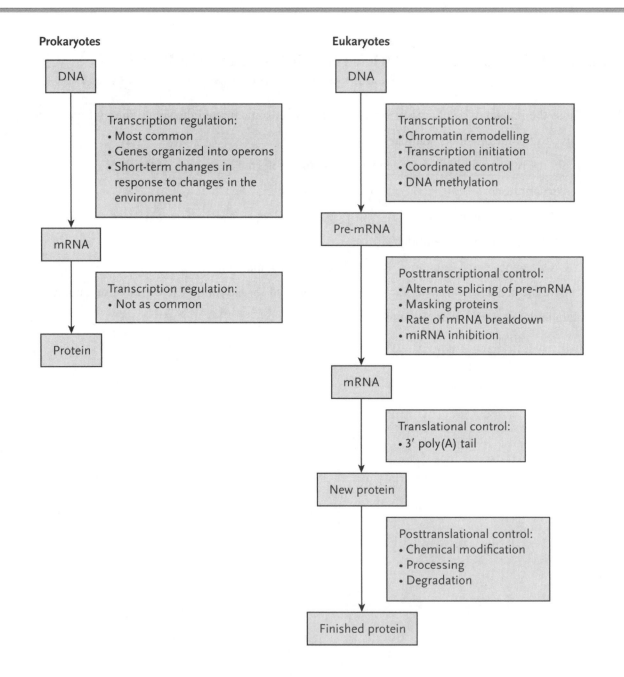

Prokaryotes

DNA

Transcription regulation:
• Most common
• Genes organized into operons
• Short-term changes in response to changes in the environment

mRNA

Transcription regulation:
• Not as common

Protein

Eukaryotes

DNA

Transcription control:
• Chromatin remodelling
• Transcription initiation
• Coordinated control
• DNA methylation

Pre-mRNA

Posttranscriptional control:
• Alternate splicing of pre-mRNA
• Masking proteins
• Rate of mRNA breakdown
• miRNA inhibition

mRNA

Translational control:
• 3′ poly(A) tail

New protein

Posttranslational control:
• Chemical modification
• Processing
• Degradation

Finished protein

LEARNING OUTCOMES AND STUDY STRATEGIES

By the end of this chapter, you should be able to

- Describe negative control of transcription in prokaryotes: that is, the *lac* and *trp* operons
- Describe positive control of transcription in prokaryotes: that is, the CAP–cAMP control of the *lac* operon
- Describe how transcriptional control in eukaryotes differs from that of prokaryotes and be able to explain the various levels of transcriptional control in eukaryotes
- Describe how gene expression is controlled posttranscriptionally, translationally, and posttranslationally and relate the breakdown of regulation of gene expression to cancer

Study strategies for this chapter:

- This chapter has extensive gene control pathways. Trying to memorize all of the steps is the most common mistake.
- Remember that the goal of this chapter is to understand how genes are controlled.
- Concentrate on the key steps for protein synthesis: transcription and translation.
- Focus on what each step is about and where changes can be made.
- Once the key steps are understood, you can then learn the regulatory pathways.
- Try comparing and contrasting the various control mechanisms, selecting different pairs where there is at least one aspect shared between the two.
- Carefully examine the figures as well as the various subject headings to keep the ideas clearly organized in your mind.
- As always, go through one section of the textbook at a time and then work through the companion section of the study guide. Make sure, as you read, that you can answer the questions in each "Study Break."
- After you have gone through the chapter, see how much you can expand on the Study Plan at the beginning of the chapter and if you can come up with alternative topic maps to the one above.

INTERACTIVE EXERCISES

Why It Matters [pp. 308–309]
14.1 Regulation of Gene Expression in Prokaryotic Cells [pp. 309–314]

Section Review (Fill-in-the-Blanks)

In multicellular organisms, all nucleated cells have the same complement of (1) _____ as the

developing embryo. The differences in cell types are instead the result of differential gene (2) _____.

(3) _____ genes, such as those for rRNA, are expressed in all cells but expression of other genes is

highly regulated. In prokaryotic cells, (4) _____ and translation occur (5) _____, allowing rapid, short-term, responses to environmental changes. The genes encoding proteins of related function are organized in (6) _____. These form a single (7) _____ unit, controlled by binding of regulatory proteins to the (8) _____ and sometimes to other sequences. The *lac* (9) _____ is the paradigm for transcriptional regulation in bacteria. It is negatively regulated by the binding of a(n) (10) _____ in the absence of lactose, to turn off transcription. Lactose is the (11) _____ for the operon, combining with the (12) _____ to relieve repression. The operon is also positively regulated, through binding of a(n) (13) _____ in the absence of glucose, turning (14) _____ transcription. The *trp* operon is also subject to (15) _____ regulation; however, in this case the repressor is normally inactive. Tryptophan is a(n) (16) _____, combining with the repressor to bind the (17) _____ sequence and turn transcription off.

Matching

Match each of the following terms with its correct definition or descriptor.

18. _____	Operon model		A.	Encodes a repressor or activator protein
19. _____	Operon		B.	An operon where the metabolite molecule represses or decreases the expression of the cluster of genes
20. _____	Regulon		C.	Proposed by Jacob and Monod to explain regulation of gene expression in *E. coli* lactose metabolism
21. _____	Regulatory gene		D.	Mechanism where a protein binds DNA to turn off gene expression
22. _____	Repressor protein		E.	Mechanism where a protein binds DNA to turn on gene expression
23. _____	Operator sequence		F.	A cluster of genes expressed as a single transcript
24. _____	Inducer		G.	Several operons controlled by the same regulator
25. _____	Inducible operon		H.	A chemical that relieves repression of transcription
26. _____	Repressible operon		I.	Tryptophan, for example
27. _____	Corepressor		J.	*LacI*
28. _____	Negative gene regulation		K.	Binding sequence for transcriptional repressors

29. _____ Positive gene regulation

30. _____ CAP

31. _____ CAP site

L. An operon where the metabolite molecule enhances or increases the expression of the cluster of genes

M. Binding sequence for the catabolite activator protein–cAMP complex

N. Central regulator protein for glucose-dependent transcriptional regulation

Complete the Table

32. Prokaryotic cells have different types of operons and gene regulation mechanisms. Provide descriptions and an example of each in the following table.

Inducible Operon	*Repressible Operon*
A.	B.
Negative Gene Regulation	*Positive Gene Regulation*
C.	D.

Short Answer

33. What would be the phenotype of a LacI⁻ *E. coli* (i.e., Lac repressor mutant) strain growing on minimal medium with lactose as the only carbon source?

_____

_____

34. What would be the phenotype of an *E. coli* strain that had a mutation in the gene for the CAP protein (i.e., Cap⁻)?

_____

_____

35. What would be the phenotype of an *E. coli* strain that had a mutation in its *Trp* repressor gene (i.e., Trp⁻)?

_____

_____

True/False

Mark if the statement is true (T) or false (F). If the statement is false, justify your answer in the lines below each statement.

36. _____ Prokaryotic mRNA is degraded, on average, after three minutes.

_____

_____

37. _____ In order to conserve energy and grow quickly, prokaryotic cells synthesize very stable metabolic enzymes.

_____

_____

Labelling

38. Label the following diagram of the *E. coli lac* operon.

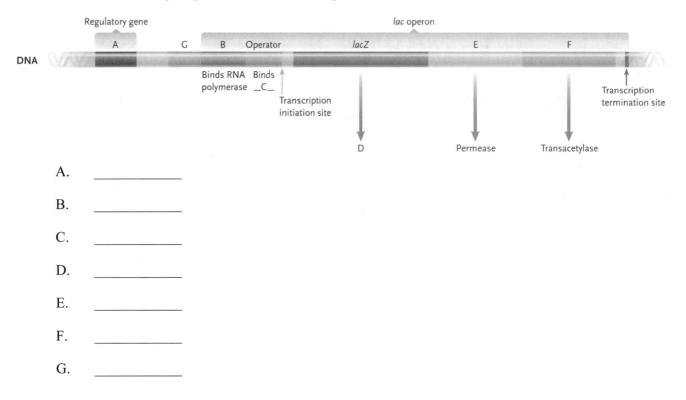

A. _____

B. _____

C. _____

D. _____

E. _____

F. _____

G. _____

14.2 Regulation of Transcription in Eukaryotes [pp. 315–322]

Section Review (Fill-in-the-Blanks)

In eukaryotes, genes for related functions are not organized in (39) _____ but are still coordinately

regulated. There are two major categories of regulation in eukaryotes: (40) _____-term regulation

allows rapid responses to environmental changes, while (41) _____-term regulation underlies

development and differentiation. Regulation of gene expression is primarily at the (42) _____ level

but can also involve post- (43) _____, translational, and post- (44) _____ mechanisms. At

protein-encoding genes, low levels of transcription occur when general (45) _____ factors bind to the

promoter and recruit RNA polymerase (46) _____. Transcription levels are increased when activator

proteins bind the promoter (47) _____ elements. Maximal transcription levels occur when activators

bind to (48) _____ sequences and to a(n) (49) _____ protein complex which, in turn, binds

proteins at the promoter. Binding of (50) _____ proteins reduces transcription levels. The net effect

on transcription depends upon the combination of regulators bound to the promoter (51) _____

elements and the (52) _____ sequences. Combinatorial regulation using different (53) _____

of regulators allows eukaryotes to coordinately regulate genes expression with relatively few

(54) _____ proteins and in a cell-specific manner; which of these binds depends upon the particular

regulatory (55) _____ associated with that gene. Transcriptionally active genes have a looser

(56) _____ structure than inactive genes. The structural change accompanying gene activation is

called (57) _____ remodelling and is dependent on chemical modification of specific

(58) _____ proteins in the region of the promoter. In vertebrates, long-term inactivation, called gene

(59) _____, occurs not through a DNA sequence change but through chemical modification of

(60) _____ bases in DNA. Permanent gene inactivation through methylation of inherited alleles is the

basis for the phenomenon of genomic (61) _____.

Matching

Match each of the following terms with its correct definition or descriptor.

62. ____   Histone methylation

A.   Protein-binding sequence ~25bp upstream from transcription start site

63. ____   Chromatin remodelling

B.   Bind TATA box or similar sequences

64. ____   Nucleosome

C.   Modification associated with heterochromatin formation

65. ____   TATA box

D.   The complex of DNA and histones H2A, H2B, H3, and H4

66. ____   General transcription factors

E.   Histone acetylation in region of promoter causing a looser DNA structure

67. ____   Transcription initiation complex

F.   Mechanisms of altering gene expression without altering gene sequence(s)

68. ____   Promoter proximal elements

G.   The process of chemically modifying cytosines in DNA to turn off the genes

69. ____   Epigenetics

H.   Located upstream of TATA box, binds activators to give medium-level activation

70. ____   Coactivator

I.   An epigenetic phenomenon that involves methylation of DNA in gametogenesis

71. ____   Hormone-receptor complex

J.   Also called a mediator, bridges regulatory proteins bound at various distances from the transcription start site

72. ____   Methylation

K.   Protein structural domain such as helix-turn-helix

73. ____   Silencing

L.   A modification of DNA associated with gene silencing in vertebrates and genomic imprinting

74. ____   Genomic imprinting

M.   Formed in cytoplasm, migrates to nucleus and binds DNA to alter gene expression

75. ____   Motif

N.   RNA polymerase II and basal transcription factors

Complete the Table

76. Eukaryotic cells have different types of gene regulation mechanisms at the transcriptional level. Complete the following table giving a short description of each type.

Mechanism	Description
Chromatin remodelling	A.
Combinatorial gene regulation	B.
Coordinated control of gene expression	C.
Alteration of gene expression by DNA methylation	D.

True/False

Mark if the statement is true (T) or false (F). If the statement is false, justify your answer in the lines below each statement.

77. _____ Long-term regulation of gene expression occurs in multicellular eukaryotes but not in unicellular eukaryotes.

_____

_____

78. _____ Acetylation is the chemical basis for chromatin remodelling, and methylation is the chemical basis for silencing.

_____

_____

79. _____ Heterochromatin is transcriptionally active while euchromatin is highly condensed and inactive.

_____

_____

Short Answer

80. How and why are histone proteins chemically modified?

_____

_____

81. What are housekeeping genes and how would their regulation differ from hormone-regulated genes?

_____

_____

82. What is the nucleosome remodelling complex?

_____

_____

Labelling

83. Label the various components of transcription regulation of a eukaryotic gene.

A. _____

B. _____

C. _____

D. _____

E. _____

F. _____

G. _____

H. _____

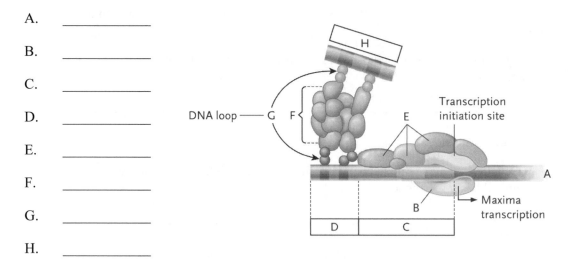

14.3 Posttranscriptional, Translational, and Posttranslational Regulation [pp. 322–326]

Section Review (Fill-in-the-Blanks)

Posttranscriptional control of gene activity may involve (84) _____-_____ processing,

altering mRNA availability for (85) _____, or the rate of mRNA (86) _____. With the first

mechanism, the process of (87) _____ _____ removes introns and different combinations of

(88) _____ to produce mRNAs for a family of related proteins. Alternatively, mRNA may complex

with (89) _____ proteins to block translation, a common control mechanism in unfertilized animal

(90) _____. Control doesn't always involve proteins: mRNA may also be protected from translation

by complexing with imperfectly complementary (91) _____ molecules (miRNA). Finally, the half-

life of mRNA may be regulated through the activity of (92) _____ such as prolactin, or by

controlling sequences in the 5′ (93) _____ or through perfect base pairing to a miRNA, leading to

(94) _____ of the complexed mRNA. Finally, posttranslational controls include reversible chemical

(95) _____ to alter protein activity, activation through (96) _____ of an inactive precursor or

by controlling proteolytic degradation, for example through the use of the "doom tag" (97) _____.

Matching

Match each of the following terms with its correct definition or descriptor.

98. ____	Alternative splicing	A.	A complex containing RNA and proteins that base pairs to 3′ UTR sequences and silences gene expression
99. ____	Masking proteins	B.	Large cytoplasmic complex involved in post-translational regulation of gene expression
100. ____	miRISC	C.	Typically derived from an infecting virus through Dicer activity
101. ____	Poly(A) tail	D.	Bind mRNA to block translation
102. ____	Ubiquitin	E.	Increased length gives increased translation
103. ____	Proteasome	F.	A regulatory mechanism in plant and animal cells that involves small, single-stranded RNA molecules
104. ____	RNAi	G.	The protein tag that targets proteins for proteolytic degradation
105. ____	siRNA	H.	Generates a family of proteins from the same pre-mRNA

Complete the Table

106. Complete the table, describing each type of regulation of gene expression in eukaryotic cells.

Mechanism	Underlying Process(es)	Result of Regulatory Mechanism(s)
Posttranscriptional control	Alternative splicing of pre-mRNA; masking proteins; control of mRNA half-life; RNAi	A.
Translational control	B.	Increase or decrease of translation through unknown mechanism,
Posttranslational control	C.	Reversible alteration of protein activity; activation of inactive precursor; alteration of protein half life

True/False

Mark if the statement is true (T) or false (F). If the statement is false, justify your answer in the lines below each statement.

107. _____ Viruses may use RNAi to inhibit translation of host proteins.

_____

_____

108. _____ Although the 3′ UTR of eukaryotic mRNA molecules may play a role in regulation of gene expression, this is not true of the 5′ untranslated region.

_____

_____

Short Answer

109. Explain how the phenomenon of RNAi can be exploited in the laboratory.

_____

_____

110. Explain how the rate of degradation of mRNA and proteins is regulated to control gene expression.

_____

_____

14.4 The Loss of Regulatory Controls in Cancer [pp. 326–329]

Section Review (Fill-in-the-Blanks)

Cancer cells are partially or completely (111) _____, causing them to revert to an embryonic

developmental state where they divide rapidly and uncontrollably. (112) _____ tumours are those

that break loose and spread to other parts of the body. Cancers are genetic diseases and are associated with

alterations in (113) _____-_____, (114) _____ suppressor genes and/or miRNA

genes. The first type encodes proteins that stimulate cell division; the altered form in cancer cells, the so-

called (115) _____, is abnormally active. The second type encodes proteins such as P53, that

normally (116) _____ cell division and when mutated, lose this (117) _____ activity. In

many cancers, miRNA genes show cancer-specific alterations that either (118) _____ translation of

proto-oncogene mRNA or (119) _____ translation of tumour suppressor gene mRNA, leading to cell

proliferation. Although mutations in these genes are associated with cancer, most cancers result from a

(120) _____ progression of changes in multiple genes.

Matching

Match each of the following terms with its correct definition or descriptor.

121. ____	Mutation	A.	Tumour-suppressor gene that is altered in many different types of cancer cells
122. ____	Sporadic cancer	B.	The tumour whose cells separate and spread to other tissue and organs
123. ____	Malignant tumour	C.	An inherited change in the DNA
124. ____	Dedifferentiation	D.	Nonhereditary
125. ____	Metastasis	E.	Mutated to cause cells to progress unregulated through the cell cycle
126. ____	Proto-oncogene	F.	Encodes proteins that inhibit cell division
127. ____	Oncogene	G.	The process by which specialized cells revert to the embryonic state
128. ____	TP53	H.	Encodes proteins that stimulate cell division in normal cells
129. ____	Tumour-suppressor genes	I.	Spreading of malignant tumours

Complete the Table

130. Complete the following table by comparing the cancer-related terms.

Terms	Differences
Benign vs. malignant tumours	A.
Proto-oncogenes vs. oncogenes	B.
Differentiation vs. dedifferentiation	C.
Tumour-suppressor genes vs. TP53	D.

Short Answer

131. What are the four types of types of genetic changes that can give rise to an oncogene?

_____

_____

132. What is meant by the term "predisposed to cancer" and why does this relate specifically to tumour suppressor genes and not proto-oncogenes?

_____

_____

SELF-TEST

1. Which term refers to a cluster of prokaryotic genes and the sequences involved in regulation of the cluster? [pp. 309–310]

   a. promoter
   b. operator
   c. operon
   d. regulon

2. To which region does the RNA polymerase bind? [p. 310]

   a. the operator
   b. the promoter

   c. the operon
   d. the regulon

3. How does lactose affect expression of the *lac* operon? [pp. 310–311]

   a. It represses expression.
   b. Its isomer acts as a corepressor, turning expression off.
   c. It is the activator for the operon.
   d. Its isomer induces the operon.

4. Which is NOT a term associated with the regulation of diverse operons in response to glucose levels? [pp. 311–313]

    a. catabolite activator protein
    b. cAMP
    c. a regulon
    d. *LacI*

5. How does tryptophan affect expression of the *trp* operon? [pp. 313–314]

    a. Its isomer represses expression.
    b. It acts as a corepressor, turning expression off.
    c. It is the activator for the operon.
    d. Its isomer induces the operon.

6. Which statement does NOT explain why eukaryotic gene expression is more complex than in prokarhotes? [pp. 309, 315]

    a. Eukaryotes have a nucleus and prokaryotes don't.
    b. Multicellular eukaryotes undergo cellular differentiation and prokaryotes don't.
    c. Eukaryotes have their chromosomes condensed into chromatin.
    d. Eukaryotes have to adapt to more rapid and extreme environmental changes.

7. Which statement about eukaryotic promoters is true? [pp. 315–316]

    a. They are associated with operons containing genes of related function.
    b. They contain a DNA sequence that is recognized by RNA polymerase.
    c. They bind activator proteins.
    d. They bind general transcription factors.

8. Which is a common feature of regulation of gene expression in prokaryotic and eukaryotic cells? [pp. 315–319]

    a. Short-term regulation occurs at the level of transcription initiation.
    b. Transcriptional regulation is based on differing combinations of activators.
    c. Both may be controlled by hormones.
    d. Both involve nucleosome remodelling.

9. Which is NOT associated with the ability of prokaryotic cells to adapt and replicate quickly? [pp. 309, 315]

    a. mRNA with a half-life on the order of minutes
    b. the absence of a nuclear membrane
    c. rapid processing of pre-mRNA
    d. simultaneous transcription and translation

10. Which binds directly to DNA to alter transcription in eukaryotes? [pp. 315–320]

    a. repressors
    b. promoter-proximal elements
    c. RNA polymerase
    d. coactivators

11. Which is not associated with steroid hormone-mediated gene regulation? [pp. 320–321]

    a. a steroid-specific cytoplasmic receptor protein
    b. a masking protein
    c. a steroid-specific regulatory DNA sequence
    d. tissue-specific transcriptional activation

12. Which is involved in silencing of eukaryotic genes? [p. 321]

    a. acetylation of the cytosines in all or part of a chromosome
    b. acetylation of some of all of the histones
    c. methylation of all or part of a chromosome
    d. phosphorylation of all or some of the nucleosomes

13. Which is NOT associated with the phenomenon of epigenetics? [p. 321]

    a. methylation of cytosines
    b. genomic imprinting
    c. X chromosome inactivation
    d. acetylation of histone tails

14. Which is NOT associated with chromatin remodelling? [pp. 321–322]

    a. ATP-powered movement of the H2A, H2B, H3, and H4 complex
    b. acetylation of histone lysine residues
    c. methylation of cytosines
    d. activator binding

15. Which is the normal mechanism of gene regulation in unfertilized animal eggs? [p. 323]

    a. inhibition of translation by proteins associated with the mRNA
    b. methylation of cytosines
    c. acetylation of histone proteins
    d. ubiquitin-dependent protein degradation

16. Which statement about RNA interference is false? [pp. 323–325]

    a. It is restricted to animal cells.
    b. It may involve nuclear-encoded miRNAs.
    c. It may involve viral-encoded siRNAs.
    d. Dicer activity is a critical component.

17. Which description of miRNA is correct? [pp. 323–325]

    a. They are single-stranded RNAs for posttranslational regulation.
    b. They are single-stranded RNAs for posttranscriptional regulation.
    c. They are eukaryotic mRNA prior to processing.
    d. They are microbial RNA.

18. Which is NOT involved in translational regulation in eukaryotes? [p. 324]

    a. the 3′ poly(A) tail
    b. ubiquitin
    c. the 5′ UTR
    d. a proteasome

19. Which is most likely to be involved in regulating the half-life of short-lived proteins? [p. 326]

    a. the poly (A) tail
    b. ubiquitin
    c. processing of preproteins
    d. oncogenes

20. Which is NOT associated with tumours spreading from one site to another tissue? [pp. 326–327]

    a. a benign tumour
    b. metastasis
    c. invasion of surrounding tissue
    d. cancer

21. Which is associated with the process of dedifferentiation? [pp. 326–328]

    a. siRNAs
    b. masking proteins
    c. proto-oncogenes
    d. a mutation in *TP53*

INTEGRATING AND APPLYING KEY CONCEPTS

1. This chapter presented the details of control systems for gene expression in prokaryotes and eukaryotes and revealed the relative simplicity of the systems used in the relatively simple prokaryotic cells versus those in the larger, more complex, and often multicellular eukaryotes. One of the terms used to describe the CAP–cAMP system of control in prokaryotes is a regulon (p. 313). Compare and contrast the prokaryotic regulon with the steroid hormone–regulated systems/mechanism of regulation in eukaryotes.

2. Explain how red blood cells are able to make the blood protein hemoglobin while the other body cells do not.

3. Researchers think that there are approximately 120 genes for miRNA in worms but approximately 250 in humans. (a) Speculate on why there would be such differing levels of these genes in these two organisms. (b) Explain how miRNA exerts control over gene expression and how the viral equivalent, siRNA, can play a role in viral infections.

15 DNA Technologies and Genomics

TOPIC MAP

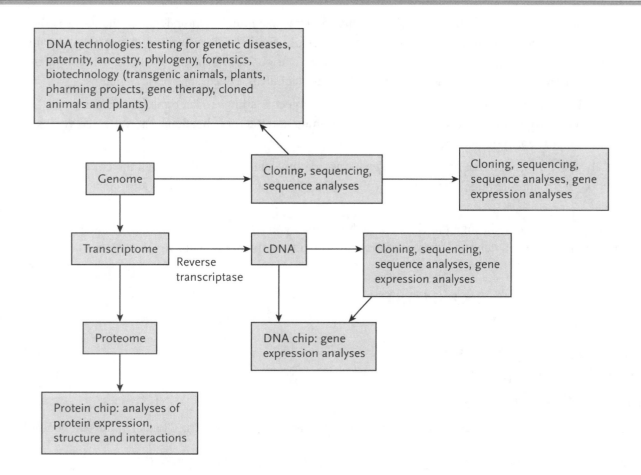

LEARNING OUTCOMES AND STUDY STRATEGIES

By the end of this chapter, you should be able to

- Explain what restrictions enzymes are and how they can be used for cloning or examining RFLPs
- Describe the two ways you can amplify a gene: by cloning and PCR
- Understand what cDNA is and why one would clone cDNA rather than the gene itself
- Explain what a gene library is, and distinguish that from a cDNA library
- Define the terms RFLP and DNA fingerprinting, explain how they work, and what they are used for
- Describe some of the applications of genetic engineering and some of the ethical and legal considerations associated with it

- Explain how a genome sequence is generated and, for humans, what the data revealed
- Distinguish between structural genomics, functional genomics, and comparative genomics, and what kinds of information result from each

Study strategies for this chapter:

- In order to understand this chapter, you must review DNA structure, its replication, and its organization in prokaryotic and eukaryotic cells.
- This chapter has extensive terminologies. Trying to memorize rather than understand the terms is the most common mistake. It also has extensive examples of genetic engineering and its uses; you do not need to memorize all of these but simply appreciate the various approaches that can be used, some of the advances that have been made and where there are technical, ethical, and legal concerns.
- Carefully examine the figures as well as the various subject headings to keep the ideas clearly organized in your mind. The study plan at the beginning and the topic headings should guide you as the major concepts you need to understand.
- As always, go through one section of the textbook at a time and then work through the companion section of the study guide. Make sure, as you read, that you can answer the questions in each Study Break.
- After you have gone through the chapter, see how much you can expand on the Study Plan at the beginning of the chapter and if you can come up with alternative topic maps to the one above.

INTERACTIVE EXERCISES

Why It Matters [pp. 332–333]
15.1 DNA Cloning [pp. 333–341]

Section Review (Fill-in-the-Blanks)

DNA (1) _____ is a technique that generates multiple copies of genes. The technique can be used to

understand the structure and (2) _____ of genes or for manipulating genes. (3) _____

enzymes are used to cut the DNA of interest and a cloning (4) _____ such as a plasmid. The

fragments are joined using the enzyme DNA (5) _____ to produce (6) _____ plasmids.

These are then (7) _____ into a living cell such as a bacterium, where they are (8) _____ as

the cell grows and divides. Clones containing the specific gene of interest are identified using a

complementary (9) _____ nucleic acid probe, a technique called DNA (10) _____. A

genomic (11) _____ is a collection of plasmids containing a copy of every DNA sequence in the

genome. A cDNA (12) _____, in contrast, contains only the sequences of the (13) _____

genes. With this technique, the cellular (14) _____ is purified and converted to complementary

(15) _____ sequences using the enzyme reverse (16) _____. Instead of cloning, large

quantities of DNA may be obtained using the (17) _____ _____ _____, or PCR.

The technique amplifies a specific sequence defined by a pair of (18) _____. It uses a heat stable

(19) _____ _____ with the reaction mixture cycling between three temperatures to

facilitate (20) _____ of the template DNA , (21) _____ the primers to the template, and

(22) _____ the primers. With each cycle, the amount of DNA (23) _____. A more recent

DNA technology, (24) _____, uses DNA purified directly from the environment. This technique

provides insights into the genetics of the (25) _____ world, the vast majority of which has not yet

been (26) _____ in the laboratory.

Matching

Match each of the following terms with its correct definition or descriptor.

27.	_____	Biotechnology	A.	Porous material for electrophoresis of DNA
28.	_____	DNA technology	B.	Contains cloned DNA insert
29.	_____	β-galactosidase	C.	Techniques used to make improvements in living organisms or their products
30.	_____	Agarose gel	D.	Site-specific endonucleases for cloning
31.	_____	Plasmids	E.	Single-stranded DNA ends produced by some restriction enzymes
32.	_____	Restriction enzymes	F.	Generated from mRNA and reverse transcriptase activity
33.	_____	DNA ligase	G.	Small, circular independently replicating DNA molecules in bacteria
34.	_____	Recombinant plasmid	H.	Separates charged macromolecules using an electrical field
35.	_____	Gel electrophoresis	I.	Produces millions of copies of a target DNA sequence without cloning
36.	_____	Sticky ends	J.	A collection of recombinant plasmids representing all genetic sequences of an organism
37.	_____	Transformation	K.	Techniques for the isolation, analysis, and manipulation of DNA

38. ____ Genomic library

39. ____ cDNA

40. ____ PCR

41. ____ DNA primer

42. ____ Genetic engineering

L. Techniques using biological systems or organisms to make or modify desired products

M. Enzyme used to generate intact, double-stranded recombinant DNA molecule

N. Single-stranded molecule complementary to template for replication

O. Absorption of extracellular DNA by bacteria

P. Enzyme cleaves lactose and X-gal and is often encoded by cloning vectors

Short Answer

43. Why are restriction enzymes so valuable to the generation of recombinant DNA molecules?

_____

_____

44. What is the value of a cDNA library versus a genomic library?

_____

_____

45. What is DNA hybridization? What role does it play in DNA cloning?

_____

_____

46. Explain why PCR is only an option under certain circumstances.

_____

_____

True/False

Mark if the statement is true (T) or false (F). If the statement is false, justify your answer in the lines below each statement.

47. _____ Metagenomics uses DNA purified straight from an environmental source.

_____

_____

48. _____ Bacteria producing restriction enzymes acetylate their DNA to protect it from digestion.

_____

_____

49. _____ In the presence of X-gal, colonies of bacteria producing β–glactosidase will appear blue.

_____

_____

Sequencing

50. Arrange the following steps of DNA cloning in the correct sequence:

____ ____ ____ ____ ____

A. Transformation of bacteria

B. Hybridization with labeled DNA probe

C. Restriction digestion of DNA

D. Selection of antibiotic-resistant colonies

E. Ligation of mixed DNA

15.2 Applications of DNA Technologies [pp. 341–352]

Section Review (Fill-in-the-Blanks)

Recombinant (51) _____ and PCR techniques are used in molecular testing for human

(52) _____ diseases. These tests often involve digesting the genomic DNA with a specific

(53) _____ enzyme, to identify restriction fragment (54)) _____ _____ (RFLPs)

between the normal and mutant (55) _____. The fragments are separated in (56) _____, and

the bands detected and compared using Southern (57) _____ _____ with a labelled nucleic

acid probe to the allele. Alternatively, the gene can be amplified by (58) _____, and the products

digested and compared in gels. DNA (59) _____ are also valuable for establishing paternity,

ancestry, and in forensics: they are generated by (60) _____ amplifying specific (61) _____

_____ _____ (STR) loci within the genome, and comparing the products. The lengths of

these regions vary between individuals, except between (62) _____ _____. Genetic

(63) _____ uses DNA technologies to alter the genes of humans and other animals,

(64) _____, and microorganisms. It has been used to improve domestic (65) _____ and crop

plants to provide large amounts of (66) _____ for research and medicine and, with less success, to

correct human (67) _____ defects. Although genetic (68) _____ has enormous potential, the

possible risks have led to the establishment of national and international guidelines on the use of

(69) _____ _____ _____ or GMOs.

Matching

Match each of the following terms or names with the appropriate definition or contribution.

70. _____	RFLP	A.	Normal genes are inserted into a fertilized egg to correct a genetic disorder
71. _____	Southern blot analysis	B.	The crown-gall-inducing DNA produced by certain bacteria and which is exploited in making transgenic plants
72. _____	STR locus	C.	Cloning vector containing regulatory sequences for translation of proteins from cloned genes
73. _____	Somatic gene therapy	D.	A technique for the detection of specific sequences using labelled DNA probes and a filter paper imprint of an agarose gel containing digested DNA
74. _____	Germ-line gene therapy	E.	Most commonly a crop, for example BT corn or round-up ready soy beans
75. _____	Ti plasmid	F.	An organism that contains a foreign gene
76. _____	Transgenic	G.	Using a transgenic organism to produce large volumes of proteins for pharmaceutical purposes
77. _____	GMO	H.	Sequences in noncoding regions of genome that differ in the number of repeat sequences between all individuals except twins
78. _____	Expression vector	I.	Sequence differences between alleles are reflected in changes to the relative positions of specific restriction sites
79. _____	Pharming	J.	Where normal genes are inserted into diploid cells of the body to correct a genetic disorder

Short Answer

80. Discuss how DNA technology can be used to determine if someone has sickle cell trait.

_____

_____

81. Provide an explanation for the term "transgenic."

_____

_____

82. Describe how an animal protein might be synthesized at high levels in a recombinant bacterium.

_____

_____

83. Compare embryonic stems cells with adult stem cells.

_____

_____

True/False

Mark if the statement is true (T) or false (F). If the statement is false, justify your answer in the lines below each statement.

84. _____ Normal genes introduced into somatic cells with a defective gene will ensure that the next generation does not inherit the mutant allele.

_____

_____

85. _____ A tobacco plant with a firefly gene is called a transgenic plant.

_____

_____

86. _____ Germ-line therapy can be used to correct certain human genetic diseases.

_____

_____

87. _____ Round-up ready soy beans are GMOs resistant to a commonly used pesticide.

_____

_____

88. _____ Knock-out mice are genetically engineered gene mutants.

_____

_____

15.3 Genome Analysis [pp. 353–361]

Section Review (Fill-in-the-Blanks)

Genome analysis can be divided into two parts: (89) _____ genomics is the actual sequence of the

genome, while (90) _____ genomics studies the functions of the genes and noncoding sequences.

DNA sequences can be generated using Sanger (91) _____ sequencing, an in vitro DNA

(92) _____ technique that uses fluorescently labelled (93) _____. Incorporation of these

modified substrates causes chain (94) _____ and the lengths of the terminated chains, combined with

the particular (95) _____ on each, provides the sequence for the template DNA. Genome sequencing

is generally done using the whole-genome (96) _____ method where random, overlapping

(97) _____ of the entire genome are (98) _____ and each is then sequenced. Overlapping

(99) _____ are then assembled into the genome sequence using computer (100) _____.

Computer analysis can also identify potential (101) _____-coding genes; this is easiest in prokaryotes

where open (102) _____ frames are identified by reading (103) _____ bases at a time from

an ATG (104) _____ _____ to a stop codon. (105) _____ genomics is used to

understand evolutionary relationships: such studies revealed that humans share approximately

(106) _____ percent of our genes with (107) _____, our closest relative. Additionally, all

eukaryotes have been shown to share (108) _____ sequences, allowing prediction and analyses of

certain human genes through studies of the non-human (109) _____. (110) _____ genomics

focuses on the functions of genes and other genomic sequences. These studies have been advanced by the

development of DNA (111) _____ or "chips", which allow comparison of gene expression between

cell types or under various conditions. A related approach using protein (112) _____ has provided

inroads into the field of (113) _____, which studies the complete set of (114) _____ and

protein interactions in a cell type or organism.

True/False

Mark if the statement is true (T) or false (F). If the statement is false, justify your answer in the lines below each statement.

115. _____ Molecular phylogenetics uses DNA or amino acid sequence comparisons to determine evolutionary relationships.

_____

_____

116. _____ The human genome has about 100 000 protein-coding genes.

_____

_____

117. _____ Systems biology compares the genetic systems of different organisms to try to understand evolutionary relationships.

_____

_____

Short Answer

118. Discuss how Sanger sequencing works.

_____

_____

119. What is bioinformatics?

_____

_____

120. How does a BLAST analysis help assign function to genes?

_____

_____

121. What is the difference between gene knock-outs and gene knock-downs and why are they done?

_____

_____

1. Which statement about metagenomics is true? [pp. 332–333]

    a. It uses DNA purified from a lab culture.
    b. It refers to the method of assembling sequence data to generate a genome sequence.
    c. It is a culture-independent method of obtaining sequence data from environmental samples.
    d. It is a scientific field that combines genetics, computer science, mathematics and statistics to analyze and interpret genomic data.

2. Which term most accurately describes the use of a recombinant bacterium to produce human insulin? [p. 333]

    a. biotechnology
    b. a DNA technology
    c. genetic engineering
    d. metagenomics

3. Which would be a necessary step in generating a recombinant DNA molecule? [pp. 333–334]

    a. PCR amplification
    b. restriction digestion of the insert and vector
    c. agarose gel electrophoresis
    d. Sanger sequencing reaction

4. Which is associated with "sticky ends"? [pp. 334–335]

    a. some DNA restriction fragments
    b. PCR amplicons
    c. recombinant bacterial plasmids
    d. dideoxynucleotides

5. What is the role of ligase in DNA cloning? [pp. 334–335]

    a. to covalently join DNA fragments to make recombinant molecules
    b. to amplify DNA in the polymerase chain reaction
    c. to cleave the DNA insert and cloning vector
    d. to generate cDNA from RNA prior to cloning

6. Which is NOT associated with a typical bacterial cloning vector? [pp. 334–336]

    a. the gene for β-galactosidase
    b. a unique/single restriction enzyme sites
    c. an antibiotic resistance gene
    d. an X-gal sequence

7. Which describes DNA hybridization? [pp. 337–338]

    a. complementary base pairing of a labelled RNA probe with recombinant DNA
    b. in vitro replication of recombinant DNA
    c. sequence-specific cleavage of DNA molecules using restriction endonucleases
    d. protection of restriction sites in the DNA of organisms producing that restriction enzyme

8. Which type of molecule is used to make cDNA? [p. 337]

    a. mRNA
    b. eukaryotic genes
    c. proteins
    d. plasmids

9. Which scientist developed PCR? [p. 337]

    a. Paul Berg
    b. Edward Southern
    c. Kary Mullis
    d. Frederick Sanger

10. Which is NOT an advantage of a cDNA library over a genomic library? [p. 337]

    a. It allows you to clone only those genes that are being expressed under specific conditions.
    b. It allows you to express eukaryotic genes in bacterial hosts.
    c. It can provide information on the changes in gene expression during differentiation.
    d. It can be used to generate a genome sequence.

11. Which is a shared feature of in vivo DNA replication and PCR? [pp. 337, 339–340]

    a. The polymerization reactions proceed $5' \rightarrow 3'$.
    b. Both use RNA primers.
    c. Both require a helicase to unwind the double-stranded template.
    d. The products of both are hybrids of the original template and a newly replicated daughter strand.

12. Which is a limitation of the PCR technique? [pp. 339–341]

    a. You need a relatively concentrated DNA sample.
    b. You have to know the sequence of your target.
    c. You need a pure DNA sample.
    d. You have to know the size of your target.

13. Which is NOT associated with agarose gel electrophoresis? [pp. 340–341]

    a. identification of bacterial clones using labelled probes
    b. separation of molecules based on size
    c. separation of molecules based on charge
    d. separation of PCR amplicons using an electrical current

14. Which describes an application of RFLP analysis? [pp. 341–342]

    a. identification of successful PCR reactions
    b. identification of gene sequence variations using restriction endonucleases
    c. identification of successful cloning reactions
    d. identification of paternity using PCR

15. Upon what is DNA fingerprinting based? [pp. 342–344]

    a. Every person produces unique hemoglobin proteins.
    b. Every person has a unique genome sequence.
    c. Individuals each have a unique combination of STR alleles.
    d. Individuals can be identified by Southern blot analysis.

16. Which would be considered transgenic? [pp. 345–346]

    a. a bacterial strain with an antibiotic resistance plasmid
    b. a bacterial chromosome with the *lac* operon
    c. a differentiated human cell
    d. a bacterial strain containing the insulin gene

17. What are knock-out mice? [p. 346]

    a. They are homozygous mutants in a specific gene used to elucidate the normal function of the gene.
    b. They contain a transgenic gene for a rat growth hormone, making them grow much bigger than normal.
    c. They were the first animals to be cloned.

18. Which statement is false regarding gene therapy? [pp. 346–348]

    a. Normal genes are introduced into somatic cells that have a defective gene.
    b. Normal genes are introduced into fertilized eggs that have a defective gene.
    c. It has been successfully used to correct heritable diseases in human germ cells.
    d. It has been successfully used to correct somatic cell mutations in humans with genetic diseases.

19. Which statement about transgenic animals is NOT true? [p. 348]

    a. They can be used as pharmaceutical protein factories.
    b. A transgenic sheep was made to secrete a human blood-clotting factor in its milk.
    c. They are used in pharming projects.
    d. They are illegal according to the Cartagena Protocol.

20. What does the term "pharming projects" refers to? [p. 348]

    a. the cloning of animals
    b. the use of transgenic animals to produce proteins of medicinal value
    c. gene therapy projects
    d. the use of antibiotic resistance genes in bacterial cloning vectors

21. What was the source of the nucleus used to clone Dolly the sheep? [pp. 348–349]

    a. a somatic cell
    b. an unfertilized egg cell
    c. an embryonic stem cell
    d. an adult stem cell

22. Which statement about transgenic plants is false? [pp. 349–352]

    a. Transgenic plants have been created to produce vitamins.
    b. Transgenic plants are relatively easy to make.
    c. Transgenic plants are relatively widely accepted GMOs.
    d. One common method of generating a transgenic plant is to infect the plant with *Rhizobium radiobacter*.

23. Which is NOT used in Sanger sequencing? [pp. 353–355]

    a. two primers flanking the gene of interest
    b. dideoxyribonucleotides
    c. DNA polymerase
    d. fluorescent dye molecules

24. Which would NOT be a component of annotation of a genome sequence? [p. 356]

    a. bioinformatics analyses of the sequence data
    b. identification of open reading frames
    c. assembly of overlapping sequences to generate a contiguous chromosomal sequence
    d. BLAST analyses

25. What has comparative genomics revealed? [pp. 356–358]

    a. Bigger organisms have bigger genomes.
    b. The complexity of an organism does not correlate with the number of genes in its genome.
    c. The size of an organism's proteome is reflected in the number of genes in its genome.
    d. The bigger the genome size, the higher the number of genes within the genome.

26. Which statement regarding the human genome is true? [p. 357]

    a. It contains 1/5 the number of genes as predicted based on the total number of different human proteins.
    b. The protein-coding regions of the genome represent ~50% of the total genome.
    c. Functions could be assigned to the majority of the sequences.
    d. Only about 2% of the genome consists of non-coding regulatory sequences.

27. Which of the following is NOT a tool of functional genomics? [pp. 357–358, 361]

    a. DNA microarrays
    b. BLAST homology searches
    c. protein microarrays
    d. gene knockdown experiments

INTEGRATING AND APPLYING KEY CONCEPTS

1. Describe the experimental steps in generating a recombinant, insulin-expressing *E coli*.

2. Provide some examples of genetically engineered food products that are commercially available. What is the rationale for the skepticism in our community to buy these products? What kinds of regulations have been established?

3. The Human Genome Project identified a much smaller number of protein-coding genes in the human genome than was expected. How might they have come up with the number of 100 000 protein-coding genes, and how do they explain the discrepancy between that predicted value and the observed value of ~20 000 protein-coding sequences?

16 Microevolution: Genetic Changes within Populations

TOPIC MAP

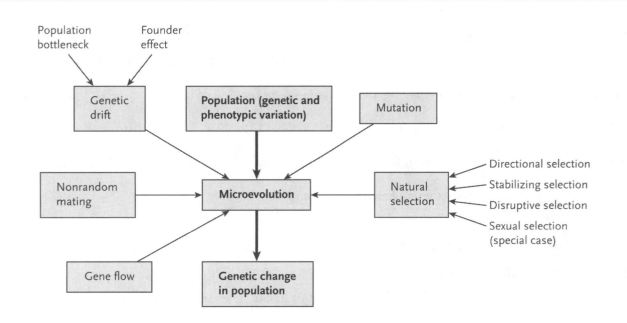

LEARNING OUTCOMES AND STUDY STRATEGIES

By the end of this chapter, you should be able to

■ Explain the sources of variation in populations and describe examples and experiments relating to the variation

■ Describe the Hardy–Weinberg principle in terms of its equations and the conditions that must exist for a population to be in genetic equilibrium

■ Explain the three modes of natural selection, as well as sexual selection, and their effect on the phenotypic variation of a population

■ Explain how variation is maintained in populations

Study strategies for this chapter:

■ This chapter introduces many new terms and concepts, so focus on descriptions and examples to make it easier to distinguish between them.

- Familiarize yourself with the Hardy–Weinberg principle, both its equations and associated conditions. As you read through the chapter, keep relating the various agents of microevolution back to the Hardy–Weinberg principle to discern which aspect of the principle is being violated.

- Carefully examine the figures, examples, and various subject headings to keep the concepts clearly organized in your mind.

INTERACTIVE EXERCISES

Why It Matters [pp. 364–365]

Section Review (Fill-in-the-Blanks)

(1) _____ is a drug used to fight bacteria that enter through the skin and saved many lives after the

Cocoanut Grove nightclub fire in 1942. Its overuse led to the evolution of (2) _____ strains of

Staphylococcus. The increase of these strains is an example of (3) _____, that is, a heritable change

in the genetics of a population. A population of organisms includes all the individuals of the same

(4) _____ that live together in the same place and time.

16.1 Variation in Natural Populations [pp. 365–368]

Section Review (Fill-in-the-Blanks)

Most individuals in a population differ in structure and/or function; that is, they show (5) _____

variation. If the variation among individuals is generally small and incremental, it is said to be

(6) _____; however, if it occurs in two or more discrete states—for example, blood type in humans—

the variation is said to be (7) _____. Data relating to the former are generally depicted on a(n)

(8) _____ graph if it is a small population or as a(n) (9) _____ if the population is large. The

width of the plot reflects the amount of (10) _____ among the individuals, and the mean describes

the average value of the character. Traits that display discrete variants are said to be (11) _____, and

each variant of a trait is described quantitatively as a percentage or (12) _____.

Short Answer

Provide an explanation for each of the following statements.

13. Phenotypic variation in individuals may have an environmental as well as a genetic basis.

_____

_____

14. Only variation based on genetic differences is subject to evolutionary change.

_____

_____

15. Differences in the DNA of organisms do not always produce phenotypic differences.

_____

_____

For each of the following statements, provide an example that supports the statement.

16. The behaviour of animals may be influenced by genetic differences between individuals.

_____

_____

17. Humans have traits that vary quantitatively.

_____

_____

Complete the Table

Complete the following table.

Term/Process	Description/Function
Polymorphism	18.
Microevolution	19.
20.	A technique that can identify different forms of a protein and is useful in analyzing genetic differences between individuals
Population	21.

16.2 Population Genetics [pp. 368–370]

Matching

Match each of the terms with its correct definition.

22. ____	Hardy–Weinberg principle	A.	Relative abundance of each allele
23. ____	Genotype frequencies	B.	Reference point that predicts outcome if studied factor has no effect
24. ____	Allele frequencies	C.	State where the genetic structure of a population is NOT evolving
25. ____	Gene pool	D.	Proportion of individuals possessing each of the possible genotypes in a population
26. ____	q	E.	Sum of all allele at all gene loci in all individuals in a population
27. ____	Heterozygous	F.	Mathematical model that acts as reference point to study circumstances under which evolution may occur
28. ____	Genetic equilibrium	G.	In diploid organisms, an individual's two alleles at a gene locus
29. ____	Null model	H.	Genotype comprised of two copies of the same allele
30. ____	Homozygous	I.	Frequency of one of the versions of a gene
31. ____	Genotype	J.	Genotype comprised of two different alleles

Short Answer

List the five conditions that must be met for a population to be in Hardy–Weinberg equilibrium.

32. _____

_____

33. _____

_____

34. _____

_____

35. _____

_____

36. _____

_____

16.3 The Agents of Microevolution [pp. 370–378]

Section Review (Fill-in-the-Blanks)

If any of the conditions necessary for a population to be in Hardy–Weinberg equilibrium are not met,

(37) _____ (a change in allele frequencies over time) will occur. The following sentences describe

processes that result in a change to a population's allele frequencies, and consequently cannot occur if Hardy–

Weinberg equilibrium is maintained. A(n) (38) _____ is a heritable change in a gene or chromosome

and may impact allele frequencies. Likewise, (39) _____ caused by immigrants entering a population

or emigrants leaving it can change the genetic structure of the population. Changes in allele frequencies may

also occur due to chance events, an effect referred to as (40) _____; this is minimized in very large

(or infinite) populations. When populations are dramatically reduced in size, the result may be the loss of

alleles or a reduction in genetic (41) _____. Two general circumstances give rise to this situation:

population (42) _____ and (43) _____ effects. The former results when disease, drought, or

starvation kills many individuals in a population and may eliminate a(n) (44) _____ in the process;

this is what is being seen with (45) _____ species. The latter effect results when a small number of

individuals start a new (46) _____; this will inevitably result in a limited number of alleles compared

to "normal," as is seen with captive (47) _____ programs. Natural selection is the process where

certain individuals with specific, (48) _____ traits produce relatively more offspring than individuals

lacking these traits. This difference in reproductive success is reflected in an individual's (49) _____,

a measure that reflects the number of surviving offspring an individual produces compared with other

members of the population.

Choose

Identify the condition that is NOT being met in each of the situations provided. Note that the conditions of the Hardy–Weinberg principle can be used more than once.

50. _____ New phenotype appears as a result of a new allele in the population.

A. Infinite population size

51. _____ Individuals of a forest population that have dark-coloured fur coats are better able to avoid predators.

B. No mutations

52. _____ Tsunami catastrophe kills more than 90% of a population.

C. Closed to migration

53. _____ Breeding occurs between individuals of neighbouring populations.

D. All genotypes survive and reproduce equally well

54. _____ Female birds in a population prefer male birds with louder mating calls.

E. Individuals mate randomly

55. _____ A new population is formed on an isolated island by colonization of a few individuals of a species.

56. _____ Predation occurs by fish that prefer to feed on the smaller individuals of the prey species.

Matching

Match each of the processes associated with natural selecton on the left with the most appropriate example on the right.

57. _____ Directional selection

A. Babies with very low or very high birth weights suffer higher than average mortality.

58. _____ Disruptive selection

B. Very large elephant seals win battles with smaller males. The winner of one of these encounters attains dominant status and gets to mate with females.

59. _____ Intersexual selection

C. During droughts, cactus finches with very long or very deep bills enjoy higher survival than those with average-sized bills.

60. _____ Intrasexual selection

D. Female bowerbirds prefer males with extremely long tails.

61. _____ Stabilizing selection

E. A horse breeder mates the fastest males with the fastest females.

16.4 Maintaining Genetic and Phenotypic Variation [pp. 378–381]
16.5 Adaptation and Evolutionary Constraints [pp. 381–383]

Section Review (Fill-in-the-Blanks)

Despite the combined effects of stabilizing selection and genetic drift, most natural populations exhibit a

tremendous amount of (62) _____ and (63) _____ variation. One reason for this is that in

(64) _____ eukaryotes, a recessive trait is masked in individuals with a(n) (65) _____

genotype, meaning that the trait, even if undesirable, will not be eliminated. Another reason for high levels of

variation is the phenomenon of balanced (66) _____, which occurs when two or more phenotypes are

maintained in fairly stable proportions in a population. This is commonly seen in situations where a)

heterozygotes enjoy a higher relative (67) _____ than either homozygote, an effect named the

(68) _____ _____; b) when different (69) _____ are favoured in different

environments; or c) when rare phenotypes have higher (70) _____ compared with more common

phenotypes. Some biologists believe in the (71) _____ _____ hypothesis, which suggests

that not every genetic variant is maintained by (72) _____ _____. In these situations the

variation is said to be (73) _____ _____ and no allele is favoured. This hypothesis

explains why large populations and ones that have not experienced a recent population (74) _____

exhibit the highest levels of genetic variation. There appears to be agreement that (75) _____ traits—

that is, those that increase the relative fitness of an individual—exist and are products of natural selection. The

accumulation of these traits over time—that is, (76) _____—is constrained by several factors: most

adaptive traits represent compromises among conflicting needs; most environments are constantly

(77) _____; and natural selection can only work on (78) _____ traits; it cannot create new

(better) traits.

Matching

Match each of the processes related to natural selection listed on the left with the most appropriate definition or example on the right.

79. ____	Adaptive trait	A.	A mutation changes the base sequence in DNA, but the protein it codes for is unchanged.
80. ____	Frequency-dependent selection	B.	The proportions of two or more phenotypes continue to be stable over many generations.
81. ____	Heterozygote advantage	C.	Different shell patterns in snails are favoured in different environments.
82. ____	Selectively neutral	D.	In malaria-prone areas, individuals with homozygous genotype for hemoglobin have lower fitness than individuals with the HbA/HbS genotype.
83. ____	Selection in varying environments	E.	Rare or unusual phenotypes in a population enjoy higher than average reproductive success.
84. ____	Balanced polymorphism	F.	Frogs that can best mimic the colour of the rocks that they live on are best able to escape from predators.

SELF-TEST

1. How does diploidy maintain genetic variability in a population? [p. 379]
   a. It doubles the number of gametes produced by individuals.
   b. It hides recessive alleles from natural selection.
   c. It increases mutation rate.
   d. It promotes genetic drift.

2. Which of the following factors can influence an individual's phenotype? [pp. 366–367]
   a. environmental factors
   b. genetic factors
   c. quantitative factors
   d. environmental and genetic factors

3. Which type of variation is subject to evolutionary change? [p. 367]
   a. acquired
   b. anatomic
   c. genetic
   d. environmental

4. Which of the following processes can create a new allele, potentially producing a novel genotype and phenotype? [pp. 367, 370]
   a. mutation
   b. nonrandom mating
   c. genetic drift
   d. sexual reproduction

5. What does a population bottleneck cause to occur? [p. 373]
   a. gene flow
   b. genetic drift
   c. mutation
   d. polymorphism

6. Which term refers to one individual's success in producing surviving offspring compared to other members within a population? [p. 374]

    a. allele frequency
    b. gene flow
    c. heterozygote advantage
    d. relative fitness

7. How are lethal recessive alleles able to persist in a population? [p. 374]

    a. They transform into the dominant allele in a population.
    b. They are hidden in heterozygous individuals and passed onto their offspring.
    c. They alter the individual's structure or function in a beneficial way.
    d. They are only found in homozygous recessive genotypes, which are passed onto their offspring.

8. Which will reduce genetic variability in a population? [p. 375]

    a. directional selection
    b. disruptive selection
    c. stabilizing selection
    d. sexual selection

9. Which natural selection process results in the evolution of showy structures and behaviours in males of many animal species? [p. 376]

    a. directional selection
    b. disruptive selection
    c. sexual selection
    d. stabilizing selection

10. Which statement is true? [pp. 382–383]

    a. No organism is perfectly adapted; evolutionary compromises must always be made.
    b. In the absence of human intervention, natural selection produces organisms perfectly adapted to all conditions.
    c. Biologists are in agreement that all genetic change has fitness implications.
    d. Traits evolved for a specific function cannot be co-opted for other purposes.

11. Which statement is false? [p. 367]

    a. Sexual reproduction contributes to phenotypic diversity.
    b. In humans, 10^{600} combinations of alleles are estimated to be possible in human gametes.
    c. Sexual reproduction can create new alleles.
    d. Inbreeding is a form of nonrandom mating that increases the frequency of homozygous individuals.

12. Which statement about the evolution of antibiotic resistance is true? [pp. 365, 374]

    a. It is the result of balanced polymorphism.
    b. It is an example of directional selection.
    c. It is an example of frequency-dependent selection.
    d. Antibiotics cause the accumulation of mutations.

13. If the protein products of two alleles from the same locus differ, which indicates the difference that gel electrophoresis is unable to identify? [pp. 367–368]

    a. difference in size between the two proteins
    b. difference in one or two codons between the two proteins
    c. difference in shape between the two proteins
    d. difference in net charge between the two proteins

14. Which of the following does NOT cause genetic variation? [pp. 365]

    a. the overuse of antibiotics
    b. rearrangement of existing alleles
    c. gene flow between populations
    d. mutation

15. What is the definition of gene pool? [p. 368]

    a. all alleles at all gene loci in all individuals in a population
    b. all alleles of all genes loci in a given individual
    c. all of the various alleles of a particular gene/locus
    d. the degree of variation at a given locus within a population

16. When does balanced polymorphism arise? [pp. 379–380]
    a. when a small group of individuals moves into a new environment
    b. when heterozygote individuals have increased fitness
    c. when males develop exaggerated traits to attract mates
    d. when there is inbreeding

17. Which of the following is a qualitative variation? [pp. 366]
    a. birth size
    b. dwarfism
    c. sickle cell disease
    d. sickle cell trait

18. Which of the following human traits would be measured in terms of frequencies? [p. 366]
    a. birth size
    b. height
    c. dwarfism
    d. athletic ability

19. Suppose that a particular virus is introduced into a small population and proves lethal for the very young and the elderly. How would geneticists identify this? [pp. 373, 375]
    a. as a bottleneck effect
    b. as stabilizing selection
    c. as a founder effect
    d. as disruptive selection

20. Which of the following statements is correct? [pp. 382–383]
    a. Organisms can willfully change their DNA to be better adapted to their environment.
    b. Adaptation of organisms to their environment results from variation arising from the environmental conditions.
    c. An individual in a population with an adaptive trait will have higher relative fitness in its environment.

INTEGRATING AND APPLYING KEY CONCEPTS

1. Investigators studying genetic variation in humpback whales, with an average life span of 30 to 40 years, were surprised to learn that two of the three populations that survived until whale hunting was outlawed retained relatively high levels of variability. Would you expect to obtain similar results if you were studying a bird species with a comparatively short generation time? Explain why or why not.

2. If a population geneticist finds that a population is not in Hardy–Weinberg equilibrium, he or she will probably want to determine which of the required assumptions is violated. What sorts of things might he or she do to determine whether each condition is met?

3. Genetic studies of individuals who are resistant to HIV infection have identified, in at least some cases, a homozygous mutation in an immune cell surface receptor gene, *ccr5*. Heterozygous individuals appear to have higher levels of resistance compared to homozygous wild-type (normal) individuals. Discuss how these observations may have been determined and how researchers would ethically prove or disprove this association.

17 Darwin, Fossils, and Developmental Biology

TOPIC MAP

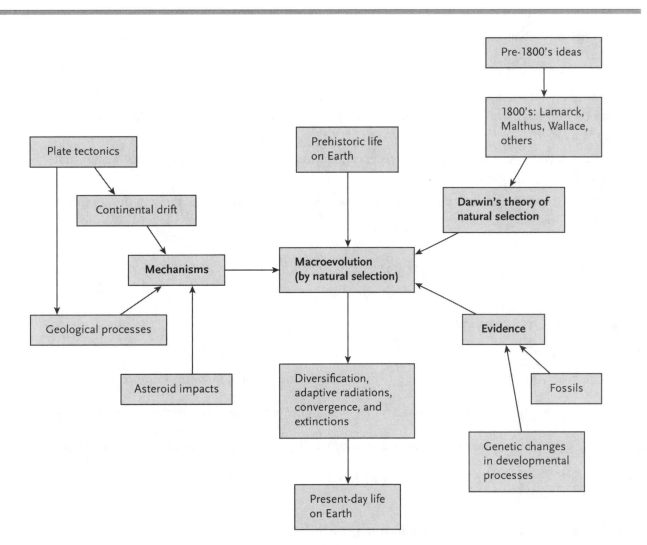

LEARNING OUTCOMES AND STUDY STRATEGIES

By the end of this chapter, you should be able to

■ Provide the names and contributions of various people who contributed to the world-view of evolutionary change

- Describe the Earth as a dynamic planet and relate changes in its physical properties (e.g., climatic change, movement of continents) to changes in species composition and diversity (i.e., new species evolve and existing species go extinct)
- Describe the role of paleobiology in our knowledge of evolutionary theory, including why the fossil record paints an incomplete picture
- Explain why convergent evolution results in superficial similarities among distantly related species
- Identify and be familiar with both types of evolutionary change, anagenesis and cladogenesis, as well as their underpinnings: the gradualist hypothesis and the punctuated equilibrium hypothesis
- Identify some macroevolutionary trends in morphology
- Describe how changes in the timing of various developmental events can lead to evolutionary change

Study strategies for this chapter:

- Remember that macroevolution is essentially the same as microevolution but over much longer time periods with large-scale changes. Keep referring to the topic map to help you maintain this perspective.
- Make sure you pay attention to the subject headings and especially the examples that demonstrate each concept or process.
- As always, go through one section of the textbook at a time and then work through the companion section of the study guide.

INTERACTIVE EXERCISES

Why It Matters [pp. 385–387]

Fill-in-the-Blanks

In Medicine Hat, Alberta, (1) _____ of riverbanks has resulted in the appearance of

(2) _____, the remains of organisms that lived in the past. These discoveries, as well as present-day

(3) _____ organisms, help identify evolutionary (4) _____ on Earth. This was studied by

(5) _____ and led to his theory of evolution by natural selection.

17.1 Recognition of Evolutionary Change [pp. 387–388]
17.2 Changes in Earth [p. 388]
17.3 Charles Darwin [pp. 388–391]

Section Review (Fill-in-the-Blanks)

Historically, there has been considerable change from ideas from the Greek philosopher (6) _____,

who believed that all organisms were created by (7) _____ and that they did not (8) _____

over time, to the theory of (9) _____ _____ proposed by Charles Darwin. As the *H.M.S.*

Beagle's (10) _____, Darwin was able to study organisms from all over the world, including those living in the (11) _____ _____. Darwin's familiarity with animal breeding, which he termed (12) _____ _____, as well as his readings promoted the development of his ideas. Two of the books that had a great impact on Darwin were by (13) _____ _____ and (14) _____ _____, the former expressing ideas on how overpopulation results in competition and the latter on how geological processes are changing the Earth. Based on his observations, Darwin suggested that variation exists among living organisms in a(n) (15) _____ and that only those individuals with the more successful variations in a given environment could survive and (16) _____. He realized that this would give rise to a change in the population's characteristics in subsequent (17) _____. His theory of evolution through natural selection paralleled a proposal by (18) _____ _____ _____ and both theories were presented to the Linnaean Society of London on July 1, 1858. A few months later, Darwin published his book, (19) _____.

Complete the Table

Complete the following table with the scientist's name or contribution to the recognition of evolutionary change.

Name	Name or Title Given to Concept, Book, or Theory	Description of Contribution
20.	Book: 21.	Wrote essay on the inevitable deaths from starvation as a result of a higher rate of population growth versus agricultural growth in England; provided a model for Darwin's theory of natural selection
Charles Lyell	Concept: 22.	Geological processes are the same as in the past and changes to the Earth's surface takes a long time period
23.	Concept: Parallel to Darwin's mechanism on how species change over time	Contacted Darwin about this ideas; paper presented with Darwin's paper at Linnaean Society of London
24.	Principles: Mechanisms of "use and disuse" and the "inheritance of acquired characteristics"	Although principles are erroneous, fostered discussion relating to mechanisms of evolution

Name	Name or Title Given to Concept, Book, or Theory	Description of Contribution
James Hutton	Concept: 25.	26.
27.	Concept: "Organisms were conceived by Nature and produced by Time"	Recognized animals must have changed since created due to presence of 28. _____ organs
29.	Concept: "Great Chain of Being"	Developed ladder of life to classify non-changing organisms according to purpose and position
Georges Cuvier	Theory: 30.	31.

Choose

Identify the letter(s) associated with the individual(s) whose proposed theory is associated with each of the following points.

32. _____ All species change over time

33. _____ Organisms with favourable heritable traits in their environment will survive and reproduce more readily

34. _____ Individuals of a species can pass on acquired characteristics to offspring

35. _____ Variation exists among individuals in a population

36. _____ Some organisms function better than others in a particular environment

A. Charles Darwin

B. Jean Baptiste de Lamarck

17.4 Evidence for Evolution: The Fossil Record [pp. 391–393]

Section Review (Fill-in-the-Blanks)

(37) _____ is the study of fossils and is our primary source of data about the evolutionary history of

organisms. Fossils can be formed in a number of ways. Ideal conditions for fossil formation include low

(38) _____ levels and/or high (39) _____. Hard structures such as (40) _____,

bones, and shells of animals and the (41) _____ and wood of plants are more likely to form fossils

through the slow replacement of the original material by dissolved (42) _____. Some fossils are formed as casts or (43) _____. When oxygen is scarce even soft-bodied organisms may be preserved

since (44) _____ does not occur. Unfortunately, not all environments favour (45) _____.

There are a number of methods used to estimate the relative age of fossils, but primarily this is done by

studying their location; (46) _____ geological strata contains older fossils than (47) _____

strata. To determine the absolute age of a fossil (48) _____ _____ is used, which is based

on measuring the amount of a specific unstable isotope in a fossil and knowing its (49) _____-

_____. Fossils that still contain organic material can be dated by calculating the ratio of

(50) _____:_____.

True/False

Mark if the statement is true (T) or false (F). If the statement is false, justify your answer in the lines below each statement.

51. _____ Fossils form when organisms are buried under sediment or are preserved in mountain forests.

_____

_____

52. _____ The fossil record provides a complete record of life throughout evolutionary history.

_____

_____

53. _____ The half-life of ^{14}C is approximately 5600 years. At death, a piece of wood contains all of the ^{14}C found in a living specimen and after 5600 years contains half the amount.

_____

_____

Short Answer

54. Explain why soft-bodied animals are preserved in peat bogs, tar pits, and glacial ice.

_____

_____

55. What is the relevance of amber to paleontology?

_____

_____

17.5 Earth History, Biogeography, and Convergent Evolution [pp. 393–396]

Section Review (Fill-in-the-Blanks)

The theory of (56) _____ _____ explain shifts in geography, the movement of pieces of

Earth's crust on its semisolid (57) _____. This movement underlies the phenomenon known as

(58) _____ _____ and explains the gradual changes in Earth's past climate. Living

organisms are affected by prevailing climates and conditions in the (59) _____. Catastrophic events,

such as massive volcanic eruptions or the impact of (60) _____ with Earth can result in massive

extinctions of species over relatively short geological time scales. (61) _____ is the study of the

distribution of living and ancient organisms on Earth. Some species have a (62) _____ distribution,

living in habitats throughout a geographic area, whereas others have a (63) _____ distribution. This

may be due to the process of (64) _____, which occurs when organisms move away from their place

of origin, or (65) _____, which is due to external factors that cause fragmentation. An example of the

latter is the breakup of the supercontinent (66) _____ into six biogeographic (67) _____. On

each of the resulting modern-day continents the isolation and environmental conditions experienced by the

mix of organisms living there has led to the evolution of a unique (68) _____ on each. Sometimes

distantly related species that are biogeographically isolated may evolve similar (69) _____ features as

a result of similar environmental pressures and lifestyles. These similarities are the result of

(70) _____ evolution.

Matching

Identify correct structure that describes each of the processes occurring in the theory of plate tectonics.

71. _____ Semi-solid structure below the crust | A. Oceanic trench

72. _____ Location where upward movement of magma separates plates | B. Continental crust

73. _____ Lighter crust that is pushed upwards by old crust | C. Young crust

74. _____ Results from the movement of the continental crust | D. Mantle

75. _____ Forms on either side of oceanic ridge   E.   Oceanic ridge

76. _____ Location where old crust is recycled into mantle   F.   Continental drift

True/False

Mark if the statement is true (T) or false (F). If the statement is false, make it correct by changing the underlined word(s) and writing the correct word(s) in the lines below each statement.

77. _____ <u>Historical biogeography</u> attempts to explain the geographic distribution of organisms.

_____

_____

78. _____ The present distribution of magnolia trees, which was continuous in the past, is explained by <u>vicariance</u>.

_____

_____

79. _____ The theory of <u>plate tectonics</u> helps explain continental drift and historical biogeography.

_____

_____

80. _____ The redfin darter (a small fish) is found only in the rivers of the Ozarks and therefore is <u>endemic</u> to the region.

_____

_____

81. _____ The ring-billed gull is found in all coastal regions of the continental U.S. Its distribution is <u>disjunct</u>.

_____

_____

82. _____ Organisms living in Australian and Neoartic biogeographical realms belong to <u>the same biota</u>.

_____

_____

83. _____ The marsupial mole in Australia and the golden mole in Africa show <u>divergent</u> evolution.

_____

_____

17.6 Interpreting Evolutionary Lineages [pp. 396–402]
17.7 Macroevolutionary Trends in Morphology [pp. 402–404]

Section Review (Fill-in-the-Blanks)

The evolution and adaptive radiation of horses reveal that the evolution of a species is not

(84) _____; many previous species have arisen through branching of the evolutionary tree and then

subsequently become (85) _____. The gradual evolutionary transformation of an existing species into

a new one is called (86) _____ and does not increase the number of existing species. In contrast,

(87) _____ is the evolution of two or more descendant species from a single ancestral species, giving

rise to an increase in the number of existing species. The former is prevalent in the (88) _____

hypothesis since it is the slow, continuous accumulation of small changes at a steady rate that results in

speciation. An alternate hypothesis, the (89) _____ _____ hypothesis, describes rapid

macroevolutionary change, with new species forming through (90) _____, followed by little change

in these species for prolonged periods. There are examples of both of these extreme hypotheses in the

(91) _____ record. Some evolutionary lineages exhibit a trend toward greater size and

(92) _____, while others exhibit the development of novel (93) _____. To explain how

novel morphological structures evolve, various mechanisms have been proposed including

(94) _____, which occurs when a trait that serves one function is later co-opted for another;

(95) _____ _____, which is based on the differential growth rates of specific anatomical

structures; and (96) _____, which leads to different morphologies between species due to changes in

the timing of developmental events. Two phenomena that can be involved in the latter mechanism are

(97) _____ and (98) _____. The former occurs when larvae (juveniles) acquire the ability to

(99) _____ and the latter occurs when adults retain (100) _____ _____.

Building Vocabulary

Using the definitions of the prefixes below, assign the appropriate prefix to the appropriate suffix for the following:

Prefix	Meaning
allo-	different
clado-	a branch
hetero-	different
pedo-	child

	Prefix	Suffix	Definition
101.	_____	-morphosis	Retention of juvenile characteristics into adulthood
102.	_____	-chrony	Changes in timing of developmental events
103.	_____	-metric	Different relative sizes of structures in related species
104.	_____	-genesis	Evolution of two or more descendant species from a common ancestor

Matching

Match each of the following names or mechanisms with the correct concept or example.

105. ____	Preadaptation	A.	Rule identifying the macroevolutionary trend toward greater size in a lineage.
106. ____	Allometric growth	B.	Description of the phylogeny of horse species.
107. ____	Punctuated equilibrium	C.	Gill retention in some amphibian species into adulthood, possibly due to a mutation in a gene for metamorphosis.
108. ____	Rapid evolution (36 years)	D.	Feathers and wing-like forelimbs may have originally evolved among some dinosaurs as a means of capturing prey and conserving body heat.
109. ____	Edward Drinker Cope	E.	The skulls of newborn chimps resemble those of newborn humans; however, by the time skull development is complete, significant changes are apparent.
110. ____	Pedomorphosis	F.	Morphological differences found between new and original populations of Italian wall lizards.

True/False

Mark if the statement is true (T) or false (F). If the statement is false, justify your answer in the lines below each statement.

111. _____ Heterochrony is believed to be the explanation for the difference in flower morphology and pollination species in the compared with the ancestral species *D. decorum*.

_____

_____

17.8 Evolutionary Developmental Biology [pp. 404–409]
17.9 Evolutionary Biology since Darwin [p. 409]

Section Review (Fill-in-the Blanks)

(112) _____ _____ biology or "evo-devo" is the study of changes in regulatory genes that

affect development and can create morphological changes. In studying the development of body plan, it has

been found that most animals contain a highly conserved (106) "_____ _____-

_____" composed of several hundred of the same (114) _____ genes. These genes are

regulatory genes that code for (115) _____ _____ that bind to regulatory sites in order to

(116) _____ (turn on) or (117) _____ (turn off) expression of other genes. Among these

genes are the (118) _____ family of genes, which controls the overall body plan of animals by

expressing different genes at different positions along the (119) _____-to-_____ axis of the

developing embryo. These tool-kit genes, as well as others, may have differing (120) _____ of

activity at different (121) _____ in the embryonic development of different species, resulting from

the regulatory site acting as a(n) (122) _____. Based on this concept, (123) _____

_____ could arise from evolutionary changes in developmental switches that cause certain body parts

to grow larger or more quickly than others. Other changes in developmental switches would also provide an

explanation for (124) _____ so that the development of adult characteristics is either delayed or the

development of reproductive maturity is sped up.

Matching

Identify the correct term associated with each of the definitions relating to genes for development.

125. _____ Large set of homeotic genes that controls the basic design of the body plan

    A.   Homeotic genes

126. _____ Location where a transcription factor binds; acts as a switch to activate/repress a downstream gene

    B.   Transcription factor

127. _____ Regulatory genes that code for transcription factors that bind regulatory sites

    C.   Genetic took-kit

128. _____ Produce transcription factors to activate genes for the correct development of appendages

    D.   Hox genes

129. _____ Nucleotide sequence that codes for a homeodomain

    E.   Regulatory site

130. _____ Protein that binds to a regulatory site, controlling the activity of a downstream gene

    F.   Homeobox

True/False

Mark if the statement is true (T) or false (F). If the statement is false, justify your answer in the lines below each statement.

131. _____ *Pitx1* regulates genes that control the development of light-sensing organs in a wide variety of animals.

_____

_____

132. _____ Evolutionary developmental biology was made possible by the evolution of the science of genomics.

_____

_____

133. _____ The morphological differences between mice and fruit flies are the result of the evolution of different tool-kit genes.

_____

_____

Short Answer

134. How does evo-devo help shed light on macroevolutionary trends and adaptive radiations?

_____

_____

135. Explain how a single mutation combined with natural selection could provide an explanation for the differing morphologies of stickleback fish.

_____

_____

136. What is the evidence that the *Pax-6* gene has been conserved over the course of hundreds of millions of years?

_____

_____

SELF-TEST

1. What does the term "natural theology" refer to? [p. 387]
   a. the scientific pursuit of classifying all of God's creations prevalent in 14th-century Europe
   b. the study of the form and variety of organisms in their natural environments
   c. the story of creation
   d. the classification of all animals on Earth as being below minerals

2. What did Le Comte de Buffon propose to explain the existence of two toes on some mammals that never touch the ground? [p. 387]
   a. the hypothesis of adaptive radiation
   b. the theory of gradualism
   c. the idea that some animals must have changed since their creation
   d. the theory of cladogenesis

3. Which of the following relates to the theory of catastrophism? [p. 387]
   a. It refers to the presence of different fossils in abruptly changing geological strata.
   b. It refers to the extinction of certain lineages of an organism.
   c. It was proposed by Charles Lyell.
   d. It is used to determine the relative ages of fossils.

4. Which of the following is a specific proposal made by Jean Baptiste de Lamarck that ultimately contributed to an evolutionary worldview? [pp. 387–388]
   a. Vestigial structures must have served a purpose in an ancestral species.
   b. Organisms change in response to their environments.
   c. Slow and continual geological processes shape, and continue to shape, Earth's geology.
   d. All life forms have arisen from a common ancestor.

5. On whose writings was Darwin's idea of natural selection based? [pp. 389–390]
   a. Charles Lyell
   b. Alfred Russell Wallace
   c. Thomas Malthus
   d. Jean Baptiste de Lamarck

6. Which statement most directly relates to Darwin's theory of evolution by natural selection? [p. 390]

    a. Individuals within a population compete for limited resources.

    b. Certain hereditary characteristics allow some individuals to survive longer and reproduce more than others.

    c. Many variations among individuals have a genetic basis and so are inherited by subsequent generations.

    d. A population's characteristics will change over generations.

7. When are fossils most likely to form? [p. 391]

    a. when aquatic invertebrates are exposed to the air and are preserved by dehydration

    b. when hard parts of organisms are buried under sediments in anaerobic conditions

    c. when soft-bodied organisms are buried under sediments in aerobic conditions

    d. when volcanoes erupt

8. What information is required for radiometric dating of a fossil? [p. 393]

    a. amount of isotope present in the fossil and its decay rate

    b. its location with the sedimentary stratum

    c. amount of various isotopes in the fossil and the variation in amounts among them

    d. size of particles comprising the fossil and its location in the strata

9. Which of the following correctly describes continental drift? [pp. 393–394]

    a. It can be explained by plate tectonics.

    b. It is the result of currents in Earth's oceans.

    c. It is another term for cladogenesis.

    d. It is the layers of strata in which fossils are found.

10. Which of the following can be explained by continental drift? [p. 394]

    a. continuous distribution

    b. preadaptation

    c. dispersal

    d. disjunct distribution

11. What are endemic species? [p. 394]

    a. They exhibit a continuous distribution.

    b. They exhibit a disjunct distribution.

    c. They are unique to a single location/ region.

    d. They are from lineages that became extinct.

12. Why are North American cacti and African spurges almost identical? [p. 395]

    a. They share the same recent common ancestor.

    b. They are the product of convergent evolution.

    c. They are different species of the same genus.

    d. They are the product of a recent vicariance.

13. Which of the following is NOT one of Wallace's six biogeographical realms? [pp. 394–395]

    a. Australian

    b. Ethiopian

    c. Neotropical

    d. Arctic

14. What is adaptive radiation? [p. 398]

    a. all organisms living in an area

    b. evolution of similar morphologies between distantly related organisms

    c. a burst of speciation resulting from a move to a new situation

    d. transformation of a species due to the accumulation of changes

15. What does the term "anagenesis" refer to? [pp. 399–400]

    a. the gradual change of individuals in a lineage as they adapt to changing environments

    b. the rapid diversification of a population into two or more descendant species

    c. the differential growth rates of different parts of the body

    d. a change in the timing of developmental events

16. Which hypothesis for evolutionary change is described as periods of stability followed by periods of rapid evolutionary change? [p. 400]

a. convergence
b. gradualism
c. heterochrony
d. punctuated equilibrium

17. Which of the following terms identifies the type of trend within evolutionary lineages alluded to by Cope's Rule? [p. 402]

a. allometric growth
b. pedomorphosis
c. increase in size
d. vicariance

18. What term can be associated with observed relative size differences between human anatomical features during development? [p. 403]

a. adaptive radiation
b. allometric growth
c. pedomorphosis
d. preadaptation

19. What mechanism for the evolution of a novel feature describes the morphology and pollination of the recently evolved species *Delphinium nudicaule*? [p. 404]

a. heterochrony
b. pedomorphosis
c. cladogenesis
d. tectonics

20. In what way do homeotic genes serve as a "tool-kit"? [pp. 404–405]

a. They link regulatory genes on a single chromosome.
b. They are species specific.
c. They regulate the timing and sequence of developmental processes.
d. They encode different morphological structures.

INTEGRATING AND APPLYING KEY CONCEPTS

1. Based on what you have learned about homeotic genes, why is it not surprising that organisms with serially repeating segments are most likely to show extreme organ displacement, for example, substitution of legs for antennae in Drosophila? Arthropods, which exhibit this pattern of segmentation, are the most diverse group in the animal kingdom. How might these two facts relate to each other?

2. The evolution of placental mammals resulted in the extinction of most marsupials in most parts of the world. Having learned about the impact of continental drift on the distribution of flora and fauna, what would be the explanation for the fact that marsupials are so common in Australia? What do you think would be the fate of Australian marsupials if placental animals from other parts of the world were introduced without regulation?

3. The research described on page 407, "From Fins to Fingers," indicates that tetrapod digits are a morphological novelty. Can you suggest any further experiments or observations that could determine whether fish have the genetic capacity to form digits?

18 Classification, Evolution, and Phylogeny

TOPIC MAP

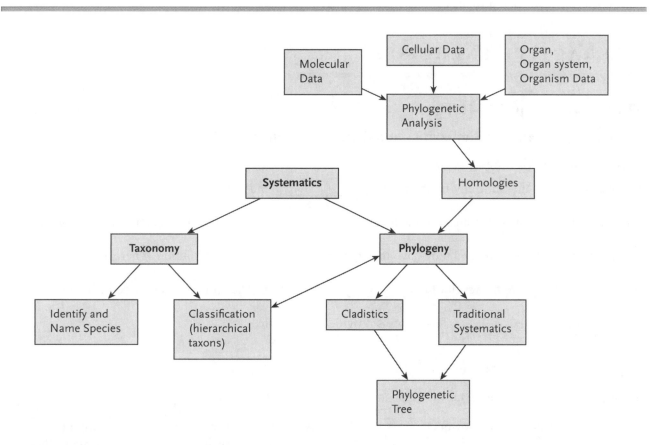

LEARNING OUTCOMES AND STUDY STRATEGIES

By the end of this chapter, you should be able to

- Describe the difficulties in determining phylogeny and building relationships based strictly on morphology or observed similarities

- Define the terms "Linnaean classification," "systematics," "phylogeny," and "taxonomy"

- Explain how phylogenetic trees are derived, using both the traditional evolutionary systematic approach and the cladistic approach; you should also be able to explain why cladistics is now more widely used than the traditional approach

- Derive a simple phylogenic tree given relevant information

- Explain the process of molecular phylogeny and why, with examples, it often sheds light on relationships that previously could not be determined
- Differentiate between the characteristics and timeline of present and past hominids

Study strategies for this chapter:

- This chapter has many new terms and concepts. You will want to pay attention to the subject headings and examples that demonstrate each concept or process.
- Make your way through the various phylogenetic trees that are depicted, noting the specific information that each provides.

INTERACTIVE EXERCISES

Why It Matters [pp. 412–415]

18.1 The Significance of Similarities and Differences [pp. 415–417]

Section Review (Fill-in-the-Blanks)

Organisms living in the same environmental (1) _____ tend to evolve similar body forms even

though they have not arisen from an immediate (2) _____ (phylogenetic) history. In this situation, if

two organisms are closely related they have undergone (3) _____ evolution, whereas if they are more

distantly related they are the result of (4) _____ evolution. The similarities between edible true

morels and the (5) _____ false morels provide an example.

Matching

Match each of the following terms or organisms with its correct description.

6. ____	Carnivorous flowers	A.	Similar traits evolved by distantly related organisms living under the same conditions
7. ____	African spurges	B.	Poisonous mushrooms that resemble the edible chanterelles
8. ____	Jack-o'-lanterns	C.	Similar traits evolved by closely related organisms living under the same conditions
9. ____	Convergent evolution	D.	Plants that show convergent evolution with North American cacti
10. ____	Parallel evolution	E.	A group of organisms that trap insects as a source of nitrogen and that do not all share the same recent common ancestor

18.2 Systematic Biology: An Overview [p. 417]
18.3 The Linnaean System of Classification [p. 418]
18.4 From Classification to Phylogeny [p. 418]

Section Review (Fill-in-the-Blanks)

The (11) _____ system of classification was developed in the 1700s by Carl von Linné and is still

used today. Organisms are grouped into increasingly inclusive categories, so this system demonstrates

(12) _____ hierarchy. According to his system, the most specific (13) _____ is species and

the most inclusive is (14) _____. While he based his classifications on organismal

(15) _____ traits, more recently, other criteria have been incorporated into classification schemes.

These include cellular information such as chromosomal anatomy, morphology of (16) _____

structures, and gene and protein (17) _____. At higher levels, organism physiology, organ system

and organ morphology, and (18) _____ patterns have been used. Classification requires the

identification and naming of species, all of which are components of (19) _____. This is one goal of

the science of (20) _____ and the second goal is to reconstruct the (21) _____, or

evolutionary history of organisms. These relationships are illustrated using (22) _____

_____, which can be used to distinguish similarities inherited from a common ancestor from those

that evolved (23) _____ (e.g., wings).

Sequence

Arrange each of the following taxa in the correct sequence, from the most inclusive group to the least
inclusive.

24. ____	A.	Family
25. ____	B.	Phylum
26. ____	C.	Genus
27. ____	D.	Order
28. ____	E.	Domain
29. ____	F.	Species
30. ____	G.	Kingdom
31. ____	H.	Class

Matching

Match each of the following with its correct definition.

32. _____	Species	A.	An illustration that identifies likely evolutionary relationships among species
33. _____	Taxon	B.	A species that is not hybridizing with any other species
34. _____	Oviparous	C.	The science devoted to naming and organizing organisms
35. _____	Taxonomy	D.	The science of determining evolutionary histories of organisms and naming and classifying those organisms
36. _____	Taxonomic hierarchy	E.	The group of organisms at a given taxonomic level
37. _____	Phylogenetic tree	F.	An arrangement of organisms into ever more inclusive groups
38. _____	Systematics	G.	The science of determining evolutionary histories of organisms
39 _____	Closed genetic system	H.	The least inclusive of Linnaean taxa
40. _____	Phylogeny	I.	Organisms that lay eggs when reproducing

True/False

Mark if the statement is true (T) or false (F). If the statement is false, justify your answer in the lines below each statement.

41. _____ All life on Earth can be classified into three kingdoms.

_____

_____

42. _____ Phylogenetic trees are considered to be scientific hypotheses because they are testable and as data is collected they can be revised.

_____

_____

18.5 Evaluating Systematic Characters [pp. 418–420]
18.6 Phylogenetic Inference and Classification [pp. 420–423]

Section Review (Fill-in-the-Blanks)

In order to prepare a phylogenetic hypothesis, systematists use two important criteria to identify characters to

study: phenotypic variation must reflect (43) _____ differences rather than environmental ones and the traits must be genetically (44) _____, reflecting different parts of the organism's genome.

(45) _____ characters have the same developmental histories, reflecting underlying

(46) _____ similarities as a result of their relationship with a common ancestor. Phenotypic

similarities that evolved independently in different lineages are called (47) _____ or homoplasious

characters and are not used in systematic analyses. The term (48) _____ evolution refers to the fact

that some characters evolve slowly while others evolve rapidly. As a result, every species displays old forms

of traits, (49) _____ characters, and new forms of traits, (50) _____ characters. The latter is

inherited by all subsequent descendents thereby acting as a marker for its evolutionary (51) _____.

There are primarily two views on how to classify species. Using traditional evolutionary systematics, species

that share both ancestral and derived (52) _____ are grouped together so classification reflects both

(53) _____ branching and (54) _____ divergence. Alternatively, (55) _____ is a

classification approach based solely on evolutionary relationships. In this approach, species that share derived

characters are grouped together in a(n) (56) _____ and, using the principle of (57) _____,

the hypothesized evolutionary branching of groups is illustrated using a(n) (58) _____. The latter

system is favoured because it clearly and precisely relates species in terms of their (59) _____

history.

Matching
Match each of the following terms with its correct definition.

60. _____	Cladogram	A.	A phenomenon that describes how some characters evolve slowly and others evolve rapidly
61. _____	Outgroup comparison	B.	Traits that have remained unchanged in a species
62. _____	Homoplasies	C.	A group that possesses a unique set of derived characters
63. _____	Mosaic evolution	D.	The assignment to a taxon based on presumed evolution from a single ancestral species
64. _____	Clade	E.	Species from several evolutionary lines but a common ancestor is not included

65. ____	PhlyoCode	F.	The idea that the same change evolved more than once in a lineage is extremely unlikely
66. ____	Principle of monophyly	G.	A tree that illustrates a hypothesized sequence of evolutionary branchings
67. ____	Polyphyletic taxon	H.	Similarities that result from shared ancestry
68. ____	Paraphyletic taxon	I.	Traits not present in ancestors
69. ____	Monophyletic taxon	J.	An alternative system for identification and naming based on clades rather than familiar taxonomic levels
70. ____	Homologies	K.	A technique that compares a group under study to a distantly related species
71. ____	Ancestral characters	L.	Groups of species consisting of a common ancestor and some but not all of its descendants
72. ____	Derived characters	M.	Similarities that evolved independently in different lineages
73. ____	Assumption of parsimony	N.	A common ancestral species and all species descended from it

True/False

Mark if the statement is true (T) or false (F). If the statement is false, justify your answer in the lines below each statement.

74. _____ Cladistics is based on derived and ancestral features.

_____

_____

75. _____ Homologous characters can differ markedly in form and function.

_____

_____

76. _____ The evolution of flight is convergent between vertebrates and parallel between insects and vertebrates.

_____

_____

77. _____ The PhyloCode system divides organisms into domains, kingdoms, phyla, classes, and orders but not families, genera, and species.

_____

_____

Short Answer

78. Explain how embryonic developmental patterns are related to homologous characters.

_____

_____

79. Explain why derived traits provide more useful information about evolutionary relatedness than ancestral traits.

_____

_____

Complete the Table and Fill-in-the-Blank

A particular character may be considered ancestral or derived, depending upon what organisms are being considered. For the following pairwise comparisons of organisms, determine if the vertebral column is derived or ancestral.

Paired Comparison	Presence/Absence of Vertebral Column	Ancestral or Derived Trait
Humans: chimps	Yes/yes	80. _____
Birds: insects	Yes/no	81. _____
Fish: frogs	Yes/yes	82. _____
Crocodiles: wolves	Yes/yes	83. _____

84. For the purposes of deriving a cladogram of all of the eight organisms in the above table, the outgroup would be _____.

18.7 Molecular Data [pp. 423–427]
18.8 Clarifications from Molecular Phylogenetics [p. 428]
18.9 Phylogeny: Contributions from Bayesian, Bootstrap, and Parsimony Analysis [pp. 428–430]

Section Review (Fill-in-the-Blanks)

Because DNA is inherited, differences in DNA, RNA, or (85) _____ sequences can provide

information for determining relatedness. The advantages of using molecular sequence data include the large number of independent (86) _____ that can be compared, availability of genes that are

(87) _____ among organisms, even those that share no morphological similarities, and the fact that

the sequences are not affected by developmental or (88) _____ factors. Some sequences evolve more

rapidly than others: for example, mitochondrial DNA evolves relatively (89) _____, whereas

chloroplast DNA evolves relatively (90) _____, a demonstration of the phenomenon of

(91) _____ evolution. Regardless of the speed of evolution, as long as mutations occur at a

(92) _____ rate, one can use the degree of change as a (93) _____ _____. Large

differences would therefore indicate divergence in the (94) _____ past and minor differences would

be indicative of divergence in the (95) _____ past. Computer programs are often used to precisely

(96) _____ sequence data, taking into account insertions and deletions. Similarities and differences

are then used to construct (97) _____ _____, often using a group of statistical approaches

called the (98) _____ _____ methods to determine the likelihood of a particular sequence

change being a shared (99) _____ trait (i.e., inherited from a common ancestor) rather than having

arisen independently. Such independently arising changes are more likely with DNA sequences than protein

sequences as there are only (100) _____ possible bases for any position in the sequence.

Choose

Identify the domain(s) that each of the 1960s kingdoms belong to based Woese's data using small subunit
rRNA data. Note: more than one choice may be required.

101.	_____	Protista	A.	Archaea
102.	_____	Animal	B.	Eukarya
103.	_____	Plant	C.	Bacteria
104.	_____	Monera		
105.	_____	Fungi		

Sequence

Arrange each of the following steps used in the practice of molecular phylogenetics in the correct order.

106. _____

A.   Align sequences, determining where insertions and deletions occur

107. _____

B.   Use statistical analysis programs to group species accordingly

108. _____

C.   Select an appropriate protein molecule or region of nucleic acids

109. _____

D.   Determine the sequence of the chosen protein molecule or nucleic acid segment

110. _____

E.   Compare sequences, looking for similarities and differences

True/False

Mark if the statement is true (T) or false (F). If the statement is false, justify your answer in the lines below each statement.

111. _____   Sequence data from mitochondrial DNA are more useful for dating evolutionary divergence from the distant past.

_____

_____

112. _____   Analysis of rRNA in the 1970s was able to provide information to produce a tree of life composed of 5 kingdoms.

_____

_____

113. _____   Prior to the development of molecular phylogenetics, the prokaryotes were assigned to a single polyphyletic kingdom.

_____

_____

Short Answer

114. Differentiate between the terms "genetic distance" and "maximum likelihood method."

_____

_____

115. Describe what is meant by the term "molecular clock."

_____

_____

18.10 The Evolution of Humans [pp. 430–437]

Section Review (Fill-in-the-Blanks)

The (116) _____ includes modern humans and their bipedal ancestors. The (117) _____

posture associated with bipedal movement impacts various structures in these organisms, such as an increase

in the number of (118) _____ vertebrae, lengths and concavity of these vertebrae, and freeing of

(119) _____ resulting in the (120) _____ characters of power and/or precision grips. There

are two hypotheses that explain the origin and timing of modern humans. The (121) _____

_____ hypothesis suggests that we arose from an African ancestor, whereas the (122) _____

hypothesis suggests that *H. sapiens* evolved in many areas, such as Africa, Europe, and Asia, simultaneously.

Two studies provide support for the former hypothesis: a study by Cann and colleagues shows that the

greatest variation in (123) _____ _____ occurs in African populations, indicating they are

the (124) _____ on Earth, and a study by Whitfield found that there is little diversity in the

(125) _____ _____ globally, indicating a common ancestor from a single migration out of

Africa.

Matching

Match each of the human ancestral species with the correct character(s) or description(s).

126. _____	*Ardipithecus ramidus*	A.	Thick enamel teeth (derived character) on oldest species of this genus
127. _____	*Australopithecus anamensis*	B.	Taller than ancestors with a relatively large brain in a thick skull; spread out from Africa to Eurasia and Europe
128. _____	*Australopithecus afarensis*	C.	Lived at approximately same time as *H. erectus* and had 20% larger brain than *Paranthropus*
129. _____	*Homo habilis*	D.	Heavier body and triple the differences in mtDNA compared to within *H. sapiens* individuals
130. _____	*Homo erectus*	E.	Lived about 5 million years ago and had ape-like teeth in its 120 cm tall body
131. _____	*Homo neanderthalensis*	F.	Relatively small brain (ancestral character), large and pointed canines, and scapulae that indicate vertical climbing and suspension from tree limbs did not occur

1. Which statement about the animal *Castor canadensis* is NOT true? [pp. 415–416]

   a. It is the classification of the Canadian beaver.
   b. It is closely related to the "Mesozoic beaver" identified by fossil evidence from China.
   c. *Canadensis* is the species name.
   d. *Castor* is the genus name.

2. What does the science of systematics study? [p. 417]

   a. the evolutionary history, identification, and naming of organisms
   b. the evolutionary history of organisms
   c. the identification and naming or organisms
   d. the development of organisms

3. Which taxon comprises related species? [p. 418]

   a. Class
   b. Family
   c. Genus
   d. Order

4. Which statement is true? [p. 418]

   a. The class taxon is more inclusive than the phylum taxon.
   b. The family taxon is more specific than the genus taxon.
   c. Pine trees all belong to the genus *Pinus.*
   d. All prokaryotes belong to the same domain.

5. Which term refers to phenotypic similarities that evolved independently in different lineages? [p. 419]

   a. homologous characters
   b. evolutionary mosaics
   c. feathers
   d. analogous characters

6. What structure in tetrapod vertebrates is homologous to the hyomandibula, a bone that braced the lower jaw in early jawed fishes? [p. 419]

   a. inner ear
   b. mandible
   c. stapes
   d. femur

7. Which of the following statements do NOT apply to homologous characters? [pp. 419–420]

   a. They arise from a common ancestry.
   b. They will show genetic relatedness.
   c. They are affected by environmental conditions.
   d. They are the product of comparable embryonic structures.

8. According to scientific evidence, which of the following are derived characters (within group indicated in brackets)? [pp. 420–421, 428]

   a. vertebral column (animals)
   b. rRNA molecule (animals)
   c. six walking legs (insects)
   d. internal skeleton (mammals)

For questions 9 to 13, refer to the following figure.

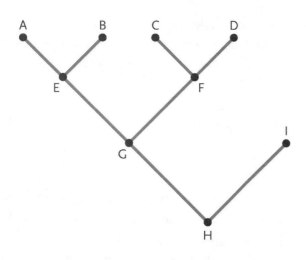

9. Species C and D are part of a monophyletic taxon. Which is the ancestor for this taxon? [p. 421]

   a. species A
   b. species B
   c. species E
   d. species F

10. Which of the following terms best describes the taxon containing Species B and C? [p. 421]

    a. monophyletic
    b. polyphyletic
    c. paraphyletic

11. What is the most recent common ancestor for species A and B? [p. 421]

    a. species E
    b. species F
    c. species G
    d. species H

12. In order to determine which shared characteristics are derived versus ancestral when comparing organisms A, B, and C, which would be a likely outgroup? [p. 421]

    a. species E
    b. species G
    c. species H
    d. species I

13. If this tree were derived using cladistics, which statement would be true? [p. 422]

    a. The various branches would be paraphyletic.
    b. The phylogenetic tree would be based on evolutionary and morphological divergence.
    c. The various species (A–I) could be PhyloCode designations rather than species, genera, families, etc.

14. When comparing two phylogenetic trees containing species A to D, if both agreed with the evidence but there were fewer branches on the first tree than on the second tree, which of the phylogenetic trees would be correct? [pp. 421–422, 427]

    a. The first was most likely to be correct.
    b. The second was most likely to be correct.
    c. The one based on molecular data would be more likely to be correct.

15. Which of the following would cladistics consider when classifying organisms? [p. 422]

    a. shared ancestral characters
    b. shared derived characters
    c. a combination of ancestral and derived characters
    d. morphology

16. Why are changes in the amino acid sequence of a protein of more value in determining evolutionary divergence than DNA base changes? [p. 423]

    a. because protein sequences evolve at a more constant rate compared to DNA sequences
    b. because there is a higher likelihood that similarities in DNA sequence arose independently since there are only 4 bases but 20 amino acids
    c. because there is a higher likelihood that similarities in protein sequence arose independently since there are only 4 DNA bases but 20 amino acids,
    d. because translation is more accurate than DNA replication

17. Which of the following would a molecular systematists be least interested in when conducting phylogentic analyses? [pp. 423, 425]

a. protein
b. DNA
c. RNA
d. morphology

18. Which three major lineages have been identified by molecular phylogentics? [p. 428]

a. Prokarya, Eukarya, Protista
b. Archaea, Animalia, Plantae
c. Bacteria, Archaea, Eukarya
d. Protista, Monera, Plantae

19. What does the fossil record indicate regarding the evolution of humans from apes? [p. 430]

a. insects are more closely related to humans than apes
b. human evolutionary lineage diverged from gorillas and chimps 6 million years ago
c. humans have recently (less than 1 million years ago) evolved from apes
d. the fossil record provides no information about the evolutionary relationship between humans and apes

20. What characteristic are Australopithicus, Paranthropus, Ardipithecus, and Homo genera known to have in common? [pp. 432–435]

a. protruding brow ridges
b. protruding jaw
c. bipedalism
d. ape-like appearance

INTEGRATING AND APPLYING KEY CONCEPTS

1. Given that bacteria were first discovered more than 300 years ago, why is it only with the advent of molecular phylogeny that the polyphyletic nature of the Monera has come to light?

2. Remembering what you learned about transcription and translation, why is rRNA such a good molecular clock and mRNA is not?

3. Construct a cladogram based on the information below and identify (a) which organism would be the outgroup; and (b) for the most right-hand branch, the derived trait.

Species	Vertebral Column	Swim Bladder or Lungs	Mammary Glands	Extraembryonic Membrane
Lancelets	−	−	−	−
Amphibians	+	+	−	−
Birds	+	+	−	+
Lizards	+	+	−	+
Mammals	+	+	+	+
Sharks	+	−	−	−

19 Species

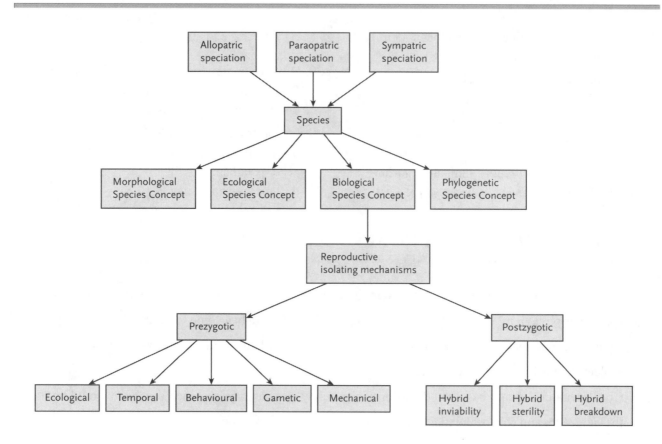

LEARNING OUTCOMES AND STUDY STRATEGIES

By the end of this chapter, you should be able to

- Discuss the four species concepts used by biologists and explain why biologists cannot agree on a single concept and why, specifically, there are limitations associated with the Biological Species Concept

- Relate the importance of reproductive isolation between species to maintaining species integrity

- Identify and describe the various pre- and postzygotic isolating mechanisms

- Identify the three generally recognized models of speciation and explain how reproductive isolation can evolve in each model

- Describe the genetic mechanisms of speciation and explain how they also give rise to reproductive isolating mechanisms

Study strategies for this chapter:

- Make sure you pay attention to the subject headings and examples that demonstrate each concept or process related to species and speciation, ensuring that you can differentiate between them

- Make sure you are clear on the meaning of the prefixes allo-, para-, sym-, and auto- as well as the suffix -ploidy. Remember the difference between mitosis and meiosis and the change in chromosome number resulting from the latter.

INTERACTIVE EXERCISES

Why It Matters [pp. 441–442]
19.1 What's in a Name? [pp. 442–443]
19.2 Definition of *Species* [pp. 443–444]

Section Review (Fill-in-the-Blanks)

Within the giraffe species *Giraffa camelopurdalis,* morphological and (1) _____ evidence indicates

(2) _____ variation, suggesting that this group of animals should be divided into (3) _____,

each composed of one or more genetically discrete populations. This is an example of the difficulties inherent

in (4) _____ and classifying organisms. Biologists use latinized names to identify (5) _____,

subspecies, or varieties. Many animals rely on their own methods of naming, using (6) _____ to refer

to different organisms. The term "species" is a fundamental (7) _____ unit of biological

classification, and one of the many ways that biologists define "species" is the (8) _____ Species

Concept, which is based on the ability of a group of organisms to breed in nature and produce fully

(9) _____ offspring. There are several problems with this definition, including the exclusion of

organisms that reproduce (10) _____, such as any of the prokaryotes, and organisms of different

species that produce (11) _____ and fit offspring. Androdioecous species also pose a problem: they

are composed of only males and (12) _____ (produce both sperm and eggs). (13) _____

species consist only of females, and their eggs begin development after being mechanically

(14) _____ by male sperm of another species. (15) _____ is a principal advantage of sexual

reproduction, the most prevalent type of reproduction in the biological world. This is supported by genetic

studies of water fleas, since the asexually reproducing fleas experienced higher levels of (16) _____

in their mitochondrial protein-encoding genes than fleas that reproduced sexually.

Matching

For each of the following concepts, choose the most appropriate definition from the list below.

17. _____ Biological Species Concept

    A.   A group of organisms that share a distinct ecological niche

18. _____ Ecological Species Concept

    B.   A group of organisms that share a unique evolutionary ancestry

19. _____ Phylogenetic Species Concept

    C.   A group of organisms that interbreed to produce fully fertile offspring

True/False

Mark if the statement is true (T) or false (F). If the statement is false, justify your answer in the lines below each statement.

20. _____ Bacteria reproduce asexually and so are not given species names.

_____

_____

21. _____ Gynogenetic organisms do not reproduce sexually.

_____

_____

22. _____ Zebras and horses cannot interbreed.

_____

_____

Short Answer

23. Explain what is meant by the term "hybridization."

_____

_____

24. Describe what is meant by hybrid vigour.

_____

_____

19.3 One Size Does Not Fit All [pp. 444-446]
19.4 Gene Flow: Four Examples [pp. 446-448]

Section Review (Fill-in-the-Blanks)

No single definition of species satisfies all biologists or applies to all (25) _____; this is not surprising

as organisms are the product of (26) _____, a very dynamic process. The Biological Species Concept

assumes an unchanging or (27) _____ world in which gene (28) _____ is thought to be the

"glue" that holds members of a species together, making them a(n) (29) _____ group. This concept also

assumes that members of a species are reproductively (30) _____ from members of other species,

making each species genetically (31) _____ from each other and they cannot interbreed. Although gene

(32) _____ is assumed to explain the genetic cohesiveness of members of the same species, for a

species with widely but sparsely distributed populations, a(n) (33) _____ force may not explain its

distribution. The use of (34) _____ technology has assisted in providing information to explain

(35) _____ patterns and (36) _____ differences. An alternate approach to defining a species is

based on the (37) _____ Species Concept of the 1800s, which identifies organisms of the same species

based on shared (38) _____ traits. This approach has practical application, especially for naturalists

working in the field and paleontologists identifying (39) _____ species.

Matching

Match the organism with the best proposed explanation for its distribution.

40.	_____	*Balea perversa*	A.	Restricted distribution due to limited areas of habitat availability
41.	_____	*Mus musculus*	B.	Distribution explained by bird migratory pathways due to its ability to hitchhike on these birds
42.	_____	Frosted glass whiskers (lichen)	C.	Pine tree plantation provided forest habitat that mixed previously isolated populations
43.	_____	*Rattus norvegicus*	D.	Continuous distribution as a result of wide availability of human-created habitats
44.	_____	Eurasian red squirrels	E.	Distribution due to social behaviour; no interbreeding when males introduced to population but increased gene flow when females introduced

Short Answer

45. Explain how distribution can affect gene flow of a species.

_____

_____

46. Explain how social behaviour can influence gene flow of a species.

_____

_____

47. Explain how the gene flow of one species may be dependent upon another.

_____

_____

19.5 Geographic Variation [pp. 448–449]

Section Review (Fill-in-the-Blanks)

When there is genetic or (48) _____ variation between different populations of a species, each

populations is referred to as a(n) (49) _____, race, or breed or, in the case of plants, a(n)

(50) _____ or variant. Members of different subspecies may interbreed when their distributions

(51) _____, with the resulting offspring generally having a phenotype that is (52) _____

between the parents. Species with geographic distributions in which (53) _____ _____ can

occur between adjacent populations, due to interbreeding, but not between distant populations are called

(54) _____ species. Other species that occupy a wide geographic range and show gradual and

continuous genetic and phenotypic variation in a trait, known as a(n) (55) _____, may result in

(56) _____ populations at either end of the distribution.

57. Explain how a particular type of geography gives rise to a ring species.

_____

_____

58. Explain how a particular type of geography gives rise to clinal variation.

_____

_____

59. Why are rat snakes considered to exist as subspecies?

_____

_____

19.6 Reproductive Isolation [pp. 450–452]

Section Review (Fill-in-the-Blanks)

(60) _____ _____ mechanisms are biological characteristics that prevent the gene pools of

two sympatric species from mixing. This can be accomplished in two basic ways: (61) _____

isolating mechanisms prevent the fusion of gametes and the production of a zygote, whereas

(62) _____ isolating mechanisms operate after fertilization has occurred. There are at least

(63) _____ mechanisms that can prevent fertilization. When the sperm of one species does fertilize

an egg of another species, the offspring of such a mating, that is, the (64) _____ hybrids, may have

reduced fitness compared with (65) _____ offspring (parents from the same species). There are three

mechanisms that can result in postzygotic isolation.

Complete the Table

66. Fill in the blanks with the proper term or description associated with reproductive barriers.

Reproductive Barrier	Mechanism	Description
A.	Prezygotic	Individuals occupy different habitats.
B.	Postzygotic	Hybrid offspring do not make functional gametes
Mechanical isolation	Prezygotic	C.
Hybrid breakdown	D.	E.
F.	Postzygotic	Abnormal embryonic development
Behavioural isolation	G.	H.
I.	J.	Incompatibility between gametes of different species
Temporal isolation	K.	L.

True/False

Mark if the statement is true (T) or false (F). If the statement is false, justify your answer in the lines below each statement.

67. _____ Sympatric species are the product of interspecific matings.

_____

_____

68. _____ Song birds of different species are reproductively isolated by behavioural isolation.

_____

_____

69. _____ The zero fitness of mules is the result of hybrid inviability.

_____

_____

70. _____ *Pinus radiata* and *P. muricata* do not interbreed even though they are sympatric species due to temporal isolation.

_____

_____

Short Answer

71. Provide an explanation for the evolution of species-specific courtship displays.

_____

_____

72. Provide a molecular explanation of how gametic isolation occurs.

_____

_____

73. Provide an explanation of how mechanical isolation would be accomplished by plants.

_____

_____

19.7 Geography of Speciation [pp. 452–457]
19.8 Genetic Mechanisms of Speciation [pp. 457–461]
19.9 Back to the Species Concept in Biology [pp. 461–462]

Section Review (Fill-in-the-Blanks)

If a population is subdivided by a physical barrier to gene flow, speciation may occur: this is called

(74) _____ speciation. Sometimes the barrier may subsequently be removed, allowing

(75) _____ contact. If the evolution of prezygotic isolating mechanisms is not complete, individuals

from the two populations may interbreed in (76) _____ zones, producing fertile offspring. If the hybrid

offspring have lowered fitness, selection will favour individuals that mate only with members of their own

species, a phenomenon known as (77) _____. (78) _____ speciation occurs when a species is

distributed across a discontinuity in environmental conditions so that natural selection favours different

(79) _____ on either side of the discontinuity, which limits gene flow. (80) _____ speciation

occurs among individuals of a continuously distributed population. Extensive studies with the apple maggot, a

possible example of this type of speciation, point to genetic changes yielding a switch in preferred

(81) _____ plant species and, thus, reproductive isolation. When this kind of isolation results in the

development of a subspecies, the subspecies is called a(n) (82) _____ race. Geographic isolation results

in the loss of gene (83) _____, which, in turn, allows allopatric populations to accumulate

(84) _____ differences; these may result in postzygotic reproductive isolation upon secondary

(85) _____. The genetic basis for postzygotic isolating mechanisms may be as simple as the two

alterations that cause hybrid (86) _____ through the development of lethal tumours in the hybrid

offspring of swordtails and platys aquarium fish; in other cases, many more genes are involved. When hybrid

offspring instead have reduced fitness, natural selection may then (87) _____ the evolution of pre-

zygotic isolating mechanisms. As with postzygotic mechanisms, these mechanisms may also have a simple

genetic basis, as in the case of the single mutation that causes the (88) _____ isolation of oppositely

coiled snails. Reproductive isolation among sympatric populations can result from changes in the numbers of

sets of chromosomes, a phenomenon more common in (89) _____ than in animals and is referred to

as (90) _____. When an error in mitosis (in the germ line) or (91) _____ occurs within one

or more individuals of the same species such that gametes are unreduced, this is called (92) _____.

Unreduced gametes ($2n$) may fuse in a self-fertilizing plant or between two plants of the same species,

producing tetraploid offspring, which can reproduce by either self-pollination or by breeding with other

(93) _____. Speciation may result because tetraploids are (94) _____ isolated from the original

diploid population as a result of differences in chromosome numbers; that is, hybridization would be result in

(95) _____ triploid individuals. Speciation resulting from (96) _____ occurs when two closely

related species hybridize. Although the two sets of parental chromosomes are unable to pair in meiosis,

nondisjunction during mitosis of germ-line cells will (97) _____ the chromosome number, giving $4n$

germ cells, which can be reduced during meiosis to give viable (98) _____ or $2n$ gametes. These can

fuse by self-pollination or with another diploid gamete; either process gives rise to (99) _____ or $4n$

offspring and can yield a new (100) _____ within a single generation, without geographic isolation.

Building Vocabulary

Using the definitions of the prefixes below, assign the appropriate prefix to each suffix:

Prefix	Meaning
allo-	different
auto-	self
para-	beside
sym-	together

	Prefix	Suffix	Definition
101.	_____	-patric	A type of speciation that results from a sudden discontinuity in environmental condition
102.	_____	-polyploidy	Chromosome duplication within a species from the production of unreduced gametes; it may lead to speciation
103.	_____	-polyploidy	Hybrid offspring become polyploid; it may lead to speciation
104.	_____	-patric	A type of speciation that occurs within one continuously distributed population
105.	_____	-patric	Speciation that requires geographic isolation of subpopulations

True/False

Mark if the statement is true (T) or false (F). If the statement is false, justify your answer in the lines below each statement.

106. _____ Natural selection selects for prezygotic reproductive isolation mechanisms in allopatric populations.

_____

_____

107. _____ In the case of behavioural isolation, individuals can often successfully interbreed in captivity, producing viable and fertile offspring.

_____

_____

Short Answer

108. Provide an explanation of how structural alterations of chromosomes can give rise to a new species.

_____

_____

109. Define a species cluster.

_____

_____

110. Explain why an organism that is 4*n* is reproductively isolated from its 2*n* parent species.

_____

_____

SELF-TEST

1. If two populations can and do interbreed in nature and produce fully fertile offspring, what species concept would they exemplify? [p. 443]

    a. the Biological Species Concept
    b. the Morphological Species Concept
    c. the Phylogenetic Species Concept
    d. the Ecological Species Concept

2. Which species concept relies mainly on visible anatomical characters to define species? [p. 446]

    a. the Biological Species Concept
    b. the Morphological Species Concept
    c. the Phylogenetic Species Concept
    d. the Ecological Species Concept

3. Which term refers to the local variants of an animal species that interbreed where their distributions overlap? [p. 448]

    a. cultivars
    b. clines
    c. subspecies
    d. clusters

4. What do traits that vary along an environmental gradient represent? [p. 449]

    a. a cline
    b. a hybrid zone
    c. a reproductive isolating mechanism
    d. a subspecies

5. How have elaborate courtship displays of many animal species evolved? [pp. 450–451]

    a. as mechanical isolating mechanisms
    b. as ecological isolating mechanisms
    c. as behavioural isolating mechanisms
    d. as temporal isolating mechanisms

6. In some cases, the genitalia of closely related insect species do not fit and, thus, prevent successful mating. What is this an example of? [p. 451]

    a. behavioural isolation
    b. ecological isolation
    c. hybrid inviability
    d. mechanical isolation

7. Mules, the hybrid offspring of horses and donkeys, are sterile. What is this the result of? [p. 452]

    a. a postzygotic isolating mechanism
    b. a prezygotic isolating mechanism
    c. allopolyploidy
    d. clinal variation

8. Suppose that an earthquake causes the course of a river to change and separates a subpopulation of mammals from the main body of the population. Over time, this isolated population accumulates enough genetic variation to be considered a new species. What is this an example of? [pp. 452]

    a. allopatric speciation
    b. autopolyploidy
    c. parapatric speciation
    d. sympatric speciation

9. What type of speciation is associated with polyploidy? [pp. 457–458]

    a. allopatric

    b. nongenetic

    c. parapatric

    d. sympatric

10. Which statement is false? [p. 458]

    a. Autopolyploidy is common in animals.

    b. Chromosomal rearrangements may foster speciation.

    c. Speciation may occur between adjacent populations.

    d. Sympatric speciation may occur within a continuously distributed population.

11. Which of the following provides the greatest opportunity for gene flow within a species? [pp. 444]

    a. diverse habitat availability

    b. formation of a geographic barrier that separates individuals of a population

    c. distant populations of a ring species

    d. continuous distribution of conspecifics

12. Which of the following is NOT a synonym for subspecies? [pp. 448–449]

    a. race

    b. cline

    c. variant

    d. cultivar

13. Which term refers to a species that spreads through an ecologically varying region surrounding an uninhabitable zone with the accumulation of habitat-specific traits among the different populations but where the overlapping populations can breed and give fertile, fully viable, hybrid offspring? [pp. 449]

    a. cline species

    b. race species

    c. ring species

    d. species cluster

14. Which term describes a trait that exhibits a gradual and continuous variation over a large, environmentally diverse region? [p. 449]

    a. cline

    b. race

    c. ring

    d. cluster

15. Which term refers to a species that spreads into isolated pockets, which then allows the evolution of behavioural differences that prevent the mating upon secondary contact even though the different individuals can breed and give fertile, fully viable, hybrid offspring in captivity? [p. 454]

    a. distinct species

    b. race species

    c. ring species

    d. cline species

16. Which statement is true? [pp. 459]

    a. Polyploidy is common in some animals and plants.

    b. Plant breeders use certain chemicals to create polyploidy plant species.

    c. Polyploidy is a temporary and harmful condition.

    d. Alloploidy can result in speciation only if the polyploidy individuals are geographically isolated from the parent species.

17. Which mechanism has been suggested as resulting in the evolution of humans and chimps from their recent common ancestors? [pp. 460–461]

    a. geographic isolation

    b. temporary polyploidy

    c. chromosomal alterations

    d. mutations

18. Which statement is true? [pp. 460]

   a. Chromosomal alterations can be visualized with certain dyes.

   b. Chromosomal alterations can only be identified by DNA sequence analysis.

   c. Unless chromosomal inversions include the centromeric region, they will not have an identifiable effect on the organism.

   d. The degree of genetic divergence between two species is directly related to the phenotypic differences between those species.

19. Which statement is true? [pp. 458–459]

   a. Sterile autopolyploids can be more robust compared to their diploid parents.

   b. Sterile allopolyploids can have a higher relative fitness than their diploid parents.

   c. Polyploid crop plants are rare.

   d. The wheat strain commonly used for bread making was created by hybridization and autopolyploidy possibly thousands of years ago.

20. Which statement does NOT accurately describe the process of speciation? [p. 456, 458]

   a. It is a highly dynamic process.

   b. It requires geographic isolation and adaptation to differing environments.

   c. It can happen in a single generation.

   d. It results in the formation of a new species.

INTEGRATING AND APPLYING KEY CONCEPTS

1. Most of the small number of "speciation genes" that have been identified so far affect postzygotic reproductive isolating mechanisms. Speculate on why this might be so and why it may be more difficult to identify genes that contribute to the evolution of prezygotic reproductive isolating mechanisms.

2. Studies of fruit flies in Hawaii indicate that flies from older islands in the Hawaiian archipelago colonized the young island of Hawaii at least 19 different times. Describe the mechanisms of speciation that would have been involved and speculate on how sexual selection could have hastened the evolution of prezygotic isolating mechanism and, hence, speciation.

3. If you observed organisms in a region surrounding an uninhabitable zone and they seemed to be morphologically similar but not identical, how would you determine if these were all subspecies of a ring species or had evolved to be separate species?

20 Bacteria and Archaea

TOPIC MAP

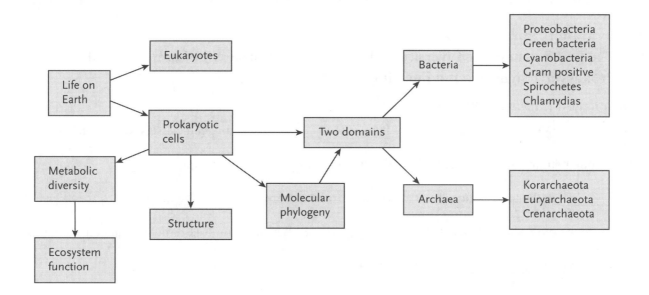

LEARNING OUTCOMES AND STUDY STRATEGIES

By the end of this chapter, you should be able to

- Describe the structure of prokaryotic cells and explain how Archaea and Bacteria are identified and how they differ structurally and metabolically

- Identify the four types of metabolism in Bacteria and Archaea and the different types of oxygen requirements

- Understand why prokaryotes are critical to biogeochemical cycling, using the nitrogen cycle as an example

- Explain how bacteria can cause illness, including through formation of biofilms, and how they may resist the effects of antibiotics

- Provide examples of the different types of lineages of the Bacteria and Archaea and describe the unique aspects or a few different types of members of each

Study strategies for this chapter:

- This chapter is fairly simple: pay particular attention to the various examples of the diversity of these organisms. There are some new terms to remember; keep a list of these new terms and their definitions.

- Pay attention to the figures, figure legends, and tables.
- As always, go through one section of the textbook at a time and then work through the companion section of the study guide.
- When you are done, try devising your own topic map and expanding upon the one above.

INTERACTIVE EXERCISES

Why It Matters [pp. 465–466]
20.1 The Full Extent of the Diversity of Bacteria and Archaea Is Unknown [p. 466]
20.2 Prokaryotic Structure and Function [pp. 466–475]

Section Review (Fill-in-the-Blanks)

Escherichia coli O157:H7, occurs in the GI tract of (1) _____ and can cause severe disease in

humans; other strains of this bacterium are essential to human health, producing (2) _____

_____ in the human gut. The Bacteria and Archaea represent two of the three (3) _____ of

life and are the most abundant and (4) _____ life forms on Earth. It is estimated that only 1% has

actually been (5) _____ in the lab. Prokaryotic cells generally have a single, (6) _____

chromosome, packaged into a(n) (7) _____. They may also possess a smaller, circular DNA

molecule called a(n) (8) _____, which replicates independently of the chromosome and may be

spread to other cells by (9) _____ gene transfer. This is a common cause of the spread of antibiotic

(10) _____. Outside the plasma membrane is the (11) _____ _____, which, in

bacteria, is the basis for differential staining using the (12) _____ stain. (13) _____ positive

and negative bacteria both have a cell wall of (14) _____; this layer is relatively thick in

(15) _____-_____ bacteria. In (16) _____-_____ bacteria it occurs as a thin

layer and is surrounded by a(n) (17) _____ membrane that contains the unique lipid LPS. Many

bacteria and archaea are surrounded by a protective polysaccharide layer called the (18) _____.

Prokaryotic organisms are divided into four metabolic types based on their source of (19) _____ and

carbon. Two types are also seen among the eukaryotes: some are (20) _____, like animals, and

others, like plants, are (21) _____. Two other types are unique: (22) _____ oxidize inorganic

substances for energy and use CO_2 as their carbon source, while (23) _____ obtain energy from

photosynthesis but use organic chemicals as their carbon source. Prokaryotes are also diverse in their

(24) _____ or tolerance for oxygen; some perform aerobic (25) _____, but others may

perform anaerobic (26) _____, and still others may perform various types of (27) _____

reactions. Because of the metabolic diversity, prokaryotes are critical for (28) _____ cycling. For

example, the cellular nitrogen in all life forms ultimately depends upon the nitrogen (29) _____

reactions of organisms such as *Rhizobium*, combined with the ability of others to oxidize (30) _____

to nitrate, a process called nitrification. Bacteria and archaea normally reproduce asexually by

(31) _____ fission and, under favourable conditions, can grow extremely rapidly. Although essential

to the function of any ecosystem, a small number are (32) _____, causing disease through the

production of secreted (33) _____ or the LPS-associated (34) _____.

Matching

Match each of the following terms with its correct definition or descriptor.

35. _____	Biofilm	A.	DNA molecules that may be spread among bacterial cells through sex pili
36. _____	Plasmid	B.	A slimy, polysaccharide substance critical to biofilm formation
37. _____	Nucleoid	C.	Bacterial pili that conduct electricity
38. _____	Pilus	D.	Contains the condensed bacterial and archaeal chromosome
39. _____	Flagella	E.	A rigid surface protein structure that may facilitate attachment of bacteria and archaea
40. _____	Capsule	F.	The conversion of atmospheric nitrogen to ammonia
41. _____	EPS	G.	Helical surface protein structures that move by rotation, providing motility to the prokaryotic cell
42. _____	Nitrogen fixation	H.	A complex aggregation of microorganisms attached to a solid surface
43. _____	Nitrification	I.	An extracellular polysaccharide layer that may protect against dessication
44. _____	Coccus	J.	Spherical prokaryotic cell
45. _____	Gram positive	K.	An LPS-containing feature of Gram-negative bacteria

46. ____ Nanowires

47. ____ Peptidoglycan

48. ____ Outer membrane

49. ____ Endotoxin

50. ____ Metagenomics

51. ____ Lithotrophs

L. Bacterial types that stain purple with the Gram staining technique and have a thick wall of peptidoglycan

M. A DNA technology that provides insight into the uncultured bacteria and archaea

N. Bacteria and archaea that derive their energy from inorganic chemicals

O. The rigid cell wall layer of bacteria

P. Bacterial and archaeal oxidation of ammonia to nitrate

Q. The toxic component of the Gram-negative bacterial cell wall

Complete the Table

52. Complete the following table with the appropriate name or description of the metabolic process in prokaryotes.

Metabolic Process	Description
A.	Obtain energy by oxidizing inorganic substances and use CO_2 as their carbon source
Heterotroph	B.
Photoautotrophs	C.
D.	Use light as their energy source and organic chemicals as their carbon source
E.	Use oxygen when present; otherwise produce energy anaerobically
F.	Do not require oxygen and cannot tolerate its presence
Obligate aerobes	G.

True/False

Mark if the statement is true (T) or false (F). If the statement is false, justify your answer in the lines below each statement.

53. _____ Botulin, the ingredient in *Botox*, is a potent bacterial exotoxin.

_____

_____

54. _____ Collectively, the Bacteria and Archaea outweigh all of the animals on Earth.

_____

_____

55. _____ Gram-negative bacteria stain purple with the Gram staining technique and have a thin wall of peptidoglycan and an outer membrane.

_____

_____

56. _____ The genetic variation in Bacteria and Archaea is, in part, the product of sexual reproduction.

_____

_____

57. _____ Some bacteria possess membrane-bound, energy-generating organelles.

_____

_____

Short Answer

58. What are some of the reasons for the fact that Bacteria and Archaea are so much more abundant and metabolically diverse than the eukaryotes?

_____

_____

59. What function does the Gram-negative outer membrane serve?

_____

_____

60. Identify some of the beneficial as well as detrimental roles of biofilms.

_____

_____

61. Identify some of the mechanisms by which bacteria may become resistant to the effects of antibiotics.

_____

_____

62. What is anaerobic respiration?

_____

_____

Labelling

63. Label the structures in the bacterial cell below.

A. _____   E. _____

B. _____   F. _____

C. _____   G. _____

D. _____   H. _____

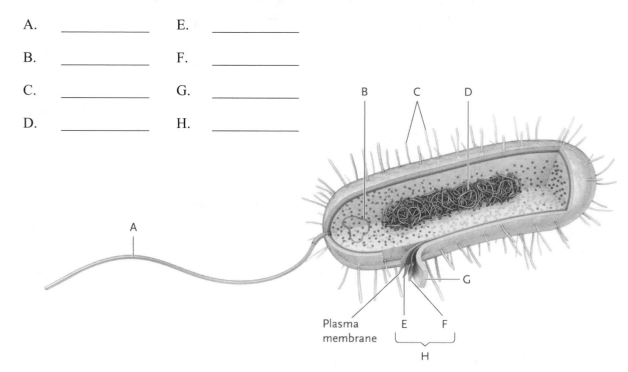

20.3 The Domain Bacteria [pp. 476–479]
20.4 The Domain Archaea [pp. 479–482]

Section Review (Fill-in-the-Blanks)

Based on molecular phylogeny, the bacteria are currently divided into more than a dozen evolutionary

(64) _____ . One of the most diverse, the (65) _____ , are thought to have evolved from a

purple (66) _____ ancestor. This branch includes chemoorganotrophs, such as *E. coli*, some of which

are human or plant (67) _____ . The group also contains photosynthetic bacteria that may be

photoautotrophs or (68) _____ ; the (69) _____ _____ are similar to the purples in that they may be photoautotrophs or (70) _____, and do not produce oxygen during photosynthesis. The remaining photosynthetic bacteria are in a third branch, the (71) _____. They ancestor to the chloroplast was probably from this group and, like the eukaryotic organelle, they release (72) _____ as a photosynthetic by-product. The (73) _____-_____ bacteria is a large group that includes the sometimes pathogenic *Streptococcus* and the fermentative (74) _____ bacteria used to make yogurt. The chlamydias are unusual because they lack (75) _____ in their cell wall and are all obligate intracellular (76) _____ of animals. The (77) _____ contain spiral-shaped bacteria, including *Treponema pallidum,* the causative agent of syphilis. Far less is known about the Archaea, in part because most have not been (78) _____. Evidence indicates they share some characteristics with bacteria, others with (79) _____, and some, such as certain membrane (80) _____, are unique. Based on (81) _____ studies, the Archaea are classified into three evolutionary lineages, including one, the (82) _____, has no cultured representatives. The (83) _____ include methanogens, extreme (84) _____ (salt-loving), and some extreme (85) _____. Most of the known extreme (86) _____ are, however, found in the third major group, the (87) _____. Strangely, the remaining members of this group are cold-loving (88) _____.

Matching

Match each of the following terms with its correct definition or descriptor.

89. ____	Extremophile		A.	Archaea that comprise the plankton in cool marine waters, for example
90. ____	Mesophile		B.	Archaea that live in high-temperature environments
91. ____	Methanogens		C.	Psychrophiles, thermophiles, and halophiles would all be examples
92. ____	Halophiles		D.	Archaea that live in high-salt environments
93. ____	Thermophiles		E.	Archaea that live in cold environments
94. ____	Psychrophiles		F.	Archaea associated with low oxygen environments such as the rumen of cows and sheep and the large intestine of dogs and humans

True/False

Mark if the statement is true (T) or false (F). If the statement is false, justify your answer in the lines below each statement.

95. _____ Green bacteria perform the same type of photosynthesis as green plants and are believed to be the ancestor of the chloroplast.

_____

_____

96. _____ *Treponema pallidum* is a coccus-shaped, Gram-positive bacterium that causes strep throat.

_____

_____

97. _____ The ability of certain Archaea to survive boiling in harsh detergents is at least partly due to the unique structures of their membrane lipids.

_____

_____

98. _____ The chemoheterotrophic proteobacteria are believed to have evolved from a photosynthetic predecessor through the loss of photosynthetic ability.

_____

_____

99. _____ The ancestors of the eukaryotic mitochondrion and chloroplast are believed to have been ancient proteobacteria.

_____

_____

Short Answer

100. Discuss how the bacteria and archaea are classified.

_____

_____

101. Compare the myxobacteria with the mycoplasmas.

_____

_____

1. Which is NOT an explanation for why we have only identified ~ 1% of the Bacteria and Archaea? [p. 466]

   a. Most of them are too dangerous to try to isolate.

   b. Most of them grow in inaccessible places.

   c. Most of them cannot yet be cultured in the lab.

   d. Many require extreme conditions to grow.

2. Which statement is false? [p. 466]

   a. The total biomass on Earth of the bacteria and archaea exceeds that of the animals.

   b. An average human contains more bacterial cells than human cells.

   c. Prokaryotic cells appeared on Earth shortly before the eukaryotes.

   d. The average prokaryotic cell measures only 1 to 2 μm.

3. Which is absent in Bacteria and Archaea? [pp. 467–468]

   a. a cytoskeleton

   b. a cell wall

   c. ribosomes

   d. a nucleus

4. Which statement is false regarding bacterial plasmids? [p. 468]

   a. They are circular DNA molecules.

   b. They can be transferred from one cell to another through pili.

   c. They generally contain essential genes for things like antibiotic resistance.

   d. They provide a means of horizontal gene transfer.

5. Which statement about Gram-negative bacteria is false? [p.469]

   a. They have a thin peptidoglycan layer.

   b. Their cell walls include an outer membrane.

   c. They are more resistant to penicillin than Gram-positive bacteria.

   d. They stain purple with the Gram staining technique.

6. Which function or property is NOT associated with capsules? [p. 470]

   a. protection against dessication

   b. movement along a surface

   c. protection against viruses

   d. virulence

7. Which statement about eukaryotic and prokaryotic flagella is true? [p. 470]

   a. Their structure and pattern of movement differs.

   b. Their structure differs but their pattern of movement is the same.

   c. The structure is the same but their pattern of movement differs.

8. Which is NOT associated with prokaryotic pili? [p. 470]

   a. attachment to other prokaryotes

   b. attachment to surfaces

   c. conduction of electricity

   d. active movement through liquids

9. Which of the following types of bacteria use inorganic chemicals as their energy source and CO_2 as their carbon source? [p. 471]

   a. lithotrophs

   b. chemoheterotrophs

   c. photoautotrophs

   d. photoheterotrophs

10. Which of the following types of bacteria obtain energy from sunlight and use organic chemicals as their carbon source? [p. 471]

    a. chemoautotrophs

    b. chemoheterotrophs

    c. photoautotrophs

    d. photoheterotrophs

11. Which can produce energy with and without oxygen? [pp. 471–472]

    a. facultative anaerobes
    b. obligate aerobes
    c. obligate anaerobes
    d. lithotrophs

12. Which statement about nitrogen fixation is true? [p. 472]

    a. It can be done by certain bacteria and certain eukaryotes.
    b. It is the conversion of ammonium to nitrate.
    c. It is an essential part of biogeochemical cycling.
    d. It is also called nitrification.

13. Which does NOT contribute to the tremendous genetic variability in bacteria and archaea compared to the eukaryotes? [pp. 472–473]

    a. short generation times
    b. a relatively high mutation rate
    c. their ability to colonize any niche that supports life
    d. horizontal gene transfer

14. Which is associated with pathogenesis? [p. 473]

    a. the bacterial plasma membrane
    b. some species of bacteria and archaea
    c. some types of Gram-negative LPS
    d. the proteins of some bacterial flagella

15. Which does NOT cause bacteria to become antibiotic resistant? [pp. 473–474]

    a. horizontal transfer of plasmids
    b. routine use of antibiotics
    c. enzymatic inactivation
    d. mutation

16. Which statement about biofilms is false? [pp. 474–475]

    a. Biofilm infections typically respond to antibiotic treatment.
    b. They require the production of an extracellular polymeric substance.

    c. They are the predominant form of prokaryotic growth in nature.
    d. They generally form from a complex assortment of different microbes.

17. Which is NOT a member of the proteobacteria? [pp. 476–477]

    a. *Lactobacillus*
    b. *E. coli*
    c. the photosynthetic purple bacteria
    d. the sometimes multicellular *Myxobacteria*

18. Which statement about the ancestor to the chloroplast is true? [pp. 477–478]

    a. They likely evolved from early cyanobacteria.
    b. They likely evolved from early purple photoautotrophs.
    c. They likely evolved from early green photoautotrophs.
    d. They likely evolved from an early proteobacterium.

19. Which statement about spirochetes is false? [p. 479]

    a. They may cause human disease.
    b. They are often nonpathogenic components of the human mouth.
    c. They may be symbiotic partners with fungi in lichens.
    d. They are spiral shaped.

20. Which has been identified solely on the basis of DNA isolated from the environment? [p. 481]

    a. the Crenarchaeota
    b. the Korarchaeota
    c. the Green bacteria
    d. the Euryarchaeota

21. Which type of archaeon is associated with high-salt environments? [pp. 481–482]

    a. psychrophiles
    b. halophiles
    c. thermophiles
    d. mesophiles

22. Which type of archaeon is associated with methane production? [p. 481]

    a. psychrophiles
    b. halophiles
    c. some of the Crenarchaeota
    d. some of the Euryarchaeota

23. Which type of archaeon is associated with the plankton of cool marine waters? [p. 482]

    a. psychrophiles
    b. halophiles
    c. some of the Crenarchaeota
    d. some of the Euryarchaeota

INTEGRATING AND APPLYING KEY CONCEPTS

1. As you learned, the chlamydias are all obligate intracellular parasites of animals. They also have the smallest genomes of any other known life form. Can you draw a connection between these two facts?

2. Since the purple and green photosynthetic bacteria do not produce oxygen as a by-product, unlike the cyanobacteria, speculate on where they might be isolated compared with the cyanobacteria.

3. Why would penicillins be able to kill bacteria such as *Streptococcus pneumoniae* but not kill the host cells? Why might organisms in nature, such as the fungus *Penicillium*, produce such chemicals?

21 Viruses, Viroids, and Prions: Infectious Biological Particles

TOPIC MAP

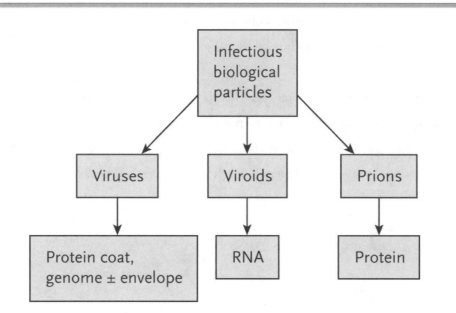

LEARNING OUTCOMES AND STUDY STRATEGIES

By the end of this chapter, you should be able to

- Describe the structure of viruses and their life cycles, giving examples
- Describe the differences between certain bacteriophages and animal and plant viruses
- Describe the structure and infectious processes of viroids and prions
- Understand the challenges of treating viral infections

Study strategies for this chapter

- This chapter is fairly simple: pay particular attention to the similarities and differences between the viruses of the different host types. There are some new terms to remember, particularly those associated with the different types of viral life cycle.
- Pay attention to the figures: they are quite helpful in depicting the various viral morphologies and life cycle processes.

- Compare the viroids and prions to the viruses.
- As always, go through one section of the textbook at a time and then work through the companion section of the study guide.
- Finally, try devising your own topic map after completing the chapter.

INTERACTIVE EXERCISES

Why It Matters [pp. 484–485]
21.1 What Is a Virus? Characteristics of Viruses [pp. 485–487]
21.2 Viruses Infect Bacterial, Animal, and Plant Cells by Similar Pathways [pp. 487–492]

Section Review (Fill-in-the-Blanks)

Free virus particles consist of one or more (1) _____ _____ molecules, surrounded by a

protein coat called a(n) (2) _____. In some viruses, the protein coat is surrounded by a(n)

(3) _____ that is derived from the host cell's membrane. They are not cells and most biologists do

not consider them (4) _____. Their genome may be either (5) _____ or (6) _____,

(7) _____-stranded or (8) _____-stranded. Viruses infect bacteria, animals, and plants:

which type of host is recognized and infected depends upon the specific (9) _____ proteins on the

(10) _____ of infectious viruses. As with bacteria and archaea, the vast majority of viruses have not

been (11) _____. However, it appears that they are vital components of (12) _____.

Regardless of the host cell, viral infection ultimately follows a similar (13) _____, beginning when

the virus (14) _____ the cell. Viruses are replicated when their genome directs the host's cellular

(15) _____ to synthesize more (16) _____ of the same kind. Phages are viruses that infect

(17) _____. Those that kill their host after each cycle of infection are referred to as

(18) _____, whereas (19) _____ phages enter an inactive phase after infection, being passed

on to multiple generations of (20) _____ cells before becoming active, replicating, and

(21) _____ the host. Animal viruses exhibit a similar inactive period in their host, a period called the

(22) _____ phase.

Matching

Match each of the following terms with its correct definition.

23. _____ Capsid

A. Viruses that have a membrane acquired from the host

24. _____ Helical viruses

B. The part of a complex virus such as lambda that contains the viral chromosome

25. _____ Polyhedral viruses

C. Bacteriophage equivalent to a latent phase in animal viruses

26. _____ Enveloped viruses

D. A member of the *Coronaviridae* family

27. _____ T-even phage

E. Protein coat of a virus

28. _____ Virus head

F. A virus made of triangular units joined together like a soccer ball

29. _____ Virus tail

G. An animal virus that remains in certain host cells for the life of the individual

30. _____ Virions

H. Cytoplasmic connections between plant cells

31. _____ Prophage

I. Critical to phage entry into, and exit from, host cells

32. _____ Lytic cycle

J. Bacteriophages that have a lysogenic phase

33. _____ Lysogenic cycle

K Viruses of complex morphology consisting of a DNA-containing head

34. _____ Plasmodesmata

L. The extracellular form of viruses

35. _____ Herpesvirus

M. Bacteriophages that always lyse their host cells

36. _____ Influenza virus

N. State of a bacteriophage when its genome is incorporated into the bacterial chromosome

37. _____ Virulent bacteriophages

O. Tobacco mosaic virus is an example

38. _____ Temperate bacteriophages

P. The part of a complex virus such as T4 that injects the viral chromosome into the host cell

39. _____ Lysozyme

Q. Ends with the rupture of the virus-infected host cell

True/False

Mark if the statement is true (T) or false (F). If the statement is false, justify your answer in the lines below each statement.

40. _____ Viruses are not living but can replicate and evolve.

_____

_____

41. _____ Viruses may effect nutrient cycling in some environments.

_____

_____

42. _____ The viral genome directs the synthesis of the viral envelope.

_____

_____

43. _____ Although viruses may leave their hosts through different mechanisms, they all enter the same way.

_____

_____

44. _____ A pandemic is an epidemic that spreads worldwide.

_____

_____

45. _____ Animal viruses may cause symptoms through the production of toxins.

_____

_____

Short Answer

46. Compare generalized transduction with specialized transduction.

_____

_____

47. Why are viruses considered vital components of ecosystems?

_____

_____

48. Compare and contrast bacteriophages T4 and λ.

_____

_____

49. What are some of the differences between animal and plant viruses?

_____

_____

Labelling

50. Label the various components of the complex polyhedral bacteriophage.

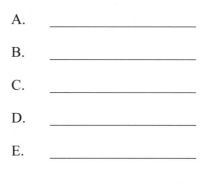

A. _____

B. _____

C. _____

D. _____

E. _____

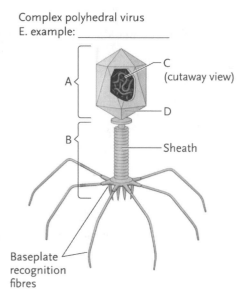

Complex polyhedral virus
E. example: _____

C
(cutaway view)

A

D

B

Sheath

Baseplate
recognition
fibres

21.3 It is Typically Difficult to Treat and Prevent Viral Infections [pp. 492–493]
21.4 Viruses May Have Evolved from Fragments of Cellular DNA or RNA [p. 493]

Section Review (Fill-in-the-Blanks)

Viruses cannot be treated with (51) _____ because they do not have the same structures as bacteria.

In fact, viral infections are difficult to treat because they are usually (52) _____ inside host cells and

they use host (53) _____ to replicate. Although most viral infections are just left to run their course,

some (54) _____ drugs have been developed for some of the more (55) _____ infections.

The (56) _____-_____ drug zanamavir is one example. For some viral diseases, efforts are

focused on prevention of infection, through the use of (57) _____. However, in the case of the

influenza virus, these are of limited use due to the fact that the multiple viral (58) _____ may reassemble in new combinations and to the high (59) _____ rate of the virus. Influenza virus and

(60) _____ are both examples of viruses that have evolved from viruses that previously infected

other (61) _____. Although it is clear that viruses do not share a common (62) _____, their

origins are not known. One theory suggests they evolved after the appearance of the first (63) _____

and that they arose from "escaped" (64) _____ _____ _____. Alternatively, it is

hypothesized they may predate the first (65) _____, and it has even been suggested that they may

have given rise to the eukaryotic (66) _____.

True/False

Mark if the statement is true (T) or false (F). If the statement is false, justify your answer in the lines below each statement.

67. _____ The high mortality rates of the 1918 pandemic strain of influenza were simply due to the lack of available vaccines.

_____

_____

68. _____ Certain antibiotics are effective against some viral infections.

_____

_____

Short Answer

69. What kind of virus has been suggested to have lead to the evolution of the eukaryotic nucleus?

_____

_____

70. Explain why a new "flu" vaccine is developed every year.

_____

_____

71. What are some of the causes of the evolution and spread of new human viruses?

_____

_____

21.5 Viroids and Prions Are Infective Agents Even Simpler in Structure than Viruses [pp. 494–495]

Section Review (Fill-in-the-Blanks)

Viroids are simpler than viruses and are small infectious pieces of single-stranded (72) _____. They

infect (73) _____ plants and cause diseases through an unknown mechanism. Prions are infectious

(74) _____ that infect animals and cause a group of diseases called (75) _____

_____, so named because of the spongy appearance of the brains of affected animals. Examples of

prion diseases include (76) _____, also known as mad cow disease; (77) _____ in sheep and

(78) _____-_____ _____, or CJD, in humans. Prions are misfolded proteins of a

normal protein of the brain; they are believed to cause disease by triggering the (79) _____ of the

normal protein, leading to abnormal (80) _____ functioning and apoptosis of infected

(81) _____.

Complete the Table

82. Complete the following table with the chemical composition of virus, viroids, and prions. Indicate
     whether the infectious agent possesses the particular polymer and if so, what is the nature of that
     material or, in the case of viruses, where in the particle is it found.

Infectious Particle	Nucleic Acid	Protein	Lipid
A. Virus			
B. Viroid			
C. Prion			

Short Answer

83. Explain the connection between scrapie, BSE, and variant CJD.

     _____

     _____

1. Which statement about The Spanish flu is NOT true? [pp. 484–485]

   a. It was responsible for a pandemic
   b. It was responsible for killing 1 in 20 people worldwide
   c. It was a virus that infected almost half the world's population in 1918
   d. It caused severe and often fatal gastro-intestinal illness throughout the world.

2. Which would not be associated with viruses? [pp. 485–486]

   a. ribosomes
   b. RNA chromosome
   c. double-stranded RNA chromosome
   d. multiple chromosomes

3. Which statement is true? [pp. 486–487]

   a. Although not living, viruses have their own evolutionary tree.
   b. The genome of an enveloped virus includes genes that direct the synthesis of the viral envelope.
   c. Some viruses are photosynthetic.
   d. The viral genome of enveloped viruses contains genes for membrane proteins.

4. How do viruses affect nutrient cycling in an environment? [pp. 486–487]

   a. Some are photosynthetic, using the energy from the sun to convert CO_2 to organic molecules.
   b. They are species-specific agents of mortality of prokaryotes, which are central to nutrient cycling in the environment.
   c. Some are capable of converting atmospheric nitrogen to organic nitrogen-containing molecules.
   d. They may cause certain animals to consume more food, resulting in higher production of CO_2.

5. Which describes the T-even bacteriophages? [pp. 488–489]

   a. They are temperate bacteriophages.
   b. They are virulent bacteriophages.
   c. They may perform generalized transduction.
   d. They are enveloped viruses.

6. Which is associated with the process of generalized transduction? [p. 489]

   a. It may result from infection with some lytic bacteriophages.
   b. It may result from infection with some lysogenic bacteriophages.
   c. It is a process where certain viruses can transfer genes from bacteria to animal cells.
   d. Certain T-even phages may perform generalized transduction.

7. Which describes bacteriophage lambda? [pp. 489–490]

   a. It is a virulent bacteriophage.
   b. It is a polyhedral virus.
   c. It may perform specialized transduction.
   d. It is an enveloped virus.

8. Which statement about herpesvirus is false? [p. 490]

   a. It is an enveloped virus.
   b. It is a latent virus.
   c. It is a virus that causes symptoms when it is released by rupturing the host cell plasma membrane.
   d. It is an enveloped virus that enters host cells by fusion with the plasma membrane.

9. Which statement about animal viruses is false? [p. 490]

 a. Viruses with an inactive phase are called "lysogenic" and incorporate their DNA into the host chromosome.

 b. Latent viruses may reside in the cytoplasm of the infected cell.

 c. Many viral infections are asymptomatic.

 d. Symptoms may arise when enveloped viruses are released at a rate that proves fatal for the host cell.

10. Which property is not associated with plant viruses? [p. 490]

 a. an envelope

 b. RNA chromosomes

 c. DNA chromosomes

 d. polyhedral morphology

11. Which does NOT explain the challenges of treating and preventing influenza virus? [p. 493]

 a. It has a high mutation rate and so can evolve into new strains.

 b. It has multiple chromosomes, which, in mixed infections, can randomly assort into new viral particles.

 c. No successful antiviral drugs have been developed because the virus largely remains hidden in host cells.

 d. It can change its protein coat, making it unrecognizable to the host's immune system.

12. Which is NOT associated with current theories on the evolution of viruses? [p. 493]

 a. They started as escaped fragments of eukaryotic and prokaryotic DNA and RNA.

 b. They may have evolved from the primordial gene pool before life evolved.

 c. They may have formed when nuclei escaped from their host cells.

 d. They have arisen on more than one occasion so do not all share a single ancestor.

13. Which description about viroids is NOT correct? [p. 494]

 a. They may be DNA or RNA molecules.

 b. They are double-stranded molecules.

 c. They are single-stranded RNA molecules.

 d. They cause host proteins to misfold.

14. Which is NOT involved in prion infections? [pp. 494–495]

 a. The prion protein enters by consumption of contaminated meat.

 b. vCJD arises rapidly after consumption of BSE-contaminated beef.

 c. The prion protein enters through contaminated surgical instruments.

 d. The prion protein enters through contaminated corneas in corneal transplants.

15. Which statement about prion diseases is true? [pp. 494–495]

 a. Scrapie is a disease seen in cannibal populations of New Guinea.

 b. Cattle with BSE likely acquired the disease from scrapie-affected sheep.

 c. CJD is a slowly progressing disease resulting from the consumption of beef contaminated with the BSE prion.

 d. Stanley Prusiner is famous for developing the first vaccine against prion diseases.

16. Which statement about "normal" prion proteins is true? [p. 495]

 a. They are essential for production of fibrils surrounding neurons.

 b. They are found in the membranes of nerves throughout the body.

 c. They are a normal part of the human brain.

INTEGRATING AND APPLYING KEY CONCEPTS

1. Provide an explanation for the fact that people who get cold sores will get them for the rest of their lives but only have occasional symptoms.

2. The primary reason for developing vaccines such as Gardasil, against human papilloma virus, are due to the fact that it mat progress in infected patients to cervical cancer. Suggest how this may occur.

3. Why do common antibiotics not work against viruses?

4. Why does the World Health Organization (WHO) determine the composition of a new flu vaccine each year, and why are the WHO and the world's governments worried about a possible flu pandemic?

22 Protists

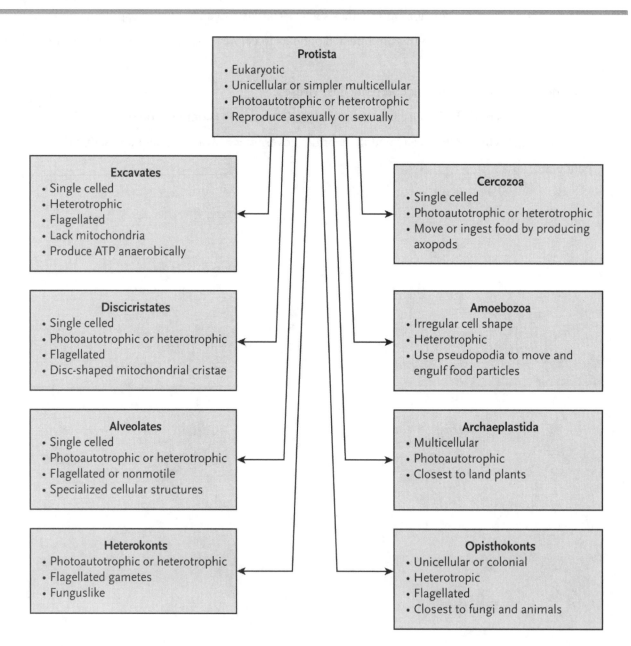

Protista
- Eukaryotic
- Unicellular or simpler multicellular
- Photoautotrophic or heterotrophic
- Reproduce asexually or sexually

Excavates
- Single celled
- Heterotrophic
- Flagellated
- Lack mitochondria
- Produce ATP anaerobically

Cercozoa
- Single celled
- Photoautotrophic or heterotrophic
- Move or ingest food by producing axopods

Discicristates
- Single celled
- Photoautotrophic or heterotrophic
- Flagellated
- Disc-shaped mitochondrial cristae

Amoebozoa
- Irregular cell shape
- Heterotrophic
- Use pseudopodia to move and engulf food particles

Alveolates
- Single celled
- Photoautotrophic or heterotrophic
- Flagellated or nonmotile
- Specialized cellular structures

Archaeplastida
- Multicellular
- Photoautotrophic
- Closest to land plants

Heterokonts
- Photoautotrophic or heterotrophic
- Flagellated gametes
- Funguslike

Opisthokonts
- Unicellular or colonial
- Heterotropic
- Flagellated
- Closest to fungi and animals

LEARNING OUTCOMES AND STUDY STRATEGIES

By the end of this chapter, you should be able to

- Understand how the mitochondria and chloroplasts evolved; it began with these organisms
- Identify what features distinguish the protists from the prokaryotes, fungi, animals, and plants and what features resemble these other groups
- Explain why the classification of the protists is so problematic
- Identify some of the protists that cause disease or blights
- Identify some of the other important groups: the brown algae with the kelp "forests," the green algae and their relationship with land plants, and the opisthokonts and their relationship with the animals and fungi
- Identify the very basic characteristics for the different groups

Study strategies for this chapter:

- There is a huge amount of new information and new names for organisms and structures. Do not worry too much about remembering all the details; the goal of this chapter is to understand what protists are, why they are important, and how they differ in their structure, metabolism, and reproduction.
- Keep track of the headings and subheadings as you go through the various protist groups. Look for figures or examples (e.g., of pathogens) that will help you remember something about that particular group. Pay particular attention to the derivation of the names for the various groups—these often have key meanings related to that group.
- As always, go through one section of the textbook at a time and then work through the companion section of the study guide.
- Use the Study Break sections of the textbook and the Review section of the textbook as well as this study guide section to help guide you on the level of detail.
- When you are finished, see if you can derive an alternative topic map to the one above.

INTERACTIVE EXERCISES

Why It Matters [pp. 498–499]
22.1 The Evolution of Protists Involved Endosymbiosis [p. 500]
22.2 Characteristics of Protists [pp. 500–501]
22.3 Protists' Diversity Is Reflected in Their Metabolism, Reproduction, Structure, and Habitat [pp. 501–503]

Section Review (Fill-in-the-Blanks)

"Beaver fever" is a water-borne infection caused by the protist (1) _____ _____, the most

common intestinal parasite in North America. Traditionally, protists are grouped together in the kingdom

(2) _____; however, this is for convenience only since the different lineages do not share a common

(3) _____. The protists are believed to have first appeared 1.5–2 billion years ago through the process of (4) _____. The (5) _____ arose through a single endosymbiotic event involving a free-living aerobic, heterotrophic prokaryote. Some protists are photosynthetic; however, the (6) _____ appears to have evolved through more complex (7) _____ events. Protists are eukaryotes and so share a number of characteristics with the other eukaryotic kingdoms, that is, the (8) _____, _____, and _____; however, they also have some striking differences. Unlike the (9) _____, they have a motile stage and their cell walls contain (10) _____, not chitin. Unlike plants, multicellular forms do not have (11) _____, _____, and _____, and do not retain embryos in parental tissue. Unlike animals, which are always multicellular, they are commonly (12) _____ and lack collagen, nerve cells, and a digestive tract. Metabolically, protists are aerobic and can live as heterotrophs or as (13) _____ or switch between the two. Protists live in aquatic or moist (14) _____ habitats or as parasites within (15) _____ organisms. Single-celled species can be highly complex, with a wide variety of complex (16) _____ structures and motile species move using (17) _____, cilia, or by amoeboid movement using (18) _____. Reproduction may be asexual by (19) _____ divisions or sexual, producing gametes by (20) _____.

Matching

Match each of the following terms with its correct definition.

21. _____	Pellicle	A.	Small photosynthetic protists that collectively live in ponds, lakes, and oceans
22. _____	Contractile vacuole	B.	Heterotrophic protists, bacteria, and small animals that live in ponds, lakes, and oceans
23. _____	Phytoplankton	C.	Catch-all term for all photosynthetic protists
24. _____	Zooplankton	D.	Most common intestinal parasite in North America
25. _____	Pseudopodia	E.	A membrane-bound organelle that helps a protist get rid of excess water
26. _____	*Giardia lamblia*	F.	A supportive layer of protein fibres under the plasma membrane
27. _____	Algae	G.	Cytoplasmic and cellular extensions of protists that help them move

Complete the Table

28. Complete the following table for the characteristics of protists.

Major Characteristic	Description
Habitat	A.
Structures involved in movement	B.
Metabolism	C.
Reproduction	D.

True/False

Mark if the statement is true (T) or false (F). If the statement is false, justify your answer in the lines below each statement.

29. _____ Animals, fungi, and plants all evolved from protists.

_____

_____

30. _____ Protists are generally unicellular and microscopic.

_____

_____

Short Answer

31. How would you distinguish sea weeds from aquatic plants?

_____

_____

22.4 The Protist Groups [p. 503–520]

Section Review (Fill-in-the-Blanks)

The Excavates are flagellated, single cells that lack typical (31) _____ but often have organelles

derived from these. They are named for the "excavated" ventral (32) _____ groove found in most

members and are exemplified by the (33) _____ (e.g., Giardia) and the parabasalids. The

Discicristates are flagellated, single cells that may be photosynthetic and/or (34) _____. They are

named for their disc-shaped mitochondrial (35) _____. This group includes the Kinetoplastids,

which, in turn, includes (36) _____ _____, the causative agent of African Sleeping

Sickness. Alveolates are single cells that may be (37) _____ or heterotrophic. They are named for

their characteristic small, membrane-bound vesicles called (38) _____, located in a layer under the

plasma membrane. They comprise three major groups, the first two being motile and primarily free living: the

heterotrophic (39) _____ swim using cilia, while the photosynthetic (40) _____ may be

bioluminescent and possess two (41) _____ that make them move in a whirling pattern. The third

group, the (42) _____, are nonmotile animal parasites such as Plasmodium, the pathogen that causes

malaria. The ciliates are the only type of eukaryote that has two distinct types of (43) _____. The

Heterokonts are named for their two different (44) _____, one smooth and one hairy. This group

includes the fungus-like (45) _____which secrete (46) _____ _____ and may grow

as saprophytes or parasites and, also like fungi, form multicellular (47) _____ and mycelia. Another

group, the (48) _____ have glassy (49) _____ shells and are unicellular photoautotrophs.

The remaining two groups are also photoautotrophic: the colonial Chrysophyta or (50) _____ algae

and the multicellular, plant-like Phaeophyta or (51) _____ algae. The latter includes large sea

(52) _____. The Cercozoa are amoebas with stiff filamentous (53) _____. Radiolarians have

microtubule-supported extensions called (54) _____; Foraminifera form calcium carbonate–

reinforced chambered, spiral (55) _____, through which extend cytoplasmic projections. Both groups

(56) _____ their prey using these projections. Chloroarachniophyta are photosynthetic and

heterotrophic amoeba, using (57) _____ to capture their food. The Amoebozoa are all heterotrophic

and live in marine, (58) _____ _____ and soil environments. The group includes most of the (59) _____ as well as the cellular and plasmodial (60) _____ _____. All use

(61) _____ to move and to engulf food particles. Both types of (62) _____ moulds may live

as individual amoeboid cells but when conditions deteriorate, the (63) _____ slime moulds aggregate

and move as individual (64) _____ within a multicellular mass, whereas the (65) _____

slime moulds form a multinucleate (66) _____, with masses of nuclei suspended in a common

(67) _____. The Archaeplastida includes the red and green (68) _____ and the land plants of

the kingdom (69) _____. The red (70) _____ are typically multicellular and primarily

photosynthetic inhabitants of (71) _____ habitats. The (72) _____ _____ are the

most diverse of the algae, primarily found in freshwater habitats; they are believed to have been the ancestor

of (73) _____ _____. The Opisthokonts are named for the single, posterior

(74) _____ they possess at some point in their life cycle. The group includes the Choanoflagellates,

so named for the (75) _____ of finger-like projections or microvilli surrounding their

(76) _____. This group is believed to have been the ancestor to the (77) _____.

Matching

Match each of the following terms with its correct definition.

78. ____	Bioluminescent	A.	Refers to leaflike structures of algae
79. ____	Diplomonad	B.	Refers to rootlike structures of algae
80. ____	Blades	C.	Structures found in ciliates such as *Paramecium* for eliminating excess water
81. ____	Stipes	D.	Light released by dinoflagellates when they are disturbed
82. ____	Holdfast	E.	Ground fossilized protist shells used in toothpaste and other commercial products
83. ____	Axopods	F.	Incudes the giant kelp
84. ____	Red tide	G.	Slender strands of cytoplasmic extensions in Radiolarians
85. ____	*Plasmodium*	H.	Named for the small sunbeam they resemble
86. ____	Pseudopodia	I.	Looks like two symmetrical cells, example *Giardia*

87. _____ *Euglena*

J. Possess an undulating membrane and single large mitochondrion with visible deposit

88. _____ Contractile vacuole

K. Structures that facilitate movement of amoebae

89. _____ Brown algae

L. Refers to stemlike structures of algae

90. _____ Diatomaceous earth

M. Oomycete that caused the Irish Potato Famine

91. _____ Kinetoplastids

N. Photosynthetic organisms that possess a light-sensing eyespot

92. _____ Radiolarians

O. Associated with population blooms of dinoflagellates

93. _____ *Phytophthora infestans*

P. A multinucleate form of slime mould

Complete the Table

94. Fill in the following table with the name of the organism or the disease/disease features associated with the organism.

Organism	Disease
A.	Sleeping sickness
Giardia lamblia	B.
Trichomonas vaginalis	C.
Plasmodium species	D.
E.	Apicomplexan disease contracted by inhalation of cysts from cat feces
F.	Causes amoebic dysentery
G.	Caused the Irish potato famine of the 1800s and has emerged as a serious disease of potato crops in Canada and the United States

Short Answer

95. Explain the relationship between the colour in the white Cliffs of Dover, in England, and the protists.

_____

_____

96. What is the explanation for the phenomenon of coral bleaching?

_____

_____

Building Vocabulary

Using the definitions of the prefixes below, assign the appropriate prefix to the appropriate suffix:

Prefix	Meaning	Prefix	Meaning
Hetero-	different	Proto-	first
Chloro-	green	Dino-	spinning
Rhodo-	rose	Opistho-	posterior
Diplo-	double	Foramin-	little hole
Choano-	collar		

	Prefix	Suffix	Protist group
97.	_____	-monads	Organisms with two equal and functional nuclei; include Giardia
98.	_____	-zoa	Alternate name for the discicristates based on the fact that they ingest food and move by themselves, similar to ancient animals
99.	_____	-flagellates	Protists with a shell formed from cellulose plates and flagella that fit in the groove between the plates, causing the cells to move by spinning
100.	_____	-konts	Possess two different flagella: one smooth and one covered with bristles
101.	_____	-ifera	Protists with pseudopodia projecting through small perforations in their shells
102.	_____	-phyta	Red algae used to wrap sushi and as a source of agar and carageenan and important in corals
103.	_____	-phyta	Green algae that include the likely ancestor to land plants
104.	_____	-konts	Protist group named for the single flagellum located at the end of the cells from some stages of their life cycle
105.	_____	-flagellata	Protist group named for the collar surrounding the flagellum; includes what is thought to be the ancestor of animals

22.5 Some Protist Groups Arose from Primary Endosymbiosis and Others from Secondary Endosymbiosis [pp. 520–522]

Section Review (Fill-in-the-Blanks)

The red and green (106) _____ and the land plants contain chloroplasts that arose through primary

endosymbiosis where a eukaryotic cell engulfed a (107) _____, which then became the chloroplast.

Other photosynthetic protists, such as the (108) _____ (the "eyespot organisms"),

(109) _____ (the "spinning" protists), (110) _____ (with their smooth and hairy flagella),

and chlorarachniophytes, were produced by secondary endosymbiosis: a nonphotosynthetic protist engulfed a

photosynthetic (111) _____. Organisms that formed from secondary endosymbiosis have

chloroplasts surrounded by (112) _____ membranes derived from the engulfed phototroph and the

(113) _____ _____ membrane of the original host cell.

SELF-TEST

1. Which is a characteristic of Protist? [p. 499]
   a. They are heterotrophic eukaryotes.
   b. They are photoautotrophic eukaryotes.
   c. They all share a past common ancestor.
   d. They are the eukaryotes that are neither animal, plant nor fungal.

2. Which statement is true? [p. 500]
   a. The protists and fungi share a common ancestor .
   b. The protists and fungi all have microfilaments and microtubules.
   c. The protists and fungi all have chloroplasts.
   d. The protists and fungi all have cellulose cell walls.

3. Which statement is correct? [p. 501]
   a. Animals are always multicellular, but protists may be unicellular.
   b. Animals, unlike protists, possess differentiated structures.
   c. Some animals, for example, corals, contain chloroplasts, as do some protists.
   d. All protists and animals possess mitochondria.

4. Which describes how photosynthetic protists differ from plants? [pp. 501, 519]
   a. The photosynthetic protists form leaves and stems but not roots.
   b. The photosynthetic protists retain parental tissue in their embryos.
   c. Unlike plants, the photosynthetic protists do not use starch as storage reserve.
   d. The photosynthetic protists form the same structures as plants, but these are given different names.

5. Which structure is involved in getting rid of excess water? [p. 502]
   a. the food vacuole
   b. the contractile vacuole
   c. the pseudopodia
   d. the axopods

6. Which protist group can only make ATP via glycolysis? [p. 503]
   a. the Chlorophyta
   b. the Apicomplexans
   c. the Excavates
   d. the diatoms

7. Which group of protists has a light-sensing eyespot? [p. 504]

    a. *Euglena*
    b. *Paramecium*
    c. *Giardia lamblia*
    d. Giant kelp

8. Which statement about the ciliates (Ciliophora) is NOT true? [pp. 505–506]

    a. They possess two functionally and structurally different nuclei.
    b. They use cilia rather than flagella to swim.
    c. They possess contractile vacuoles as well as food vacuoles.
    d. They have a flagellum for swimming and use the cilia to guide food into their gullet.

9. Which is NOT true of the dinoflagellates? [pp. 506–508]

    a. They are part of the zooplankton.
    b. They cause red tides.
    c. They may cause food-borne intoxication that results in paralysis.
    d. They glow in the dark.

10. Which statement about the apicomplexans is false? [pp. 508–509]

    a. They have a structure at one end that is involved in attaching to and invading hosts.
    b. They are parasites of animals.
    c. They may be motile or nonmotile.
    d. They include the genus *Plasmodium*.

11. Which statement about the Oomycota is false? [pp. 509–510]

    a. They include the water moulds and downy mildews.
    b. They were responsible for the Irish potato famine.
    c. They are fungi that used to be considered protists.
    d. They are key decomposers in freshwater environments.

12. Which statement about diatoms is false? [pp. 510–511]

    a. They may be unicellular or multicellular.
    b. Their shells represent a major component of the sediments of lakes and seas.
    c. They have silica cell walls.
    d. Their shells are ground up and put in toothpaste.

13. Which pigments are responsible for the distinctive colours of golden algae? [p. 511]

    a. phycobilins
    b. fucoxanthin
    c. chlorophylls
    d. β-carotene

14. Which is NOT associated with brown algae? [pp. 511–512]

    a. gas bladders
    b. agar
    c. blades
    d. holdfasts

15. Which is NOT a characteristic of Cercozoa? [pp. 512–514]

    a. They move through cytoplasmic extensions called pseudopodia.
    b. They include the "shape-shifting" amoeba.
    c. They contribute to the formation of the sedimentary rock.
    d. They are the basis for the distinctive appearance of the White Cliffs of Dover.

16. Which is NOT a member of the Amoebozoa? [pp. 514–516]

    a. the water moulds
    b. the cellular slime moulds
    c. the plasmodial slime moulds
    d. *Dictyostelium discoideum*

17. Which group of protists has been a model system for the eukaryotic processes of cell differentiation and signalling? [p. 514]

    a. the Choanoflgellates
    b. the Cercozoa
    c. the water moulds
    d. the slime moulds

18. Which pigment gives red algae their colour? [p. 517]

    a. phycobilin

    b. fucoxanthin

    c. agar

    d. carotenoid

19. Which group includes the land plants? [p. 517]

    a. the Opisthokonts

    b. the Archaeplastida

    c. the Excavates

    d. the Alveolates

20. Which may have been the ancestor to the animals? [p. 520]

    a. the Opisthokonts

    b. the Archaeplastida

    c. the Excavates

    d. the Alveolates

21. Which organism was engulfed in the primary endosymbiotic event that gave rise to the red algae? [pp. 520–521]

    a. an aerobic heterotrophic prokaryotic cell

    b. a photosynthetic prokaryotic cell

    c. an aerobic heterotrophic eukaryotic cell

    d. a photosynthetic eukaryotic cell

22. Which organism was engulfed in the secondary endosymbiotic event that gave rise to the Euglenoids? [pp. 521–522]

    a. a cyanobacterium

    b. an aerobic heterotrophic bacterium

    c. red algae

    d. green algae

INTEGRATING AND APPLYING KEY CONCEPTS

1. Discuss why it is difficult to classify protists.

2. Following from question 1, go through the various groups of protists that you have learned about and look for examples of organisms from different groups of protists that may have been assigned to the same taxonomic group prior to the advent of molecular phylogeny, or to another kingdom within the Eukarya.

3. Using one example for each, explain the process of primary and secondary endosymbiosis, the evidence, and why proving such events would have been impossible prior to the advent of genomics.

23 Fungi

TOPIC MAP

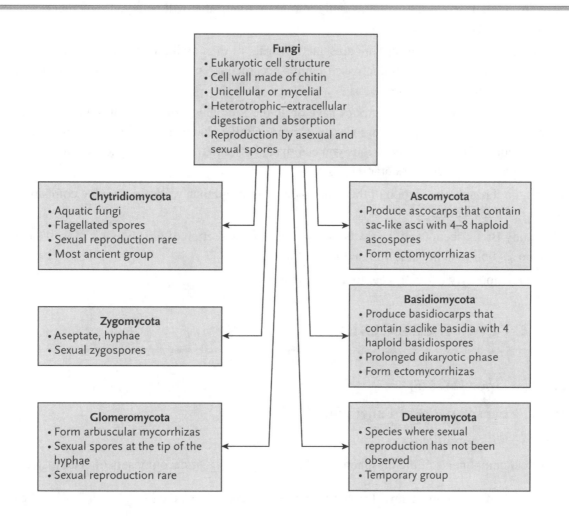

Fungi
- Eukaryotic cell structure
- Cell wall made of chitin
- Unicellular or mycelial
- Heterotrophic–extracellular digestion and absorption
- Reproduction by asexual and sexual spores

Chytridiomycota
- Aquatic fungi
- Flagellated spores
- Sexual reproduction rare
- Most ancient group

Ascomycota
- Produce ascocarps that contain sac-like asci with 4–8 haploid ascospores
- Form ectomycorrhizas

Zygomycota
- Aseptate, hyphae
- Sexual zygospores

Basidiomycota
- Produce basidiocarps that contain saclike basidia with 4 haploid basidiospores
- Prolonged dikaryotic phase
- Form ectomycorrhizas

Glomeromycota
- Form arbuscular mycorrhizas
- Sexual spores at the tip of the hyphae
- Sexual reproduction rare

Deuteromycota
- Species where sexual reproduction has not been observed
- Temporary group

LEARNING OUTCOMES AND STUDY STRATEGIES

By the end of this chapter, you should be able to

- Identify what features distinguish each of the five evolutionary lineages of the fungi

- Understand why the classification of the Deutromycota and fungi in general is likely to change with time and increasing molecular data

- Understand the various important roles of the fungi as saprotrophs and symbionts

- Identify some of the fungi that cause disease or crop losses

- Describe the structure and importance of the lichens, mycorrhizas, and endophytes

Study strategies for this chapter:

- This chapter contains a fair amount of new information and new names for organisms, phyla, and structures. Do not worry too much about remembering all the details; the goal of this chapter is to understand what fungi are, why they are important, and how they differ in their reproduction, reproductive structures, and life styles.

- Keep track of the headings and subheadings as you go through the six fungal groups. Look for figures or examples (e.g., of pathogens, commercially important fungi) that will help you remember something about that particular group.

- It helps to notice that the six groups are presented in order of their evolutionary age, and that as the fungi evolved/radiated, their reproductive structures became larger and more complex, and sexual reproduction became more prevalent.

- Try keeping separate lists of which groups have or do the following: fruiting bodies, yeasts, form mycorrhizas, a dikaryotic stage, no or rare sexual reproductive phases, are animal pathogens versus animal symbionts. The more connections you can make between the various aspects of the members of this kingdom, the better your comprehension.

- As always, go through one section of the textbook at a time and then work through the companion section of the study guide.

- Use the Study Break sections of the textbook and the Review section of the textbook as well as this study guide section to help guide you on the level of detail.

- When you are done, try deriving your own topic map(s).

INTERACTIVE EXERCISES

Why It Matters [pp. 524–525]

23.1 General Characteristics of Fungi [pp. 526–528]

Section Review (Fill-in-the-Blanks)

Fungi are critical components of the biosphere, as (1) _____ or decomposers of dead material, or as

(2) _____ of living organisms. The former process is essential to the (3) _____ of carbon in

terrestrial ecosystems. The fungal association with the leaf-cutter ants is a(n) (4) _____ one;

however, fungi may also be (5) _____, causing disease of animals and plants. Some fungi form

single-celled (6) _____, but most form filamentous (7) _____, growing throughout the

substrate on which they are feeding. Fungi have cell walls of (8) _____ and in most species, porous

(9) _____ partition hyphae into cell-like compartments. These pores permit cytoplasm and

sometimes (10) _____ to move between the compartments. Fungi obtain nutrients by secreting

(11) _____ enzymes then (12) _____ the resulting smaller molecules into their cells.

Extracellular digestion occurs at the growing hyphal (13) _____. All fungi reproduce asexually by producing large numbers of haploid (14) _____ but also sometimes through budding. Most also reproduce sexually, usually involving three stages: (15) _____ or the fusion of the cytoplasm of two haploid hyphae or gametes, followed at some point by (16) _____ or fusion of the two parental nuclei to form a (17) _____ zygote. This is followed by meiosis to give (18) _____ spores.

Matching

Match each of the following terms with its correct definition.

19. ____	Hypha		A.	Involves secretion of degradative enzymes to release small molecules that are easily transported into the cell
20. ____	Mycelium		B.	Fusion of the two nuclei in a dikaryon
21. ____	Saprotroph		C.	Organisms that live on other living things and harm them
22. ____	Parasites		D.	Involves the hyphal tips only and considerable mechanical force
23. ____	Mutualism		E.	A cell with two haploid nuclei
24. ____	Spores		F.	Threadlike structure that make up most fungi
25. ____	Plasmogamy		G.	Where two organisms live together benefiting each other
26. ____	Dikaryon		H.	The movement of nutrients to nonabsorptive regions of the organism
27. ____	Karyogamy		I.	The porous cross-wall between hyphal cells
28. ____	Absorptive nutrition		J.	Antibiotics would be examples
29. ____	Apical growth		K.	Method of reproduction of yeast cells
30. ____	Cytoplasmic streaming		L.	Fusion of the cytoplasm of two hyphae or two gametes
31. ____	Septa		M.	A mass of hyphae
32. ____	Budding		N.	Organism that lives on dead organisms to get nutrients
33. ____	Secondary metabolite		O.	Reproductive structures that are may be produced sexually or asexually and require germination to grow

Complete the Table

34. Complete the following table by giving definitions of the terms used to describe different ways fungi get their nutrients.

Terms	Definitions
Saprotrophs	A.
Parasites	B.
Mutualism	C.

35. Complete the following table by giving the major characteristics of fungi.

Characteristic	Description
Cell type	A.
Cell wall	B.
Dominant growth form(s)	C.
Mode of nutrition, nutrient acquisition	D.
Reproduction, unusual aspects	E.

True/False

Mark if the statement is true (T) or false (F). If the statement is false, justify your answer in the lines below each statement.

36. _____ Leaf-cutter ants produce antibiotics to control the growth of their fungal "garden."

_____

_____

37. _____ Fungi only grow and obtain nutrients at their fungal tips.

_____

_____

38. _____ Fungi are the most common cause of plant diseases.

_____

_____

Short Answer

39. What are some examples of how humans exploit the metabolic activities of fungi?

_____

_____

40. Define the term "secondary metabolite."

_____

_____

41. How have studies with fungi helped elucidate eukaryotic cellular structures and processes?

_____

_____

23.2 Evolution and Diversity of Fungi [pp. 528–539]

Section Review (Fill-in-the-Blanks)

Based on current molecular data, the fungi are divided into (42) _____ phyla. A sixth temporary

group called (43) _____ contains fungi with no observable sexual reproduction phase. The

Chytridiomycota are the only fungi to produce (44) _____ spores, allowing them to swim through

(45) _____ or moist habitats. While generally unicellular, cells may also form chains anchored to a

substrate via (46) _____. Asexual reproduction involves the formation of haploid spores in a sac

called a(n) (47) _____. The Zygomycota hyphae are generally (48) _____, lacking cell

partitions. Asexual reproduction involves spores formed in sac-like (49) _____ at the tips of aerial

hyphae. During sexual reproduction, specialized (50) _____ of the + and – mating types grow toward

each other, producing sex organs called (51) _____ at their tips. These fuse to form a thick-walled,

multinucleate (52) _____ or zygote, which may remain (53) _____ for years; germination

involves production of a stalked (54) _____ and (55) _____ of the diploid nuclei to generate

haploid spores of both mating types. Like the Zygomycota, the Glomeromycota form (56) _____

hyphae. However, they reproduce asexually by simply walling off a section of (57) _____ to generate

a haploid (58) _____. They all form (59) _____ mycorrhizas in the (60) _____ of

many land plants. Asexual reproduction of the Ascomycota involves the production of numerous exposed

spores called (61) _____. Sexual reproduction involves fusion of + and – hyphae and

(62) _____ or fusion of the cytoplasm. (63) _____ ($n + n$) hyphae may form briefly before

(64) _____ or fusion of the two nuclei. Sacs called (65) _____ form at the tips hyphae then

the two nuclei fuse, undergo meiosis and usually also mitosis, to form eight haploid (66) _____.

Some species contain these sacs in multicellular fruiting bodies called (67) _____. Some members of

this group grow in a yeast form, reproducing asexually by (68) _____ or by binary fission. Most

Basidiomycota reproduce only sexually, forming fruiting bodies called (69) _____, mushrooms being

familiar examples. The life cycle begins with germination of haploid (70) _____. (71) _____

occurs when two hyphae fuse at their tips; however, this is usually followed by a significant delay prior to

(72) _____ or fusion of the haploid nuclei. As with the Glomeromycota, during the intervening

period, the growing mycelium is not diploid but rather ($n + n$), i.e. a(n) (73) _____. The fruiting

bodies form under (74) _____ environmental conditions, bearing the haploid (75) _____ on

club-shaped (76) _____.

Matching

Match each of the following terms with its correct definition.

77. ____	Basidiospores		A.	The sexual spores of the ascomycetes
78. ____	Mycorrhizas		B.	The multicellular fruiting body of the Ascomycota that bears sexual spores
79. ____	Arbuscule		C.	Include subgroups that are not all descended from a single ancestor
80. ____	Sporangium		D.	Fruiting bodies such as mushrooms
81. ____	Conidia		E.	A symbiotic relationship between plant roots and Glomeromycota and Ascomycota fungal species
82. ____	Ascus		F.	A multicellular structure that may anchor chytrids to a substrate
83. ____	Ascocarp		G.	The intracellular form of Glomeromycota mycorrhizae
84. ____	Basidiocarp		H.	A terminal sac that is filled with asexual spores in Chytridiomycota and Zygomycota
85. ____	Chemotaxis		I.	A thick-walled spore that may remain dormant for years; it will germinate to form a sporangium
86. ____	Basidia		J.	A temporary group of fungi for which no sexual stage has been identified
87. ____	Paraphyletic		K.	An elongated sac that contains 4–8 sexual spores
88. ____	Ascospores		L.	Swimming in response to chemicals, a characteristic of the flagellated chytrid spores
89. ____	Rhizoid		M.	$(n + n)$
90. ____	Zygospore		N.	Club-shaped spore-containing sacs associated with the "gills" of mushrooms,
91. ____	Fungi Imperfecta		O.	Sexual spores associated with the mushrooms
92. ____	Dikaryon		P.	The asexual spores formed by basidiomycetes and ascomycetes

Complete the Table

93. Complete the following table by giving the major characteristics of each phylum of the kingdom Fungi.

Phylum	Major Characteristics
Ascomycota	A.
Zygomycota	B.
Basidiomycota	C.
Chytridiomycota	D.
Glomeromycota	E.

94. For each of the phyla below, identify an associated pathogen, disease, or benefit that will help you remember this group.

Phyla/Group	Major Characteristics
Ascomycota	A.
Zygomycota	B.
Basidiomycota	C.
Chytridiomycota	D.
Glomeromycota	E.

True/False

Mark if the statement is true (T) or false (F). If the statement is false, justify your answer in the lines below each statement.

95. _____ It is estimated that there are approximately 1.6 million undiscovered species of fungi.

_____

_____

96. _____ Fungal infections in humans generally respond to antibiotics.

_____

_____

97. _____ The products of meiosis in the fungi are spores rather than gametes.

_____

_____

98. _____ The dikaryotic stage of the Basidiomycetes and the Ascomycetes allows for hyphal growth, thus greater production of sexual spores.

_____

_____

99. _____ The chytrids are relatively recently evolved fungal species.

_____

_____

Short Answer

100. What is the historical relevance of *Claviceps purpurea*?

_____

_____

101. Why is the classification of the fungi somewhat problematic?

_____

_____

102. Identify the fungal groups that include carnivorous species and the benefit of this process.

_____

_____

Labelling

103. Label the following fungal sexual or asexual reproductive structures and identify the phylum associated with each.

A. _____

B. _____

C. _____

D. _____

E. _____

F. _____

G. _____

H. _____

I. _____

J. _____

K. _____

L. _____

M. _____

N. _____

O. _____

P. _____

Q. _____

R. _____

S. _____

T. _____

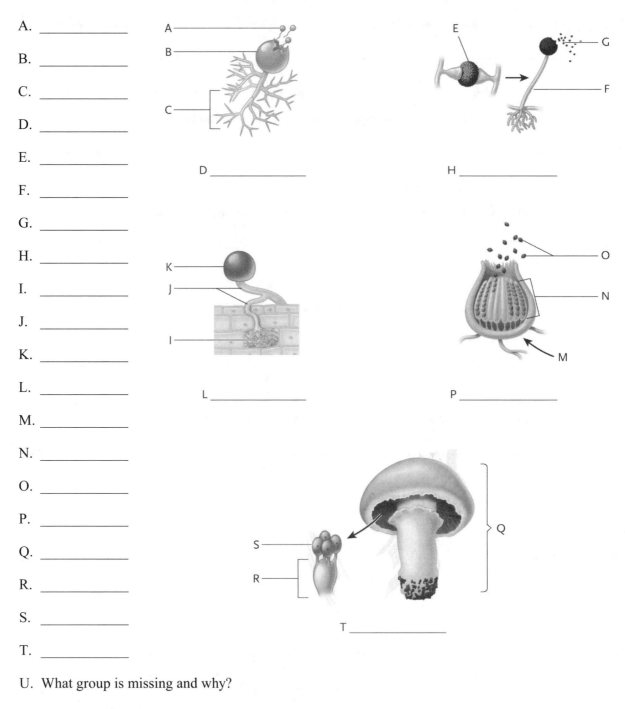

D _____

H _____

L _____

P _____

T _____

U. What group is missing and why?

_____

_____

23.3 Fungal Lifestyles [pp. 539–544]

Section Review (Fill-in-the-Blanks)

All fungi are heterotrophs, functioning as (104) _____ to break down detritus, or forming a

(105) _____ relationship with living hosts. While the former activity recycles key nutrients in

terrestrial (106) _____, it also allows fungi to grow on, and degrade the wood and

(107) _____ of buildings, weakening the building's (108) _____ integrity and posing a

potential (109) _____ hazard. (110) _____ are compound organisms formed from the

symbiosis of a fungal partner, the so-called (111) _____, and the photosynthetic partner, or so-called

(112) _____. The fungal partner is either a(n) (113) _____ or sometimes a basidiomycete,

while the photosynthetic partner may be a species of (114) _____ _____ or

(115) _____. The fungus makes up most of the body or (116) _____ of the lichen, wrapping

around the photosynthetic partner and absorbing up to 80% of the (117) _____ it produces. Fungi in

the (118) _____, Ascomycota, and Basidiomycota form mycorrhizal relationships with plant

(119) _____. The fungus obtains its organic (120) _____ from the plant and, in turn,

increases the plant's access to (121) _____ and _____. The (122) _____

mycorrhizas formed by Glomeromycota are the oldest and most (123) _____ type of mycorrhiza and

may have been critical for the (124) _____ of _____ by plants. The other two groups of

fungus form (125) _____, most commonly associated with trees. (126) _____ fungi form

symbiotic relationships with above-ground plant growth. Although not well understood, at least in some

cases, the fungal partner produces (127) _____ that deter herbivores.

Matching

Match each of the following terms with its correct definition.

128. _____ Thallus

A. A cluster of fungal and algal cells used for asexual reproduction

129. _____ Soredia

B. Edible fruiting bodies formed by ectomycorrhizal ascomycetes and oak trees

130. _____ Mycobiont

C. Symbiotic relationship between Ascomycetes and some basidiomycetes and plant roots

131. _____ Photobiont

132. _____ Arbuscular mycorrhiza

133. _____ Ectomycorrhiza

134. _____ Endophyte

135. _____ Truffles

136. _____ Taxol

137. _____ Dry rot

D. Symbiotic relationship between fungi and above-ground plant growth

E. A chemical isolated from certain endophytic fungi

F. The photosynthetic partner of a lichen

G. A type of wood decay associated with a fungus that forms mycelial cords

H. The main body of the lichen

I. Symbiotic relationship between Glomeromycota and plant roots

J. The fungal partner of a lichen

True/False

Mark if the statement is true (T) or false (F). If the statement is false, justify your answer in the lines below each statement.

138. _____ Lichens may be used to monitor air quality.

_____

_____

139. _____ Ectomycorrhizas may be a source of medicines.

_____

_____

Short Answer

140. Compare and contrast arbuscular mycorrhizas versus ectomycorrhizas.

_____

_____

_____

141. Discuss the relevance of the evolution of the fungi and the colonization of land by plants.

_____

_____

_____

1. Which best describes the fungi? [pp. 526–528]

   a. They are kingdom of generally heterotrophic but occasionally autotrophic eukaryotes.

   b. They are kingdom of unicellular and multicellular eukaryotic heterotrophs with cellulose cell walls.

   c. They are a group of heterotrophic eukaryotes that obtain their nutrients through phagocytosis and endocytosis.

   d. They are eukaryotic heterotrophs that are generally multicellular and feed by absorptive nutrition.

2. Which statement does NOT describe the fungi? [pp. 527–528]

   a. They may reproduce both sexually and asexually.

   b. The hyphae consist of chains of individual cells.

   c. Some produce antibiotics.

   d. Karyogamy and plasmogamy may be separated in time by years.

3. How do reproductive structures obtain essential nutrients? [p. 528]

   a. They ingest their food.

   b. They secrete enzymes to digest the nutrients in their substrate and then absorb them.

   c. The nutrients are transported from the environment through active transport mechanisms.

   d. Cytoplasmic streaming delivers the nutrients from absorptive regions of the mycelium.

4. Which statement is true? [pp. 528–529]

   a. The lineages leading to the fungi and animals appear to have diverged over 750 million years ago.

   b. The lineages leading to the fungi and plants appear to have diverged over 750 million years ago.

   c. The formation of mycorrhizas is thought to reflect the close evolutionary relationship between plants and fungi.

   d. The fungi are thought to have evolved from a flagellated, aquatic, heterotrophic bacterium.

5. Which statement about sexual reproduction in the fungi is NOT correct? [p. 529]

   a. Some fungi do not undergo sexual reproduction.

   b. There are more species of fungi that have not been described than have been described.

   c. The identification of arbuscules in fossils of ancient land plants suggests that the first fungi were terrestrial.

   d. As the fungi diversified, their sexual reproductive structures became more elaborate.

6. Which pair of phyla is paraphyletic? [p. 529]

   a. Chytridiomycota and Ascomycota

   b. Ascomycota and Basidiomycota

   c. Basidiomycota and Zygomycota

   d. Zygomycota and Chytridiomycota

   e. Glomeromycota and Deuteromycota

7. Which phylum includes species that produce flagellated spores? [p. 530]

   a. the Chytridiomycota

   b. the Ascomycota

   c. the Basidiomycota

   d. the Zygomycota

   e. the Glomeromycota

8. Which phylum includes bread and fruit moulds? [p. 530]

   a. the Chytridiomycota

   b. the Basidiomycota

   c. the Zygomycota

   d. the Glomeromycota

9. Which pair of phyla produces haploid spores in sporangia? [pp. 530–531]

    a. the Chytridiomycota and Zygomycota

    b. the Ascomycota and Basidiomycota

    c. the Glomeromycota and Basidiomycota

    d. the Zygomycota and Deuteromycota

10. Which phylum includes species that form arbuscular mycorrhizas? [p. 532]

    a. Chytridiomycota

    b. Ascomycota

    c. Basidiomycota

    d. Zygomycota

    e. Glomeromycota

11. Which pair of phyla includes carnivorous species? [pp. 533, 536]

    a. the Chytridiomycota and Zygomycota

    b. the Ascomycota and Basidiomycota

    c. the Glomeromycota and Basidiomycota

    d. the Zygomycota and Deuteromycota

12. Which phylum produces truffles and morels? [p. 533]

    a. the Chytridiomycota

    b. the Ascomycota

    c. the Basidiomycota

    d. the Zygomycota

    e. the Glomeromycota

13. Which describes the fungus *Claviceps purpurea*? [p. 534]

    a. It is an ascomycete.

    b. It is an edible fungus.

    c. It is a spoilage fungus that may have caused ergotism in Salem, Massachusetts, leading to the Salem witch trials.

    d. It is a deadly mushroom sometimes mistaken for an edible one.

14. Which phylum includes species that produce four to eight haploid sexual spores in a sac? [p. 535]

    a. the Ascomycota

    b. the Chytridiomycota

    c. the Basidiomycota

    d. the Zygomycota

    e. the Glomeromycota

15. Which phylum includes species that produce mushrooms? [p. 535]

    a. the Chytridiomycota

    b. the Ascomycota

    c. the Basidiomycota

    d. the Zygomycota

    e. the Glomeromycota

16. Which phylum does NOT include animal pathogens? [pp. 530, 533, 536]

    a. the Chytridiomycota

    b. the Ascomycota

    c. the Basidiomycota

    d. the Glomeromycota

17. In which group does asexual reproduction NOT include budding yeasts or conidia? [pp. 533, 537, 539]

    a. the Chytridiomycota

    b. the Ascomycota

    c. the Basidiomycota

    d. the Deuteromycota

18. Which of the following has a prolonged dikaryon stage? [p. 537]

    a. Chytridiomycota

    b. Ascomycota

    c. Zygomycota

    d. Basidiomycota

    e. Glomeromycota

19. Which group would NOT be described as lacking or rarely demonstrating sexual reproduction? [pp. 530, 532, 539]

   a. the Chytridiomycota
   b. the Ascomycota
   c. the Glomeromycota
   d. the Deuteromycota

20. Which term would NOT describe the relationship between the mycobiont and the phytobiont of lichens? [pp. 540–542]

   a. parasitic
   b. decomposers
   c. symbiotic
   d. mutualistic

21. Which does NOT appear on the fungal phylogenetic tree? [pp. 529, 539]

   a. the Chytridiomycota
   b. the Ascomycota
   c. the Deuteromycota
   d. the Zygomycota
   e. the Glomeromycota

22. Which describes soredia? [p. 541]

   a. They are clusters of fungal spores.
   b. They are clusters of algal spores.
   c. They are clusters of the mycobiont and phytobiont.
   d. They are the resting structures of lichens.

23. Which pair of phyla produces ectomycorrhizas? [p. 543]

   a. the Glomeromycota and Zygomycota
   b. the Ascomycota and Zygomycota
   c. the Zygomycota and Deuteromycota
   d. the Ascomycota and Basidiomycota

24. Which is NOT true of endophytes? [p. 543]

   a. They are of interest to biotechnology and pharmaceutical companies.
   b. They are poorly understood.
   c. They may be mutualistic symbionts of plants.
   d. They may form on the roots, shoots or leaves.

INTEGRATING AND APPLYING KEY CONCEPTS

1. Discuss how fungi play an important role in the decay and recycling processes that are critical to returning nutrients to the soil. Then relate that process to the increasingly active research on bioremediation using fungi.

2. Fungi are considered opportunistic organisms by virtue of their reproductive diversity. Explain how their reproduction helps them adapt to their environment.

3. Fungi are now believed to be closer to animals than plants. Discuss why they might initially have been though to be closer to plants and the evidence of their relationship to animals.

24 Plants

TOPIC MAP

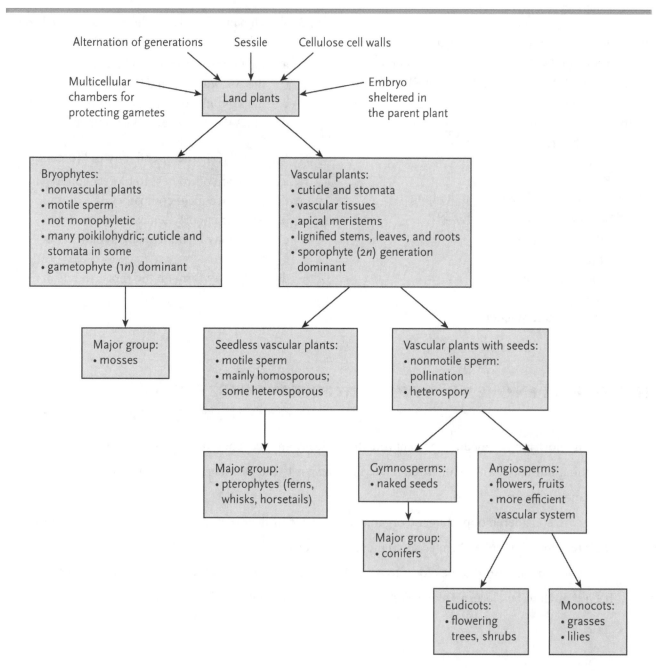

Alternation of generations

Sessile

Cellulose cell walls

Multicellular chambers for protecting gametes

Land plants

Embryo sheltered in the parent plant

Bryophytes:
- nonvascular plants
- motile sperm
- not monophyletic
- many poikilohydric; cuticle and stomata in some
- gametophyte (1n) dominant

Vascular plants:
- cuticle and stomata
- vascular tissues
- apical meristems
- lignified stems, leaves, and roots
- sporophyte (2n) generation dominant

Major group:
- mosses

Seedless vascular plants:
- motile sperm
- mainly homosporous; some heterosporous

Vascular plants with seeds:
- nonmotile sperm: pollination
- heterospory

Major group:
- pterophytes (ferns, whisks, horsetails)

Gymnosperms:
- naked seeds

Angiosperms:
- flowers, fruits
- more efficient vascular system

Major group:
- conifers

Eudicots:
- flowering trees, shrubs

Monocots:
- grasses
- lilies

LEARNING OUTCOMES AND STUDY STRATEGIES

By the end of this chapter, you should be able to

- Identify the defining features of land plants

- Describe the alternation of generations and be able to follow the process through the various major groups of plants: the bryophytes, lycophytes, ferns, gymnosperms, and angiosperms

- Distinguish between sporophytes and gametophytes, spores and gametes, including identifying that spores and gametes are both haploid and that spores, but not gametes, are the product of meiosis

- Identify the shared features (ancestral traits) as well as the distinctions (evolved traits) between the charophyte algae and the least evolved land plants, the liverworts

- Explain the role of mycorrhizas in the success of the early land plants

Study strategies for this chapter:

- Start by identifying the key adaptations that allowed the adaptive radiations of the plants, since by learning these, you will also be able to distinguish between the bryophytes, seedless vascular plants, gymnosperms, and angiosperms.

- This chapter makes use of the concepts of evolution, cell structure, mitosis, meiosis, and sexual reproduction developed earlier. You should briefly review these concepts to make sure that you understand them.

- Pay attention to the differences between the various groups and the evolutionary adaptations as you move from the least evolved bryophytes to the most evolved angiosperms.

- This chapter contains a lot of new information, names, and concepts. Do not worry about trying to memorize everything; the goal of this chapter is to understand the challenges faced by the movement to land and how the various adaptations to life on land help survive the conditions of this environment, attract a mate, reproduce, and disseminate offspring.

- Keep track of the headings and subheadings as you go through the different plant groups. Look for figures or examples (e.g., of a familiar type of plant) that will help you remember something about that particular group. As you progress through the chapter, refer back to Tables 24.1 and 24.2 as well as Figures 24.7 and 24.9; these should help you keep track of the main ideas and concepts.

- As always, go through one section of the textbook at a time and then work through the companion section of the study guide.

- Use the Study Break sections of the textbook and the Review section of the textbook, as well as this study guide section, to help guide you on the level of detail.

INTERACTIVE EXERCISES

Why It Matters [pp. 547-548]
24.1 Defining Characteristics of Land Plants [p. 548]

Section Review (Fill-in-the-Blanks)

Land plants are multicellular eukaryotes with (1) _____-containing cell walls. Most, but not all, are

(2) _____. Indian pipe is unusual in that it does not produce (3) _____ and therefore does

not perform photosynthesis; it is a (4) _____, obtaining its carbon from organic molecules through

mycorrhizas and the (5) _____ of neighbouring plants. All plants have alternation of

(6) _____ life cycles, cycling between diploid ($2n$) and haploid ($1n$) forms. Which generation is

(7) _____ by composing the majority of the life cycle varies among the different groups of plants.

During the diploid stage, specialized cells within the $2n$ (8) _____ produces haploid spores through

the process of (9) _____. These spores germinate and then undergo (10) _____ to produce a

multicellular haploid gametophyte: a structure whose function is to nourish and protect the next sporophyte

generation. Within gametophyte tissue, (11) _____ are produced and, after the process of

(12) _____, a diploid zygote forms, the first cell of the newly developing (13) _____. During

its embryonic development, embryos are retained within the parental (14) _____ tissue.

Complete the Table

15. Complete the following table, providing definitions of the terms relating to land plant structures
and processes.

Term	Definition
A. Haploid	
B. Diploid	
C. Sporophyte	
D. Gametophyte	
E. Fertilization	
F. Spores	
G. Gametes	
H. Zygote	

True/False

Mark if the statement is true (T) or false (F). If the statement is false, justify your answer in the lines below each statement.

16. _____ Plants have cell walls and are sessile.

_____

_____

Short Answer

17. Explain what is meant by the term "alternation of generations."

_____

_____

24.2 The Transition to Life on Land [pp. 548–557]

Section Review (Fill-in-the-Blanks)

Plants are thought to have evolved from (18) _____ (green algae) between 425 and 490 million years

ago. The earliest groups of land plants were the nonvascular (19) _____, which lack internal transport

vessels and are largely (20) _____ (they have little control over their internal water content).

Modern-day mosses are a good example of this group, growing close to the ground and obtaining water by

(21) _____. All later plant groups benefited from a waxy (22) _____ on their surface (to

reduce water loss) and small openings called (23) _____ that allowed for control of gas exchange and

water evaporation. These land plants are (24) _____ plants, named for their internal transport vessels

that consists of two types of vessel: (25) _____, which distributes water and ions, and

(26) _____, which distribute sugars made during photosynthesis. This system evolved to allow plants

to maximize access to (27) _____ by growing taller, which was was also further enhanced by the

production of (28) _____, a polymer that strengthens cell walls, allowing plants to grow vertically

and horizontally, against the force of gravity. Vascular plants also developed (29) _____

_____, regions of unspecialized constantly dividing cells near the tips of shoots and roots.

(30) _____ anchor the plant to the substrate and absorb water and nutrients; for the vast majority of

plants, roots are associated with fungal (31) _____, a system that vastly increases the ability of a

plant's root system to acquire (32) _____. Because fungi are believed to have colonized land first, and the soil quality would have initially been poor, these (33) _____ associations are believed to

have been critical to the evolution of land plants. As plants became more evolved, the diploid

(34) _____ generation became dominant. These eventually produce capsules called

(35) _____, which give rise to spores by (36) _____. Plants that make only one type of spore

are (37) _____, from which a "bisexual" (38) _____ is usually produced. Plants that are

(39) _____ produce two types of spores: a smaller microspore that develops into a(n)

(40) _____ gametophyte and a larger megaspore that develops into a(n) (41) _____

gametophyte, the latter of which becomes increasingly protected inside (42) _____ tissues.

Building Vocabulary

Using the definitions of the prefixes below, assign the appropriate prefix to the appropriate suffix for the
following:

Prefix	Meaning
gamet(o)-	sex cells (egg, sperm)
spor(o)-	spore
homo-	same
hetero-	different

Suffix	Meaning
-angi(o)(um)	vessel, container
-phyte	plant
-spor(e)(ous)	of or relating to a spore

	Prefix	Suffix	Definition
43.	_____	_____	structure in which gametes are formed
44.	_____	_____	structure in which spores are produced
45.	_____	_____	the gamete-producing phase in the life cycle of a plant
46.	_____	_____	the spore-producing phase in the life cycle of a plant
47.	_____	_____	production of one type of spore
48.	_____	_____	production of two different types of spores

Matching

Match each of the following structures with its correct definition.

49. _____	Stomata	A.	A region of unspecialized dividing cells near shoot and root tips
50. _____	Lignin	B.	Plants lacking internal transport vessels
51. _____	Spore	C.	Vascular tissue that distributes sugars made during photosynthesis
52. _____	Apical meristem	D.	Vascular tissue that distributes water and ions
53. _____	Cuticle	E.	The haploid generation of a plant
54. _____	Bryophytes	F.	The diploid generation of a plant
55. _____	Xylem	G.	A plant that makes two different kinds of spores
56. _____	Phloem	H.	A horizontal modified stem that can penetrate a substrate and provide support only
57. _____	Sporophyte	I.	Structure in which spores develop
58. _____	Gametophyte	J.	Formed through meiosis
59. _____	Sporangium	K.	Structure specialized for the uptake of water and nutrients
60. _____	Heterosporous	L.	Structure specialized for the absorption of light and the uptake of CO_2 from air
61. _____	Root system	M.	The waxy layer on the plant surface to reduce water loss
62. _____	Shoot system	N.	Openings in the surface of the plant for the control of gas exchange and H_2O evaporation
63. _____	Rhizome	O.	A polymer that strengthens cell walls to permit plant growth in air

24.3 Bryophytes: Nonvascular Land Plants [pp. 557–560]
24.4 Seedless Vascular Plants [pp. 561–566]

Section Review (Fill-in-the-Blanks)

Because they lack a system for conducting water, (64) _____ commonly grow in moist places. They

are generally poikilohydric, lacking a vascular system and (65) _____, relying instead on rhizoids,

stems, and leaves; they do, however, have leaflike and stemlike parts. The group includes

(66) _____, thought to be the first land plants, (67) _____, and the familiar

(68) _____ of the phylum Bryophyta. The 1*n* or (69) _____ stage is dominant. The gametes

develop in a protective layer of cells called a(n) (70) _____; for the female eggs, this structure is

flask-shaped and referred to as the (71) _____, while the sperm develop in a rounded structure called

a(n) (72) _____. The sperm are flagellated so (73) _____ of the egg requires a layer of

water. In mosses, the life cycle starts when a 1*n* spore lands on moist soil and (74) _____, elongating

and branching into a thin web of tissue called a(n) (75) _____. After several weeks, these give rise to

leafy, green (76) _____ anchored by (77) _____. The tips of the male gametophytes develop

the (78) _____, while the tips of the female gametophytes develop the (79) _____. Once

released, the sperm swim down a channel in the neck of the (80) _____ attracted by a chemical

attractant secreted by each (81) _____. The fertilized egg develops into the next (82) _____

generation, inside the gametophyte. The mature sporophyte consists of a stalk and a(n) (83) _____.

Some moss gametophytes possess rudimentary vessels for conducting (84) _____, and in some

mosses, these vessels may be surrounded by (85) _____-conducting tissue. These structures did not,

however, give rise to the xylem and (86) _____ of vascular plants.

The first vascular plants were the dominant plant life during the Carboniferous period even though

they, like bryophytes, did not produce (87) _____. Existing members include the (88) _____

(club mosses) and the pterophytes (whisks, horsetails, and (89) _____). Like bryophytes, these plants

release spores and have (90) _____ sperm; however, unlike the bryophytes, they have well-developed

(91) _____ tissues, as well as roots, stems, and (92) _____. Another difference is seen in the

life cycle: the diploid or (93) _____ generation is dominant and independent of the gametophyte.

Spores develop in (94) _____ which, in ferns, develop on the underside or margins of the leaves.

Spores are released and germinate into (95) _____, producing two different gametangia, sometimes

on the same gametophyte: a(n) (96) _____ in which the egg forms and a(n) (97) _____ in

which the sperm forms. Fertilization of the egg within its protective gametangium produces a zygote that

develops into a(n) (98) _____. In ferns, this structure remains attached to the gametophyte until it

becomes (99) _____ independent, at which point, the parent gametophyte degenerates and dies.

Some seedless vascular plants are (100) _____, producing two different types of spores in two different sporangia: microspores that give rise to the (101) _____ gametophyte and

(102) _____ that give rise to the female gametophyte.

Matching

Match each of the following terms with its correct definition.

103.	_____	Gametangium	A.	Cup-shaped gametophyte that produces the female egg
104.	_____	Protonema	B.	The phylum that contains the ferns
105.	_____	Poikilohydric	C.	Spores that give rise to the female gametophytes
106.	_____	Liverworts	D.	The phylum that contains the club mosses
107.	_____	Antheridium	E.	Spores that give rise to the male gametophytes
108.	_____	Archegonium	F.	Structure in which gametes form
109.	_____	Lycophytes	G.	Thought to be the first land plants
110.	_____	Pterophytes	H.	Filamentous web of tissue
111.	_____	Microspores	I.	The gametophyte that produces the sperm
112.	_____	Megaspores	J.	Having little control over internal water

Complete the Table

113. Complete the table with the appropriate characteristics.

Type of Plant	Major Characteristics
Bryophytes	A.
Seedless vascular plants	B.
Life Cycle	*Major Features*
Mosses	C.
Ferns	D.

True/False

Mark if the statement is true (T) or false (F). If the statement is false, justify your answer in the lines below each statement.

114. _____ The pterophyta, containing the ferns, whisks, and horsetails, are extremely diverse, growing in tropical climates, the Arctic, semi-arid deserts, and mangrove swamps.

_____

_____

115. _____ In the dry arctic tundra, the bryophytes are a critical component of the food web.

_____

_____

116. _____ Molecular studies have recently confirmed that bryophytes are all descended from a common ancestor.

_____

_____

Short Answer

117. In the fern life cycle, explain the advantage of switching from a single bisexual gametophyte to many male gametophytes.

_____

_____

118. Explain why bryophyte "stems" and "leaves" are not homologous structures to the stems and leaves of vascular plants.

_____

_____

24.5 Gymnosperms: The First Seed Plants [pp. 566–570]
24.6 Angiosperms: Flowering Plants [pp. 570–575]

Section Review (Fill-in-the-Blanks)

(119) _____, the conifers and their relatives, and (120) _____, the flowering plants, are both

seed-bearing vascular plants. Collectively, their evolution involved important reproductive adaptations,

including the use of pollen and its transfer by (121) _____, and the development of the ovule and the

(122) _____. The name "gymnosperm" comes from Greek and means (123) _____ seed, a

description that refers to the fact that the seeds are not protected inside a fruit. The predominant gymnosperms are the conifers: in these, the male sporophyte gives rise to microspores and megaspores, which form within (124) _____ cones (generally on the lower branches) and (125) _____ cones (on the upper branches) respectively. The microspores undergo mitosis to become (126) _____ grains, immature male gametophytes. The megaspores are produced inside a protective ovule: four result from meiosis, but only one survives to become a(n) (127) _____. When a pollen grain lands on a female cone, it germinates and produces a(n) (128) _____ _____. At this time sperm form and then enter the (129) _____-containing ovule when it is reached by the pollen tube. Fertilization gives rise to a (130) _____, which develops into an embryo that remains inside the gametophyte tissue and the seed coat. In the case of pine trees, the seed is the (131) _____ _____. Three other members of the gymnosperms are very restricted in numbers and habitat; for example, the (132) _____ are restricted to warmer climates. The other two types are both remnants of ancient lineages: the (133) _____, which grows in temperate forests in China, and the (134) _____. The most successful group of plants is the (135) _____; currently, they are the most diverse plant group. In addition to evolving a more efficient (136) _____ system, defining and key reproductive structures of this group are a protective (137) _____ surrounding the ovule, a(n) (138) _____ that results from double fertilization, flowers that attract (139) _____, and (140) _____ that protect and disperse the seeds. Angiosperms are assigned to the phylum (141) _____, most of which are classified as (142) _____, such as grasses and lilies, or (143) _____, such as flowering shrubs and trees. During double fertilization, the delivery of two sperm to the female (144) _____ results in one fertilizing the egg and the other fertilizing the (145) _____-producing cell. Eventually, the ovary develops into the (146) _____, which protects the seeds but also aids in (147) _____ of the seeds, often through the feces of fruit-eating animals.

Matching

Match each of the following terms with its correct definition.

148. _____ Gymnosperms		A.	Sporophyte structure within which a female gametophyte develops
149. _____ Angiosperms		B.	A structure that aids in protecting and dispersing angiosperm seeds
150. _____ Microspores		C.	Embryos generally possess two leaves
151. _____ Megaspores		D.	The interdependent evolution of two or more species
152. _____ Monocots		E.	An immature male gametophyte that gives rise to sperm
153. _____ Eudicots		F.	Produced in male cones and will form a pollen grain
154. _____ Ovule		G.	Plants with "naked" seeds
155. _____ Ovary		H.	The process of transferring pollen to female reproductive structures
156. _____ Pollen grain		I.	An important structure of angiosperms for pollinators
157. _____ Fruit		J.	Plants with seeds that develop in a carpel
158. _____ Coevolution		K.	Produced in female cones and will form a gametophyte
159. _____ Seed		L.	The process by which flowering plants gives rise to an embryo and to nutritive tissue
160. _____ Flowers		M.	Plants with embryos possessing a single leaf
161. _____ Double fertilization		N.	A structure formed after fertilization that includes the embryo sporophyte, nutritive tissue, and a protective cover
162. _____ Pollination		O.	The part of a carpel that matures into a fruit following fertilization

Complete the Table

163. Complete the table with the appropriate characteristics.

Type of Plant	Major Characteristic(s)
Cycads	A.
B.	Only one living species; found in China and used for herbal remedies
Conifers	C.
D.	Contains only three genera with a total of approximately 70 species; ancient lineage
Type of Plant	Representative(s)
Monocots	E.
Eudicots	F.

True/False

Mark if the statement is true (T) or false (F). If the statement is false, justify your answer in the lines below each statement.

164. _____ Coconuts are the seeds of palm trees like pine nuts are the seeds of pine trees.

_____

_____

165. _____ Pine resin is the sap that flows through the phloem of these trees.

_____

_____

166. _____ Despite their distinctive structures, the fossil record of the evolution of the angiosperms is very poor.

_____

_____

Short Answer

167. Explain why plants that evolved to produce ovules had a selective advantage.

_____

_____

168. Explain how the evolution of pollen represented an adaptive advantage.

_____

_____

169. Explain the phenomenon of coevolution as it relates to the angiosperms.

_____

_____

SELF-TEST

1. Which statement about the sporophyte generation of a plant is incorrect? [p. 548]
   a. It is the haploid generation.
   b. It is the diploid generation.
   c. The sporophyte produces spores by meiosis.
   d. The sporophyte is multicellular.

2. Which type of organisms are land plants thought to have evolved from? [p. 548–549]
   a. green algae
   b. fungus
   c. red algae
   d. cyanobacteria

3. How are new metabolic pathways thought to evolve? [pp. 548–549]
   a. through species sensing what they need
   b. through organisms trying to develop the right genes
   c. through natural selection in which more offspring are produced by organisms with beneficial traits
   d. through natural selection in which organisms acquiring what they need to survive

4. What trait did plants NOT have to develop in their move to land? [pp. 548–549]
   a. taking up nutrients from soil
   b. developing ability to live in a wet environment
   c. undertaking sexual reproduction in a dry environment
   d. growing a plant body in air

5. Which statement is NOT true about spores? [p. 548]
   a. They form within sporangia.
   b. They grow into sporophyte plants.
   c. They are haploid.
   d. They form from meiosis.

6. Which adaptation did NOT facilitate an increase in vertical growth as plants colonized land? [pp. 549–553]
   a. lignified stems
   b. root systems
   c. xylem and phloem
   d. heterospory

7. Which group of plants avoids desiccation by being a drought tolerator? [pp. 549–551]

   a. gymnosperms

   b. mosses

   c. angiosperms

   d. ferns

8. Which statement correctly describes apical meristems? [p. 551–553]

   a. They are differentiated cells.

   b. They give rise to sporangia.

   c. They are the growth sites of roots and shoots.

   d. They are present in all branching bryophytes.

9. Which statement correctly describes mycorrhizas? [pp. 550–554]

   a. They are algae symbionts.

   b. They are associated with uptake of carbon uptake through stomata.

   c. They are the symbiotic association between plants and fungi.

   d. They control the evaporation of water from plants.

10. Which group of plants has a dominant gametophyte phase in its life cycle? [pp. 553–555]

   a. gymnosperms

   b. mosses

   c. angiosperms

   d. ferns

11. In what structures do Bryophyte and seedless vascular plant sperm form? [pp. 557–565]

   a. diploid gametophyte plants

   b. archegonia

   c. haploid sporophyte plants

   d. antheridia

12. Which statement correctly describes both rhizomes and roots? [pp. 561–564]

   a. They both provide water and ions to land plants.

   b. They both provide an anchor for land plants.

   c. They are both associated with mycorrhizas.

   d. They both function as part of a vascular system.

13. Where is a strobilus found? [pp. 562–565]

   a. at the stem tips of whisk ferns

   b. on the root tips of *Pterophyta*

   c. at the base of specialized leaves of lycophytes (club mosses)

   d. on the thallus of liverworts

14. Which statement regarding the sporangia of ferns is correct? [pp. 562–565]

   a. They are formed by the haploid generation.

   b. They are usually on the fiddleheads.

   c. They are often arranged in a sorus.

   d. They are a precursor to the fiddlehead.

15. Which of the following do NOT assist gymnosperms in their adaptation to dry environments? [pp. 566–567]

   a. thick cuticle

   b. sunken stomata

   c. resin production

   d. needle-shaped leaves

16. Which of the following is NOT associated with pine trees? [pp. 567–569]

   a. double fertilization

   b. megasporangia on female cones

   c. production of two sizes of spores

   d. female cones that are larger than male cones

17. Which statement correctly describes the fossil record of angiosperms? [pp. 570–571]

   a. It is complete.

   b. It is nonexistent.

   c. It lacks any transition stages.

   d. It is quite extensive.

18. In which case is double fertilization required? [pp. 573–575]
    a. for development of endosperm in angiosperm plants
    b. for development of a zygote in heterosporous plants
    c. for development of fruit in angiosperms
    d. for pollination in gymnosperms

19. What flower trait would be most useful to a bat pollinator? [pp. 573–575]
    a. tube-like flower shape
    b. dark flower colour
    c. sweet flower odour
    d. flower nectar guides

20. Which of the following was NOT a factor contributing to the adaptive success of angiosperms? [pp. 572–575]
    a. more efficient transport of water and nutrients
    b. enhanced nutrition and physical protection of embryos
    c. enhanced dispersal of seeds
    d. increased requirement of water for sperm to fertilize egg

INTEGRATING AND APPLYING KEY CONCEPTS

1. What is the adaptive significance of flowers? What has made angiosperms so successful? Are they more successful than the gymnosperms? If so, why?

2. What are the problems with tracing the evolution of the land plants? How was the current classification of land plants, as depicted in Figure 24.9, derived? Is it likely to change? If so, why? If not, why not?

3. Without looking at the topic map at the beginning of this study guide chapter, try to derive your own topic map, focusing on the major evolutionary steps in the structures and reproductive strategies of land plants, starting with the presumed first ones (or most ancient), the liverworts, and progressing through to the angiosperms.

25 Diversity of Animals 1: Sponges, Radiata, Platyhelminthes, and Protostomes

TOPIC MAP

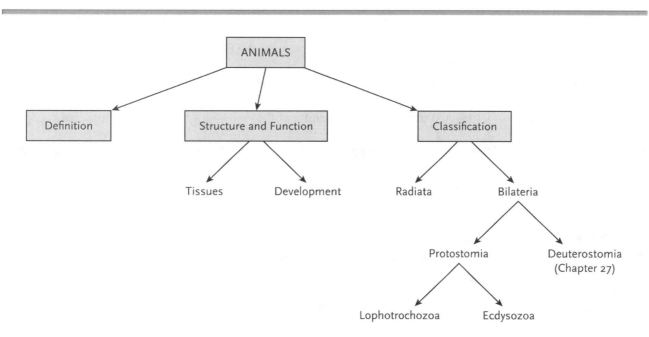

LEARNING OUTCOMES AND STUDY STRATEGIES

By the end of this chapter, you should be able to

- Explain the present animal phylogenetic tree in terms of the overall classification down to phylum within the protostomes
- Describe morphological innovations and developmental patterns that are the basis for animal classification
- Define terms relating to structural, functional, and developmental differences between groups of animals

Study strategies for this chapter:

- Become familiar with an overview of animal phylogeny, comparing and contrasting characteristics that produced the groupings.

- Examine the morphological innovations, developmental patterns, and molecular analyses associated with animals.
- Make comparisons within and between the various animal classification groups, focusing on diversity and success of animal groups in their environments.

INTERACTIVE EXERCISES

Why It Matters [pp. 578–579]

Section Review (Fill-in-the-Blanks)

During the "(1) _____ Explosion," approximately 540 million years ago (mya), a large number of

new (2) _____ evolved. Due to a(n) (3) _____ of the Cathedral Escarpment about 509 mya,

fossilized animals in the mud were preserved and have now been discovered in (4) _____

_____, an area in British Columbia. Although some of these fossils appear familiar, such as

(5) _____ and trilobites, other species appear strange (such as *Opabinia* with its five eyes) and can

only be seen as fossils, as they are now (6) _____.

25.1 What Is an Animal? [pp. 579–580]
25.2 Key Innovations in Animal Evolution [pp. 580–584]

Section Review (Fill-in-the-Blanks)

Animals are a(n) (7) _____ group, a kingdom that has arisen from a common ancestor. Like plants,

animals are multicellular organisms composed of (8) _____ (nucleus-containing) cells; however,

unlike plants, animal cells (9) _____ cell walls. Animals acquire (10) _____ for their

processes and activities by eating plants and other (11) _____; thus, they are (12) _____.

Typically, animals are (13) _____, able to move away from any inhospitable environments, although

some animals are (14) _____ at least in a portion of their life cycle. Reproduction is either

(15) _____, requiring the production of egg or (16) _____, or (17) _____.

Structurally, animals have a wide array of (18) _____ plans. In terms of development, more highly

developed animals, the (19) _____, contain embryonic tissues. Embryos that are (20) _____

are composed of only an outer tissue called the (21) _____ and an inner tissue called the

(22) _____, whereas those with three (23) _____ layers are triploblastic and contain a third

tissue in the middle called the (24) _____. Another body plan addresses animal shape, primarily in

terms of the amount of symmetry present. Animals such as sponges are (25) _____, showing no

symmetry; animals such as crayfish show (26) _____ symmetry, since a mirror image is only

observed between the right and left sides; and animals such as jellyfish show (27) _____ symmetry,

since mirror images can be observed in many planes along a(n) (28) _____ axis. The body plan for

bilateral animals can be (29) _____ if there is no body cavity present, (30) _____ if there is a

body cavity but no (31) _____ lining the endoderm, or (32) _____ if there is a body cavity

and the endoderm is lined with mesoderm tissue.

Matching

Match each of the following terms with its correct definition.

33.	_____	Front	A.	True fluid-filled, lined body cavity
34.	_____	Lower	B.	Cleavage pattern of protostomes
35.	_____	Head end	C.	Solid body, no body cavity
36.	_____	Upper	D.	Cavity from the splitting of mesoderm
37.	_____	Back	E.	Blocks of repeating tissue
38.	_____	Coelom	F.	Developmental fate determined at cleavage
39.	_____	Peritoneum	G.	Ventral
40.	_____	Spiral cleavage	H.	Posterior
41.	_____	Determinate cleavage	I.	Cleavage pattern of deuterostomes
42.	_____	Acoelomates	J.	Space pinched off from outpockets of archenteron
43.	_____	Indeterminate cleavage	K.	Anterior
44.	_____	Mesenteries	L.	Surrounds internal organs that are suspended in the coelom
45.	_____	Schizocoelom	M.	Cephalization
46.	_____	Enterocoelom	N.	Dorsal
47.	_____	Segmentation	O.	Tissue that lines a coelom
48.	_____	Radical cleavage	P.	Development fate determined after cleavage

25.3 An Overview of Animal Phylogeny and Classification [pp. 584–585]

Section Review (Fill-in-the-Blanks)

Relationships between animals have previously been based on (49) _____ (study of structure) and

(50) _____ (study of prebirth development). With advances in technology, these relationships are

now also based on (51) _____ analysis, usually resulting from studies of (52) _____

sequences from ribosomal RNA, (53) _____ DNA, or specific (54) _____ . In some cases,

the molecular analyses have supported the major (55) _____ already identified, such as the grouping

of the (56) _____ and the Bilateria; however, in other cases, the molecular analyses have compelled

re-evaluation of an original classification, such as the new evidence that indicated that segmentation evolved

by convergent evolution independently in (57) _____ lineages rather than in two lineages. A(n)

(58) _____ tree could be revised at any time as further molecular studies are completed.

25.4 Phylum Porifera [pp. 585–587]
25.5 Metazoans with Radial Symmetry [pp. 587–591]

Section Review (Fill-in-the-Blanks)

Originally believed to be Parazoan, the (59) _____ phylum is actually (60) _____ , although

it has no symmetry and no nerves. Sponges are (61) _____ feeders, taking in water through

(62) _____ (perforations) located in the two layers of cells that compose the body wall.

(63) _____ as adults, sponges are only motile as (64) _____ . There are two phyla of

Metazoans with radial symmetry: the (65) _____ , which include corals and jellyfish, and the

(66) _____ , the comb jellies. Organisms in both of these phyla have body walls composed of

(67) _____ layers of cells that surround a(n) (68) _____ cavity, which has a large opening,

the (69) _____ , at one end. Cnidarians, whether they have an upright (70) _____ form or a

bell-shaped (71) _____ form, have an interesting way of capturing prey; specialized cells called

(72) _____ release whipping threads, (73) _____ , that sting or paralyze their prey.

Ctenophores, which use (74) _____ filaments to capture their prey, are the largest animals to use

(75) _____ for movement.

Choice

For each of the following terms, choose all phyla that it applies to (i.e., a term may apply to more than one phylum).

76.	____	Nematocysts	A.	Phylum Porifera
77.	____	Mesoglea	B.	Phylum Cnidaria
78.	____	Sea anemones	C.	Phylum Ctenophora
79.	____	Filter feeder		
80.	____	Comb jellies		
81.	____	Either polyp and/or medusa form		
82.	____	Sessile during part/all of life cycle		
83.	____	Metazoan		
84.	____	Venus flower basket		
85.	____	Gastrovascular cavity		
86.	____	Spongocoel		
87.	____	Nerve cells		
88.	____	Corals		
89.	____	Asymmetrical		
90.	____	Use cilia for locomotion		

25.6 Lophotrochozoan Protostomes [pp. 592–604]

Section Review (Fill-in-the-Blanks)

The protostomes, all of which show (91) _____ symmetry, can be divided into (92) _____

major lineages: the (93) _____, which consists of eight phyla, and the (94) _____, which

consists of (95) _____ phyla. In the Lophotrochozoan lineage, three of the phyla possess a(n)

(96) _____, a fold with ciliated tentacles around the mouth that the organisms use to

(97) _____ food as well as for (98) _____ exchange. Of these three lophophorate phyla,

organisms belonging to the (99) _____ phylum live as colonies; organisms of the

(100) _____ phylum are protected by two shells composed of (101) _____; and in the third

phylum, the (102) _____ build tubes of chitin to live in. The animals of the phylum

(103) _____ have flat bodies and so are commonly known as (104) _____. They have

relatively complex systems, including a(n) (105) _____ system, which can include a protruding pharynx; a(n) (106) _____ system, which includes an anterior concentration of nerve tissue called

a(n) (107) _____; a(n) (108) _____ system, which contains organs such as an ovary and

testis; and a(n) (109) _____ system, which uses (110) _____ cells to remove wastes. Of the

(111) _____ flatworm groups or classes, only one, class (112) _____, is free-living; the rest

are (113) _____. An individual of the phylum (114) _____ has a wheel-like structure around

its head that is covered in (115) _____, which it uses for locomotion and to obtain food. When

environmental conditions are good, rotifers reproduce by (116) _____, producing female offspring

from diploid (117) _____ eggs. Individuals in both Rotifera and Nemertea phyla have

(118) _____ digestive tracts since food enters the (119) _____, passes through the stomach

and intestines, and exits from the (120) _____. Organisms belonging to the phylum Nemertea are

unique in that they have a chamber that houses a(n) (121) _____, which they use to capture prey

when (122) _____. The characteristics of the phylum Mollusca include a body that is divided into

(123) _____ regions: the (124) _____ _____, which contains many of the major

organ systems; the (125) _____-_____, which is primarily used for locomotion; and the

(126) _____, which usually functions as a protective covering. This phylum is composed of

(127) _____ classes, the largest being class (128) _____ (comprised of snails and slugs) and

the most intelligent of the invertebrates being class (129) _____ (octopuses and related species). The

last phylum of this lineage, phylum (130) _____, is composed of (131) _____ classes of

organisms. All annelids have bodies that are divided into (132) _____ by partitions called

(133) _____. Some organ systems appear as repeating units in each of the segments, such as the

paired (134) _____ of the excretory system. Bristles called (135) _____ are used for traction

in both class (136) _____ (bristle worms) and class (137) _____ (earthworms), but they are

lacking in class (138) _____ (leeches).

Matching

Match each of the following with its correct definition.

139. ____ platys	A.	Excretory system of flatworms
140. ____ moll	B.	Soft
141. ____ Trochophore	C.	Few
142. ____ Metanephridia	D.	Wheel
143. ____ helminth	E.	Folding door
144. ____ rota	F.	Bristles
145. ____ Parthenogenesis	G.	Ring
146. ____ gaster	H.	Excretory system of segmented worms
147. ____ Radula	I.	Cephalopods and Annelids
148. ____ pod	J.	Belly
149. ____ oligo	K.	Unfertilized egg develops into a female
150. ____ Flame cells	L.	Food scraping device of molluscs
151. ____ Closed circulation	M.	Foot
152. ____ valv	N.	Worm
153. ____ annelis	O.	Larval form of molluscs
154. ____ Setae	P.	Flat

Complete the Table

Phylum	Organism (Common Name)
155.	Fluke
Nemertea	156.
157.	Earthworm
158.	Brachiopod
Rotifera	159.
160.	Clam

25.7 Ecdysozoan Protostomes [pp. 604–614]

Section Review (Fill-in-the-Blanks)

The adaptation of shedding a hard exterior cuticle, called a(n) (161) _____, is a major characteristic

of the (162) _____ phyla that comprise the (163) _____ protostome lineage. Most of the

animals in the phylum (164) _____, the round worms, are very successful (165) _____,

infecting organisms in most other phyla globally. Velvet worms, belonging to the phylum

(166) _____, have superficial segmentation and live primarily in the (167) _____

hemisphere. The phylum (168) _____ consists of a large and diverse group of animals, composing

approximately (169) _____-_____ of all living species. An arthropod sheds it exoskeleton

by the process of (170) _____ and then replaces it as the animal (171) _____. Its body is

composed of three body segments, the (172) _____, thorax, and (173) _____ (from front to

back), although in some species, the head and thorax fuse to form a(n) (174) _____.

Short Answer

175. Identify and discuss one disadvantage of shedding (moulting) the external covering or exoskeleton.

_____

_____

176. Explain how parasitic nematodes are so successful.

_____

_____

Matching

Match each of the following with its correct definition.

177.	_____	crusta	A.	Claw
178.	_____	lob	B.	Shell
179.	_____	arthros	C.	Horn
180.	_____	nemata	D.	Six
181.	_____	cheol	E.	Jointed
182.	_____	instar	F.	Thread
183.	_____	hex	G.	Lobed
184.	_____	cera	H.	Developmental stage

Choice

Given the animal characteristics, select the most appropriate phyla (and subphyla when possible).

185. ____	Cephalothorax	A.	Nematoda
186. ____	Antennae	B.	Arthropoda
187. ____	Book lungs	C.	Chelicerata
188. ____	Compound eyes	D.	Onychophora
189. ____	Malpighian tubules	E.	Subphylum Hexapoda
190. ____	Numerous unjointed legs		
191. ____	Metamorphosis		

SELF-TEST

1. Which of the following is the most unique to animals? [pp. 579–580]

   a. sexual reproduction
   b. eukaryotic
   c. heterotrophic
   d. multicellular

2. Which pair are NOT appropriately matched? [pp. 581–583]

   a. protostomes—spiral cleavage
   b. deuterostomes—radial cleavage
   c. bilateral symmetry—cephalization
   d. platyhelminthes—coelomate

3. Which characteristic is different protostomes and deuterostomes? [pp. 582–584]

   a. segmentation
   b. origin of mesoderm
   c. bilateral symmetry
   d. triploblastic

4. What is the most likely type of animal to have determinate cleavage and a nervous system located on the ventral side of the body? [pp. 582–584]

   a. protostome
   b. deuterostome
   c. asymmetrical animal

5. In protostomes, what does the blastopore develop into? [pp. 582–584]

   a. into a mouth
   b. into an anus
   c. from the mesoderm
   d. from the schizocoleom

6. What embryonic tissue is the lining of the gut formed from? [pp. 580–582]

   a. mesoderm
   b. endoderm
   c. ectoderm

7. Which type of symmetry applies to animals that have undergone cephalization in their development? [p. 581]

   a. asymmetrical
   b. radially symmetrical
   c. bilaterally symmetrical

8. Which statement describes a phylogenetic tree resulting from the collection of morphological innovation, embryological patterning, and molecular analyses? [pp. 584–585]

   a. It will appear the same as a tree developed without molecular information.
   b. It is in its final form and will not require further revision in the future.
   c. It identifies the schizocoelomate condition as ancestral.
   d. It indicates that a segmented common ancestor resulted in segmented protostome phyla.

9. Which of the following describes an animal that has the ability to produce both eggs and sperm? [pp. 585–586]

   a. able to undergo parthenogenesis
   b. monoecious
   c. able to undergo metamorphosis
   d. parasitic

10. Some sponges produce a cluster of cells that germinate only under favourable conditions. What are these called? [pp. 585–586]

    a. nematocysts
    b. gemmules
    c. polyps
    d. porocytes

11. Which of the following does NOT undergo polymorphic development during its life? [pp. 585–590]

    a. *Obelia*
    b. sponges
    c. coral
    d. *Hydra*

12. Where would you expect to find animals that have a radula? [pp. 592–604]

    a. at the bottom of a water body or among rocks
    b. in trees
    c. living in the respiratory system of other animals
    d. living on the surface of a fish

13. Cephalopods have a closed circulatory system. Why is this thought to be important to this group or organisms? [pp. 600–602]

    a. increases buoyancy
    b. provides the high oxygen requirement for movement
    c. supports beak-like jaws to capture prey
    d. provides space for the storage of sperm in males

14. Which pair is NOT appropriately matched? [pp. 593–603]

    a. flame cell excretory system—Platyhelminthes
    b. setae—Annelida
    c. corona and mastax—Nemertea
    c. mantle—Mollusca

15. What tiny Lophotrochozoan makes up a large component of fresh water zooplankton? [pp. 593–600]

    a. flatworm
    b. mussel
    c. chiton
    d. rotifer

16. How do insects differ from spiders? [pp. 606–613]

    a. only spiders modify the first pair of appendages into pedipalps
    b. only spiders have chelicerae
    c. only spiders have Malpighian tubules
    d. only spiders undergo complete metamorphosis

17. Which of the following animals has ganglia and a pair of metanephridia in each of its segments? [pp. 602–613]

    a. a roundworm
    b. an annelid
    c. an insect
    d. a spider

18. Which group of arthropods consists of individuals with a separate head and thorax (not fused)? [pp. 606–612]

    a. spiders
    b. centipedes
    c. insects
    d. shrimps

19. Why are insects that undergo complete metamorphosis successful? [pp. 603–614]

    a. because the larvae and the adults are both able to fly
    b. because the larvae and the adults are both able to undergo pupation
    c. because the larvae and the adults occupy different habitats and eat different food
    d. because the larvae and the adults have the same body form

INTEGRATING AND APPLYING KEY CONCEPTS

1. Discuss the major characteristics that make an organism an animal.

2. Why are three "worms"—tapeworms, round worms, and earthworms—not grouped in the same phylum?

3. Why is segmentation considered to be a result of convergent evolution?

26 Diversity of Animals 2: Deuterostomes: Vertebrates and Their Closest Relatives

TOPIC MAP

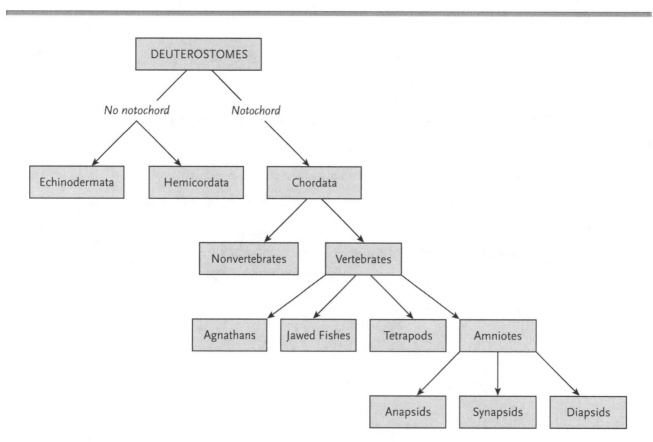

LEARNING OUTCOMES AND STUDY STRATEGIES

By the end of this chapter, you should be able to

- Differentiate between organisms within and between each of the major groups in terms of their characteristics and their habitats
- Explain the importance of interpreting information, such as molecular data, to classification
- Explain how modification of certain structures lead to the evolution of more recent or derived structures
- Explain the concept of convergent evolution

Study strategies for this chapter:

- First, focus on major groupings of deuterostomes, identifying general characteristics associated with each.
- Next, make comparisons within and between groups, looking at the tremendous diversity of these animals.
- Examine how adaptations have enhanced success in a given habitat.
- Go through one section of the textbook at a time, keeping track of the headings and subheadings. Then work through the companion section of the study guide.
- Use the Study Break sections of the textbook and the Review section of the textbook as well as this study guide section to help guide you on the level of detail.
- When you are done, try deriving your own topic map(s) or add detail to the existing topic map.

INTERACTIVE EXERCISES

Why It Matters [pp. 617–619]

Section Review (Fill-in-the-Blanks)

The use of (1) _____ _____, as well as morphology and development patterns, has provided

information for the (2) _____ of animals into (3) _____ trees. However, making correct

choices means looking beyond (4) _____ and may even require careful interpretation of the

(5) _____ data. An example is the classification of a group of ciliated marine worms called

(6) _____. Confusion about their phylogeny was resolved when it was determined that some of the

(7) _____ information obtained from the organism was actually from its (8) _____ prey.

After resolving that issue, that group of organisms was identified as a new (9) _____ within the

Deuterostomes.

26.1 Deuterostomes [pp. 619–620]
26.2 Phylum Echinodermata [pp. 620–623]
26.3 Phylum Hemichordata [pp. 623–624]

Section Review (Fill-in-the-Blanks)

One of the unifying characteristics of a deuterostome is that during development, the (10) _____

arises from a(n) (11) _____ opening and the (12) _____ from a second opening. In the

nervous system of phylum Echinodermata, nerve cords surround the (13) _____ and radiate outward

into rays, or (14) "_____," whereas in the phylum Hemichordata, a dorsal nerve (15) _____

is present but is not as developed as that found in the phylum Chordata. A(n) (16) _____ echinoderm

develops from a(n) (17) _____ symmetrical larva, which, as it develops, forms a(n)

(18) _____ symmetrical body, often with (19) _____ rays. This phylum uses a(n)

(20) _____ vascular system for movement, which involves the flow of fluid into and out of

(21) _____ feet. The phylum (22) _____ is a small group of (23) _____ worms.

These animals are organized with an anterior (24) _____ that tunnels into soil, as well as mouth and

gill slits (connected by a pharynx). Water flows into the (25) _____ from the mouth, drawn by

beating (26) _____, and exits through the gill slits; food particles are trapped and diverted to the

(27) _____ system, and gases are exchanged across the partitions between the (28) _____

_____.

Matching

Match each of the following roots with its correct definition.

29.	____	Derm	A.	Half
30.	____	Echino	B.	Opening
31.	____	Hemi	C.	Skin
32.	____	Stomia	D.	Second
33.	____	Deuteron	E.	Spiny

For each characteristics or structures, match the term with its description from the list below.

34. ____ Proboscis   A. Calcium-stiffened structures of endoskeleton

35. ____ Water vascular system   B. Surface opposite to the mouth

36. ____ Aboral   C. Sievelike plate through which water enters

37. ____ Ring canal   D. Used to burrow into sand or mud

38. ____ Tube feet   E. Location where water exits in hemichordates

39. ____ Madreporite   F. Small pincers at base of spines to remove fallen debris

40. ____ Gill slits   G. Fusion of ossicles; protection but reduced flexibility

41. ____ Test   H. Protrusions for movement using internal flow of fluids

42. ____ Pedicellariae   I. Hemichordate equivalent of the notochord

43. ____ Ossicle   J. Tube that surrounds esophagus

44. ____ Stomochord   K. System of fluid-filled canals used for movement

Short Answer

45. What is the relevance of the common name of the Ophiuroidea, "Brittle Stars"?

_____

_____

26.4 Phylum Chordata [pp. 624-626]
26.5 The Origin and Diversification of Vertebrates [pp. 626–628]

Section Review (Fill-in-the-Blanks)

All organisms in the phylum Chordata are characterized, at some point in their lives, by: paired

(46) _____ _____ in the pharynx, a dorsal hollow (47) _____ chord,

(48) _____ muscles in the body wall and tail, and a(n) (49) _____ (a flexible rod of fluid-

filled cells). The latter is the (50) _____ of invertebrate chordates. Unlike organisms in the Vertebrata

subphylum, the organisms in the other two subphyla are (51) _____, lacking a(n) (52) _____

column. With the exception of the (53) _____ fishes, the (54) _____, or spine, of the

vertebrates is made of (55) _____, an innovation unique to these animals. The other two morphological innovations of vertebrates are the (56) _____, or bony protective covering for the brain, and (57) _____ crest cells. The vertebrates are a diverse group of organisms, much of the diversity arising from repeated (58) _____ of a homeotic gene called the (59) _____ gene. These genes are arranged in a particular order to form a (60) _____, such that each of the component genes controls the (61) _____ of a particular structure (such as eyes, wings, or legs) and therefore the (62) _____ of the organism. There is a correlation between the number of these genes and the (63) _____ of an animal's structure.

Matching

Match each of the following roots with its correct definition.

64. ____	Noto	A.	Not
65. ____	Tetra	B.	Head
66. ____	Gnath	C.	Back
67. ____	Stoma	D.	Mouth
68. ____	Uro	E.	Tail
69. ____	A	F.	String
70. ____	Pod	G.	Jawed
71. ____	Cephalo	H.	Four
72. ____	Chord	I.	Foot

Choice

For each characteristic or structure, select the most appropriate animal group from the list below.

73. ____	Dorsal hollow nerve chord	A.	Subphylum Vertebrata
74. ____	Atriopore in adult	B.	Phylum Chordata
75. ____	Vertebral column	C.	Subphylum Urochordata
76. ____	Head-to-tail notochord	D.	Subphylum Cephalochordata
77. ____	Atrial siphon		
78. ____	Bone		
79. ____	Segmented muscle in body wall and tail		
80. ____	Cranium		

81. _____ Neural crest

82. _____ Gill slits in pharynx

83. _____ Oral hood with tentacles

True/False

Mark if the statement is true (T) or false (F). If the statement is false, justify your answer in the lines below each statement.

84. _____ Air breathing vertebrates have lost their gill slits.

_____

_____

85. _____ The purpose of the vertebrate backbone is to protect the dorsal nerve chord.

_____

_____

86. _____ Adult sea squirts are sessile and have lost their gill slits and dorsal hollow nerve chords but retain their notochords.

_____

_____

87. _____ The lancelets and sea squirts both expel water through atriopores.

_____

_____

Short Answer

88. What is the invertebrate equivalent to the vertebrate brain?

_____

_____

89. Among the vertebrates, why are the sharks and rays unique?

_____

_____

90. What makes up the axial skeleton of vertebrates?

_____

_____

26.6 Agnathans: Hagfishes and Lampreys, Conodonts, and Ostracoderms [pp. 628–630]
26.7 Jawed Fishes: Jaws Expanded the Feeding Opportunities for Vertebrates [pp. 630–635]

Section Review (Fill-in-the-Blanks)

The jawless fishes or (91) _____, were the earliest vertebrates. They suck water into their mouths

using a muscular (92) _____; (93) _____ filter out the food and exchange gases. Today, only

two groups remain: the (94) _____, which feed on invertebrates and dead or dying fish, and the

(95) _____, many of which feed by rasping a hole in a live fish with its (96) _____ disk and

ingesting the body fluids. Jaws evolved from fish gill (97) _____, and provided an advantage by

allowing fish to eat (98) _____ food pieces. One group of jawed fish, the class (99) _____,

has derived a trait from the ancestral bony endoskeleton; these fish are entirely cartilaginous. Both skates and

rays, which have a(n) (100) _____ flattened shape, belong to this group, as well as

(101) _____, a dominant predator in the ocean. All three groups belong to the subclass

(102) _____. Based on sheer numbers, the (103) _____ fishes are the most successful of all

vertebrates. They have a lightweight (104) _____, consisting of a cranium, a vertebral column, and

bones supporting fins, as well as a covering of smooth and lightweight (105) _____ that are coated

with (106) _____. Fish of the class Actinopterygii, i.e., the (107) _____-_____ fish

outnumber those of class Sarcopterygii , the (108) _____-_____ fish. The most recently

evolved subclass within the Actinopterygii, the (109) _____, have a(n) (110) _____, a flap

of the body wall on each side of the head to protect the gills. They also have an improved sensory system,

which includes a(n) (111) _____ line system that allows them to detect (112) _____ in

water.

Matching

Match each of the following roots, terms, or structures with its correct definition or descriptor.

113.	_____	Plac	A.	Oil in liver of sharks
114.	_____	Chondr	B.	Sarcopterygii
115.	_____	Lateral line system	C.	Ray
116.	_____	Ichthy	D.	Increases surface area in digestive tract
117.	_____	Sturgeons	E.	Hydrostatic organ
118.	_____	Claspers	F.	Fish
119.	_____	Acanth	G.	Plate
120.	_____	Squalene	H.	Cartilage
121.	_____	Acti	I.	Flap covering chamber containing gills
122.	_____	Spiral valve	J.	Actinopterygii
123.	_____	Swim bladder	K.	Reproductive specializations on the dorsal fins of male chondrichthyans
124.	_____	Lungfish	L.	Spine
125.	_____	Ptery	M.	Detects vibrations in water
126.	_____	Operculum	N.	Fin

True/False

Mark if the statement is true (T) or false (F). If the statement is false, justify your answer in the lines below each statement.

127. _____ The hagfish have a larval stage that may last years; however, the lamprey has no larval stage.

_____

_____

128. _____ The nerve chord of lampreys is partially protected by cartilage, unlike hagfish.

_____

_____

129. _____ The elasmobranches possess electroreceptors and some rays possess an electric organ that allow them to stun prey with electrical shocks.

_____

_____

130. _____ Hagfish and lampreys are chondrichthyans.

_____

_____

Short Answer

131. In addition to feeding, what are some other functions that jaws serve?

_____

_____

132. What adaptations allow sharks to swim after their prey so quickly?

_____

_____

133. What is the purpose of the mucous layer on bony fishes?

_____

_____

134. What is the difference between ray-finned and fleshy-finned fishes?

_____

_____

26.8 Early Tetrapods and Modern Amphibians [pp. 635–638]

Section Review (Fill-in-the-Blanks)

Life on land requires several important characteristics, including a system for locomotion and adaptations for

survival in a(n) (135) _____-breathing environment. For example, early tetrapods developed a(n)

(136) _____ system that included a more robust vertebral column and a(n) (137) _____ girdle

that was not fused with the cranium (both of which aided in movement), as well as a(n) (138) _____, or

eardrum, on either side of the head to detect (139) _____ waves. Many adult amphibians have thin,

scaleless skin through which (140) _____ exchange can occur. For this kind of exchange to occur,

however, the skin must be kept (141) _____, limiting such organisms to moist environments. Most have

(142) _____ and use these in gas exchange. Amphibians at the (143) _____ stage, the

developmental portion of their life cycle, often require a(n) (144) _____ habitat, but as adults, they may live on land or in water or move between (145) _____ habitats. There are three groups of amphibians:

the (146) _____, which consists of frogs and (147) _____; the (148) _____, which are

the salamanders; and the (149) _____, which are the caecilians.

Matching

Match each of the following with its correct definition.

150. ____	Gymnos	A.	Bone homologous to support structure of jaws, involved in hearing
151. ____	Bios	B.	Both
152. ____	Stapes	C.	Membrane that vibrates with sound waves
153. ____	Del	D.	Snakelike
154. ____	Amphi	E.	Naked
155. ____	Ophioneos	F.	Tail
156. ____	Tympanum	G.	Life
157. ____	Uro	H.	Visible

26.9 The Origin and Mesozoic Radiations of Amniotes [pp. 638–643]

Section Review (Fill-in-the-Blanks)

Amniotes are characterized by a fluid-filled (158) _____ that surrounds the (159) _____, called

the (160) _____. These animals have several important characteristics that enhance their ability to

survive in a(n) (161) _____ environment. First, their (162) _____ will not dehydrate because

its cells are filled with (163) _____ and lipids, which makes it (164) _____. Second, the

amniote egg has a hard, leathery (165) _____ containing microscopic pores and four specialized

(166) _____ that, together, make it resistant to (167) _____ (drying up). The shell facilitates

exchange of (168) _____ and water between the egg and its environment. The developing embryo

obtains its energy from the egg (169) _____ while the (170) _____ provides nutrients and

water. The third characteristic of amniotes is that they produce nontoxic (171) _____ and/or uric acid

waste instead of (172) _____. There are three groups of amniotes, distinguished by the number of bony

arches in the (173) _____ region of the skull: the (174) _____ have no temporal arches; the

(175) _____ have one temporal arch; and the (176) _____ have two.

Matching

Match each of the following with its correct definition.

177.	_____	Morph	A.	Lizard
178.	_____	Di	B.	Scale
179.	_____	Apsid	C.	With
180.	_____	Sauro	D.	Two
181.	_____	Syn	E.	Ruler
182.	_____	Archo	F.	Form
183.	_____	Lepi	G.	Connection

26.10 Subclass Testudines: Turtles and Tortoises [pp. 643–644]
26.11 Living Diapsids: Sphenodontids, Squamates, and Crocodilians [pp. 644–645]
26.12 Aves: Birds [pp. 645–650]

Section Review (Fill-in-the-Blanks)

Turtles and tortoises are amniotes that are (184) _____ since they have no temporal arches in their

skulls. An animal in this group is characterized by its boxlike (185) _____, which has the animal's

(186) _____ fused to the inside. When under attack, most (187) _____ into their shells.

Another of the amniotic groups, the diapsids, have (188) _____ temporal arches. Two lineages of

diapsids exist: the (189) _____ and the (190) _____. Arising from the former is the order

(191) _____, which includes lizards and (192) _____. Arising from the latter is the order

(193) _____, which includes the (194) _____, alligators, gavials, and the group composed of

animals with wings, the (195) _____. Three innovations to the skeleton are associated with their

ability to fly: they have a(n) (196) _____ _____ (breastbone), a(n) (197) _____

(wishbone), and (198) _____ processes on the ribs. Additional adaptations include

(199) _____ limb bones with small supporting struts to provide strength, and feathers. Birds exhibit

extensive ecological specialization: for example, (200) _____ size and shape reflect diet,

(201) _____ size and shape reflect swimming or flight requirements, and their (202) _____

vary depending upon whether they are predators or swimmers.

Choice

For each characteristic or structure, select the most appropriate animal group from the list below.

203. _____ Third eye

204. _____ Keeled sternum

205. _____ Periodically shed their skin

206. _____ Furculum

207. _____ Overlapping keratinized scales

208. _____ Possess muscles analogous to diaphragm in mammals

209. _____ Boxlike shell

210. _____ Uncinate processes on ribs

211. _____ Girdles inside rib cage

A. Turtles

B. Birds

C. Crocodiles and alligators

D. Tuatara

E. Lizards and snakes

True/False

Mark if the statement is true (T) or false (F). If the statement is false, justify your answer in the lines below each statement.

212. _____ Flightless birds generally lack a furculum but maintain the keeled sternum and uncinate processes on the ribs.

_____

_____

213. _____ Birds lack a urinary bladder.

_____

_____

214. _____ Birds' feathers are derived from the scales of their reptilian ancestors.

_____

_____

Short Answer

215. What is the function of the keeled sternum and furculum of birds?

_____

_____

26.13 Mammalia: Monotremes, Marsupials, and Placentals [pp. 650–653]
26.14 Evolutionary Convergence and Mammalian Diversity: Tails to Teeth [pp. 653–658]

Section Review (Fill-in-the-Blanks)

Mammals are part of the (216) _____ lineage, having only one (217) _____ arch. Due to their

extensive diversity, there are no definitive characteristics; however, most mammals are (218) _____, a

body covering that helps maintain a stable and elevated temperature, and are (219) _____ (endo-

thermic). Other structures usually found in these organisms include a(n) (220) _____, (a layer of muscle

separating the chest cavity and viscera), two (221) _____ condyles where the skull attaches to the neck,

a secondary (222) _____ comprising the roof of the mouth, and a brain (223) _____ for

processing information. Although some mammals have no teeth, many are (224) _____, having

different teeth for different functions, as well as (225) _____, producing an earlier set of

(226) _____ teeth and a later set of (227) _____ teeth. Many mammals feed their young

(228) _____, which is produced in mammary glands. One of the major differences between groups of

mammals is their mode of (229) _____. One group, the (230) _____ (also called Prototheria),

lay eggs; another group, the (231) _____ mammals, produce offspring that complete their embryonic

development in the uterus; and a third group, the (232) _____, produce offspring that begin their

development in the uterus but finish their development attached to a(n) (233) _____ located in an

abdominal pouch called the (234) _____.

Matching

Match each of the following derivatives and characteristics with its correct definition.

235.	____	Eu	A.	Wild beast
236.	____	Heterodont	B.	Hoof
237.	____	Diphyodont	C.	Between
238.	____	Precocial	D.	Helpless at birth
239.	____	Marsupium	E.	Two generations of teeth
240.	____	Theri	F.	Individual teeth specialized for different functions
241.	____	Proto	G.	Quickly mobile when born
242.	____	Atricial	H.	Good

243.	____	Meta	I.	Cheek teeth
244.	____	Ungula	J.	First
245.	____	Molar	K.	Purse

SELF-TEST

1. Which is characteristic of Deuterostomia? [pp. 619–624]
   a. Their anus develops from a blastopore and their mouth from a second opening.
   b. They have two openings in their bodies.
   c. The have bilateral symmetry.
   d. They have a dorsal hollow nerve chord.

2. Which characteristics are correct for Echinoderms? [pp. 620–622]
   a. The larvae are radially symmetrical.
   b. The adults are bilaterally symmetrical.
   c. They have tube feet that attach to substrate when filled with water.
   d. They have internal sexual reproduction with the male gametes entering through the madreporite.

3. If an animal has pedicellariae and a larval form with bilateral symmetry, to which group would it belong? [p. 622]
   a. Ophinuroidea
   b. Asteroidea
   c. Echinoidea
   d. Urochordata

4. Which structure is unique to the Echinodermata? [pp. 620–622]
   a. a notochord
   b. gill slits
   c. a proboscis
   d. a water vascular system

5. Which is characteristic of sea cucumbers? [p. 623]
   a. The larvae have bilaterally symmetrical bodies.
   b. They have ten rows of tube feet.
   c. They have a symbiotic relationship with pearl fish.
   d. They belong to the Asteroidea group.

6. Which subphylum of chordates are free-living larvae and sessile adults? [pp. 624–625]
   a. Echinodermata
   b. Hemichordata
   c. Urochordata
   d. Cephalochordata
   e. Vertebrata

7. Which group would you expect to have the greatest number of *Hox* gene complexes? [pp. 626, 633–634]
   a. Lamprey
   b. Hagfish
   c. Placoderm
   d. Seahorse

8. Which of these classes of fish do NOT contain any bone (totally cartilaginous)? [pp. 628–635]
   a. Actinopterygii
   b. Chondrichthyes
   c. Placodermi
   d. Sacropterygii

9. Which of the following are believed to have given rise to the jaw? [p. 630]

   a. gill arches
   b. gill slits
   c. the notochord
   d. the cranium

10. Which of the following belong to the Gnathostomata lineage? [pp. 630–631]

    a. Hagfishes
    b. Lampreys
    c. Conodonts
    d. Acanthodian

11. If the swim bladder of a bony fish were destroyed, what would be the effect? [p. 633]

    a. The fish would be unable to excrete waste.
    b. The fish would not be able to breathe underwater.
    c. The fish would be closer to the surface of the water.
    d. The fish would be farther away from the surface of the water.

12. Which would be a problem associated with moving from an aquatic environment to a terrestrial one? [pp. 635–639]

    a. The organism could become easily dehydrated.
    b. The organism could become face increased predation.
    c. The organism would be less likely to find a mate.
    d. The organism could die from starvation due to lack of food.

13. Why are blood vessels under the skin in adult amphibians important? [pp. 636–637]

    a. They keep the animals warm.
    b. They carry gases to and from the site of gas exchange.
    c. They provide a method of sensing sound waves.
    d. They provide support for this class of tetrapods.

14. Which of the following is NOT an adaptation associated with colonization of a terrestrial environment? [pp. 638–639]

    a. keratin and lipid in skin cells
    b. ammonium as a waste product
    c. perforated pharynx in the adult form
    d. lateral line system

15. Which diapsids have a four-chambered heart? [pp. 639–645]

    a. Tuataras
    b. Crocodiles
    c. Turtles
    d. Lizards
    e. Snakes

16. Of the following, which is the most advantageous for flight? [pp. 645–646]

    a. an amniotic egg
    b. bipedal locomotion
    c. hollow limb bones
    d. a dorsal hollow nerve chord

17. Which group of amniotes detects prey using a long tongue and has the associated sensory receptors in the roof of its mouth? [p. 645]

    a. birds
    b. alligators
    c. turtles
    d. tortoises
    e. snakes

18. Which of the following does NOT have a prototheria reproductive mode? [pp. 649–653]

    a. monotremes
    b. mammals that lay eggs
    c. duck-billed platypus
    d. Aves

19. Which of the following is example of convergent evolution? [pp. 653–654]

    a. a dorsoventrally flattened tail
    b. development of feathers
    c. teeth used for different functions, such as crushing or cutting
    d. development of bone

20. How many times can mammals replace teeth?
    [pp. 653–656]

    a. > 10 times
    b. 2 to10 times
    c. one time
    d. not all mammals have teeth

INTEGRATING AND APPLYING KEY CONCEPTS

1. Discuss how the adult echinoderm—a sea star—is significantly different from a human, yet both are considered to be deuterostomes.

2. Address the major characteristics or adaptations that enhanced or allowed movement from an aquatic to a terrestrial environment.

3. What are some of the defensive structures or responses seen in extant deuterostomes?

27 The Plant Body

TOPIC MAP

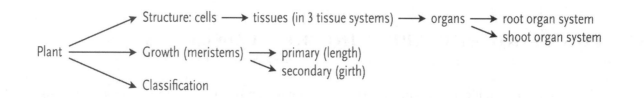

LEARNING OUTCOMES AND STUDY STRATEGIES

By the end of this chapter, you should be able to

- Describe differences between plant and animal structure and growth
- Differentiate between root system and shoot system structures, components, and functions
- Identify and describe three different ways to classify angiosperms
- Describe plant primary and secondary growth in stems and roots

Study strategies for this chapter:

- Concentrate on the key concepts of the overview of plant structure and growth before tackling the specifics (review of Chapter 24 may be helpful).
- Focus on terminology, categorizing plant components and their functions upon which to build in terms of forming the plant body and its processes for growth.

INTERACTIVE EXERCISES

Why It Matters [pp. 662–663]

Section Review (Fill-in-the-Blanks)

Most plants develop from seeds located in soil, producing an underground (1) _____ system that

accesses (2) _____ and nutrients and an above-ground (3) _____ system that provides

energy from sunlight. Banyan trees, however, produce seeds that germinate in the (4) _____ of a host

tree, aggressively form (5) _____ downward around the host's trunk and into the ground, and then

develop morphologically thick (6) _____ that allow them to (7) _____ the host tree for light,

eventually strangling the host tree.

27.1 Plant Structure and Growth: An Overview [pp. 663–668]

Section Review (Fill-in-the-Blanks)

Focusing on flowering plants, called (8) _____, stems, leaves, and, if present, flowers are organs that

make up the (9) _____ system of a plant. Within an organ, each tissue is composed of groups of

(10) _____ that function together to perform specific tasks. Although animal and plant cells contain

many of the same components, only plant cells contain (11) _____, which function in photosynthesis;

(12) _____, which can provide storage and assist in cell elongation and cell rigidity; and

(13) _____, which give cells strength and flexibility. Many plants have a secondary cell wall within

their cells that is laid down inside the primary, cellulose cell wall. The secondary cell wall contains

(14) _____, which is a waterproof substance that also strengthens the cell wall.

Choice

For each of the following characteristics, choose whether it belongs to a terrestrial PLANT (P) or a
terrestrial ANIMAL (A).

15. _____ Presence of an apical meristem

16. _____ A chemoheterotroph

17. _____ Determinate growth

18. _____ Can undergo totipotency

19. _____ Presence of a cell wall containing cellulose

20. _____ Sessile

21. _____ Growth occurs primarily by mitosis (not cell elongation)

True/False

Mark if the statement is true (T) or false (F). If the statement is false, make it correct by changing the
underlined word(s) and writing the correct word(s) in the lines below each statement.

22. _____ Plants undergoing totipotency are <u>unable</u> to dedifferentiate.

_____

_____

23. _____ Solutes move between adjacent plant cells through <u>plasmodesmata</u>.

_____

_____

24. _____ Increases in the height of a plant are due to cell divisions in the <u>root apical meristem</u>.

_____

_____

25. _____ Lateral meristems give rise to <u>primary</u> tissues.

_____

_____

26. _____ <u>Herbaceous</u> plants show little or no secondary growth.

_____

_____

Complete the Table

Complete the following tables. In A, provide the appropriate description of monocots or eudicots for each of the traits identified; in B, use three different methods of classification to categorize each plant.

A.

Trait	Monocots	Eudicots
Flower parts	27.	Multiples of 4 or 5
Vascular bundles in stem	28.	Arranged in a ring
Leaf veins	Parallel	29.
Root systems	Fibrous	30.

B.

Plant (Common Name)	Life Span	Monocot or Dicot	Herbaceous or Woody Plant
Willow Tree	31.	Dicot	32.
Corn	Annual	33.	Herbaceous
Carrot	34.	35.	Herbaceous

27.2 The Three Plant Tissue Systems [pp. 668–672]

Section Review (Fill-in-the-Blanks)

Plants have three tissue systems that are the basis of plant organs. These tissue systems are the

(36) _____ _____ _____, which makes up most of the plant body; the

(37) _____ _____ _____, which makes up the transport system in the plant; and

(38) _____ _____ _____, which forms the "skin" of the plant. There are three types

of cells that make up ground tissue. Thin-walled and irregularly shaped (39) _____ cells comprise most

of the primary body (roots, stems, leaves, flowers, and fruits), (40) _____ cells provide flexible support

and tend to be elongated, and (41) _____ cells provide rigid support and protection.

Compare and Contrast

Provide the similarities and differences between the structures identified in the following questions.

42. Compare and contrast the structure of the three types of tissues that can be found in the ground tissue system.

    _____

    _____

43. Compare and contrast the structure and function of tracheids and vessel members.

    _____

    _____

Match

Match each of the types of cells with the description(s) of its structure.

44. _____	Tracheids	A.	Contain perforations at the ends for water and mineral movement
45. _____	Parenchyma	B.	Produces lignified secondary walls; dead at maturity
46. _____	Vessel members	C.	Have plate containing pores at each end
47. _____	Epidermal cells	D.	Primary cell walls of cellulose and pectin
48. _____	Sieve tube members	E.	Specialized form controls size of stomata
49. _____	Collenchyma	F.	Many contain chloroplasts
50. _____	Sclerenchyma	G.	Tapered cells that use pits for water transport

Choice

For each of the following plant functions, choose the most appropriate tissue and/or tissue systems associated with it. (Note that choices may be used more than once.)

51. _____ Provides protection and reduces plant water loss

A. Dermal tissue system

52. _____ Gives plant structure and rigidit.

B. Ground tissue system

53. _____ Provides colour to flowers to attract pollinators

C. Vascular tissue system

54. _____ Transports sugar molecules

D. Xylem

55. _____ Produces majority of leaf sugar molecules (and other products of photosynthesis)

E. Phloem

56. _____ Transports water and minerals

F. Epidermis

57. _____ Produces specialized structures to maximize water and mineral uptake

27.3 Primary Shoot Systems [pp. 672–677]

Section Review (Fill-in-the-Blanks)

A leaf stalk is a (58) _____ that attaches to a stem at a(n) (59) _____. The distance between

two of them is a(n) (60) _____. Buds at the tip of the main shoot are (61) _____, while buds

that produce branches are (62) _____. Terminal buds produce a hormone that inhibits the

development of nearby lateral buds, a phenomenon known as (63) _____. When a cell in an apical

meristem divides, one of the daughter cells gives rise to one of three types of (64) _____,

unspecialized tissues. One of these tissues, the (65) _____, becomes the stem's epidermis; a second

tissue, the (66) _____, ultimately forms the ground tissue of the plant; and the primary vascular

tissues are derived from the third type of tissue, the (67) _____. These Along the sides of shoot apical

meristems (68) _____ give rise to mature leaves. A mature leaf has an upper and a lower epidermis,

between which is the (69) _____ region, which can be divided into a palisades layer and a spongy

layer. The vascular bundles of leaves are arranged in various patterns visible on the surface and are known as

leaf (70) _____.

Matching

Match each of the following plant parts with its appropriate term.

71. _____ Onion "head"

A. Bud

72. _____ Venus flytrap insect trap

B. Bulb

73. _____ Strawberry stem

C. Rhizome

74. _____ Potato "eye"

D. Tendril

75. _____ *Urtica dioica* defense system

E. Trichomes with stinging chemical

76. _____ Cactus leaf

F. Petiole

77. _____ Celery stalk

G. Stolon

78. _____ Ginger "root"

H. Spine

79. _____ Sweet pea modified leaf for climbing

I. Spiny leaf margins

Short Answer

80. What is a leaf vein (composition and function)?

_____

_____

81. How does the arrangement of vascular bundles differ between eudicot and monocot stems?

_____

_____

27.4 Root Systems [pp. 677–680]
27.5 Secondary Growth [pp. 681–685]

Section Review (Fill-in-the-Blanks)

The roots of most eudicots exhibit a(n) (82) _____ system, which consists of a main, large root with

smaller branching roots called (83) _____ _____. Most monocots have a highly branched

root systems know as a(n) (84) _____ _____ system. Roots that emanate from the stem or

some other region of a plant, such as the prop roots of corn, are called (85) _____ roots.

Primary growth occurs in roots and shoots at (86) _____ _____. Secondary growth

arises from two types of lateral meristems: (87) _____ _____ (which gives rise to secondary

xylem and phloem) and (88) _____ _____, both of which increase plant

(89) _____. In stems and roots, (90) _____ cells form from the vascular cambium toward the centre of the plant and (91) _____ cells form outward from the vascular cambium.

The age of wood in plant stems can be determined by counting (92) _____ _____ produced by the alternating light-coloured large xylem cells of (93) _____ _____ and dark-coloured smaller xylem cells of (94) _____ _____. All living tissue between the vascular cambium and the surface of the stem comprises the (95) _____. It consists of secondary phloem, cork cambium, and cork.

Complete the Table

Cell Activity	Name of Zone	Relative Location
Cells are increasing in length.	Zone of (96) _____	Located ABOVE the zone of (97) _____
Cells are NOT dividing nor lengthening, but they may be (98) _____.	Zone of (99) _____	Zone located FARTHEST from the root cap.
Cells are (100) _____ rapidly.	Zone of cell division	Contains the root (101) _____.

True/False

Mark if the statement is true (T) or false (F). If the statement is false, make it correct by changing the underlined word(s) and writing the correct word(s) in the lines below each statement.

102. _____ Root hairs form in the zone of elongation.

_____

_____

103. _____ The three primary meristems are formed in the zone of cell division.

_____

_____

104. _____ The exodermis regulates water and ion uptake into the vascular tissue system.

_____

_____

105. _____ Chemical growth regulators influence the growth of lateral roots from the pericycle.

_____

_____

106. _____ Primary phloem cells are present in woody plants.

_____

_____

107. _____ Heartwood consists of xylem vessels that are clogged and no longer conduct water.

_____

_____

108. _____ In roots, cork cambium arises from pericycle tissue.

_____

_____

109. _____ Cork cambium produces phelloderm tissue towards the center of the cell and secondary phloem tissue towards the outside of the stem.

_____

_____

SELF-TEST

1. Consider the height of a lily plant's stem. What is it an example of? [p. 663]

   a. anatomy
   b. physiology
   c. morphology
   d. life span

2. Which term refers to the pathways connecting the cytoplasm contents of adjacent plant cells? [p. 664]

   a. middle lamellae
   b. protoplasts

   c. vascular cambium
   d. plasmadesmata

3. Which of the following is NOT a characteristic of a plant primary cell wall? [p. 664]

   a. provides support
   b. acts as a solid barrier
   c. has flexibility
   d. contains cellulose

4. Which of the following describes the order of the major components of a plant cell in a woody plant from the centre outward? [pp. 664–665]

   a. cell membrane, cytoplasm, primary cell wall, secondary cell wall
   b. cytoplasm, cell membrane, secondary cell wall, primary cell wall
   c. cell membrane, primary cell wall, cytoplasm, secondary cell wall
   d. cytoplasm, secondary cell wall, cell membrane, primary cell wall

5. Which term refers to the self-perpetuating embryonic cells of plants? [p. 666]

   a. dermal tissue
   b. ground tissue
   c. meristematic tissue
   d. vascular tissue

6. Which term refers to the tissue responsible for growth in the diameter of a plant? [p. 667]

   a. lateral mersitem
   b. root apical meristem
   c. shoot apical meristem

7. Which characteristic would you expect to find in a lily? [p. 668]

   a. two cotyledons
   b. petals in multiples of three
   c. netlike leaf veins
   d. taproot

8. Which cell type is most likely to be photosynthetic? [p. 669]

   a. collenchyma
   b. parenchyma
   c. sclerenchyma
   d. stone cell

9. Which type of ground tissue produces cells with thick secondary walls and therefore the greatest support? [p. 670]

   a. collenchyma
   b. sclerenchyma
   c. parenchyma

10. What cells of the vascular tissue system are most efficient at transporting water in angiosperms? [pp. 670–671]

    a. tracheids
    b. vessel members
    c. sieve tube members
    d. schlerids

11. What type of cells assist in the functioning of sieve tube cells? [pp. 671–672]

    a. companion cells
    b. endodermal cells
    c. pith cells
    d. cortex cells

12. Which term refers to the distance between two leaves on a stem? [pp. 672–673]

    a. axil
    b. internode
    c. leaf gap
    d. node

13. Where does shoot growth occur? [p. 673]

    a. shoot apical meristem
    b. base of stem
    c. lateral meristem
    d. tip of leaf

14. Which of the following is NOT a primary meristem produced at a shoot apex? [pp. 673–674]

    a. a ground meristem
    b. a procambium
    c. a protoderm
    d. a vascular cambium

15. In bamboo, what tissue breaks down to form the hollow centre of the stem? [pp. 674–675]

    a. cortex
    b. pith
    c. xylem
    d. phloem

16. Which of the following is a specialized trichome structure? [p. 676]

    a. leaf protrusions containing a toxin
    b. leaf primordia
    c. cuticle
    d. petiole

17. Where does most of the photosynthesis in a leaf take place? [pp. 675–676]

    a. guard cells
    b. lower epidermis
    c. palisades mesophyll
    d. spongy mesophyll

18. Why is a root cap required to cover the root apical meristem? [p. 679]

    a. for protection
    b. to break down old root cells
    c. to produce new cells
    d. (to increase uptake of water and minerals

19. What produces the alternating annual rings that form in trees in temperate climates? [p. 682]

    a. fusiform initials and ray initials
    b. heartwood and sapwood
    c. pericycle and endodermis
    d. spring wood and summer wood

20. Which of the following correctly describes a cedar tree that has 50 very narrow tree rings? [p. 683]

    a. It is 100 years old.
    b. It has grown little each year.
    c. It has grown in optimal environmental conditions.

INTEGRATING AND APPLYING KEY CONCEPTS

1. Why is it important that both plant shoot systems and root systems are dendritic?

2. Within a vegetative bud, cells must differentiate to form each of the necessary plant tissue systems. Identify the tissue system that each of the primary meristems develops into and give their resulting functions.

3. You planted a red oak tree in your backyard three years ago. Explain how growth this summer will be different from the growth that occurred in the tree's first summer.

28 Transport in Plants

TOPIC MAP

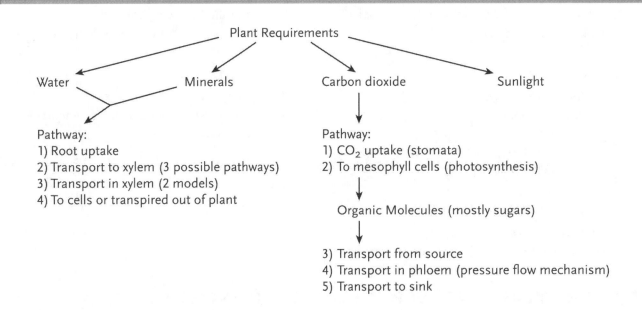

LEARNING OUTCOMES AND STUDY STRATEGIES

By the end of this chapter, you should be able to

- Differentiate between the different mechanisms that move substances across a cell membrane and how they apply to water and solute movement in plants

- Define water potential and describe how each of its two components affects its value

- Describe the pathway and mechanisms of water and minerals movement into the plant, to the xylem, within the xylem, and out of the plant

- Describe the pathway and mechanisms of organic solutes movement from the source, through the phloem, and to the sink

Study strategies for this chapter:

- Concentrate on understanding the mechanisms functioning at different steps of the pathways of water and solute movement.

- Remember that water moves from areas with high water potential to areas of low water potential (similar to its movement from high concentration to low concentration).

INTERACTIVE EXERCISES

Why It Matters [pp. 688–689]

Section Review (Fill-in-the-Blanks)

Plants must move (1) _____ and dissolved nutrients upward throughout the plant body without the

use of a (2) _____; animals differ as they have hearts that function in this way. The cumulative effect

of the rather weak forces such as (3) _____ and (4) _____ can be sufficient to move water in

some plants over 100 metres, counteracting the downward force of (5) _____.

28.1 Principles of Water and Solute Movement in Plants [pp. 689–692]

Section Review (Fill-in-the-Blanks)

Water and dissolved minerals travel from (6) _____ to shoots and leaves within the vascular tissue

called (7) _____ and sugars travel from (8) _____ and stems to other parts of the plant,

including roots, within the vascular tissue called (9) _____. In terms of the cell-to-cell movement of

water and solutes, or (10) _____-_____ transport, two types of transport move water and

solutes through plants. If the process requires no energy and involves movement of material down a

concentration gradient, it is (11) _____ _____. If energy is involved, it is a(n)

(12) _____ _____ process. Sometimes proteins embedded in the cell membrane, called

(13) _____ proteins, may assist in movement of material across the membrane.

   Between individual cells, water moves passively across individual cell membranes by

(14) _____, which is driven by energy within the water known as its (15) _____

_____. By convention, pure water at standard atmospheric pressure has a water potential value of

(16) _____ megapascals. The addition of dissolved solutes alters the water potential by an amount

referred to as the (17) _____ _____. If a cell has a lower water potential relative to outside

the cell, water will move (18) _____ the cell, increasing the physical pressure against the cells' walls

called (19) _____ _____. If this pressure increases such that it prevents further water from

entering the cell, this (20) _____ _____ offsets the solute potential, resulting in a water

potential value of (21) _____, and the cell is distended or (22) _____. Most plant cells contain a large, water-filled (23) _____ _____ surrounded by a membrane called a(n)

(24) _____, which maintains the turgor pressure of the cell. If the cytoplasm loses water, it is replaced

from the central vacuole through channel proteins in the tonoplast membrane known as (25) _____.

If a plant loses more water than it takes in over an extended period, it will (26) _____.

True/False

Mark if the statement is true (T) or false (F). If the statement is false, make it correct by changing the underlined word(s) and writing the correct word(s) in the lines below.

27. _____ In osmosis, water flows from <u>an area of higher water potential to an area of lower water potential</u>.

_____

_____

28. _____ If the solute concentration inside a cell increases due to water loss, its water potential will <u>increase</u>.

_____

_____

29. _____ Facilitated diffusion is a type of <u>passive</u> transport that uses transport proteins.

_____

_____

30. _____ Wilting is a result of loss of <u>turgor pressure</u>.

_____

_____

Matching

Match the best description of movement across a membrane with the type of short-distance transport.

31. _____ facilitated diffusion   A. Movement of a substance down its concentration gradient

32. _____ Passive transport   B. Movement of a substance down its concentration gradient using transport proteins

33. _____ Active transport   C. Movement of polar molecules across the lipid portion of a membrane

34. _____ Diffusion   D. Using energy to move a substance against its concentration gradient

Choice

For each of the following situations, select the change that would result to a solution that has a water potential of zero.

35. _____   Addition of solutes   A.   Increase in water potential

36. _____   Addition of pure water   B.   Decrease in water potential

37. _____   Addition of tension   C.   No change to water potential

38. _____   Addition of pressure

28.2 Uptake and Transport of Water and Solutes by Roots [pp. 692-694]

28.3 Long-Distance Transport of Water and Minerals in the Xylem [pp. 694-701]

Section Review (Fill-in-the-Blanks)

Water enters the plant root in one of two ways. The first is the (39) _____ _____, in which

water travels through cell walls and the intercellular spaces between cells through the root epidermis and

cortex. The second is the (40) _____ _____, in which the water moves through the

cytoplasm of adjacent cells using cytoplasmic connections called (41) _____. Water using either of

these pathways will move through the root cortex until it encounters the last layer of cells called the

(42) _____, each of which are wrapped transversely and (43) _____ in bands of waterproof

suberin called the (44) _____ _____. These bands force the soil solution to pass through the

membranes of living endodermal cells in order to reach the stele, thereby regulating water and minerals

entering the stele.

The model that describes the long-distance movement of xylem sap is called the (45) _____-

_____ model. It is based on two important physical properties of water, (46) _____ (resulting

from hydrogen bonds between water molecules) and (47) _____ (resulting from attraction of water to

xylem walls). The driving force for the movement of water is the process of (48) _____ from leaves.

Since plant water loss is primarily through (49) _____ in the leaves, plants have various controls,

such as regulating the size of the pores using surrounding (50) _____ _____. Another model

to explain movement of xylem sap in plants, especially over short distances in non-woody plants, is the

(51) _____ _____ model, which involves the active transport of ions from the soil into the

stele to create a water potential difference across the (52) _____. As water entering the xylem builds, so does a significant pressure, forcing water upward and potentially out of leaf pores, a phenomenon known

as (53) _____. Some plants that live in hot, dry environments utilize (54) _____

_____ _____ to reduce plant water loss, which involves opening stomata and fixing CO_2 into

an organic acid during the (55) _____ (when humidity is higher and temperatures are lower) and

manufacturing sugar during the (56) _____ while stomata remain closed.

Matching

Match each of the following terms with its correct definition.

57. ____	Abscisic acid (ABA)	A.	Model that explains movement of water through xylem over short distances, resulting in guttation
58. ____	Adhesion	B.	Plant adapted to hot, dry conditions
59. ____	Root pressure	C.	Suberin covering surrounding endodermal cells
60. ____	Xerophyte	D.	Pores from which water vapour leaves the plant
61. ____	Guard cells	E.	Tendency of water molecules to stick to other types of molecules, including the cell walls of xylem
62. ____	Transpiration	F.	Evaporation of water from intercellular spaces to the atmosphere
63. ____	Casparian strip	G.	Plant hormone responsible for stomatal closure under stressful conditions
64. ____	Stomata	H.	Structures that control transpiration rate, usually using K^+

28.4 Transport of Organic Substances in the Phloem [pp. 702–705]

Section Review (Fill-in-the-Blanks)

The long-distance movement of sugars and many other substances (such as proteins, fats, and hormones)

through the sieve tubes of phloem is called (65) _____, and the mix of water and dissolved

substances that flows within them is called (66) _____ _____. The point of origin of these

materials is called the (67) _____, and their destination is the (68) _____. The force that

drives this movement is known as the (69) _____ _____ mechanism because solutes in the

phloem move down (70) _____ gradients. The loading of solutes in the phloem (71) _____ the water potential of the phloem sap at the source, which causes water to follow using the process of

(72) _____. The solutes (and water) travel by (73) _____ _____ to lower pressure

regions and at the sink since solutes and water exit from the sieve tube members. In some plants, companion

cells are modified in order to actively transport large amounts of substances into the sieve tube members.

These cells are called (74) _____ _____.

True/False

Mark if the statement is true (T) or false (F). If the statement is false, make it correct by changing the underlined word(s) and writing the correct word(s) in the lines below each statement.

75. _____ Fructose is the most common type of sugar translocated in phloem.

_____

_____

76. _____ Phloem transports sap downward from the source.

_____

_____

77. _____ Translocation originates at the source and ends at the sink.

_____

_____

78. _____ Movement of solutes into companion cells is accomplished by active transport.

_____

_____

79. _____ A root is a sink throughout the growing season.

_____

_____

1. What does facilitated diffusion use to move ions through pores down a concentration gradient? [pp. 690–691]

    a. transport proteins
    b. passive proteins
    c. potential proteins
    d. active proteins

2. What are symplast and apoplast? [p. 693]

    a. different types of epidermal cells
    b. different types of xylem cells
    c. different pathways travelled by water and minerals to the endodermis
    d. different pathways travelled by sugars to the endodermis

3. Which term refers to the effect that dissolved materials have on water's tendency to move across a membrane? [pp. 690–691]

    a. membrane potential
    b. pressure potential
    c. solute potential
    d. water potential

4. What would be the water potential in a cell in which the solute potential is –0.38 and the pressure potential is 0.25? [pp. 690–692]

    a. –0.63
    b. –0.13
    c. 0
    d. 0.63

5. Which term refers to the membrane surrounding the central vacuole of a plant cell? [pp. 691–692]

    a. apoplast
    b. protoplast
    c. symplast
    d. tonoplast

6. Which term refers to a plant cell that contains enough water to exert pressure on the cell wall? [pp. 691–692]

    a. dehydrated
    b. flaccid
    c. plasmolyzed
    d. turgid

7. What pathway is taken by a molecule of soil water as it is taken up by a root hair and travels through plasmodesmata in the root cortex cells? [p. 693]

    a. the apoplastic pathway
    b. the endodermal pathway
    c. the symplastic pathway
    d. the stomatal pathway

8. What cells in the root must all water and minerals travel through (not around) before reaching the stele? [pp. 693–694]

    a. cortical parenchyma
    b. endodermis
    c. epidermis
    d. pericycle

9. Which of the following cells are alive at maturity? [pp. 702–703]

    a. tracheids
    b. vessel elements
    c. sieve tube elements

10. Which of the following terms describes the transpiration of water from leaves? [pp. 695–696]

    a. cohesion
    b. adhesion
    c. evaporation
    d. condensation

11. What causes the "stretching" of hydrogen bonds in the xylem sap resulting from transpiration? [pp. 695–696]

    a. pressure
    b. cohesion
    c. tension
    d. viscosity

12. What are the most important players in the "transpiration–photosynthesis compromise"? [p. 697]
    a. companion cells and sieve tube members
    b. guard cells and stomata
    c. spongy and palisades mesophyll
    d. xylem and phloem

13. Which ions are most important in regulating stomata function? [pp. 699–700]
    a. Ca^{++} and Mg^{++}
    b. H^+ and Cl^-
    c. H^+ and K^+
    d. K^+ and Mg^{++}

14. When a pair of guard cells have a high water potential, what is the state of the central stoma? [pp. 699–700]
    a. It will be open.
    b. It will be closed.
    c. It will quickly alternate between opening and closing.

15. Which of the following will cause stomata to close? [p. 700]
    a. low concentration of CO_2 in leaf air spaces
    b. daytime light levels
    c. abscisic acid production in roots
    d. moist soil

16. Which plant would most likely utilize CAM photosynthesis? [p. 701]
    a. maple tree
    b. moss

c. sedum
d. water lily

17. Which of the following is NOT found in phloem sap? [pp. 689, 702]
    a. sugars
    b. amino acids
    c. fatty acids
    d. minerals

18. What information did the "honeydew" from the anus of an aphid provide regarding the phloem sap in sieve tubes? [p. 703]
    a. It has a high water potential.
    b. It has a low solute potential.
    c. It is under high pressure.
    d. It is under no pressure.

19. Which of the following mechanisms is used to transport photosynthate in plants? [pp. 703–705]
    a. cohesion–tension mechanism
    b. pressure-flow mechanism
    c. guttation mechanism
    d. root pressure mechanism

20. In late summer after blooming has occurred, which of these organs is a source of organic substances? [pp. 702–703]
    a. leaves
    b. roots
    c. buds
    d. bulb

INTEGRATING AND APPLYING KEY CONCEPTS

1. Explain the process of how a stoma opens?

2. Why is xylem transport considered to be unidirectional whereas phloem transport is multidirectional?

3. Provide three examples (at least one for the root system and one for the shoot system) of adaptations used by plants to survive in drought-stressed environments. Explain how these adaptations increase water uptake or decrease water loss.

29 Reproduction and Development in Flowering Plants

TOPIC MAP

Using the following terms, identify each of the processes occurring in angiosperm reproduction: dedifferentiation, differentiation, double fertilization, germination, maturation, meiosis, mitosis, pollination. Note that terms can be used more than once.

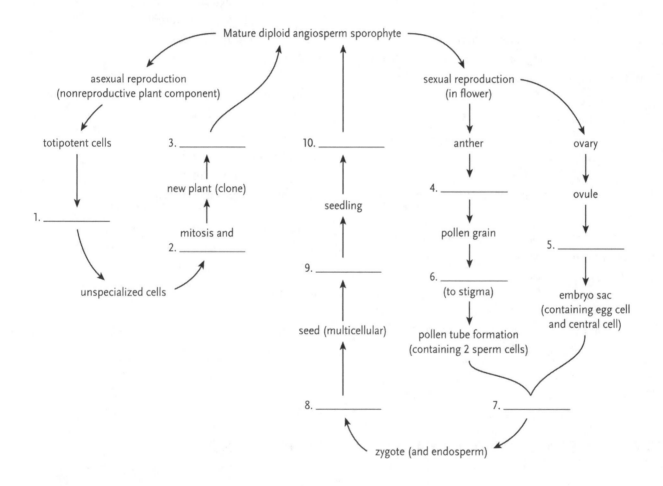

LEARNING OUTCOMES AND STUDY STRATEGIES

By the end of this chapter, you should be able to

■ Define plant structure and process-related terms and apply these terms to sexual and asexual plant reproduction processes

■ Describe an imperfect flower, differentiating between dioecious and monoecious plants

■ Describe the life cycle of a sexually reproducing angiosperm, incorporating the terms sporophyte, gametophyte, haploid, and diploid, as well as structures and processes involved

■ Explain why honeybees are important pollinators

■ Explain the importance of the *S* gene and describe two situations in which pollination does not lead to fertilization

■ Identify two functions of fruit and differentiate between different types of fruit

■ Describe how you could create a new plant from a plant cutting

Study strategies for this chapter:

■ If you are already familiar with the reproduction process in animals, you may note that some of the processes in plants are similar.

■ Concentrate on the key concepts and on the sequence of events in each process.

INTERACTIVE EXERCISES

Why It Matters [pp. 708–709]

Section Review (Fill-in-the-Blanks)

Angiosperms reproduce sexually using male and female reproductive structures found in (11) _____.

Male gametes in pollen grains are transferred to female gametes in other plants by the process called

(12) _____. Approximately one-third of North American plants are pollinated using

(13) _____. The reason for the decline in this pollinator's numbers, referred to as (14) _____

_____ _____ (or CCD), is unknown. If CCD spreads, angiosperm (15) _____, such

as cucumbers, berries, and apples, could be at risk.

29.1 Overview of Flowering Plant Reproduction [pp. 709–711]
29.2 Flower Structure and Formation of Gametes [pp. 711–714]

Section Review (Fill-in-the-Blanks)

A plant is a diploid (16) _____. It bears flowers where meiosis eventually leads to the formation of

male and female (17) _____ spores. After mitosis of these spores, each male spore will form a three-

celled (18) _____ _____, whereas a female spore will form a seven-celled

(19) _____ _____. The fusion of the haploid male and female (20) _____ forms a

(21) _____ zygote. The zygote divides by (22) _____ to eventually form a new sporophyte

plant.

Once a vegetative shoot becomes a(n) (23) _____ _____, it bears a flower or a

group of flowers called a(n) (24) _____. Each flower has four concentric whorls in which the

outermost, first whorl is made of leaf-like (25) _____ to enclose the flower as a bud; the second

whorl is composed of colourful (26) _____ to attract animals for pollination; the third whorl contains

the (27) _____, each of which is made of a thin (28) _____ upon which a sac called the

(29) _____ sits containing the (30) _____ grains; and the innermost whorl contains one or

more (31) _____, each composed of a lower (32) _____ containing ovules, an extension

called the (33) _____, and an upper flattened surface called the (34) _____.

In an anther, each (35) _____ (or microspore mother cell) undergoes meiosis, resulting in the

formation of four (36) _____. After mitosis, microspores will eventually form (37) _____

_____, each containing two (38) _____ cells and a(n) (39) _____ _____ cell.

In a(n) (40) _____, there may be one or more ovules formed. Inside each ovule, meiosis of

a(n) (41) _____ (or megaspore mother cell) results in the formation of (42) _____ mature

megaspore(s) since the three others degenerate. A megaspore undergoes mitosis divisions to form an eight-

celled female (43) _____ sac. As well as three antipodal cells, each sac has (44) _____ egg

cell(s), (45) _____ synergid(s), and (46) _____ large central cell(s). All cells in the sac are

haploid except for the (47) _____ cell, which contains two nuclei. The egg cell and the synergids are

located near the (48) _____ of the ovule.

Matching

Match each of the definitions with the correct term.

49. _____ Alternation of generations

50. _____ Sporophyte flower

51. _____ Gametophyte

52. _____ Inflorescence

53. _____ Imperfect flower

54. _____ Monoecious

55. _____ Dioecious

A. A flower that lacks one of the four whorls

B. A plant that produces male and female flowers or flower parts on different plants

C. The structure that produces diploid microsporocytes and megasporocytes

D. The haploid stage of the plant that bears the gametes

E. A life cycle that alternates between a diploid sporophyte and a haploid gametophyte

F. Flowers that are borne in a group

G. Where a plant bears both the male and female flowers or flower parts on the same plant

Match each of the following structures found in flowers with its correct definition.

56. _____ Embryo sac

57. _____ Sepal

58. _____ Style

59. _____ Petal

60. _____ Stamen

61. _____ Filament

62. _____ Anther

63. _____ Carpel

64. _____ Ovary

65. _____ Stigma

66. _____ Ovule

67. _____ Pollen grain

A. The long tube-like portion of a carpel through which the pollen tube travels to reach the micropyle

B. The third whorl of a flower that is composed of male reproductive structures

C. The innermost whorl that is composed of female reproductive structures

D. The tip of the carpel where the pollen lands during pollination

E. A leafy component of the outermost whorl

F. The male gametophyte of a plant

G. One of the brightly coloured parts of a flower that attracts pollinators

H. The female gametophyte of a plant

I. The thin stem of a stamen that bears an anther at the tip

J. The lower part of a carpel that bears ovules

K. A round structure formed inside an ovary where the female gametophyte develops

L. The sac located at the tip of a stamen that bears the pollen grains

Match each cell of the male and female gametophyte structures with its correct definition.

68. _____ Sperm cell

A. The female gamete of the plant

69. _____ Pollen tube cell

B. The male gamete of the plant

70. _____ Egg cell

C. The cell of the male gametophyte that grows inside the style of the carpel and transports the sperm cells to the ovule

71. _____ Synergids

D. Three cells located at a pole of the embryo sac that eventually degenerate

72. _____ Antipodal cells

E. The large diploid cell that fuses with one of the sperm cells and forms the triploid endosperm

73. _____ Central cell

F. The two cells that flank the egg cell in the embryo sac and degenerate to guide the sperm cells to their receptive cells in the sac

29.3 Pollination, Fertilization, and Germination [pp. 714–721]

Section Review (Fill-in-the-Blanks)

Air, water, birds, or other organisms aid in (74) _____, transferring pollen grains from the

(75) _____ of one plant to the (76) _____ of the carpel of another plant. Incompatibility

between two plants of the same species or plants of differing species is identified using the multiple

(77) _____ system of the S gene. If the pollen and stigma have the same (78) _____, pollen

may not germinate or some other process will occur to prevent fertilization. If the pollen and stigma are

compatible, after a pollen grain germinates, a(n) (79) _____ tube grows through the

(80) _____ of the carpel to reach the micropyle end of an ovule. Two haploid (81) _____

cells enter the embryo sac and (82) _____ _____ occurs, with one sperm cell fusing with

the egg cell to form a diploid (83) _____ and the other sperm cell fusing with the diploid central

nucleus to form a(n) (84) _____ cell. The first division of the zygote forms a(n) (85) _____

cell, which will form the embryo, and a basal cell, which will form a(n) (86) _____ and provide

nutrients to the developing embryo from the parent plant. Eudicot seeds have two (87) _____, which

can be thick or thin and function to provide stored nutrients to the growing embryo. Monocots have only one

(88) _____, along with its nutrient-rich (89) _____. The embryo in both has a(n)

(90) _____ that develops into a root and a shoot apical meristem that becomes a(n)

(91) _____ (leafy shoot). A seed also develops a protective seed (92) _____. In monocots, a sheath of cells covering the root meristem is called the (93) _____ and those covering the shoot meristem are the (94) _____.

In most angiosperms, while a seed develops in a(n) (95) _____, a fruit develops from the wall of the (96) _____ within the carpel. Its formation is stimulated by hormones released by the (97) _____ grain and the fruit wall becomes a(n) (98) _____. The fruit provides both (99) _____ and aids in seed (100) _____. Once a seed is formed, it usually goes into a period of (101) _____ during which it becomes metabolically inactive. Upon receiving proper environmental conditions, the process of (102) _____ begins. A seed absorbs water, a process called (103) _____, which causes the seed to swell and the seed (104) _____ to split. The increased water and oxygen reaching the embryo cause (105) _____ to be produced, which catalyze many reactions, including the release of nutrients. Cells rapidly produce new cells by (106) _____. Germination has ended when the (107) _____ emerges from inside the seed coat to become the primary (108) _____, which is followed by the (109) _____ growing to become the new foliage.

Complete the Table

110. Complete the following table by describing each process.

Events	Description
A. Pollination	
B. Fertilization	
C. Germination	

111. Complete the following table by describing each fruit type.

Fruits	Description
A. Simple fruits	
B. Aggregate fruits	
C. Multiple fruits	

Matching

Match the appropriate definition for each of the following parts a seed.

112. _____ Cotyledon

    A. The fleshy structure that is formed by the triploid cells when the haploid sperm cell fuses with the diploid central cell

113. _____ Endosperm

    B. The protective covering of a seed

114. _____ Seed coat

    C. The part of the embryo in the seed that becomes the shoot of the seedling

115. _____ Radicle

    D. A protective covering of the plumule in a monocot seed

116. _____ Plumule

    E. An embryonic structure that often becomes one of the first leaves of an eudicot seedling

117. _____ Coleorhiza

    F. The part of the embryo in the seed that becomes the primary root of the seedling

118. _____ Coleoptile

    G. A protective covering of the radicle in a monocot seed

Short Answer

119. Why is it advantageous for angiosperms to produce endosperm as a nutrient source rather than use gametophyte tissue?

_____

_____

120. Differentiate between the function of the cotyledons in a eudicot such as a sunflower seed and the cotyledon in a monocot such as a corn seed.

_____

_____

29.4 Asexual Reproduction of Flowering Plants [pp. 721–724]
29.5 Early Development of Plant Form and Function [p. 724]

Section Review (Fill-in-the-Blanks)

Producing new plants from non-reproductive parts of a parent plant is asexual reproduction, often referred to as (121) _____ reproduction. This is possible because many plant cells can dedifferentiate and divide to form a complete plant, a property called (122) _____. One type of asexual reproduction is (123) _____, which occurs when wounded cells in a plant part (such as a cutting) dedifferentiate and produce other plant parts to form a new complete plant. A somatic embryo forms in a seed when a(n) (124) _____ egg or a diploid cell around the embryo sac of an ovule undergoes cell division but not fertilization. This type of asexual reproduction is (125) _____. Plant cells grown in culture often form an undifferentiated cell mass called the (126) _____ that can be stimulated to redifferentiate by providing specific (127) _____. The result of all types of asexual reproduction is a new plant that is genetically (128) _____ to the original plant or plant cells.

As soon as a plant zygote divides, a(n) (129) _____-_____ axis is established where the (130) _____ cell will eventually form shoots and the (131) _____ cell will form the root system. These two early cells contain different transcription-regulating proteins called (132) _____ _____. This results in different genes being expressed in these cells, which leads to (133) _____ between these cells and all cells arising to form the specialized shoot and root systems.

Matching

Match each of the following terms with its correct definition.

134. _____ Totipotency

    A. Type of vegetative reproduction where a new plant forms from a detached piece of parent plant

135. _____ Dedifferentiation

    B. Result of early embryo development of apical and basal cells

136. _____ Fragmentation

    C. Ability of a cell to dedifferentiate and form a new organism

137. _____ Callus

    D. Process where a specialized cell becomes undifferentiated

138. _____ Apomixis

    E. Process in which an undifferentiated cell becomes a specialized cell

139. _____ Transcription factors

    F. Correct relative location during embryonic development of epidermal, ground, and vascular tissues

140. _____ Differentiation

    G. Mass of genetically identical cells grown in culture grown from dedifferentiated plant cells

141. _____ Outside-to-inside

    H. Mechanism resulting in development of seed containing somatic embryo

142. _____ Root-shoot axis

    I. Proteins that regulate transcription of genes

Short Answer

143. Differentiate between totipotent, pluripotent, and multipotent.

_____

_____

SELF-TEST

1. What function do pollinators provide? [pp. 708–709]

    a. They transfer sperm cells to an ovule.

    b. They transfer pollen grains to a stigma on a different plant.

    c. They transfer egg cells to an anther on a different plant.

    d. They transfer female gametophytes to a filament.

2. Which specific part of the flower transforms into a seed after fertilization? [pp. 710–711, 715]

    a. the ovary

    b. the stamen

    c. the ovule

    d. the embryo sac

3. What is a three-celled pollen grain?
   [pp. 710–713]

   a. a male sporophyte
   b. a male gametophyte
   c. a female sporophyte
   d. a female gametophyte

4. Which of these statements describes a plant with imperfect flowers that is monoecious? [p. 711]

   a. Its flowers contain both male and female reproductive structures.
   b. It has two types of flowers, those with only male reproductive structures and others with only female reproductive structures.
   c. It contains either flowers with only male reproductive structures or flowers with only female reproductive structures.
   d. Its flowers contain neither male nor female reproductive structures.

5. Which of the following represents the cells in a pollen grain? [pp. 712–713]

   a. one sperm cell and two pollen tube cells
   b. two sperm cells, one synergid, and one central cell
   c. three antipodal cells and one sperm cell
   d. one pollen tube cell and two sperm cells

6. Which of the following describes the pathway that the growing pollen tube travels through? [pp. 715–716]

   a. style, then ovule, then stigma
   b. ovule, then stigma, then anther
   c. stigma, then style, then micropyle
   d. filament, then micropyle, then anther

7. Which cell(s) of the embryo sac fuses with the sperm cell to form triploid endosperm? [pp. 716–717]

   a. the egg cell
   b. the synergids
   c. the antipodal cells
   d. the central cell

8. Which of the following situations would result in self-incompatibility, so no fertilization would occur? [pp. 716–717]

   a. When a pollen grain lands on the stigma of its own plant.
   b. When a pollen grain with a S_1 gene lands on a stigma that has a S_3 gene.
   c. When a pollen grain with a S_2 gene lands on a stigma that has a S_3 gene.
   d. When a pollen grain lands on the stigma of a plant with a different S gene.

9. How many nuclei are present in endosperm? [p. 717]

   a. one
   b. two
   c. three
   d. four

10. What type of fruit is formed from ovaries within different flowers in an inflorescence, such as the fruit produced by a pineapple? [pp. 717–718]

    a. a simple fruit
    b. an aggregate fruit
    c. a multiple fruit

11. In a developing seed, which of the following correctly describes the suspensor? [pp. 718–719]

    a. It is formed from the cotyledon(s).
    b. It transfers nutrients from the parent plant to the embryo.
    c. It forms a protective seed coat.
    d. It develops into root and shoot meristems.

12. Why does a developing eudicot embryo become heart-shaped? [pp. 718–719]

    a. The seed coat has the same shape as the embryo.
    b. The suspensor cells divide unevenly.
    c. Two cotyledons are forming.
    d. The radicle and plumule are forming.

13. For seeds requiring a dormancy period, what process begins after dormancy ends? [pp. 719–720]

    a. fertilization

    b. microspore formation

    c. megaspore formation

    d. germination

14. What type of structure does a radicle form? [pp. 719–721]

    a. stems

    b. leaves

    c. flowers

    d. roots

15. What is the correct order of processes occurring during germination? [pp. 719–721]

    a. imbibition, seed swelling, seed coat rupturing, radicle growing

    b. seed swelling, plumule growing, imbibition, seed coat rupturing

    c. radicle growing, seed coat rupturing, seed swelling, imbibition

    d. seed coat rupturing, imbibition, plumule, growing, seed swelling

16. Which of the following will NOT promote germination? [pp. 719–721]

    a. increased day length

    b. increased soil moisture

    c. increased temperature

    d. increased seed dehydration

17. Which type of cell has the potential to dedifferentiate and develop into an individual that is a clone of the parent? [p. 722]

    a. multipotent cell

    b. pluripotent cell

    c. vegipotent cell

    d. totipotent cell

18. What is an advantage of reproducing asexually? [pp. 722–723]

    a. There is greater variation between the new plants produced than those resulting from sexual reproduction.

    b. There is a lower energy cost required for asexual reproduction relative to sexual reproduction.

    c. New plants have a greater chance of survival if the environmental conditions change than those resulting from sexual reproduction.

    d. New plants from asexual reproduction are better able to attract pollinators than those produced from sexual reproduction.

19. When can a somatic embryo develop? [pp. 722–724]

    a. following fertilization

    b. following pollination

    c. following differentiation of totipotent cells

    d. following maturation of seedlings

20. Which statement describes the cells in a callus? [pp. 723–724]

    a. They are all genetically alike.

    b. They are all genetically different.

    c. They are all phenotypically alike.

    d. They are all multipotent.

INTEGRATING AND APPLYING KEY CONCEPTS

1. Totipotency is demonstrated in plants. Explain the concept by giving an example.

2. Describe the *S* gene concept to explain incompatibility between male and female reproductive tissues.

3. What is CCD, and why is it a problem for farmers growing apple trees and/or berry plants?

30 Control of Plant Growth and Development

TOPIC MAP

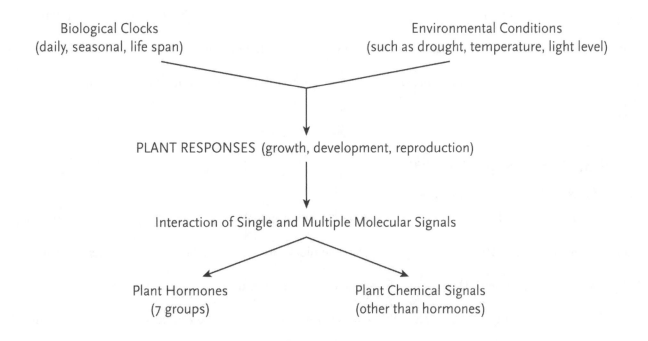

Biological Clocks
(daily, seasonal, life span)

Environmental Conditions
(such as drought, temperature, light level)

PLANT RESPONSES (growth, development, reproduction)

Interaction of Single and Multiple Molecular Signals

Plant Hormones
(7 groups)

Plant Chemical Signals
(other than hormones)

LEARNING OUTCOMES AND STUDY STRATEGIES

By the end of this chapter, you should be able to

■ Differentiate between the different plant hormones, including where each is synthesized and its effect on the plant

■ Compare and contrast different types of general and specific plant defence responses

■ Describe how plants respond to signals, from hormones or the environment, at the cellular level

■ Differentiate between the different types of tropism, describing what causes these changes to occur

■ Explain how biological clocks can affect different plants

Study strategies for this chapter:

■ This chapter can be confusing because there are a number of overlapping functions of plant-producing chemicals.

■ It helps to keep track of major functions first and then try to understand their interactions.

INTERACTIVE EXERCISES

Why It Matters [pp. 727–728]

Section Review (Fill-in-the-Blanks)

As (1) _____ organisms, plants cannot run from predators, so they have adapted by developing

(2) _____ responses. Plants produce various chemicals that can act as triggers for various metabolic

events such as seed (3) _____ (to begin growth of a new plant), phase shift from the vegetative to

(4) _____ phase, or end-of-season (5) _____ of body parts. These responses are initiated by

changes in the (6) _____, such as changes in day length, temperature, and soil moisture. Some plants

produce (7) _____ compounds, which, when released in the air, signal to animals and neighbouring

plants.

30.1 Plant Hormones [pp. 728–739]

Section Review (Fill-in-the-Blanks)

Plants respond to internal (8) _____ changes and external (9) _____ conditions by producing

special chemicals called (10) _____. These chemicals are small and organic and are required in very

(11) _____ amounts. They diffuse from one cell to another, or they may be transported by the

(12) _____ tissues. Although hormones show large variability in their effects, they can be classified

into seven major groups:

A. Auxins—They are made by apical (13) _____ and young leaves and stems. They

(14) _____ growth of stems and lateral roots, primarily through cell (15) _____. Since

auxins diffuse away from (16) _____, differential cell growth can occur that causes shoot tips or

other plant parts to (17) _____ toward the light. This response is called (18) _____. Auxins

also (19) _____ fruit development.

B. Gibberellins—They are made mostly by root and shoot (20) _____. They (21) _____ cell

division and cell elongation, most notably in stems. In some species, gibberellins cause elongation of floral

stalks in rosette plants, increasing the length of (22) _____, such that leaves no longer appear to arise from the same node. This process is called (23) _____. Gibberellins also help in breaking seed and

bud (24) _____ at the beginning of the growing season.

C. Cytokinins—Produced mainly in root (25) _____, cytokinins stimulate cell (26) _____

rather than cell elongation. Unlike gibberellins, which are transported in phloem tissue, cytokinins are

transported in (27) _____ tissue.

D. Ethylene—Produced by most parts of the plant, ethylene is in the form of a(n) (28) _____ and it

assists in regulating many processes. For example, during seedling growth, it increases cell

(29) _____ relative to cell elongation to increase stem girth, assisting in growth out of the soil.

Ethylene promotes (30) _____ ripening, as well as stimulating the process of (31) _____

(aging and cell death). With aging, ethylene stimulates digestive enzymes that break down cell walls in

(32) _____ _____, located at the base of petioles, which results in the dropping of leaves,

flowers, and fruits.

E. Brassinosteroids—These are (33) _____ hormones that were first discovered in the mustard

family. Produced primarily in (34) _____ tips, seeds, and embryos, they stimulate cell division and

(35) _____. In roots, ethylene (36) _____ root elongation.

F. Abscicic acid—This hormone is derived from (37) _____ in leaf chloroplasts. It

(38) _____ growth and promotes dormancy, in response to (39) _____ conditions. It often

accumulates in seed coats during seed development and requires a dormancy period to slowly break down

before the seed can (40) _____.

G. Jasmonates and Oligosaccharins—Jasmonates are derived from (41) _____ acids, and

oligosaccharins are derived from (42) _____. Although both of these hormones (43) _____

growth of one or more plant parts, they are best known for protecting plants from (44) _____.

Matching

Match each of the following terms with its correct definition.

45. _____	Bolting	A.	Aging process in plants that leads to breakdown and death of their cells
46. _____	Senescence	B.	Dropping of leaves, flowers, and fruits in response to environmental changes
47. _____	Phloem	C.	Tissue that cytokinins travel through
48. _____	Abscission	D.	Period when seeds and buds go into growth-inhibiting phase
49. _____	Dormancy	E.	Mechanism used by auxins to travel through a plant
50. _____	Xylem	F.	Sudden elongation of the floral stem in rosette plants
51. _____	Polar transport	G.	Tissue that gibberellins travel through

Match each of the following scientists with their major contribution.

52. _____	Eiichi Kurosawa	A.	Performed the first experiments to explain phototropism in grasses
53. _____	Francis and Charles Darwin	B.	Demonstrated that the growth-promoting chemical travels from the shoot tip downward
54. _____	Frits Went	C.	Showed that auxins move laterally in response to light exposure
55. _____	Winslow Briggs	D.	First one to discover the effect of gibberellins produced by a fungus on rice plants

Complete the Table

56. Complete the following table by describing the main actions of each hormone.

Hormone	Action
Auxins	A.
Gibberellins	B.
Cytokinins	C.
Ethylene	D.
Brassinosteroids	E.
Abscisic acid	F.
Jasmonates and oligosaccharins	G.

30.2 Signal Responses at the Cellular Level [pp. 739–740]
30.3 Plant Chemical Defences [740–744]

Section Review (Fill-in-the-Blanks)

In plants, a signal molecule, such as a hormone, initiates a(n) (57) _____ pathway that involves

converting the signal molecule into a(n) (58) _____ _____ that causes a change in a target

cell's (59) _____ or metabolism. Generally, the binding of a signal molecule to a(n)

(60) _____ molecule, located on the plasma membrane, on the endoplasmic reticulum, or in the

(61) _____, will cause a reaction to occur inside the cell. Possible reactions include activation of an

enzyme or some other (62) _____, opening of a channel for ion flow, or translation of mRNA,—all

of which result in a physiological response. In some cases, the reaction between the (63) _____

molecule (the primary messenger) and the receptor stimulates the synthesis of an internal (64) _____

messenger. It is this intermediary molecule that acts as the main signal to alter how the (65) _____

cell functions.

Plants are attacked by various organisms including (66) _____, _____,

_____, and _____. If a plant provides a general defence to an insect attack, it will likely

immediately initiate a complex signalling (67) _____ that, with the involvement of

(68) _____, ethylene, or some other hormone, will produce a chemical or physical defence at the

wound site. In tomato plants, the synthesis of (69) _____ stimulates the production of jasmonates,

which results in the expression of a protease (70) _____, preventing the insect predator from

digesting plant (71) _____. If attached by bacteria or fungi, many plants are able to provide a

(72) _____ response, which involves isolating the infection site by signalling nearby cells to release

(73) _____-_____ compounds, such as hydrogen peroxide, to kill these cells. The pathogen

is unable to survive without the plant's (74) _____ supply. Furthermore, the release of

(75) _____ _____ (SA) triggers cells to produce (76) _____-_____ (PR)

proteins, which contain hydrolytic enzymes that harm the pathogen by breaking down its cell walls.

Plants also produce protective chemicals called (77) _____ metabolites, which are not

routinely produced by plants but function to ward off feeding (78) _____. Examples include phyloauixins, alkaloids, and terpenes, with the latter being (79) _____ and therefore released into the

air during a pathogen attack, which functions to attract the pathogen's (80) _____.

Gene-for-gene recognition is a(n) (81) _____ defence response requiring a molecule

produced from a dominant (82) _____ (*Avr*) gene in the pathogen to bind to a plasma membrane

(83) _____ protein produced from a dominant (84) _____ (*R*) gene in the plant. When this

occurs, a defence response, usually the (85) _____ response, will be triggered and PR proteins will

be produced.

Plants that survive pathogen attacks produce (86) _____ _____, which stimulates

production of PR proteins. In defence of future attacks, both of these chemicals provide (87) _____-

_____ protection.

Short Answer

88. How does a secondary messenger differ from a secondary metabolite?

_____

_____

89. PR proteins function in various plant defences. What do they do, and why is this important?

_____

_____

Matching

Match each of the following terms with its correct definition.

90. _____ Salicylic acid

91. _____ Phytoalexin

92. _____ Secondary metabolite

93. _____ Hydrogen peroxide

94. _____ Receptor

A. A chemical produced by plants to prevent herbivores from consuming them

B. A chemical produced by plants infected with bacteria or fungi that acts like an antibiotic

C. A chemical similar to aspirin that is produced by some wounded plants to protect themselves from infections

D. A structure on a cell's plasma membrane that a particular hormone can bind to

E. A chemical that some plants release to kill cells surrounding a wound

30.4 Plant Responses to the Environment: Movements [pp. 744–749]
30.5 Plant Responses to the Environment: Biological Clocks [pp. 749–753]
30.6 Plant Responses to the Environment: Responses to Temperature Extremes [p. 753]

Section Review (Fill-in-the-Blanks)

Plants respond to certain environmental factors by growing away or toward the factor, a process referred to as

(95) _____. One type is (96) _____, which is plant growth toward a unidirectional light.

This occurs when a blue light–absorbing pigment, such as (97) _____, stimulates lateral movement

of auxins that eventually leads to increased growth of cells on the shaded side relative to the non-shaded side

of a plant part. (98) _____ is growth in response to gravity where roots are stimulated to grow

(99) _____ and shoots to grow (100) _____. It is hypothesized that amyloplasts in some

cells sink to the bottom of cells, an indicator of direction to ensure that auxins stimulate cell

(101) _____ to promote growth in the appropriate direction. (102) _____ is growth in

response to physical contact with another object where auxins and ethylene stimulate bending of the plant.

Specialized stems, such as (103) _____ on a pea plant, are able to grow around an object, thereby

receiving necessary (104) _____ for their slender stems. (105) _____ movement is different

from the tropisms above since it is reversible, a temporary response to a non-directional stimulus. This type of

movement is due to changes in cell (106) _____ pressure and results in movements such as folding of

leaves at night, opening or closing of stomata, and shifting of flowers or leaves as they follow the movement

of the sun.

Plants, like animals, have a (107) _____ _____ that acts as an internal time-

measuring mechanism. A 24-hour cycle, called the (108) _____ rhythm, ensures that necessary

activities occur repeatedly at a set time within this cycle. Plant activities also tend to change with seasons,

often due to changes in (109) _____, a rhythm based on the division of light and dark periods in a 24-

hour period. Plants primarily use a blue-green pigment, (110) _____, which exists in two reversible

forms (P_r and P_{fr}) to measure changes in photoperiodism. Plants may be classified as (111) _____-

_____ plants, which tend to flower in the spring, or (112) _____-_____ plants,

which flower in the fall. It is the length of (113) _____ in a 24-hour cycle that determines when a plant will initiate flowering. Some plants will not flower unless they go through a period of cold temperature, a process called (114) _____.

Plants that have seeds and buds that go through a phase of no growth (even if conditions are suitable) experience (115) _____. Environmental conditions that initiate this state include (116) _____ nights, cold temperature, dry soil, and nitrogen deficiency.

Matching

Match each of the following terms with its correct definition.

117. _____	Phototropism	A.	Amyloplasts that move in the plant root and shoot tips to help in responding to gravity
118. _____	Gravitropism	B.	A blue-green pigment that exists in two forms and signals the light switch
119. _____	Thigmotropism	C.	Refers to a low-temperature stimulation of flowering
120. _____	Nastic movement	D.	Movement or growth of a plant in response to contact with an object
121. _____	Circadian rhythm	E.	Movement or growth of a plant in response to unidirectional light
122. _____	Phytochrome	F.	Movement or growth of a plant in response to gravity
123. _____	Vernalization	G.	Reversible or temporary movement in response to unidirectional stimulus
124. _____	Statoliths	H.	A 24-hour cycle of response in plants

SELF-TEST

1. Which of the following was identified as the first plant hormone? [p. 729]

   a. auxins
   b. gibberellins
   c. cytokinins
   d. ethylene

2. How did Went prevent light "contamination" when performing his experiment using auxins? [pp. 731–732]

   a. He grew only seedlings sensitive to high light levels.
   b. He kept seedlings in the dark.
   c. He provided light for a limited period each day.
   d. He provided light for the full 24-hour cycle each day.

3. Which hormone assists in the elongation of a pollen tube after a flower is pollinated? [p. 737]

   a. ethylene
   b. a brassinosteroid
   c. abscisic acid
   d. an auxin

4. When cell elongation occurs, how do auxins (and gibberellins) cause the cell walls to stretch, according to the acid-growth hypothesis? [p. 733]
   a. by loosening the cell wall's cellulose microfibril mesh
   b. by breaking down the cell's plasma membrane
   c. by reducing the turgor pressure in the cell

5. Which hormone is involved in the breaking of seed and bud dormancy? [pp. 733–734]
   a. auxins
   b. gibberellins
   c. abscisic acid
   d. brassinosteroids

6. Which substance may be produced during a hypersensitive response that results in the death of cells surrounding an infected site? [pp. 741–742]
   a. salicylic acid
   b. jasmonates
   c. systemin
   d. hydrogen peroxide

7. Which hormone coordinates growth of roots and shoots in concert with the auxins? [p. 735]
   a. abscisic acid
   b. gibberellins
   c. cytokinins
   d. salicylic acid

8. Which hormone is synthesized by ripening fruit? [pp. 736–737]
   a. auxins
   b. systemin
   c. ethylene
   d. abscisic acid

9. You order tree seedlings for delivery in early spring. What hormone will the tree nursery apply to your seedlings to promote dormancy and minimize damage during transport? [p. 738]
   a. ethylene
   b. brassinosteroids

c. abscisic acid
d. auxins

10. Which term refers to the mechanism resulting in the dropping of flowers, fruits, and leaves? [p. 736]
    a. senescence
    b. abscission
    c. tropism
    d. bolting

11. How can the rapid stem cell elongation in rosette plants due to the addition of Gibberellins be described? [pp. 734–735]
    a. senescence
    b. abscission
    c. vernalization
    d. bolting

12. Which of the following statements does NOT describes systemin? [pp. 740–741]
    a. It functions as a defence response in tomato plants.
    b. It was the first peptide hormone discovered in plants.
    c. It binds to a receptor in a target cell plasma membrane.
    d. It causes a plant to synthesize ethylene.

13. What is shoot growth a response to? [pp. 746–747]
    a. positive gravitropism
    b. negative gravitropism
    c. neutral gravitropism

14. How are plants described that are responding to the phenomenon called thigmomorphogenesis? [p. 747]
    a. Plants are tall and thin.
    b. Plants are short and stalky.
    c. Plants produce large shoots relative to roots.
    d. Plants grow rapidly toward sunlight.

15. The temporary folding of leaflets due to changes in cell turgor pressure in *Mimosa pudica* in response to touch is an example of which type of plant response? [p. 748]

    a. phototropism
    b. photoperiodism
    c. gravitropism
    d. nastic movement

16. Which type of plant response is referred to when considering the activity of phytochrome? [pp. 749–750]

    a. phototropism
    b. gravitropism
    c. thigmotropism
    d. photoperiodism

17. Which term refers to low-temperature stimulation of flowering? [p. 751]

    a. vernalization
    b. abscission
    c. tropism
    d. bolting

18. Which group of proteins protects temperature-sensitive plant proteins during prolonged exposure to high temperatures? [p. 753]

    a. CO proteins
    b. HSPs
    c. FT proteins
    d. PR proteins

19. Which of the following molecules is NOT involved in systemic acquired resistance? [pp. 743–744]

    a. PR proteins
    b. SA
    c. JA
    d. NPR-a

20. How many genes are believed to be required for a photoperiod flowering response in *Arabidopsis*? [pp. 750–751]

    a. 0
    b. 1
    c. 2
    d. >2

INTEGRATING AND APPLYING KEY CONCEPTS

1. Knowing that ethylene is involved in fruit ripening, discuss how this information is used by fruit growers.

2. How does a plant use its phytochrome pigments to identify changes in the photoperiod?

3. Describe how an action potential leads to a change in cell turgor pressure during a nastic movement.

31 Introduction to Animal Organization and Physiology

TOPIC MAP

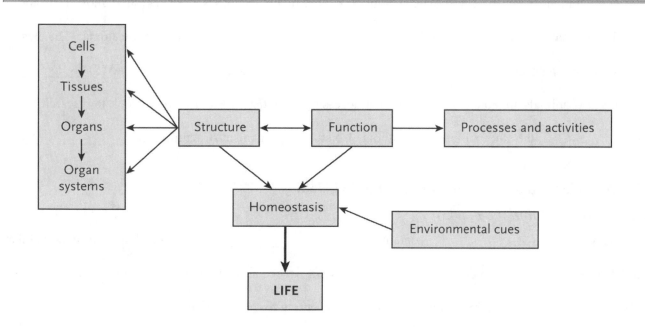

LEARNING OUTCOMES AND STUDY STRATEGIES

By the end of this chapter, you should be able to

■ Differentiate between the four tissues found in animals in terms of their structure and function

■ Explain how the major levels of organization in animals are related to each other

■ Describe how animals are able to maintain homeostasis, despite changing external and internal environments

Study strategies for this chapter:

■ First, focus on major levels of organization of animals—cells, tissues, organs, and organ systems.

■ Examine and learn the structure of the various tissues, organs, and organ systems and then associate them with their functions.

■ Evaluate the control mechanisms of feedback systems and maintenance of a constant yet dynamic internal environment.

INTERACTIVE EXERCISES

Why It Matters [pp. 756–757]

Section Review (Fill-in-the-Blanks)

All living organisms are exposed to a variety of environmental conditions. An animal must maintain

(1) _____, a stable yet dynamic (2) _____ environment, despite the external conditions and the

demands within the organism. Under these conditions, various body functions, such as digestion, movement, and

reproduction, can be carried out by different (3) _____ _____ within the animal. The close

relationship between structure (at the cell, (4) _____, organ, or organ system level) and (5) _____

explains how animals are able to coordinate their necessary activities. It is therefore difficult to research

(6) _____, the study of function, without also studying organism structure, (7) _____.

31.1 Organization of the Animal Body [pp. 757–758]

Section Review (Fill-in-the-Blanks)

Organisms that are (8) _____ contain (9) _____ _____, also known as extracellular

fluid, between their cells, which assists cells in various ways, such as supplying required ions and

(10) _____ to cells for cellular activities and accepting by-products, the (11) _____

molecules, produced from cellular activities. The concentration of ions and molecules in the extracellular

fluid must be balanced with neighbouring (12) _____ to prevent excessive water movement by

(13) _____. A group of similar cells, specialized to perform a specific (14) _____, forms

a(n) (15) _____. A(n) (16) _____ is composed of two or more (17) _____ tissues

that together perform a specific function. At the highest level within an organism, a(n) (18) _____

_____ coordinates the activities of two or more (19) _____ to carry out a major body

activity, such as digestion or reproduction.

31.2 Animal Tissues [pp. 758–767]

Section Review (Fill-in-the-Blanks)

The structure and function of a tissue are primarily determined by the (20) _____ within the cells it is

composed of, the (21) _____ matrix surrounding the cells, and the (22) _____, which hold the cells within the tissue together. Complex animals are composed of four major types of tissues. One type, (23) _____ tissue, is classified by the number of layers of (24) _____ above a basement membrane and the (25) _____ of the cells. Connective tissue structure and function are varied but are consistently composed of cells surrounded by a(n) (26) _____ matrix embedded with protein (27) _____. The consistency of the matrix ranges from liquid to (28) _____-_____ to porous, depending upon the type of connective tissue. There are (29) _____ types of (30) _____ tissue: cardiac, skeletal, and (31) _____, of which only the former two contain striations. The fourth type of tissue is (32) _____ tissue, which is composed of (33) _____ (also known as nerve cells) and supporting (34) _____ cells.

Matching

Match each of the following tissues with its correct function.

35. ____	Epithelial	A.	Supports, binds, provides structure
36. ____	Connective	B.	Responds to stimuli and communicates with other cells and tissues
37. ____	Nervous	C.	Contains actin and myosin—forcibly shortens
38. ____	Muscle	D.	Covers or lines body surfaces and cavities

Match each of the following tissues or cells with its correct description.

39. ____	Neurons	A.	Short, branched cells with intercalated disks
40. ____	Cardiac	B.	Moves bones
41. ____	Skeletal	C.	Walls of tubes and cavities, primarily autorhythmic
42. ____	Glial cells	D.	Respond to stimuli with axon and dendrites
43. ____	Smooth	E.	Support and electrical insulation

Choice

For each of the following statements, choose the most appropriate connective tissue components or type from the list below.

44. _____ Primary cell type is fibroblast; forms mesenteries

45. _____ Lipid storage

46. _____ Fibrous glycoprotein

47. _____ Function of oxygen delivery to tissues as well as immunity

48. _____ Fibroblast cells; attaches muscles to bones

49. _____ Primary cell type is the osteocyte

50. _____ Chondrocytes in collagen and chondroitin sulphate matrix

51. _____ Fibroblast cells; attaches bones to bones

52. _____ Resilient like rubber, cushioning disks between vertebrae

53. _____ Calcium–phosphate mineral deposits in extracellular matrix

A. Collagen

B. Fibrous connective tissue

C. Loose connective tissue

D. Cartilage

E. Bone

F. Blood

G. Adipose

Complete the Table

54. Complete the following table.

Tissue Type	Function	Location
Epithelial	A.	B.
C.	Support, protection, attachment	Most body structures and systems
Muscle	D.	E.
Nervous	F.	Central and peripheral nervous systems

Short Answer

55. Identify the type of junction found between cells of epithelial tissue lining the urinary bladder and explain why it is found there.

_____

_____

56. How does the function of an osteoblast differ from that of an osteoclast?

_____

_____

57. What is the benefit of storing excess carbohydrates as fat?

_____

_____

31.3 Coordination of Tissues in Organs and Organ Systems [pp. 767–768]

Section Review (Fill-in-the-Blanks)

In multicellular organisms, the (58) _____ is the unit of life, yet it does not function in isolation. It

must perform basic metabolic activities to (59) _____, and it must also perform at least one function

for each of the tissue, organ, and (60) _____ levels to which it belongs. Most animals have

(61) _____ major organ systems. These organ systems work in a coordinated fashion to accomplish

basic functions, including acquiring, processing, and distributing (62) _____ and other substances

throughout the body and disposing of (63) _____, synthesizing macromolecules, sensing and

(64) _____ to environmental changes, protecting the body, and (65) _____, and then

nourishing young.

Choice

For each of the following organs, choose the most appropriate organ system(s) it belongs to from the
list below.

66. _____ Brain   A.   Endocrine

67. _____ Heart   B.   Muscular

68. _____ Skin   C.   Nervous

69. _____ Thymus   D.   Circulatory

70. ____	Bones	E.	Lymphatic
71. ____	Thyroid	F.	Integumentary
72. ____	Stomach	G.	Reproductive
73. ____	Lungs	H.	Excretory
74. ____	Cardiac and smooth	I.	Digestive
75. ____	Spleen	J.	Respiratory
76. ____	Testes	K.	Skeletal
77. ____	Hair and nails		
78. ____	Pancreas		
79. ____	Liver		
80. ____	Spinal cord		
81. ____	Uterus		
82. ____	Kidneys		

31.4 Homeostasis [pp. 768–772]

Short Answer

83. Explain the importance of homeostasis with respect to a changing external environment.

_____

_____

84. Compare and contrast a negative and a positive feedback mechanism when a change results in excess product.

_____

_____

Matching

Match each component associated with a homeostatic mechanism with its correct definition.

85. ____	Response	A.	Control centre—compares change to set point
86. ____	Stimulus	B.	Detects change—temperature, pH, touch
87. ____	Effector	C.	Output
88. ____	Sensor	D.	Acceptable level for output
89. ____	Integrator	E.	Responds to stimulus; produces the output
90. ____	Set point	F.	Input—environmental change

1. Which factors place demands on a cell?
   [pp. 768–769]

   a. internal and external
   b. physical and anatomical
   c. functional and physiological

2. What is a muscle, such as the biceps muscle of
   your arm, composed of? [p. 765]

   a. similar tissues
   b. different tissues
   c. similar cells
   d. different organs
   e. similar organs

3. Which structure is in the highest level of
   organization (i.e., contains the other structures)?
   [pp. 757–758]

   a. the liver
   b. the epithelium
   c. the mitochondria
   d. a hepatic (liver) cell

4. Where is interstitial fluid found in an organism?
   [p. 768]

   a. in the cytoplasm
   b. in the cell membrane
   c. in the cell wall
   d. between cells

5. What is the study of animal structure called?
   [p. 757]

   a. homeostasis
   b. osmosis
   c. anatomy
   d. physiology

6. Which tissue can be best described as one that
   lines a body cavity and has little or no
   extracellular matrix? [pp. 758–761]

   a. nervous
   b. muscle
   c. connective
   d. epithelial

7. What type of junction allows ions and
   molecules to flow between cells by way of
   channels? [p. 765]

   a. tight junction
   b. gap junction
   c. anchoring junction

8. Which tissue has cells involved in immunity as
   well as oxygen delivery to cells? [pp. 761–764]

   a. nervous
   b. muscle
   c. connective
   d. epithelial

9. Which tissue is found in every organ/organ
   system and characterized by various cell types,
   fibres, and an extracellular matrix? [pp. 761–764]

   a. nervous
   b. muscle
   c. connective
   d. epithelial

10. Which term refers to a unit consisting of cells,
    concentric layers of calcium–phosphate minerals,
    a blood vessel, and nerve endings ? [p. 764]

    a. fibroblast
    b. osteon
    c. chondrocyte
    d. osteoblast

11. What type of junction connects smooth muscle
    cells such that they can contract as a unit? [p. 765]

    a. tight junction
    b. gap junction
    c. anchoring junction

12. What type of tissue contains erythrocytes and
    leukocytes? [pp. 761–764]

    a. epithelial tissue
    b. bone tissue
    c. blood tissue
    d. skeletal muscle tissue
    e. nervous tissue

13. In what direction does an electrical signal move through a neuron? [p. 766]

    a. dendrite, cell body, then axon
    b. axon, dendrite, then cell body
    c. cell body, dendrite, then axon
    d. axon, cell body, then dendrite

14. Which organ system is primarily involved in osmotic balance, electrolytes, and pH regulation? [p. 767]

    a. circulatory
    b. excretory
    c. respiratory
    d. endocrine

15. Which organ system has sweat glands and provides protection to the organism? [pp. 767–768]

    a. the muscular system
    b. the integumentary system
    c. the skeletal system
    d. the nervous system

16. What organ system functions in acquiring nutrients, such as proteins and carbohydrates, and breaks them down? [p. 767]

    a. the endocrine system
    b. the circulatory system
    c. the lymphatic system
    d. the respiratory system
    e. the digestive system

17. Which term refers to the element of a homeostatic mechanism that compares a detected change with a set point ? [pp. 768–772]

    a. effector
    b. response
    c. integrator
    d. sensor
    e. stimulus

18. Suppose the stimulus resulted in amplification of the response. What would this be an example of? [pp. 768–772]

    a. negative feedback
    b. positive feedback
    c. homeostasis
    d. integration

19. Suppose body temperature exceeded the set point of the hypothalamus. How would the stimulus that activates the sweat glands to react? [pp. 768–772]

    a. increase
    b. decrease
    c. not change

INTEGRATING AND APPLYING KEY CONCEPTS

1. Where is sweat produced, and how does it reach the system's surface?

2. Compare and contrast the bone, cartilage, and adipose tissue in terms of their structure and function.

3. Differentiate between structure and function of the three types of muscle tissue.

32 Transport in Animals: The Circulatory System

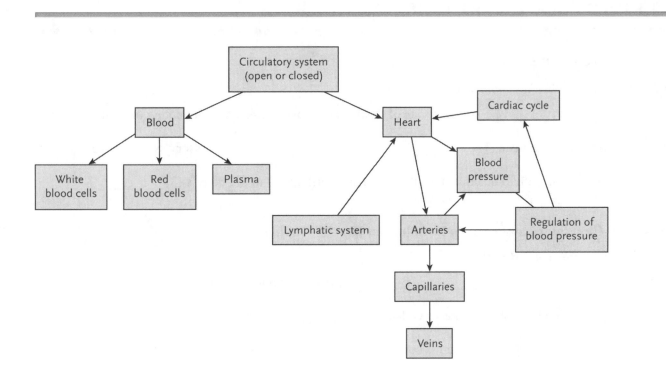

LEARNING OUTCOMES AND STUDY STRATEGIES

By the end of this chapter, you should be able to

- List the basic elements that are shared between circulatory systems of different organisms
- List the functions of the components of the circulatory system
- Explain the difference between an open and a closed circulatory system
- List and explain the functions of the components of blood
- List the components of the heart and describe the flow of blood through the heart of different organisms
- Discuss the heart cycle and how it is controlled
- Explain the changes in blood pressure during the heart cycle and how blood pressure is regulated
- Explain the roles of the lymphatic system

Study strategies for this chapter:

- This chapter is divided into sections. DO NOT try to go through them all in one sitting. Take one section at a time and then work through the companion section in the study guide.

- Draw pictures of the various circulatory systems, being careful to detail the flow of blood, especially the path through the heart.

- Develop a basic understanding of the components and functions of each part of the circulatory system.

INTERACTIVE EXERCISES

Why It Matters [pp. 774–775]

Section Review (Fill-in-the-Blanks)

The (1) _____ _____ consists of fluid, a heart, and vessels for conducting nutrients, wastes, and gases through the organism. The (2) _____ _____ is an accessory system of vessels and organs that helps balance the fluid content of the blood and participates in the body's (3) _____.

32.1 Animal Circulatory Systems: An Introduction [pp. 775–780]

Section Review (Fill-in-the-Blanks)

In a(n) (4) _____ _____ _____, vessels leaving the heart release

(5) _____ directly into body spaces called (6) _____. In a(n) (7) _____

_____ _____, the blood is confined to a network of vessels and is separated from the

interstitial fluid. In closed circulatory systems, (8) _____ conduct blood away from the heart and

break into highly branched (9) _____ that are specialized for exchange of material between the blood

and interstitial fluid. Blood then flows into (10) _____, which return it to the heart. The heart of

vertebrates, depending on the species, may consist of one or two (11) _____, which receive blood

returning to the heart, as well as one or two (12) _____, which pump blood from the heart. In

amphibians, which have a single ventricle, most of the oxygenated blood enters the (13) _____

_____, while deoxygenated blood is directed into the (14) _____ _____. In reptiles,

which also have a single ventricle, oxygenated blood enters the systemic circuit, while deoxygenated blood is

directed into a(n) (15) _____ _____. Mammals and birds have two atria and two ventricles

so that there are two separate circuits: a pulmonary circuit and a systemic circuit.

Short Answer

16. List the common features of circulatory systems in animals.

_____

_____

17. List the different functions of the circulatory system.

_____

_____

18. Distinguish between the open and the closed circulatory system.

_____

_____

Choice

For each of the following, choose the most appropriate type of circulatory system from the list below.

A. Open circulatory system   B. Closed circulatory system

19. _____   Snails

20. _____   Arthropods

21. _____   Annelids

22. _____   Squids

23. _____   Vertebrates

For each of the following, choose the most appropriate circuit of blood from the list below.

A. Systemic circuit   B. Pulmonocutaneous circuit   C. Pulmonary circuit

24. _____   The circuit that distributes oxygenated blood to the body

25. _____   The circuit in amphibians that distributes deoxygenated blood to the lungs and skin

26. _____   The circuit in reptiles, birds, and mammals that distributes deoxygenated blood to the lungs

For each of the following, choose the most appropriate chamber(s) of the heart from the list below.

A. Atrium/atria   B. Ventricle(s)

27. _____   Receive(s) blood returning to the heart

28. _____   Pump(s) blood from the heart

32.2 Blood and Its Components [pp. 780–783]

Section Review (Fill-in-the-Blanks)

Blood is a connective tissue that consists of several cell types and a liquid matrix called (29) _____.

There are three classes of protein in the liquid matrix: (30) _____, (31) _____, and

(32) _____. (33) _____, commonly called (34) _____ _____

_____, are the cells that carry O_2 to tissues. (35) _____ is a hormone produced by the kidney

and stimulates RBC production. White blod cells, or (36) _____, play a role in the body's defence

against invading organisms. (37) _____ are cell fragments that contain factors important for blood

clotting, including enzymes that convert fibrinogen into (38) _____.

Building Vocabulary

Using the definitions of the prefixes below, assign the appropriate prefix to the appropriate suffix for the following:

Prefix	Meaning	Suffix	Meaning
erythro-	red	-cyte	a cell
leuko-	white (without colour)		
hemo-	blood		

	Prefix	Suffix	Definition
39.	_____	_____	Red blood cell
40.	_____	_____	White blood cell
41.	_____	-globin	Protein in red blood cells specialized for binding O_2

Complete the Table

Cell/Component	Function
42.	Eliminates dead/dying cells; removes cellular debris
Erythrocytes	43.
44.	Cell fragments produced in bone marrow; play a role in blood clotting

Matching

Match each of the following structures with its correct definition (choices may be repeated more than once).

45.	_____	Erythrocytes	A.	Transport of oxygen
46.	_____	Leukocytes	B.	Involved in immune responses
47.	_____	Platelets	C.	Involved in blood clotting
48.	_____	Erythropoietin	D.	Red blood cells
49.	_____	Albumins	E.	Fluid component of blood that contains nutrients, ions, gases, etc.
50.	_____	Hemoglobin	F.	Proteins important for osmotic balance, pH buffering, and transport
51.	_____	Globulins	G.	Proteins important in transport and as antibodies
52.	_____	Plasma	H.	Hormone that stimulates red blood cell production
53.	_____	Fibrinogen		

Short Answer

54. Explain how hemoglobin transports oxygen.

_____

_____

55. Discuss the process of blood clotting.

_____

_____

32.3 The Heart [pp. 783–787]
32.4 Blood Vessels of the Circulatory System [pp. 787–790]
32.5 Maintaining Blood Flow and Pressure [p. 790–791]
32.6 The Lymphatic System [pp. 791–793]

Section Review (Fill-in-the-Blanks)

Oxygenated blood leaves the heart and enters the (56) _____. The cardiac cycle consists of a period

of heart muscle contraction or (57) _____ and a period of relaxation or (58) _____. As the

atria contract, blood flows through the (59) _____ _____ and into the ventricle. When the

ventricle contract, the AV valves close and blood flows through the semilunar valves in the pulmonary and systemic circuits. Some animals such as crabs and lobsters have a(n) (60) _____ _____ in which the heartbeat is under the control of the nervous system. Other animals, including all vertebrates, have (61) _____ _____ in which the heart has its own endogenous rhythm that does not require outside signals. In mammals, contraction is initiated in the right atrium by the (62) _____ _____, which contains specialized (63) _____ _____. The electrical impulse travels from the atria to the ventricles through the (64) _____ _____. The electrical activity of the heart can be recorded externally to produce a(n) (65) _____.

As blood flows from the heart, it enters progressively smaller arteries until finally reaching the (66) _____. Blood flow into individual capillary beds is controlled by a(n) (67) _____ _____. Capillaries join together to form (68) _____, which merge to form larger veins that return blood to the heart.

Blood pressure is influenced by (69) _____ _____, the degree of constriction of blood vessels (primarily arterioles), and blood volume.

The (70) _____ _____ is a network of vessels that collects excess interstitial fluid or (71) _____ and returns it to the systemic circulation (venous side). (72) _____ _____ act as filters and participate in immune responses.

Choice

For each of the following descriptions, choose the most appropriate type of heart from the list below.

A. Myogenic heart   B. Neurogenic heart

73. _____ Possesses endogenous electrical activity that initiates contraction

74. _____ Requires neural signals to initiate contraction

For each of the following descriptions, choose the most appropriate region of the heart from the list below.

A. Sinoatrial node   B. Atrioventricular node

75. _____ In the right atrium and possesses pacemaker cells; initiates contraction of atria

76. _____ Conducts electrical impulses from atria to ventricles

For each of the following descriptions, choose the most appropriate phase of the cardiac cycle from the list below.

A. Systole   B. Diastole

77. _____   Period of contraction and emptying of heart chambers

78. _____   Period of relaxation and filling of heart chambers

For each of the following descriptions, choose the most appropriate valve from the list below.

A. Atrioventricular valves   B. Semilunar valves

79. _____   Valves between atria and ventricles

80. _____   Valves between ventricles and the arteries that leave the heart

Complete the Table

Component	Function
Lymphatic system	81.
82.	Filters blood and participates in immune responses
83.	Interstitial fluid that enters lymph vessels

Short Answer

84. What is an electrocardiogram?

_____

_____

85. List the events of the cardiac cycle.

_____

_____

86. Explain the changes in blood pressure in the aorta, atria, and ventricles during the heart cycle.

_____

_____

87. Using the following diagram, describe the electrical control of the heart cycle.

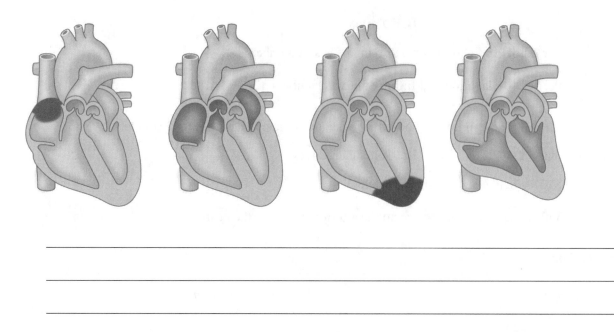

_____

_____

_____

_____

88. Draw a diagram of an electrocardiogram. Relate the characteristics of the electrocardiogram to the events of the heart cycle.

_____

_____

_____

_____

Matching

Match each of the following with its correct definition.

89. ____	Pacemaker cells	A.	Cells that initiate the endogenous rhythms of myogenic hearts
90. ____	Cardiac cycle	B.	Chronic elevation in blood pressure above normal levels
91. ____	Venules	C.	Small vessels that supply blood to capillaries
92. ____	Aorta	D.	Small vessels that drain blood from capillaries
93. ____	Cardiac output	E.	Control blood flow into capillary
94. ____	Hypertension	F.	Is a function of force of contraction and heart rate
95. ____	Precapillary sphincter	G.	The sequence of heart contraction–relaxation
96. ____	Arterioles	H.	The large vessels into which blood enters after leaving the heart

SELF-TEST

1. Which of the following is NOT a function of the circulatory system ? [p. 775]

   a. gas transport
   b. nutrient transport
   c. elimination of waste products
   d. hormone circulation

2. Which of the following is a characteristic of a closed circulatory system? [pp. 777–780]

   a. The blood is confined to blood vessels.
   b. The blood directly bathes the organs.
   c. The heart releases hemolymph into sinuses.

3. Which term refers to the fluid-filled space that surrounds organs of animals that have an open circulatory system? [pp. 776–777]

   a. coelom
   b. lymphocoel
   c. atracoel
   d. sinus

4. What type of circulatory system to bony fish have? [p. 778]

   a. an open circulatory system
   b. a single-circuit circulatory system
   c. a pulmonary circuit

5. Three-chambered hearts generally consist of how many atria and ventricles, respectively? [pp. 778–779]

   a. 2 atria and 1 ventricle
   b. 1 atria and 2 ventricles
   c. 1 atria and 1 ventricle
   d. No atria and no ventricle
   e. 3 atria but no ventricle

6. Which statement about erythrocytes is incorrect? [pp. 780–781]

   a. They are red blood cells.
   b. They are spherical shaped.
   c. They are produced in bone marrow.
   d. They are a kind of white blood cells.
   e. They are specialized for O_2 transport.

7. Which is NOT a function of the blood? [p. 780]

    a. gas transport
    b. defence
    c. clotting
    d. eliminate waste products

8. The plasma protein albumin plays a role in which biological activity? [p.780]

    a. osmotic balance
    b. lipid transport
    c. blood clotting

9. Which of the following is NOT a respiratory pigment? [p. 782]

    a. hemoglobin
    b. myoglobin
    c. hemocyanin
    d. hemerythrin
    e. globulins

10. Which statement about erythropoietin is correct? [p. 781]

    a. It is a hormone involved in the activation of the immune responses.
    b. It is a chemical signal involved in the initiation of blood clotting.
    c. It is a hormone involved in the stimulation of the production of red blood cells.
    d. It is a chemical signal involved in the maintenance of extracellular fluid.

11. Which activity is best described with neutrophils? [p.781]

    a. phagocytosis during inflammation
    b. defence against parasitic worms
    c. gas transport

12. Which statement about fibrinogen is correct? [p. 783]

    a. It is a plasma lipid.
    b. It is a gamma globulin.
    c. It is an erythrocyte.
    d. It is a precursor to fibrin.

13. In general, the path of blood in the systemic circulation in a vertebrate occurs in which order? [pp. 783–784]

    a. veins, venules, capillaries, arterioles, arteries
    b. arterioles, capillaries, arteries, venules, veins
    c. venules, veins, capillaries, arteries, arterioles
    d. arteries, arterioles, capillaries, venules, veins

14. In mammals, blood that enters the right atrium comes which vessel? [pp. 783–784]

    a. right ventricle
    b. vena cava
    c. pulmonary artery
    d. jugular vein

15. Which is correct about the blood that circulates in the pulmonary arteries? [pp. 783–784]

    a. high in O_2, low in CO_2, and on its way to the lungs
    b. high in O_2, low in CO_2, and on its way to the body
    c. low in O_2, high in CO_2, and on its way to the lungs
    d. low in O_2, high in CO_2, and on its way to the body

16. Which statement is consistent with the term systolic pressure? [p. 784]

    a. It occurs during the relaxation phase of the heart cycle.
    b. It is the blood pressure during the contraction of the heart cycle.
    c. It is the blood pressure in the venous system.
    d. It is approximately 80 mmHg.

17. Which tissue of the mammalian heart sends signals to ventricular muscle cells to stimulate contractions? [pp. 784–786]

    a. SA node
    b. AV node
    c. atria
    d. Purkinje fibres

18. An electrocardiogram measures the electrical activity of which organ? [p. 787]

    a. viscera
    b. heart
    c. skeletal muscle
    d. brain

19. Which of the following vessels are very small and supply blood to capillary beds?
    [pp. 787–789]

    a. arterioles
    b. venules
    c. arteries
    d. veins
    e. capillaries

20. Which of the following are characteristics of veins and venules? [pp. 789–790]

    a. thick walls
    b. large muscle mass in walls
    c. large quantity of elastin in the walls
    d. low blood volume compared with arteries
    e. one-way valves to prevent backflow of blood

21. Which of the following is NOT a role for the lymphatic system? [pp. 791–793]

    a. is a key component of the immune system
    b. returns excess tissue fluid to the blood
    c. produces red blood cells
    d. collects fat absorbed by the intestine

INTEGRATING AND APPLYING KEY CONCEPTS

1. What is the adaptive significance of a closed circulatory system?

2. Explain why some arterioles vasoconstrict in response to epinephrine while others vasodilate. What is the functional significance of the different responses?

33 Reproduction in Animals

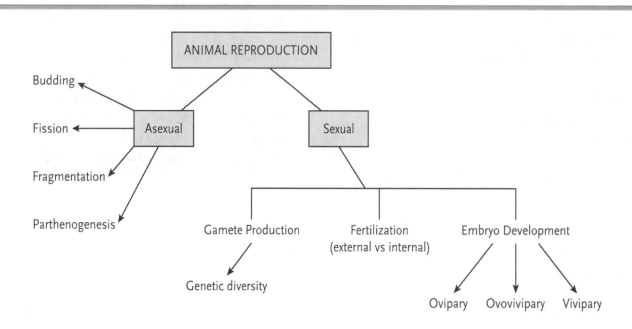

LEARNING OUTCOMES AND STUDY STRATEGIES

By the end of this chapter, you should be able to

- Describe and differentiate between the structures and processes involved in asexual and sexual reproduction
- Compare and contrast the cost and benefits of the two modes of reproduction
- Explain gamete production, fertilization, and embryo development in humans, as well as in animals

Study strategies for this chapter:

- First, focus on the purpose and overall processes required to produce offspring by asexual and sexual reproduction.
- Compare the three basic mechanisms of asexual reproduction, noting the special case of parthogenesis.
- Follow the development of the gametes, oogenesis, and spermatogenesis, identifying structures, hormones, and processes involved.
- Examine fertilization and embryo development.
- Next, expand on your knowledge of gamete production, fertilization, and embryo development with a focus on humans.

INTERACTIVE EXERCISES

Why It Matters [pp. 797–799]

Section Review (Fill-in-the-Blanks)

In many coral species, reproduction requires a mass release of both female (1) _____ cells and male

(2) _____ cells into the water a few days after a(n) (3) _____ moon. For (4) _____

fertilization to be successful, release of these gametes must be (5) _____. There is evidence that light

receptor proteins in these corals (and other animals), called (6) _____ (CRYs), sense changes in

irradiance intensity of (7) _____ light during a(n) (8) _____ cycle and trigger the mass

spawn. Fertilization can only occur between gametes of the same (9) _____ due to chemicals in the

egg (10) _____ and sperm (11) _____.

33.1 The Drive to Reproduce [p. 799]
33.2 Asexual and Sexual Reproduction [pp. 799–800]

Section Review (Fill-in-the-Blanks)

Reproduction is necessary to ensure that an organism's (12) _____ are passed on to future

generations. Aquatic invertebrates and a few vertebrates are able to reproduce by (13) _____

reproduction (or clonal reproduction), which involves the production of offspring from (14) _____

parent. There are (15) _____ major mechanisms of this type of reproduction, and each produces

offspring that are genetically (16) _____ to the parent. A special type of asexual reproduction, called

(17) _____, occurs when a new individual develops from a(n) (18) _____ egg. Sexual

reproduction results in the production of a(n) (19) _____ from the fertilization of male and female

(20) _____. In comparing the two types of reproduction, (21) _____ reproduction has

greater costs associated with it; however, it provides an overriding advantage: it generates (22) _____

_____ among offspring. In an unstable or changing (23) _____, diversity among individuals

will increase the likelihood that some will (24) _____ and reproduce. There are (25) _____

mechanisms during gamete formation that produce genetic diversity, (26) _____ _____, in

which alleles within (27) _____ from parents are mixed to form new combinations, and

(28) _____ _____, in which chromosomes from parents are (29) _____ combined.

(30) _____ is the ultimate source of variation.

Matching

Match each of the following types of asexual reproduction with its correct definition.

31. ____	Parthenogenesis	A.	Parent divides into two offspring
32. ____	Budding	B.	Separate pieces develop into offspring
33. ____	Fission	C.	Egg develops without fertilization
34. ____	Fragmentation	D.	Offspring develops directly off parent

33.3 Mechanisms of Sexual Reproduction [pp. 800–808]

Section Review (Fill-in-the-Blanks)

During (35) _____, male germ cells in the gamete-producing organ, the (36) _____, first

undergo mitosis to produce (37) _____ and then undergo (38) _____ to produce haploid

(39) _____ that will mature to become (40) _____ cells. Female germ cells in the

(41) _____ produce oogonia from mitosis, which then undergo (42) _____. Uneven division

of (43) _____ during this process results in the production of only one (44) _____, which

will mature into a functional (45) _____, and two small polar bodies. This process is called

(46) _____. Fertilization by most aquatic animals is (47) _____ and requires sperm to

(48) _____ in open water until they collide with an egg. Internal fertilization requires close

(49) _____ between individuals so that sperm can enter the (50) _____ reproductive tract

and swim in a fluid environment to the egg.

Matching

Match each of the following components of an egg or sperm with its correct definition.

51. ____	Zona pellucida	A.	Nonfunctional cells with the correct number of chromosomes but less cytoplasm
52. ____	Oviduct	B.	Embryo develops within mother's body
53. ____	Polar bodies	C.	Contains enzymes necessary for penetration of the surface coating of an egg
54. ____	Amplexus	D.	Gel-like matrix covering the egg in mammals

55. ____	Midpiece of sperm	E.	Egg-laying animals
56. ____	Acrosome	F.	Contains organelles necessary for movement of flagellum
57. ____	Viviparous	G.	More than one sperm fertilizing egg
58. ____	Oviparous	H.	Transport tube for egg
59. ____	Polyspermy	I.	Reflex response in female frogs causing egg release

Sequence

60. Arrange the following steps describing fertilization: ____ ____ ____ ____ ____ ____

    A.   Sperm nucleus enters the egg cell and fuses with egg nucleus

    B.   Enzymes in the acrosome break down jelly

    C.   Cortical granules are released from the egg cell

    D.   Sperm head fuses with the egg plasma membrane

    E.   Sperm reaches jelly layer that coats egg

    F.   Sperm binds to vitelline coat and bores a hole into it

Short Answer

61. Explain the difference between internal and external fertilization.

_____

_____

62. Explain the importance of the acrosome reaction and the fast/slow block of fertilization.

_____

_____

63. Distinguish between simultaneous and sequential hermaphroditism.

_____

_____

33.4 Sexual Reproduction in Mammals [pp. 808–817]
33.5 Controlling Reproduction [pp. 817–819]

Section Review (Fill-in-the-Blanks)

In humans, like all vertebrates, the gonads have (64) _____ functions, gamete and

(65) _____ production. In males and females, two hormones from the pituitary, (66) _____-

_____ (_____) hormone and (67) _____ (_____) hormone, are under the control of

(68) _____-_____ (_____) hormone from the hypothalamus. In females, FSH stimulates

(69) _____ to undergo meiosis, and one will develop into a mature follicle. The follicular cells

secrete (70) _____, which stimulate further development of the follicle. The second hormone from

the pituitary, (71) _____, increases just prior to and is thought to be responsible for

(72) _____. After ovulation, the follicular cells, as part of the corpus luteum, continue to secrete

estrogens but significantly increase the secretion of (73) _____, which further prepares the uterus for

implantation. In males, FSH stimulates (74) _____ cells to produce materials that are required for

(75) _____, and LH stimulates (76) _____ cells to secrete (77) _____, which also

plays a major role in spermatogenesis. Understanding the processes of reproduction in animals, including

humans, assists in controlling reproductive (78) _____, maximizing success for animals becoming

(79) _____, and reducing the possibility of becoming (80) _____ when desired.

Matching

Match each of the structures with its correct function.

81. ____	Oviduct, near ovary	A.	Entrance for sperm to enter female body
82. ____	Endometrium	B.	Group of external female organs
83. ____	Prostate gland	C.	Site where meiosis I is completed in females
84. ____	Pituitary gland	D.	Produces alkaline secretion that is component of semen
85. ____	Urethra	E.	Produces testosterone
86. ____	Vas deferens	F.	Becomes erect during ejaculation
87. ____	Ovary	G.	Site of spermatogenesis
88. ____	Vulva	H.	Location for sperm storage
89. ____	Leydig cell	I.	Muscular tube that joins urethra in males
90. ____	Epididymis	J.	Location where fertilized egg is implanted
91. ____	Vagina	K.	Location of fertilization
92. ____	Greater vestibular gland	L.	Produces lubricant for structures surrounding entrance to vagina
93. ____	Testis	M.	Tube from which semen leaves the male body
94. ____	Penis	N.	Secretes FSH and LH

Choice

For each of the following statements, choose the most appropriate definition from the list below.

A. FSH   B. LH   C. Androgens   D. Estrogens

E. Progesterone   F. GnRH   G. hCG

95. _____ Leydig cells produce this

96. _____ Corpus luteum produces large amounts of this

97. _____ Without this hormone, FSH and LH will not be released

98. _____ Responsible for development of male secondary sex/reproductive structures

99. _____ Stimulates the Leydig cells

100. _____ Stimulates primary oocytes to undergo development

101. _____ Supportive cells that surround developing spermatocytes are stimulated by this

102. _____ Hormone that is predominant during the luteal phase

103. _____ Progesterone will inhibit this hormone from being released

104. _____ Burst of this hormone results in ovulation

105. _____ Low concentration of testosterone causes this hormone to be secreted

106. _____ Enlarging follicle cells secrete this

107. _____ Secreted by embryo to prevent corpus luteum from breaking down

108. _____ Thickens mucus in uterus that forms a plug

SELF-TEST

1. What does a male acanthocephalan worm do to ensure that his genes are passed on to the next generation? [pp. 799–800]

    a. mates with female and then seals her gonopore
    b. mates with female multiple times
    c. reproduces asexually by budding

2. Suppose that a sea star was cut into two pieces and each piece developed into a complete sea star. What is this an example of? [pp. 799–800]

    a. external fertilization
    b. fission
    c. budding
    d. fragmentation

3. Which of the following is an advantage of asexual reproduction? [pp. 799–800]

    a. independent assortment
    b. synchronization of gamete release
    c. genetic diversity
    d. finding a mate is not necessary
    e. higher energy cost

4. Which of the following does NOT increase genetic diversity of offspring? [pp. 799–800]

    a. fertilization between genetically different individuals at random
    b. genetic recombination
    c. independent assortment
    d. mitosis

5. If the cortical reaction that occurs during the fast block reaction after fertilization were blocked, what might occur? [pp. 804–806]

   a. external fertilization

   b. fertilized egg would break down

   c. polyspermy and a greater than diploid number of chromosomes in offspring

6. What type of reproductive system does the duck-billed platypus have? [pp. 806–807]

   a. placental

   b. oviparous

   c. viviparous

   d. ovoviviparous

7. Which term refers to the male cell that enters meiosis I? [pp. 801–802]

   a. oocyte

   b. oogonia

   c. spermatocyte

   d. spermagonia

8. What is the chromosome number of a secondary oocyte? [pp. 801–802]

   a. haploid

   b. diploid

   c. triploid

9. What part of the sperm contains the chromosomes that will be passed on to the offspring? [pp. 801–802]

   a. the acrosome

   b. the mitochondria

   c. the tail

   d. the midpiece

10. At what stage of meiosis are the oocytes in the ovaries of a four-year-old female? [pp. 800–803]

    a. at the beginning of prophase I

    b. at the end of prophase I

    c. at the beginning of metaphase II

    d. at the end of metaphase II

11. What type of response is associated with calcium ion release from the ER to prevent polyspermy? [pp. 804–807]

    a. fast block response that occurs within seconds of fertilization

    b. fast block response that occurs within minutes of fertilization

    c. slow block response that occurs within seconds of fertilization

    d. slow block response that occurs within minutes of fertilization

12. What are hermaphrodites? [pp. 807–808]

    a. Individuals that produce eggs.

    b. Individuals that produce sperm.

    c. Individuals that produce eggs and sperm.

13. In order for progesterone to have its full effect during the luteal phase, which of the following must occur? [pp. 810–812]

    a. low levels of FSH

    b. ovulation

    c. the secretory phase

    d. stimulation of a primary oocyte

14. What is the name of the membrane that human females are born with but that is broken during the first sexual intercourse? [p. 809]

    a. labia minor

    b. labia major

    c. hymen

    d. clitoris

15. If the levels of FSH and LH were NOT high enough to inhibit the release of GnRH, what could happen? [pp. 808–812]

    a. nothing would happen

    b. no fertilization could occur

    c. possibility of having twins

    d. there would be no menstrual phase

16. If the prostate gland secretion is inhibited, one effect on the semen is a decreased volume. Which of the following is another effect on the semen? [pp. 812–816]

   a. more basic semen

   b. more acidic semen

   c. more alkaline semen

17. If a person is born without a pituitary gland, what would be the result in terms of the person's fertility? [pp. 808–817]

   a. The person would be sterile.

   b. The person would be female.

   c. It would give the person the possibility of multiple births with every pregnancy.

   d. GnRH low would be expected to be low.

18. Approximately what percentage of the oocytes in human ovaries at sexual maturity are ovulated during a female human life? [p. 810]

   a. 50%

   b. 20%

   c. 1%

   d. 0.1%

   e. 0.001%

19. As sperm cell develop and mature in human males, where do they move? [pp. 812–817]

   a. toward the centre of the seminiferous tubule

   b. toward the wall of the seminiferous tubule

   c. toward Sertoli cells

   d. toward Leydig cells

20. Home pregnancy tests evaluate which of the following hormones? [p. 817]

   a. FSH

   b. LH

   c. relaxin

   d. hCG

INTEGRATING AND APPLYING KEY CONCEPTS

1. Explain why species recognition is important for animals using external fertilization.

2. Identify the components of semen and provide at least one function for each.

3. Assume that pregnancy has occurred. Predict the effect if progesterone levels started to drop instead of increasing.

34 Animal Development

TOPIC MAP

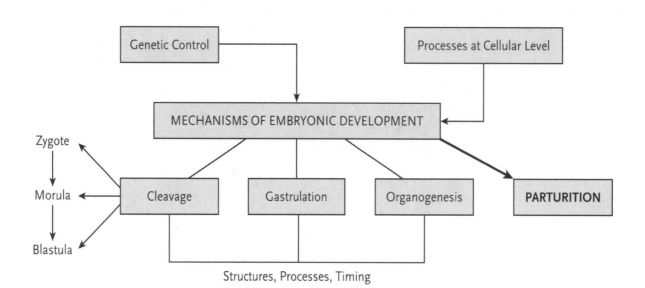

LEARNING OUTCOMES AND STUDY STRATEGIES

By the end of this chapter, you should be able to

- Describe the major stages of development from zygote to a whole organism, with a focus on humans
- Explain how genes are able to control processes of embryo development
- Describe how cells change shape, move, and become specialized

Study strategies for this chapter:

- First, focus on major events of embryological development from fertilization, through cleavage, gastrulation, and organogenesis, to parturition.
- Look for developmental patterns at the different stages, including overall structure of the adult form.
- Next, make comparisons between the embryonic development of humans and other deuterostomes.
- Evaluate the mechanisms of development from a cellular perspective, focusing on genetic and molecular controls.

INTERACTIVE EXERCISES

Why It Matters [pp. 821–822]

Section Review (Fill-in-the-Blanks)

During (1) _____, the birth process, a mammalian offspring travels through the mother's birth

(2) _____ and leaves the body through the opening between bones of the (3) _____ girdle.

This opening is often too (4) _____ for the young to pass through, especially in species that give

birth to large young. A hormone, (5) _____, which is produced by the (6) _____, assists in

parturition by relaxing the (7) _____ fibres of the interpubic (8) _____ surrounding the

opening, maximizing their (9) _____ so that the opening is enlarged.

34.1 Housing and Fuelling Developing Young [pp. 822–824]

Section Review (Fill-in-the-Blanks)

The higher the parental investment in caring for offspring, the (10) _____ the likelihood that the

parent's (11) _____ will be passed on to future generations. An animal that carries a developing

embryo inside its body not only provides (12) _____ against predators but also ensures the best

conditions for embryo (13) _____. After parturition, parents that provide nutritious food, such as

(14) _____ (primarily mammalian species) or other high-quality food, are investing their energy to

promote survival and (15) _____ of young.

34.2 Mechanisms of Embryonic Development [pp. 824–827]
34.3 Major Patterns of Cleavage and Gastrulation [pp. 827–831]

Section Review (Fill-in-the-Blanks)

All instructions for development are located in the nucleus of the (16) _____, the fertilized egg. Since

the contribution of the sperm is primarily (17) _____ material, it is the (18) _____

determinants from the (19) _____, consisting of the cytoplasm, all organelles, and mRNA, that play

key roles in the initial activities of the zygote. In most species, the nucleus in the zygote is located at one end

of the cell, the (20) _____ pole, and the other components are at the (21) _____ pole. Even

at this early stage in development, (22) _____ in the egg assists in defining the (23) _____ body axes. During embryo development, there are (24) _____ major development stages. The first

stage, (25) _____, progresses through two steps: (i) formation of a solid ball of cells, the

(26) _____, resulting from (27) _____ cell divisions; and (ii) the hollowing of the ball of

cells to form a(n) (28) _____. Next, the embryo enters the second phase, (29) _____, where

indentations and rearrangement of dividing cells result in the formation of three primary tissues: the outer

(30) _____ tissue, the inner (31) _____ tissue, and the (32) _____ in between. The

cavity that forms in the embryo, the (33) _____ (or gut), has an opening at one end, the

(34) _____. If this opening forms a mouth, the animal is classified as a(n) (35) _____,

whereas if it forms an anus, it is a(n) (36) _____. The third stage is (37) _____, and it gives

rise to all major (38) _____ systems. Six major mechanisms play key roles in these developmental

stages: mitotic divisions, cell movements, selective cell (39) _____, induction, determination, and

(40) _____ (cell-specific structure and function).

Choice

For each of the following statements, choose the most appropriate gastrulation pattern from the list below.
There may be more than one correct answer.

A.   Gastrulation with even distribution of yolk

B.   Gastrulation with uneven distribution of yolk

C.   Gastrulation at one side of yolk

41. _____   Blastodisk is composed of the epiblast and hypoblast

42. _____   Pattern found in amphibians

43. _____   Invagination begins at the vegetal pole of the blastula

44. _____   Blastopore becomes the anus

45. _____   Pattern typically found in amniotes

46. _____   Dorsal lip cells control blastopore formation

47. _____   Primitive streak defines the right and left sides of the embryo

48. _____   Extraembryonic membranes are common

49. _____   Hypoblast cells become germ cell line

50. _____   Involution results in the pigmented cells of the animal half enclosing the vegetal half

Matching

Match each of the following with its correct definition.

51. _____ Chorion

A. Stores nitrogenous wastes produced by the embryo

52. _____ Primitive groove

B. Cell of early developmental cleavage

53. _____ Determination

C. Cell-to-cell contact influencing developmental pathway of group of cells

54. _____ Blastomere

D. Layer that gives rise to primary tissues

55. _____ Amnion

E. Membrane that surrounds the embryo and yolk sac

56. _____ Allantois

F. Membrane that encloses the embryo

57. _____ Epiblast

G. Developmental fate of the cell is set

58. _____ Induction

H. Entrance to archenteron

59. _____ Blastopore

I. Means for cells to move into the blastocoels

Choice

For each of the following organs, choose the primary tissue type from the list below.

A.   Endoderm   B.   Mesoderm   C.   Ectoderm

60. _____ Muscles

61. _____ Bone

62. _____ Lining of respiratory tract

63. _____ Spinal cord

64. _____ Heart and kidneys

65. _____ Lining of mouth

66. _____ Lining of digestive tract

67. _____ Cornea of eye

34.4 Organogenesis: Gastrulation to Adult Body Structures [pp. 831–834]

Section Review (Fill-in-the-Blanks)

During the third major developmental stage, (68) _____, the three primary tissues develop into

(69) _____. This stage involves several major changes that occur in rapid succession. A rod of tissue,

the (70) _____, providing organization along the entire length of the embryo, is derived from

(71) _____. Very rapidly, ectoderm will give rise to the (72) _____ system in a process

called (73) _____. Above the notochord, cells undergo (74) _____ and develop into the

neural (75) _____, which gives rise to the central nervous system. At the same time, blocks of

(76) _____ develop into (77) _____, which will develop into organs and tissues associated

with the embryo. In addition to cellular mechanisms used in cleavage and gastrulation, organogenesis has

programmed cell death or (78) _____.

Sequence

79. Put the following steps of eye development in sequence, starting with D:

_D_ ____ ____ ____ ____ ____ ____

A. Ball of cells forms the lens vesicle

B. Optic vesicles grow outward

C. Outpocket forms optic cup

D. Neural tube forms

E. Lens placode forms from thickened ectoderm

F. Ectoderm closes over lens and forms the cornea

G. Lens synthesizes crystallin

4.5 Embryonic Development of Humans and Other Mammals [pp. 835–839]

Section Review (Fill-in-the-Blanks)

Human gestation is completed in approximately (80) _____ weeks and can be divided into three

(81) _____. The first trimester includes three development events (in order): (82) _____,

(83) _____, and (84) _____. After the first trimester, the developing embryo is called a(n)

(85) _____ until birth. A successful pregnancy requires that (86) _____ occurs in the first

(87) _____ of the oviduct. By the time that (88) _____ in the uterine wall occurs, the

embryo is in the form of a(n) (89) _____. This structure contains a fluid-filled cavity, the

(90) _____, a(n) (91) _____ _____ _____ that is pushed to one side of the

structure, and an outer layer of cells, the (92) _____. The latter secretes (93) _____ that

create a hole in the (94) _____, providing a space for implantation of the blastocyst. The inner cell

mass divides into a two-layered embryonic (95) _____, in which the inner layer, the

(96) _____, develops into the (97) _____ and the outer layer, the (98) _____, assists

in the development of extra-embryonic (99) _____. All organs and organ systems are formed at

(100) _____ weeks, with the remaining weeks providing a time for embryo (101) _____ and

development. Gastrulation and organogenesis of a human embryo are similar to the pattern found in

(102) _____ or (103) _____.

Matching

Match each of the following with its correct definition.

104. ____	Chorionic villi	A.	Connecting stalk between the embryo and placenta
105. ____	Umbilical cord	B.	Produces the yolk sac
106. ____	Parturition	C.	Develops into female reproductive system
107. ____	Wolffian duct	D.	Extensions that increase surface area
108. ____	Müllerian duct	E.	Develops into male reproductive system
109. ____	Hypoblast	F.	Process involving extracting fluid from cavity containing embryo
110. ____	Amniocentesis	G.	Birth

Choice

For each of the following processes, choose the correct time period for when it would occur.

A. First trimester   B. Second and third trimesters   C. Birth   D. After birth

111. _____ Mammary glands are stimulated by prolactin

112. _____ Blastocyst breaks out of zona pellucida

113. _____ Cervix dilates

114. _____ Fetus grows

115. _____ Formation of chorionic villi for gas and nutrient exchange between parent and embryo

116. _____ Expulsion of the placenta out of vagina

117. _____ Amniotic membrane bursts and amniotic fluid is released

118. _____ Embryo develops tail and pharyngeal slits

Short Answer

119. Identify and describe the gene that determines whether an embryo develops into a male or a female.

_____

_____

120.   How are the extraembryonic membranes formed?

_____

_____

34.6 Cellular Basis of Development [pp. 840–845]
34.7 Genetic and Molecular Control of Development [pp. 845–851]

Section Review (Fill-in-the-Blanks)

The final shape and size, as well as the location of organs in the embryo, are determined by the

(121) _____, due to the location of cleavage furrows, and (122) _____ of cellular divisions

during development. Division rate is determined by the time of the (123) _____ period of interphase.

The actual mechanisms for these events are not totally understood; however, scientists do know that various

structures and mechanisms influence embryonic development, including cell components

(124) _____ and (125) _____, which can lead to cell movement and change in cell shape;

the (126) _____ process that uses cells to define the fate of other cells, called (127) _____,

and usually results in cell differentiation; and the presence or absence of cell (128) _____ molecules,

which allows entire cells to move during embryonic development. At all stages of development,

(129) _____ control necessary processes, which are often regulated by master (130) _____

genes. An example is the (131) _____ gene, a homeotic gene that specifies what each embryo

segment will become after (132) _____.

True/False

Mark if the statement is true (T) or false (F). If the statement is false, make it correct by changing the
underlined word(s) and writing the correct word(s) in the lines below each statement.

133. _____   Broad regions along the anterior–posterior axis of the embryo are controlled by segment
                polarity genes.

_____

_____

134. _____   The genes that control the polarity of the zygote and subsequent cleavage events of the
                embryo are from a maternal source.

_____

_____

135. _____ Fate mapping of embryos allows a clear understanding of cell lineage.

_____

_____

136. _____ Products of segmentation genes divide the embryo into units of two segments each.

_____

_____

137. _____ Homeotic (*Hox*) genes have been identified in animals but not plants.

_____

_____

138. _____ Differentiation leads to determination of a cell's development.

_____

_____

139. _____ A death signal binding to a cell's plasma membrane receptors activates genes that produce killer proteins.

_____

_____

140. _____ The BICOID protein is concentrated at the posterior end of a zygote.

_____

_____

141. _____ Master regulatory genes control the expression of other genes.

_____

_____

142. _____ The MyoD transcription factor converts somite cells into differentiated muscle cells.

_____

_____

143. _____ The sliding movement of microtubules causes column-shaped cells to become wedge-shaped cells.

_____

_____

1. Which of the following animals feed skin to their offspring? [pp. 823–824]

   a. humans

   b. cockroaches

   c. caecilians

   d. pigeons

2. During which stage of development do cytoplasmic determinants have the greatest effect? [pp. 824–825]

   a. gastrulation

   b. organogenesis

   c. cleavage

   d. the second and third trimesters

3. Which term is most consistent with the two major groups of animals?[pp. 827–831]

   a. archenteron

   b. blastopore

   c. grey crescent

   d. blastocoel

4. If the endoderm tissue in a developing animal were labelled with a coloured marker, where would you expect to find the marked tissue in the adult? [pp. 826–831]

   a. in the nervous system

   b. in muscle and bone

   c. in coverings of the animal or structures

   d. in linings of major organ systems

5. If you were working with a blastodisc of a bird embryo, which portion will develop into the germ cell line in the adult? [pp. 829–831]

   a. the epiblast

   b. the hypoblast

   c. the primitive streak

   d. the primitive groove

6. If the primitive streak were blocked or removed, what do you predict would be the effect on the embryo? [pp. 827–831]

   a. The adult could not reproduce.

   b. Organization, including axes would be lost.

   c. Extra-embryonic membranes would be lacking.

   d. The blastocoel would collapse.

7. Which of the extra-embryonic membranes surrounds the sac containing nitrogenous wastes? [pp. 830–831]

   a. the amnion

   b. the allantoic

   c. the chorion

   d. the yolk sac

8. What is neurulation? [p. 831]

   a. development of a blood vessel from the mesoderm

   b. development of a blood vessel from the endoderm

   c. development of nervous tissue from the endoderm

   d. development of nervous tissue from the ectoderm

9. What are the cranial nerves in an adult vertebrate derived from? [p. 831]

   a. from the neural crest cells

   b. from the ectoderm

   c. from the mesoderm

   d. from the somites

10. Which processe does NOT happen during development of an eye? [pp. 832–834]

    a. Genes coding for keratin are activated.

    b. Genes coding for crystallin are activated.

    c. Optic vesicles induce lens formation.

    d. Ectoderm cells form a cornea.

11. Which test evaluates the fluid that surrounds a developing fetus? [p. 835–839]

    a. chorionic villus sampling

    b. umbilical cord sampling

    c. amniocentesis

    d. blastocoel sampling

12. Why must maternal blood be isolated from embryonic blood? [pp. 835–839]

    a. because maternal blood is toxic to the baby

    b. to prevent an immune reaction if blood cells are seen as "foreign"

    c. to limit the addition of excessive nutrients to baby

    d. to prevent maternal wastes from entering into the allantois

13. What does the embryonic disc consist? [pp. 835–839]

    a. trophoblast cells

    b. epiblast and hypoblast cell layers

    c. amniotic fluid

    d. blood vessels

14. Which statement is true if the embryo is lacking the SRY protein? [pp. 835–839]

    a. The Wolffian ducts develop into the male reproductive structures.

    b. The Wolffian ducts develop into female reproductive structures.

    c. The Müllerian ducts develop into male reproductive structures.

    d. The Müllerian ducts develop into female reproductive structures.

15. If you wanted to change the orientation or axes of early cleavage, which of the following would you manipulate? [pp. 835–839]

    a. the microtubules and microfilaments

    b. the Wolffian or Müllerian ducts

    c. the blastopore location

    d. the chorion

16. Which end of a polar egg undergoes cell division more quickly? [pp. 845–851]

    a. the animal pole

    b. the vegetal pole

    c. the end containing the yolk

17. Somites, which are derived from the mesoderm, are ultimately formed from the products of which genes? [pp. 845–851]

    a. maternal-effect genes

    b. segment polarity genes

    c. segmentation genes

    d. homeotic genes

18. Which statement is correct about the specialized cells resulting from differentiation? [pp. 845–851]

    a. They contain more genes than the original cells.

    b. They contain different genes than the original cells.

    c. They contain the same genes as the original cells.

    d. They contain fewer genes than the original cells.

19. Why was *C. elegans* able to provide a detailed fate map of every cell during embryonic development? [pp. 845]

    a. because it contains very few cells

    b. because its development is very simple

    c. because only one cell lineage is involved in development

    d. because it is transparent, so markers could be followed

20. Which statement about *Hox* genes in a human is true?[pp. 845–851]

    a. They are in the same order as the *Hox* genes for *Drosophila.*

    b. They are in a different order from *Hox* genes in *Drosophila.*

    c. They are a different group of genes than the *Hox* genes in *Drosophila.*

INTERACTIVE EXERCISES

1. If each of the primary tissues were assigned a different colour, predict how those colours would be distributed in any given organ or organ system.

2. Address the role and importance of apoptosis in development.

3. Explain how entire cells move during embryonic development.

35 Control of Animal Processes: Endocrine Control

TOPIC MAP

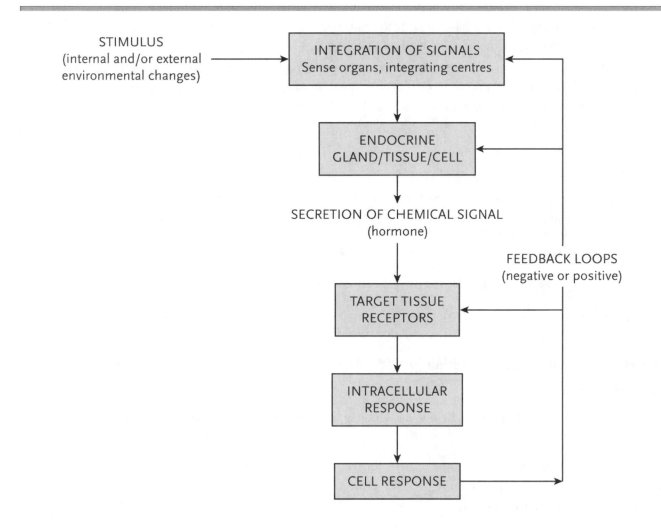

LEARNING OUTCOMES AND STUDY STRATEGIES

By the end of this chapter, you should be able to

- Describe the functions of the endocrine system, differentiating it from the nervous system
- Describe the four major types of cell signalling
- List and describe the groups of hormones based on their chemical structures and describe their mechanisms of action

- Explain the role of feedback mechanisms in the control of hormone secretion (provide examples)
- List the major human endocrine glands and hormones and provide the functions for each
- Describe the endocrine system in invertebrates

Study strategies for this chapter:

- This chapter is extremely long and has many terms. DO NOT try to go through the chapter all in one sitting. Take one section at a time and then work through the companion section in the study guide.

- Through the study of the endocrine system, one quickly recognizes that the concepts can be broken down into a number of steps that can be discussed in a sequence. By understanding a basic diagram (see the topic map) outlining the endocrine system, you can then apply the same basic series of steps to any system and hormone to understand its basic functions.

- Draw diagrams of the various endocrine pathways (source organ, target organ, feedback loops), being sure to label the various parts, noting the chemical nature of the hormone and its actions on the target organ. Some of these pathways are complex and involve intermediate or multiple targets as well as multiple hormone players.

INTERACTIVE EXERCISES

Why It Matters [pp. 854–855]

Section Review (Fill-in-the-Blanks)

(1) _____ are chemicals released by one cell that affect the activity of another cell. The network of

cells that produces hormones is the (2) _____.

35.1 Hormones and Their Secretion [pp. 855–858]

Building Vocabulary

Using the definitions of the prefixes below, assign the appropriate prefix to the appropriate suffix for the following:

Prefix	Meaning	Suffix	Meaning
neuro-	of or relating to a nerve	-crine	secretion
endo-	within, to the inside		
hyper-	over		
hypo-	under		

	Prefix	Suffix	Definition
3.	_____	-hormone	A hormone secreted by a neurosecretory cell
4.	_____	-secretion	A diminished or undersecretion
5.	_____	-secretion	An excessive or oversecretion
6.	_____	-glycemia	An abnormally high level of glucose in the blood
7.	_____ _____		A mode of secretion from cells in a ductless gland

8. Outline the differences between the endocrine system and the nervous system.

_____

_____

9. Define the term "hormone."

_____

_____

10. In your own words, what is the role of the endocrine system?

_____

_____

_____

11. Explain how the secretion of hormones is regulated by feedback pathways. Provide an example of positive and negative feedback pathways. What would be the benefits of such regulatory pathways?

_____

_____

_____

12. Explain what is meant by "the body processes are regulated by coordinated hormone secretion."

_____

_____

_____

Fill-in-the-Blanks

(13) _____ are ductless glands that secrete hormones. (14) _____ _____ are specialized neurons that also secrete hormones. Hormones can be classified into four chemical types:

(15) _____, (16) _____, (17) _____, and (18) _____ _____

_____. (19) _____ _____ are examples of peptide hormones, and

(20) _____ are examples of a fatty acid derivative. Only the (21) _____ _____ of a

hormone, those with (22) _____ _____ recognizing and binding that hormone, respond to it.

Complete the Tables

Mode of Secretion	Description
23.	The release of a hormone from a neuron
Endocrine	24.
Paracrine	25.
26.	The release of a chemical into the extracellular fluid that regulates the activity of the cell that secreted it

Chemical Type	Hormonal Example
Amine	27.
Peptide	28.
Steroid	29.
30.	Prostaglandins

Matching

Match each of the following structures with its correct definition.

31. _____ Growth factor

    A.   A chemical signal released from one cell that affects another cell, usually at a distance from its site of secretion

32. _____ Neurosecretory neuron

    B.   Network of cells/glands that secrete hormones

33. _____ Endocrine system

    C.   A group of peptide hormones that regulate growth and differentiation

34. _____ Hormone

    D.   A neuron specialized to release hormones

35.2 Mechanisms of Hormone Action [pp. 858–862]

Short Answer

35. Hormones are not always secreted in an active form. Discuss how hormones may become active. Draw a diagram of hormone activation.

_____

_____

36. Compare the mechanisms of hormone actions for hydrophilic and hydrophobic hormones. For each, provide a concrete example by drawing a diagram of the mechanisms of hormone action. In each, outline the four features of a hormone mechanism.

_____

_____

37. Explain why cells may respond to more than one hormone, and different target cells may respond differently to the same hormones, while other cells may not respond to these hormones.

_____

_____

Predict the Mechanisms of Hormone Action

Determine the mechanism of hormone action for the following chemical signals. Hint: Are these chemical signals hydrophobic or hydrophilic? Would these chemicals bind to surface receptors or intracellular receptors? Justify your answers.

38. Epinephrine:

   _____

   _____

39. Insulin:

   _____

   _____

40. Testosterone:

   _____

   _____

41. Oxytocin:

   _____

   _____

42. Estrogen:

   _____

   _____

43. Aldosterone:

   _____

   _____

44. Thyroid hormone:

   _____

   _____

45. Prostaglandin:

   _____

   _____

35.3 The Hypothalamus and Pituitary [pp. 862–865]

Section Review (Fill-in-the-Blanks)

The (46) _____ _____ consists of two lobes: the (47) _____ _____,

which contains axons and nerve endings that originate in the hypothalamus, and the (48) _____

_____. Some of the axons that terminate in the posterior pituitary release (49) _____

_____ that travel through the portal veins and affect the secretions of the anterior pituitary, while

others release nontropic hormones that enter the general blood circulation. The two types of tropic hormones

are (50) _____ _____ and (51) _____ _____. The two nontropic

hormones that enter the general circulation are (52) _____ _____ (_____), which helps

regulate water balance, and (53) _____, which stimulates milk ejection from the mammary glands of

mammals. The anterior pituitary produces and secretes (54) _____, (55) _____

_____, (56) _____ _____ _____ (_____), (57) _____

_____ (_____), (58) _____ _____ _____ (_____), and

(59) _____ _____ (_____). FSH and LH are referred to as (60) _____ because of

their action on gonads. In some species, the anterior pituitary has a distinct intermediate lobe that produces

and releases (61) _____ _____ _____ (_____) and (62) _____; in those

species without an intermediate lobe, these hormones are produced by cells dispersed in the other regions of

the anterior pituitary.

Distinguish between Members of the Following Pairs of Terms

63. Anterior pituitary and posterior pituitary

_____

_____

Chapter 35 Control of Animal Processes: Endocrine Control

Complete the Table

Hormone	Chemical Type	Site of Secretion	Function
Growth hormone	64.	65.	66.
67.	68.	69.	Influence reproductive activity, stimulate milk synthesis
70.	71.	Anterior pituitary	Stimulates thyroid gland to produce T_4
ACTH	Peptide	72.	73.
FSH	74.	75.	76.
LH	77.	78.	79.
80.	81.	82.	Controls pigmentation/coloration
Endorphin	83.	84.	85.
ADH	86.	87.	88.
89.	90.	91.	Stimulates smooth muscle contraction (includes milk "letdown" or secretion)

Labelling

Identify each numbered part of the following illustration.

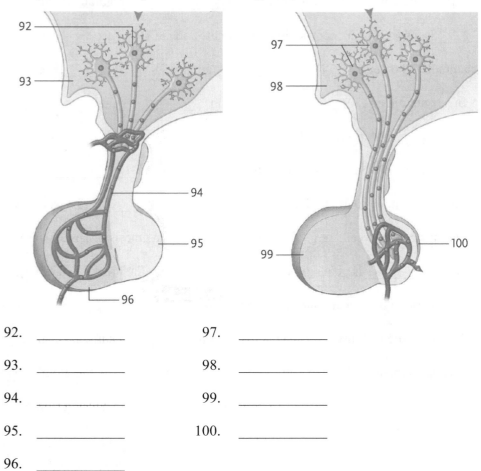

92. _____   97. _____

93. _____   98. _____

94. _____   99. _____

95. _____   100. _____

96. _____

35.4 Other Major Endocrine Glands of Vertebrates [pp. 865–871]

Section Review (Fill-in-the-Blanks)

The (101) _____ _____ produces (102) _____ (_____), which is converted to its

biologically active form, (103) _____ (_____), prior to binding to intracellular receptors. In amphi-

bians, T_4 triggers (104) _____. In mammals, the thyroid gland also produces (105) _____,

which helps lower blood calcium levels. (106) _____ _____ is produced by the

(107) _____ _____ and increases blood calcium. PTH also promotes the conversion of

(108) _____ _____ to its active form, the latter of which increases calcium absorption by the

gut and synergizes with PTH to release calcium from bone. The adrenal gland has two parts: a centrally

located (109) _____ _____ and a peripherally located (110) _____ _____.

The medulla releases two (111) _____, hormones derived from the amino acid tyrosine:

(112) _____ and (113) _____. The cortex produces two classes of steroid hormones:

(114) _____ (regulate carbohydrate metabolism) and (115) _____ (help regulate ion and

water balance). (116) _____ is a specific glucocorticoid in mammals and (117) _____ is a

specific mineralocorticoid in mammals. The gonads, (118) _____ and (119) _____, are a

primary source of three classes of sex steroids: (120) _____, (121) _____, and

(122) _____. (123) _____ is a specific androgen, whereas (124) _____ is a specific

estrogen, and (125) _____ is a specific progestin. The (126) _____ of _____ of the

(127) _____ produces several hormones that regulate metabolism. (128) _____ is generally

anabolic, stimulating the uptake of nutrients into cells (e.g., glucose) as well as the synthesis of large macro-

molecules (e.g., glycogen). (129) _____ is generally catabolic and stimulates the breakdown of large

macromolecules in tissues and the release of monomers into the blood. (130) _____ _____

can result from several defects, including the inability to produce insulin or the failure of insulin to function

properly in targets cells; conditions that generally all lead to abnormally high glucose levels in the blood. The

(131) _____ _____ produces (132) _____, which helps maintain daily biorhythms.

Matching

Match each of the following with its correct definition.

133. _____	Metamorphosis	A.	Change in body form (e.g., tadpole to adult)
134. _____	Catecholamines	B.	Steroid-like molecule that when activated stimulates Ca^{2+} absorption
135. _____	Pancreas	C.	Class of amines derived from tyrosine
136. _____	Gonad	D.	Steroid hormones that stimulate muscle development
137. _____	Estrogen	E.	Typically has both exocrine and endocrine (islets of Langerhans) components
138. _____	Progestin	F.	A disease that typically displays abnormally high glucose levels in the blood
139. _____	Diabetes mellitus	G.	Organ that produces gametes and sex steroids
140. _____	Androgen	H.	Class of sex steroid primarily produced in males
141. _____	Vitamin D	I.	An example is estradiol
142. _____	Anabolic steroid	J.	An example is progesterone

Complete the Table

Hormone	Chemical Type	Site of Secretion	Function
Thyroxine	143.	Thyroid gland	144.
145.	Peptide	146.	Lowers blood calcium
Parathyroid hormone	Peptide	Parathyroid gland	147.
148.	Amine	149.	Increase blood flow to muscles; stimulates breakdown of macromolecules
150.	151.	Adrenal cortex	Promotes fat and protein breakdown; stimulates gluconeogenesis
Aldosterone	152.	153.	154.
155.	Steroid	Testes	Stimulates sperm maturation/maintenance of secondary sexual characteristics
156.	157.	Ovary	158.
Progesterone	Steroid	Ovary	159.
160.	Peptide	161.	Stimulates secretion of FSH and LH
Insulin	162.	163.	164.
165.	166.	167.	Stimulates glycogen breakdown
168.	169.	Pineal gland	170.

35.5 Endocrine Systems in Invertebrates [pp. 871–873]

Section Review (Fill-in-the-Blanks)

The three hormones that regulate moulting and metamorphosis in insects are (171) _____

_____, (172) _____, and (173) _____ _____. In crustaceans,

(174) _____-_____ _____ helps regulate moulting by inhibiting ecdysone secretion.

Matching

Match each of the following hormones with its correct definition.

175. _____ Brain hormone   A. Peptide hormone that stimulates prothoracic glands

176. _____ Moult-inhibiting hormone   B. Steroid hormone secreted by prothoracic glands

177. _____ Ecdysone   C. Peptide hormone secreted by corpora allata

178. _____ Juvenile hormone   D. Peptide hormone secreted by gland in eye stalk

SELF-TEST

1. Which term refers to a chemical that is released from an epithelial cell in a gland and which enters the blood to affect the activity of another cell some distance away? [p. 855]
   a. hormone
   b. neurohormone
   c. pheromone
   d. bile

2. Which of the following best describes autocrine regulation? [p. 855]
   a. A local regulator acts on the same cell that released it.
   b. A local regulator is secreted from a neuron and acts on a distant target organ.
   c. A local regulator acts on cells neighbouring the cell that released it.
   d. A local regulator acts on a distant organ.

3. What type of molecule is epinephrine? [pp. 856]
   a. a fatty acid-derived hormone
   b. a steroid hormone

   c. an amine hormone
   d. a peptide hormone

4. Which of the following is generally included in the control of hormone secretion by a negative feedback mechanism?[p. 857]
   a. no change in hormone secretion
   b. decrease in hormone secretion
   c. increase in hormone secretion

5. Which statement is true about peptide hormones? [p. 857]
   a. They are hydrophilic and bind to intracellular receptors.
   b. They are hydrophobic and bind to cell surface receptors.
   c. They are hydrophilic and bind to cell surface receptors.
   d. They are hydrophobic and bind to intracellular receptors.

6. Which of the following chemical signals is NOT a hydrophobic hormone that form hormone-receptor complexes in the cytoplasm of target cells? [pp. 856–857]

    a. steroids
    b. thyroid hormone
    c. prolactin
    d. catecholamines

7. What causes pituitary dwarfism? [p. 864]

    a. hypersecretion of cortisol
    b. hyposecretion of growth hormone
    c. hyposecretion of thyroid hormone
    d. hyposecretion of insulinlike growth factor

8. Which hormones are secreted from the posterior pituitary? [p. 861]

    a. antidiuretic hormone (ADH) and ACTH
    b. antidiuretic hormone (ADH) and CRH
    c. oxytocin and ACTH
    d. oxytocin and antidiuretic hormone

9. Catecholamines cause which of the following during an acute stress response? [p. 867]

    a. a decrease in heart rate
    b. a decrease in blood pressure
    c. the breakdown in glycogen and fatty acids
    d. constriction of airways

10. Which hormone and target are involved in elevating blood glucose by glycogenolysis and gluconeogenesis? [p. 870]

    a. insulin and pancreas
    b. glucagon and liver
    c. TSH and thyroid
    d. ACTH and adrenal cortex
    e. T_4 and skeletal muscle

11. What causes the initiation of metamorphosis in lampreys? [p. 866]

    a. low metabolic rate
    b. decreasing T_4 levels
    c. increasing levels of T_4
    d. aldosterone
    e. prolactin

12. The activity of which hormone, directly and/or indirectly, can increases skeletal growth? [p. 864]

    a. aldosterone
    b. growth hormone
    c. progestin
    d. epinephrine

13. Which hormone has an involvement in the control of the activity of the anterior pituitary?[pp. 865–866]

    a. prolactin
    b. ADH
    c. epinephrine
    d. TRH

14. The hormones LH and FSH are involved in which activity?[pp. 868–869]

    a. in the control of gonadal function
    b. in the control of adrenal gland function
    c. in osmoregulation
    d. in the control of plasma calcium concentration

15. Which statement is true about prolactin? [pp. 862–864]

    a. It stimulates the development of the mammary glands.
    b. It is a nontropic hormone.
    c. It stimulates salt excretion.
    d. It regulates pancreatic secretions.

16. Which is NOT a role for the pineal gland? [pp. 870–871]

    a. regulation of blood glucose levels
    b. regulation of biological rhythms
    c. production of the hormone melatonin
    d. synchronization of the biological clock
    e. may be considered a third eye

17. Which of the following is characteristic of diabetes mellitus?[p. 870]

    a. lack of insulin
    b. lack of glucagon
    c. lack of antidiuretic hormone (ADH)
    d. lack of cortisol

18. Which hormone is bound by β-Adrenergic receptors? [p. 860]

   a. thyroxine
   b. glucagon
   c. epinephrine
   d. antidiuretic hormone
   e. insulin

19. Which is NOT a role for aldosterone? [pp. 859, 861]

   a. is a mineralocorticoid
   b. increases the amount of Na^+ in the blood
   c. increases the rate of K^+ excretion
   d. is synthesized in the adrenal cortex
   e. is a stress hormone

20. Suppose you removed the eye stalk of a lobster. Which of the following would occur? [pp. 871–873]

   a. decrease secretion of ecdysone
   b. accelerate the moult cycle
   c. decelerate the moult cycle
   d. have no effect on ecdysone

INTEGRATING AND APPLYING KEY CONCEPTS

1. Discuss the validity of the following statement: *The endocrine system and the nervous system are separate and distinct systems that serve to coordinate the function of animals.*

2. The fight-or-flight response leads to the secretion of the stress hormones epinephrine, norepinephrine, and cortisol from the adrenal gland. Describe the regulation of the hypothalamic–pituitary adrenal gland axis (cortisol secretion) and the hypothalamic–adrenal medulla axis (catecholamine secretion).

3. The control of hormone secretion is central for the proper functioning of physiological systems. Explain what effects, if any, disruptions to feedback loops would have to endocrine axes.

36 Control of Animal Processes: Neural Control

TOPIC MAP

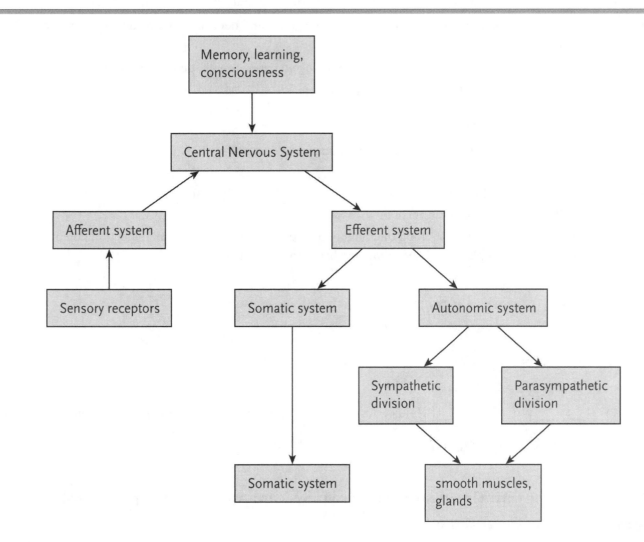

LEARNING OUTCOMES AND STUDY STRATEGIES

By the end of this chapter, you should be able to:

■ Discuss the organization of nervous systems

■ Draw the structure and identify the major parts of a neuron

■ Explain how neurons communicate with each other

- Explain how resting membrane potential is established and how it changes during an action potential
- Provide a graphic representation of an action potential and discuss the reasons for the changes
- Explain how a nerve impulse travels down a neuron and how this nerve impulse is conducted to another neuron or muscle or gland
- List different types of neurotransmitters and receptors involved in chemical synapses
- Explain how neurons integrate incoming signals from other neurons
- Compare the organization of the nervous systems of protostomes
- Identify the major divisions and structures of the brain of vertebrates and discuss their roles
- Explain how the spinal cord relays signals between the peripheral nervous system and the brain and controls reflexes
- Compare the organization and roles of the sympathetic and parasympathetic nervous systems
- Discuss the organization of the somatic nervous system

Study strategies for this chapter:

- The study of neurons and neural circuits is important for understanding how animal function is controlled.
- This chapter contains a lot of new and unfamiliar material. Go slowly. Take one section at a time and then work through the companion section in the study guide.
- Practise drawing neurons and labelling their component parts. Also practise drawing action potentials, being sure to label each phase and describing the bases for each phase.

INTERACTIVE EXERCISES

Why It Matters [pp. 876–877]

Section Review (Fill-in-the-Blanks)

The (1) _____ _____ integrates a variety of sensory inputs and then makes compensating

adjustments to the activities of the body.

36.1 Neurons and Their Organization in Nervous Systems: An Overview [pp. 877–880]

Section Review (Fill-in-the-Blanks)

(2) _____ _____ is communication by (3) _____, which has four components.

(4) _____ is the detection of a stimulus. (5) _____ is the sending of a message along a

neuron and then relaying the message to another neuron or to a muscle or gland. (6) _____ is the

sorting and interpretation of the message. (7) _____ is the output or action that results from the

message. (8) _____ _____, also known as (9) _____ _____, transmit

sensory stimuli to (10) _____, which integrate the information to formulate an appropriate response.

(11) _____ _____ carry response signals to (12) _____, such as muscles and

glands. The (13) _____ _____ of a neuron contains the nucleus. (14) _____ receive

signals and transmit them toward the cell body, whereas (15) _____, which arise from the

(16) _____ _____, conduct impulses away from the cell body. Axons end in buttonlike

swellings called (17) _____ _____. The association of neurons (connected from the axon of

one to the dendrite of another) forms a chain called a(n) (18) _____ _____.

(19) _____ _____ provide nutrition and support to neurons. Star-shaped

(20) _____ provide physical support and help maintain ion concentrations in the extracellular fluid.

In vertebrates, (21) _____ in the central nervous system and (22) _____ _____ in

the peripheral nervous system wrap around axons to form sheaths. Gaps between Schwann cells along an

axon are called (23) _____ of _____. A(n) (24) _____ is the junction between a

neuron and another neuron or between a neuron and a muscle cell. On one side of the synapse is the

(25) _____ cell and on the other side is the (26) _____ cell. Communication across the

synapse occurs in one of two ways: (a) by direct flow of electrical current, making a(n) (27) _____

_____, or (b) by chemical transmission, making a(n) (28) _____ _____. A(n)

(29) _____ is the chemical released by a presynaptic cell at a chemical synapse, which crosses a

narrow gap or (30) _____ _____ and then binds to receptors on the postsynaptic cell.

Building Vocabulary

Using the definitions of the prefixes below, assign the appropriate prefix to the appropriate suffix for the
following:

Prefix	Meaning	Suffix	Meaning
pre-	before, prior to	-neuro(n)	of or relating to a nerve
post-	after, following		
inter-	between, among		

	Prefix	Suffix	Definition
31.	_____	-synaptic	The neuron that transmits a signal to a specific synapse
32.	_____	-synaptic	The neuron that receives the signal at a specific synapse
33.	_____	_____	Neurons that integrate information

Choice

For each of the following characteristics, choose the most appropriate type of synapse.

A. Chemical synapse   B. Electrical synapse

34. _____   Plasma membranes of presynaptic cells and postsynaptic cells are in direct contact, and the electrical response flows between the two cells through gap junctions.

35. _____   Plasma membranes of presynaptic cells and postsynaptic cells are separated by a cleft, and the electrical impulse is conveyed by neurotransmitters.

For each of the following descriptions, choose the most appropriate type of cell.

A. Presynaptic cell   B. Postsynaptic cell

36. _____   Neuron that transmits signal

37. _____   Neuron that receives signal

For each of the following descriptions, choose the most appropriate type of cell.

A. Afferent neuron   B. Interneuron   C. Efferent neuron

38. _____   Transmits stimuli collected by sensory neurons

39. _____   Integrates sensory information to formulate appropriate response

40. _____   Carries impulses to effectors such as muscles and glands

Making Comparisons

41. Distinguish between motor neurons and efferent neurons.

_____

_____

_____

Sequence

Arrange the following events in neural signalling in the correct order.

42. _____   A. Integration

43. _____   B. Transmission

44. _____   C. Response

45. _____   D. Reception

Complete the Table

Type of Cell	Description
Glial cells	46.
47.	Star-shaped cells that provide physical support and help maintain ion concentration
Oligodendrocytes	48.
Schwann cells	49.
50.	Cells of the nervous system specialized to generate electrical impulses

Matching

Match each of the following with its correct definition.

51. _____ Synapse

52. _____ Neural circuit

53. _____ Neurotransmitter

54. _____ Node of Ranvier

55. _____ Effector

56. _____ Synaptic cleft

57. _____ Neural signalling

A. Communication by neurons

B. Target of efferent neurons such as muscles and glands

C. Chain of neurons

D. Gap between Schwann cells that expose axons

E. A special junction between a neuron and another neuron or between a neuron and other effector cell

F. Chemical released from an axon terminus into a synapse

G. The narrow gap of a chemical synapse

Identify

Identify the various parts on the neuron.

58. _____

59. _____

60. _____

61. _____

62. _____

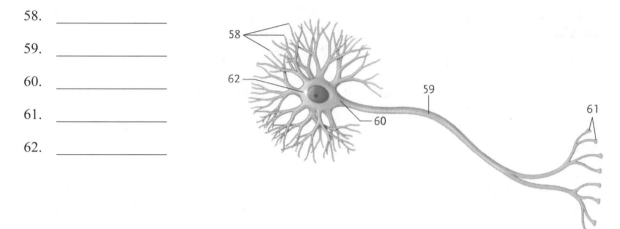

36.2 Signal Initiation by Neurons [pp. 881–887]
36.3 Conduction of Action Potentials along Neurons and across Chemical Synapses [pp. 887–893]
36.4 Integration of Incoming Signals by Neurons [pp. 894–895]

Section Review (Fill-in-the-Blanks)

(63) _____ _____ is the difference in charge across the membrane of all animal cells. The

steady negative membrane potential of a neuron that is not conducting is called the (64) _____

_____, which makes the cell (65) _____. When a neuron conducts an impulse, there is an

abrupt transient change in membrane potential called the (66) _____ _____. As the

membrane becomes less negative, the membrane becomes (67) _____. Depolarization proceeds

slowly at first until (68) _____ _____ is reached, and then the potential changes rapidly,

rising to as much as +30 mV inside with respect to the outside. The potential then falls, sometimes dropping

below the resting level and resulting in the membrane becoming (69) _____. An action potential only

results if the stimulus is strong enough to cause the membrane potential to reach threshold; once triggered, the

action potential results regardless of stimulus strength. This phenomenon is known as the (70) _____-

_____-_____ _____. At the peak of the action potential, the membrane enters a(n)

(71) _____ _____, which lasts until the resting potential is reestablished. During this time,

the neuron cannot be stimulated again, which keeps the impulses travelling only in one direction. The action potential is produced by movements of Na^+ and K^+ through (72) _____-_____

_____ _____. (73) _____ of the electrical impulse occurs along the axon as a wave

of depolarization. Impulses are sped when action potentials hop along the axon in a process called

(74) _____ _____.

In chemical synapses, neurotransmitters are released from the (75) _____ _____,

diffuse across the cleft, and alter ion conduction by activation of (76) _____-_____

_____ _____ on the (77) _____ _____. Neurotransmitters are stored in

presynaptic cells in (78) _____ _____ and are released by the process of

(79) _____. (80) _____ _____ directly bind ligand-gated channels to alter the flow

of ions. (81) _____ _____ bind to G protein–coupled receptors that trigger the generation of

a second messenger (e.g., cAMP); the second messenger then affects ion channels to alter ion movement.

Many different types of chemicals serve as neurotransmitters, including amines, amino acids, and peptides.

Neurotransmitters may stimulate or inhibit the generation of action potentials in the postsynaptic cell.

Stimulation opens a ligand-gated sodium channel, depolarizing the cell and driving closer to threshold. Such a

potential change is called a(n) (82) _____ _____ _____ (_____). An inhibitory

neurotransmitter opens a ligand-gated channel that allows Cl^- to flow into the cell and K^+ to leave, causing the

cell to become hyperpolarized and taking the cell further from threshold; such a potential change is called a(n)

(83) _____ _____ _____ (_____). In contrast to all-or-nothing action potentials,

EPSPs and IPSPs are (84) _____ _____. (85) _____ _____ is the

accumulation of EPSPs from a single presynaptic neuron over a short period of time. (86) _____

_____ is the accumulation of EPSPs produced from several different presynaptic neurons.

Building Vocabulary

Using the definitions of the prefixes below, assign the appropriate prefix to the appropriate suffix:

Prefix	Meaning
neuro-	of or relating to a neuron
hyper-	above, to a greater extent
de-	to undo

	Prefix	Suffix	Definition
87.	_____	-transmitter	The chemical released at a chemical synapse
88.	_____	-polarized	A change in membrane potential that makes the cell less negative inside compared with outside
89.	_____	-polarized	A change in membrane potential that makes the cell more negative inside compared with outside

Choice

For each of the following characteristics, choose the most appropriate term from the list below.

A.   Presynaptic membrane   B.   Postsynaptic membrane

90. _____ Membrane from which exocytosis occurs to release neurotransmitters

91. _____ Membrane on which neurotransmitters bind

For each of the following characteristics, choose the most appropriate neurotransmitter from the list below.

A.   Indirect neurotransmitter   B.   Direct neurotransmitter

92. _____ Neurotransmitter that binds to a ligand-gated channel

93. _____ Neurotransmitter that binds to a receptor to trigger production of a second messenger

For each of the following, choose the most appropriate potential from the list below.

A.   Excitatory postsynaptic potential   B.   Inhibitory postsynaptic potential

94. _____ Change in membrane potential of postsynaptic cells that brings it closer to threshold

95. _____ Change in membrane potential of postsynaptic cells that brings it further from threshold

For each of the following characteristics, choose the most appropriate type of summation from the list below.

B.   Temporal summation   B.   Spatial summation

96. _____ Change in membrane potential of postsynaptic neuron produced by the firing of several presynaptic neurons

97. _____ Change in membrane potential of postsynaptic neuron produced by successive firing of a single presynaptic neuron over a short period of time

For each of the following characteristics, choose the most appropriate type of channel from the list below.

A. Ligand-gated channel   B. Voltage-gated channel

98. _____ Membrane proteins that control ion flow by opening and closing as membrane potential changes

99. _____ Membrane proteins that control ion flow in response to binding a neurotransmitter

Making Comparisons

100. Distinguish between membrane potential and resting potential.

_____

_____

Matching

Match each of the following aspects of neural signalling with its correct description.

101. _____ All-or-nothing principle

102. _____ Synaptic vesicles

103. _____ Action potential

104. _____ Propagation

105. _____ Salutatory conduction

106. _____ Graded potential

A. An abrupt, transient change in membrane potential

B. Secretory vesicles that contain neurotransmitters

C. Rapid conduction of an impulse in which action potentials "hop" along an axon

D. Progression of action potentials along an axon

E. Once triggered, the change in membrane potential that takes place regardless of stimulus strength

F. Potential that moves up or down in response to stimulus without triggering an action potential; amplitude depends on the strength of the stimulus

Identify

Identify the various parts of an action potential.

107. _____

108. _____

109. _____

110. _____

111. _____

112. _____

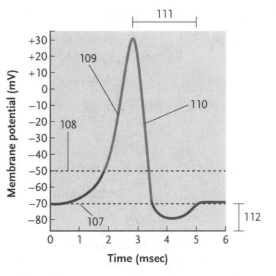

36.5 Evolutionary Trends in Neural Integration: Networks, Nerves, Ganglia, and Brains [pp. 895–901]

Section Review (Fill-in-the-Blanks)

Radially symmetrical animals such as cniderians (jellyfish) and echinoderms (starfish, sea urchins) possess

loose meshes of neurons called (113) _____ _____. Groups of nerve cells with localized

interconnections are called (114) _____. There is an evolutionary trend toward cephalization in which a

distinct head region forms that contains a central ganglion or (115) _____ connected to one or more

(116) _____ _____ that extend to the rest of the body. The brain and nerve cord constitute

the (117) _____ nervous system (_____), and the nerves that extend from this to the rest of the body

make up the (118) _____ nervous system (_____). During embryonic development, the nervous

system of vertebrates arises from a hollow (119) _____ _____, the anterior portion of which

develops into the brain, and the rest gives rise to the (120) _____ _____. The central cavity

of the neural tube persists in adults as the (121) _____ of the brain and the (122) _____

_____ of the spinal cord. The (123) _____, (124) _____, and (125) _____

are the three distinct regions of the brain early in development that give rise to the adult brain.

Building Vocabulary

Using the definitions of the prefixes below, assign the appropriate prefix to the appropriate suffix:

Prefix	Meaning
hypo-	under, below
post-	behind, after
pre-	before, prior to

	Prefix	Suffix	Definition
126.	_____	-thalamus	Part of the brain located below the thalamus and primary integration centre for regulation of the viscera
127.	_____	-ganglionic	Relates to a neuron leading away from a ganglion
128.	_____	-ganglionic	Relates to a neuron leading into a ganglion

Choice

For each of the following descriptions, choose the most appropriate term from the list below.

A. Ventricle   B. Central canal

129. _____ Space within the brain

130. _____ Space within the spinal cord

Complete the Table

Structure	Feature/Description
Nerve ring	131.
132.	Functional cluster of neurons
Nerve cord	133.

Component	Subcomponent	Function
Somatic		134.
135.		Control internal organs and blood vessels (most involuntary)
	136.	Predominates in situations involving stress, excitement, etc.
	137.	Predominates in low-stress situations

SELF-TEST

1. What does is NOT involved in neural signalling? [p. 877]
   a. differentiation
   b. integration
   c. response
   d. transmission
   e. reception

2. What statement is true about efferent neurons? [p. 879]
   a. They integrate information.
   b. They transmit electrical impulses away from interneurons.

   c. They transmit electrical impulses from sensory receptors.

3. What is NOT true about the nodes of Ranvier?[pp. 879, 888–889]
   a. They speed up conduction of electrical impulses.
   b. They make up a myelin sheath.
   c. They expose the axon.
   d. They are gaps between adjacent Schwann cells.

4. Which of the following are glial cells? [pp. 878–879]

    a. astrocytes, Schwann cells, and oligodendrocytes

    b. interneurons, afferent neurons, and efferent neurons

    c. neurosecretory cells, cells of endocrine glands, cells of exocrine glands

5. Which is a characterisitic of electrical synapses?[p. 880]

    a. They are plasma membranes of postsynaptic cells that are in direct contact with muscles

    b. They have narrow gaps called clefts between cells.

    c. They are electrical impulses that flow between cells through gap junctions.

    d. They involve release of neurotransmitters.

6. What does the resting potential result from? [pp. 881–882]

    a. differential permeability of membranes that results in accumulation of proteins and other anions on the inside of a cell

    b. opening of voltage-gated sodium channels

    c. opening of ligand-gated sodium channels

7. Which of the following describes the ion movement accomplished by the Na^+/K^+ pump? [pp. 881–882]

    a. Na^+ in and K^+ out

    b. both Na^+ and K^+ in

    c. more K^+ out than Na^+ in

    d. more Na+ out than K+ in

8. Which statement is true about the refractory period? [pp. 883–884]

    a. It is initiated with the closing of the inactivation gate of the Na^+ voltage-gated channel.

    b. It is initiated with the opening of the activation gate of the Na^+ voltage-gated channel.

    c. It ceases with the opening of the activation gate of the K^+ voltage-gated channel.

9. Which is a characteristic of a nerve impulse? [pp. 887–889]

    a. It always travels in both directions along an axon.

    b. It always travels with the same intensity along the length of an axon.

    c. It diminishes in intensity as it travels along an axon.

10. Which is NOT a characteristic of neurotransmitters? [pp. 890–893]

    a. travel through gap junctions

    b. are released from presynaptic cells through the process of exocytosis

    c. can bind to ligand-gated ion channels

    d. can bind to G protein–coupled receptors

11. What is responsible for inhibitory postsynaptic potentials (IPSPs)?[p. 894]

    a. result from K^+ influx into a cell

    b. result from an increase of Na^+ into a cell

    c. they occur or don't occur (all-or-none effect)

    d. are graded

12. What is spatial summation? [p. 894]

    a. It is the change in membrane potential of a postsynaptic cell brought on by the firing of different presynaptic neurons.

    b. It is the change in membrane potential of a postsynaptic cell brought on by the successive firing of a single presynaptic neuron over a short period of time.

    c. It is the total of the membrane potentials that occur along an axon as the electrical impulse is transmitted.

13. Which is the principal integration centre of homeostatic regulation and leads to the release of hormones? [p. 898]

    a. the cerebellum

    b. the cerebrum

    c. the thalamus

    d. the hypothalamus

    e. the association area

14. Which system is responsible for the regulation of blood pressure? [pp. 899–901]

    a. the somatic nervous system
    b. the autonomic nervous system
    c. the sensory nervous system

15. Which system is responsible for the regulation of feeding and digestion?[pp. 899–901]

    a. the somatic nervous system
    b. the parasympathetic division
    c. the sympathetic division

16. Which part of the mammalian brain integrates information about posture and muscle tone? [pp. 898–901]

    a. the cerebrum
    b. the cerebellum
    c. the myencephalon
    d. the medulla oblongata

17. Which part of the brain coordinates muscular activity? [pp. 899–901]

    a. the cerebrum
    b. the hypothalamus
    c. the myencephalon
    d. the medulla oblongata

INTEGRATING AND APPLYING KEY CONCEPTS

1. The salivary glands of vertebrates are innervated with adrenergic neurons (neurons that release epinephrine from their axon termini). Epinephrine stimulates both fluid and amylase (a carbohydrate hydrolyzing enzyme) secretion from the salivary gland. The fluid secretion is calcium dependent (can be inhibited by calcium channel blockers), while amylase secretion is cAMP dependent. Explain.

2. Discuss the selective pressure for cephalization in animals. Would there be a difference between those with sessile or motile life histories?

37 Control of Animal Processes: Neural Integration

TOPIC MAP

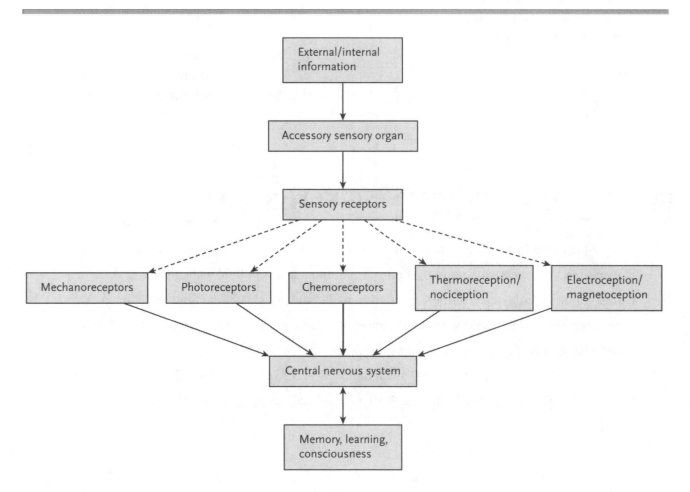

LEARNING OUTCOMES AND STUDY STRATEGIES

By the end of this chapter, you should be able to

- Explain how sensory information is detected and how this message is transduced and decoded by the central nervous system

- Draw the general structure of sensory receptors

- List and define the different types of sensory receptors

- Describe the structure and function of the accessory organs and mechanoreceptors involved in the detection of touch and pressure and maintainance of body balance and orientation
- Describe the structure and function of the accessory organs and mechanoreceptors involved in the detection of sound
- Describe the structure and function of the accessory organs and photoreceptors involved in the detection of light and formation of images
- Describe the structure and function of the accessory organs and chemoreceptors involved in the detection of chemicals
- Describe the structure and function of the accessory organs and thermoreceptors and nociceptors involved in the detection of heat and pain
- Describe the structure and function of the accessory organs and electroreceptors and magnetoreceptors involved in the detection of electric and magnetic fields
- Identify, label the parts of, and draw the different accessory organs involved in the detection of external and internal information

Study strategies for this chapter:

- This chapter makes use of the concepts of cell structure, cell communication, and nerve function developed earlier. You should briefly review these concepts to make sure that you understand them.
- This chapter is extremely long. DO NOT try to go through it all in one sitting. Take one section at a time and then work through the companion section in the study guide.
- Draw pictures of the various sensory systems, being sure to label the various parts and noting their linkage to the nervous system.

INTERACTIVE EXERCISES

Why It Matters [pp. 904–905]
37.1 Overview of Sensory Integration [pp. 906–907]
37.2 Mechanoreceptors and the Tactile and Spatial Senses [pp. 907–911]
37.3 Mechanoreceptors and Hearing [pp. 911–913]

Section Review (Fill-in-the-Blanks)

(1) _____ _____ are formed by dendrites of a neuron or are specialized cells that synapse

with afferent neurons. The conversion of a stimulus into a change in membrane potential is called

(2) _____ _____. The five types of sensory receptors are (3) _____,

(4) _____, (5) _____, (6) _____, and (7) _____. The intensity and extent

of a stimulus are registered by the (8) _____ of _____ _____ and the

(9) _____ of _____ _____. (10) _____ _____ is the effect of

reducing the response to a stimulus at a constant level.

Some mechanoreceptors that detect touch and pressure are free nerve endings, while others, such as

(11) _____ _____, have structures that surround the nerve ending to help detect stimuli.

(12) _____ detect stimuli that provide information about the position of limbs and are used to

maintain balance. (13) _____ are fluid-filled chambers that contain (14) _____ and

(15) _____ _____ _____ to detect position in some invertebrates. Fish and some

amphibians detect vibrations and water current with a(n) (16) _____ _____

_____. Some fish also have dome-shaped (17) _____ that contain sensory hair cells covered

with (18) _____ that extend into a gelatinous (19) _____ and are used to detect orientation

and velocity.

The (20) _____ _____ perceives position and motion of the head and consists of

three (21) _____ _____ and two chambers, the (22) _____ and the

(23) _____, which contain small crystals called (24) _____. The two types of

(25) _____ _____ that detect the position and movement of limbs are called

(26) _____ _____ in muscles and (27) _____ _____ _____ in

tendons.

Some invertebrates have auditory organs that consist of a thinned region of exoskeleton or

(28) _____ stretched over a hollow chamber. The (29) _____ of the (30) _____

ear focuses sound waves into the auditory canal, where they strike the (31) _____ _____.

The (32) _____ ear is an air-filled cavity containing three interconnected bones, the (33)

_____, (34) _____, and (35) _____, the latter of which is attached to an elastic

(36) _____ _____. The (37) _____ ear contains several fluid-filled compartments,

(38) _____ _____, (39) _____, and (40) _____, as well as a spiralled

(41) _____. Within the cochlea is the (42) _____ of _____, which contains

sensory hair cells that detect sound vibrations that dissipate when they reach the (43) _____

_____. Many vertebrates locate prey and avoid obstacles by (44) _____, a process that

involves generating sounds and listening for the echoes that bounce back.

Building Vocabulary

Using the definitions of the prefixes below, assign the appropriate prefix to the appropriate suffix for the following:

Prefix	Meaning	Suffix	Meaning
chemo-	chemical	-lith	stone
oto-	ear		
proprio-	one's own		
thermo-	heat, warm		
photo-	light		
noci-	pain, injury		

	Prefix	Suffix	Definition
45.	_____	-receptor	Specialized to detect chemical stimuli
46.	_____	-receptor	Specialized to detect heat/temperature
47.	_____	_____	Calcium carbonate crystals in inner ear of vertebrates
48.	_____	-ceptor	Sensory receptors in muscles, tendons, and joints
49.	_____	-receptor	Specialized for the detection of radiant energy at particular wavelengths
50.	_____	-ceptor	Specialized for the detection of tissue damage/noxious chemicals

Complete the Table

Structure	Description
51.	Detects vibrations and currents in water
Statocysts	52.
Vestibular apparatus	53.
54.	Detects stretch of muscle
55.	Contains sensory hairs that detect sound waves
Golgi tendon organ	56.
57.	Provides information about orientation and velocity of fish

Matching

Match each of the following structures with its correct definition.

58. _____ Proprioceptor

59. _____ Echolocation

60. _____ Tympanum

61. _____ Cupula

62. _____ Otolith

63. _____ Stereocilia

64. _____ Stretch receptor

65. _____ Statolith

66. _____ Sensory hair cell

A. Type of mechanoreceptor that detects position and movement of body parts

B. Type of proprioceptor that detects position and movement of limbs

C. Calcium carbonate crystal inside vestibular apparatus

D. Sensory cell with long hairlike projection of plasma membrane

E. Gelatinus matrix inside neuromasts

F. Stonelike body inside statocysts

G. Microvilli on hair cells of neuromasts

H. Process of generating sound waves and detecting echoes

I. Thinned region of exoskeleton on some invertebrates specialized for detecting vibrations

Labelling

Identify each numbered part of the following illustration.

67. _____   74. _____

68. _____   75. _____

69. _____   76. _____

70. _____   77. _____

71. _____   78. _____

72. _____   79. _____

73. _____   80. _____

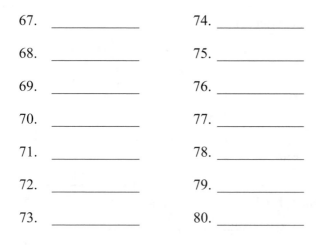
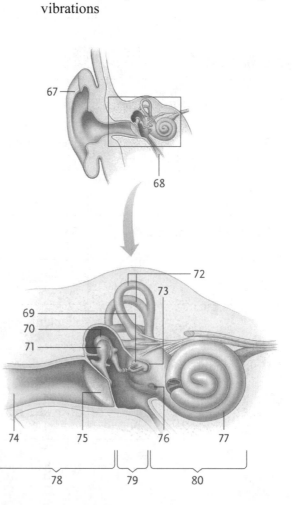

37.4 Photoreceptors and Vision [pp. 914–921]
37.5 Chemoreceptors [pp. 921–925]
37.6 Thermoreceptors and Nociceptors [pp. 925–927]
37.7 Electroreceptors and Magnetoreceptors [pp. 927–928]

Section Review (Fill-in-the-Blanks)

The simplest eye in invertebrates, a(n) (81) _____, detects light but does not form an image. One

type of image-forming eye in invertebrates is the (82) _____ eye, which has hundreds to thousands of

faceted visual units called (83) _____, which in insects are focused by a(n) (84) _____ onto

a bundle of photoreceptive cells containing the (85) _____, rhodopsin. The other type of image-

forming eye in invertebrates is the (86) _____-_____ eye, which resembles the eye of

vertebrates in its camera-like operation. Light is concentrated by the (87) _____ onto the

(88) _____, a layer of photoreceptors at the back of the eye. Muscle of the (89) _____

adjusts the size of the (90) _____ to regulate the amount of light entering the eye.

(91) _____ is a process by which the lens changes to enable the eye to focus on objects at different

distances. The structures of the vertebrate eye are similar to those of the invertebrate single-lens eye.

(92) _____ _____ fills the space between the cornea and the lens, and the jellylike

(93) _____ _____ fills the main chamber of the eye between the lens and the retina. The

lens of many vertebrates is focused by changing its shape by contraction of muscles of the

(94) _____ _____ and adjusting the tension of the ligaments that anchor the lens to the

muscles. The two types of photoreceptors in the vertebrate eye are (95) _____, which are specialized

for detection of light at low intensities, and (96) _____, which are specialized for detection of

different wavelengths (colours). In mammals and birds, cones are concentrated in and around the

(97) _____. Images focused there can be seen distinctly, while the surround image is termed

(98) _____ _____. (99) _____ are composed of the light-absorbing molecule

(100) _____, covalently bound to proteins called (101) _____. (102) _____ is the

photopigment in rods. Photoreceptors are linked to a network of neurons that integrate and process initial

visual information. (103) _____ cells synapse with rods and cones on one end and with

(104) _____ cells on their other end. In addition, (105) _____ cells connect photoreceptor

cells and bipolar cells. (106) _____ cells connect bipolar cells with ganglion cells. In

(107) _____ _____, horizontal cells inhibit bipolar cells that are outside a spot of light,

striking the retina; this visual processing sharpens the edges of the image and enhances contrast. Many

animals have colour vision, which depends on the number and types of cones. Humans and other primates

have three types of cones, based on the form of (108) _____ that they possess. Just behind the eye,

optic nerves converge and a portion of each optic nerve crosses over to the opposite side of the brain, forming

the (109) _____ _____. Axons enter the (110) _____ _____

_____ of the thalamus, where they synapse with neurons leading to the visual cortex.

Insects have taste receptors inside hollow sensory bristles called (111) _____.

(112) _____ _____ of vertebrates have distinct receptors that respond to sweet, sour, salty,

bitter, and umami (savoury). Olfactory receptor cells possess (113) _____ _____; the

density of these receptors determines olfactory sensitivity.

The (114) _____ _____ _____ (_____)-gated calcium channel family

acts as heat receptors; different channels have different temperature thresholds. Pain receptors do not exhibit

adaptation. Electroreceptors are specialized for detecting electric fields. (115) _____ detect Earth's

magnetic field and help provide directional information important for navigation.

Distinguish between Members of the Following Sets of Terms

116. Compound eye and single-lens eye

_____

_____

117. Opsins, rhodopsins, and photopsins

_____

_____

Short Answer

118. What is accommodation?

_____

_____

119. Describe the difference between electroreceptors and magnetoreceptors.

_____

_____

Complete the Tables

Cell Type	Function
120.	Neurons that synapse with rods/cones on one end and ganglion cells on the other end
Ganglion cell	121.
122.	Connect with bipolar cells and ganglion cells
Horizontal cell	123.

Type of Receptor	Stimuli	Function
124.	125.	Visual image formation
Taste bud	Chemicals	126.
127.	128.	Perception of smell
129.	Electric field	130.
Magnetoreceptor	131.	Directional movement and navigation
132.	133.	Perception of pain

Matching

Match each of the following terms with its correct definition.

134. ____	Ocellus	A.	A simple photoreceptor that does not form a visual image
135. ____	Photopigment	B.	The individual visual unit of an invertebrate compound eye
136. ____	Optic chiasm	C.	Specialized for detecting light of low intensity
137. ____	Rod cell	D.	Specialized for detecting light of different wavelengths
138. ____	Cone cell	E.	Type of visual processing that sharpens edges and enhances contrast
139. ____	Ommatidia	F.	Region where portions of each optic nerve cross over
140. ____	Lateral inhibition	G.	Region in the thalamus where optic nerve axons terminate
141. ____	Lateral geniculate nuclei	H.	Hollow sensory bristle that contains taste receptors in insects
142. ____	Sensilla	I.	Light-absorbing complex of retinal and protein
143. ____	Organ of Corti	J.	Contain sensory hair cells that detect vibrations transmitted to the inner ear

Labelling

Identify each numbered part of the following illustration.

144. _____

145. _____

146. _____

147. _____

148. _____

149. _____

150. _____

151. _____

152. _____

153. _____

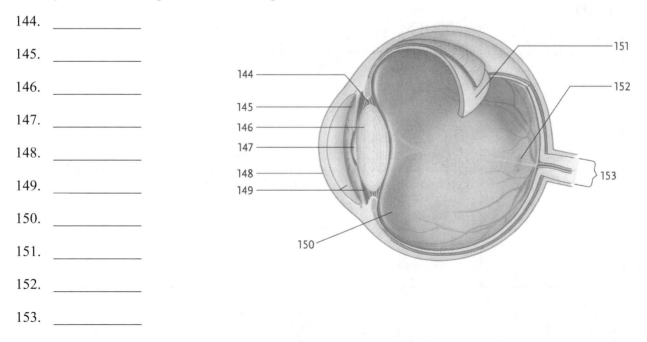

37.8 Overview of Central Neural Integration [pp. 928–929]
37.9 The Central Nervous System and Its Functions [pp. 929–935]

Section Review (Fill-in-the-Blanks)

The (154) _____ surrounds and protects the brain and spinal cord. (155) _____

_____ _____ circulates in the central canal and in the ventricles. The butterfly-shaped core

of the spinal cord is (156) _____ _____, which is surrounded by (157) _____

_____. Interneurons in the grey matter are involved in (158) _____. The

(159) _____ _____ connects the forebrain with the spinal cord. The surface layer of the

forebrain is the (160) _____ _____. Tight junctions between cells of brain capillaries form

a(n) (161) _____–_____ _____ and prevent the movement of many substances.

Incoming sensory information is filtered by the (162) _____ _____ before going to

other CNS centres. The (163) _____ helps fine-tune balance and body movements. The

(164) _____ relays sensory information to regions of the cerebral cortex concerned with motor

responses. The (165) _____ helps coordinate temperature and osmotic homeostasis. The

(166) _____ _____ surrounds the thalamus and moderates voluntary movements directed by

motor centres in the cerebrum. The (167) _____ _____ is made up of the thalamus,

hypothalamus, and basal nuclei, as well as the (168) _____, (169) _____, and

(170) _____ _____. The two cerebral hemispheres are connected via the

(171) _____ _____. The (172) _____ _____ _____ in each

hemisphere of the cerebral cortex registers information on touch, pain, temperature, and pressure.

(173) _____ _____ of the cerebral cortex integrate information from the sensory areas,

formulate responses, and pass them on to the (174) _____ _____ _____. The

localization of some brain functions in one of the two hemispheres is called (175) _____.

Choice

For each of the following descriptions, choose the most appropriate structure from the list below.

A. Spinal nerves   B. Cranial nerves

176. ____ Connect with the CNS at the level of the brain

177. ____ Connect with the CNS at the level of the spinal cord

For each of the following descriptions, choose the most appropriate characteristic from the list below.

A. Efferent   B. Afferent

178. _____ Neuron that conducts information away from the CNS

179. _____ Neuron that conducts information toward the CNS

For each of the following descriptions, choose the most appropriate characteristic from the list below.

A. Grey matter   B. White matter

180. _____ Consists of nerve cell bodies and dendrite

181. _____ Consists of axons, many of which are surrounded my myelin sheaths

Complete the Table

Structure	Function
Corpus callosum	182.
183.	Registers information about touch, pain, temperature, and pressure
184.	Causes movement of specific part of the body (each hemisphere controls the opposite side)
Association areas	185.

Matching

Match each of the following terms with its correct definition.

186. _____ Meninges   A. Connective tissue layers that surround and protect brain and spinal cord

187. _____ Basal nuclei   B. Fluid that circulates in central canal and the ventricles of the brain

188. _____ Amygdala   C. Programmed movement that takes place without conscious effort

189. _____ Lateralization   D. Results from tight junction between capillary cells in the brain

190. _____ Cerebral cortex   E. Phenomenon in which some brain functions are localized to one hemisphere or the other

191. ____	Reflex	F.	Connects brain with spinal cord
192. ____	Blood–brain barrier	G.	Surface layer of cerebrum
193. ____	Thalamus	H.	Part of the brain stem that connects thalamus to spinal cord
194. ____	Hippocampus	I.	Receives sensory information and relays it to high CNS centres
195. ____	Hypothalamus	J.	Moderates voluntary movements directed by the cerebrum
196. ____	Reticular formation	K.	Sends information to frontal lobes
197. ____	Olfactory bulb	L.	Relays information about experience and emotions
198. ____	Cerebrospinal fluid	M.	Relays olfactory information to cerebral cortex
199. ____	Brain stem	N.	Regulates basis homeostatic functions

37.10 Memory, Learning, and Consciousness [pp. 935–936]

Section Review (Fill-in-the-Blanks)

(200) _____ is the storage of an experience. (201) _____ involves a change in the response to a stimulus based on information or experience stored in memory. (202) _____ is awareness of oneself and one's surroundings. (203) _____-_____ memory stores information for up to an hour or so, whereas (204) _____-_____ memory stores information for days, years, or even for life. (205) _____-_____ _____ is a lasting increase in the strength of synaptic connections in neural pathways. Changes in neural activity can be recorded by a(n) (206) _____.

During (207) _____ _____ _____ (_____) _____, an individual's heart rate and respiration decrease, their limbs twitch, and their eyes move rapidly behind closed eyelids.

Choice

For each of the following descriptions, choose the most appropriate structure from the list below.

A. Short-term memory   B. Long-term memory

208. ____ Lasts up to an hour or so

209. ____ Lasts for days, years, or even life

Matching

Match each of the following terms with its correct definition.

210. _____ Memory

211. _____ Long-term potentiation

212. _____ Rapid eye movement (REM) sleep

213. _____ Consciousness

214. _____ Learning

A. Storage/retrieval of a sensory or motor experience

B. Changes in response to a stimulus

C. Awareness of self and surroundings

D. Long-lasting increase in strength of response

E. A phase of sleep in which brain waves similar to those in the waking state are observed

SELF-TEST

1. What does sensory transduction involve? [p. 906]

   a. one sensory stimulus being converted to another

   b. an increase in the amplitude of an action potential

   c. a stimulus causing a change in membrane potential of a sensory cell

   d. a reduced response of a sensory cell in the face of constant intensity of stimulus

2. Which sensory structure does NOT help provide information about the position/orientation of a body? [pp. 907–910]

   a. statocysts

   b. vestibular apparatus

   c. organ of Corti

   d. neuromasts

3. How are variations in the quality of sound recognized? [pp. 911–913]

   a. by the number of hair cells stimulated

   b. by the pattern of hair cells stimulated

   c. by the amplitude of action potential

   d. by the frequency of action potential

4. How is the movement of limbs detected? [pp. 910–911]

   a. by muscle spindles and the Golgi tendon organ

   c. by the joint receptors

   d. by the baroreceptors

   e. by the carotid bodies

5. Which term refers to the membrane in contact with the stapes and which transmits sound waves to the inner ear? [pp. 911–913]

   a. the oval window

   b. the round window

   c. the tympanic membrane

   d. the basilar membrane

6. How can visual images be focused? [pp. 914–921]

   a. by lateral inhibition

   b. by altering the number of ommatidia

   c. by changing the shape of the lens

7. What is responsible for differences in absorption characteristics that underlie colour vision? [pp. 920–921]

   a. rod cells
   b. retinal
   c. carotine
   d. opsin
   e. cone cells

8. Which term refers to photoreceptive cells that are specialized for detection of light of low intensity? [pp. 917–919]

   a. rod cells
   b. ganglion cells
   c. horizontal cells
   d. cone cells
   e. bipolar cells

9. Which chemical acts as a "natural painkiller"? [pp. 926–927]

   a. capsaicin
   b. substance P
   c. insulin
   d. endorphins

10. Which of the following is NOT used by animals for the location and capture of food? [pp. 905, 925, 927–928]

    a. echolocation
    b. electroreceptors
    c. pit organs
    d. Pacinian corpuscle

11. What statement about sensory receptors is true?[p. 905]

    a. They detect external and internal information.
    b. They convert external and internal information into somatic messages.
    c. They transduces the messages to the autonomic nervous system.
    d. They are decoded and processed by the somatic nervous system.

12. Which term refers to a touch and pressure receptor in human skin? [pp. 907–911]

    a. stereocili
    b. Pacinian corpuscles
    c. Golgi tendon organs

13. Which term refers to the "ears" on the head, thorax, and abdomen of insects? [p. 911]

    a. cupula
    b. pinna
    c. organ of Corti
    d. tympanum

14. Which structure is formed by when a portion of each optic nerves crosses over to the opposite side? [p. 920]

    a. chiasmata
    b. optic chiasm
    c. lateral geniculate nuclei
    d. lateral line

15. Which statement is true about electroreceptors? [p. 927]

    a. They depolarize in an electric field.
    b. They depolarize in a magnetic field.
    c. They hyperpolarize in an electric field.
    d. They hyperpolarize in a magnetic field.

16. What statement about proprioceptors of the tendon is correct? [pp. 910–911]

    a. They are called Golgi tendon organs.
    b. They measure stretch and compression of muscles as they contract.
    c. They are called muscle spindles.
    d. They measure the speed of muscle contractions.

17. How can information about the intensity and extent of a stimulus be indicated? [p. 906]

    a. by the frequency of action potentials and number of afferent neurons sending them
    b. by the summation of the activities of different types of sensory receptors
    c. by the duration of the action potentials

18. What is the vestibular apparatus responsible for? [pp. 908–910]

    a. heat
    b. tasting
    c. equilibrium
    d. vision

19. What are nociceptors sensitive to? [pp. 925–927]

    a. heat
    b. pain
    c. touch
    d. vibrations

INTEGRATING AND APPLYING KEY CONCEPTS

1. Despite the independence of sensory quality and information at the receptor level, animals perceive a unified representation of their environment within which information from the entire complement of sensory channels is seamlessly integrated. Why is such integration important? How is the integration accomplished?

2. *Insights from the Molecular Revolution*: Explain the body's responses to eating spicy food in light of capsaicin. Discuss the adaptive significance of temperature-sensitive calcium channels.

38 Muscles, Skeletons, and Body Movements

TOPIC MAP

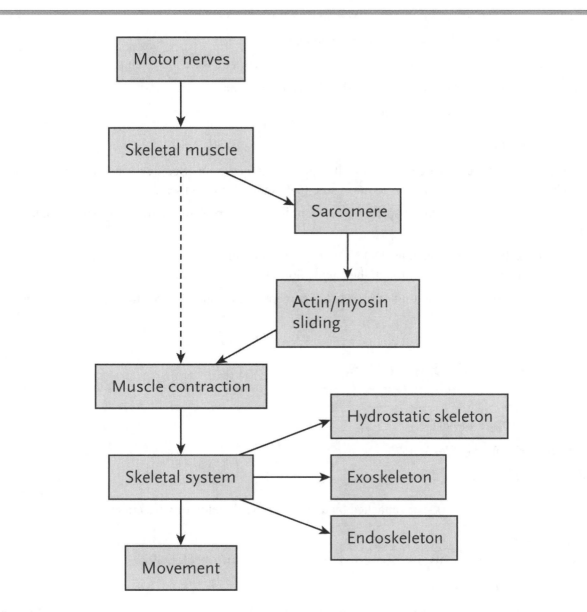

LEARNING OUTCOMES AND STUDY STRATEGIES

By the end of this chapter, you should be able to:

- Describe the internal organization of skeletal muscles
- Explain the sliding filament mechanism of muscle contraction
- List the molecular factors involved in muscle contraction
- Explain the role of calcium and ATP during muscle contraction and relaxation
- List the events of the crossbridge cycle during muscle contraction
- Explain the neural control of skeletal muscle contraction
- Describe the role of skeletal systems and list the different types of skeletal systems
- Contrast between hydrostatic skeleton, exoskeleton, and endoskeleton
- Explain the interactions between muscles and bones

Study strategies for this chapter:

- This chapter makes use of the concepts of cell structure and nerve function developed earlier. You should briefly review these concepts to make sure that you understand them.
- While many of the terms in this chapters may be familiar, others probably will not be, so do not be hasty in your study.
- This chapter is divided into sections. DO NOT try to go through them all in one sitting. Take one section at a time and then work through the companion section in the study guide.
- Draw pictures of the functional unit of muscle (sarcomere), being sure to label the various parts and note their role in contraction.

INTERACTIVE EXERCISES

Why It Matters [pp. 940–941]

Section Review (Fill-in-the-Blanks)

There are three types of muscle tissue: (1) _____, (2) _____, and (3) _____. Most

(4) _____ _____ are attached by tendons to the skeleton of vertebrates.

38.1 Vertebrate Skeletal Muscle: Structure and Function [pp. 941–949]

Section Review (Fill-in-the-Blanks)

Skeletal muscle consists of elongated, cylindrical cells called (5) _____ _____. Inside the

cell, there are contractile elements or (6) _____ that consist of regular arrangements of

(7) _____ _____, containing the protein myosin, and (8) _____ _____,

containing the protein actin. The functional unit of the myofibril is the (9) _____, which extends Z line to Z line. The plasma membrane of the muscle cell folds into the muscle fibre to form

(10) _____ _____, which are in close association with the cell's complex network of

endoplasmic reticulum called (11) _____ _____. A neuron comes in contact with a muscle

cell to form a(n) (12) _____ _____. The release of (13) _____ from the neuron

causes the muscle cell to depolarize, release calcium from the lumen of the sarcoplasmic reticulum, and raise

cytosolic calcium concentration. Calcium enables the interaction between myosin and actin so that the

filaments move relative to one another in a process called the (14) _____ _____

_____; this movement shortens the sarcomere and results in muscle contraction. A single action

potential arriving at the neuromuscular junction usually causes a single weak contraction of the muscle cell

called a(n) (15) _____ _____. (16) _____ results when muscle fibres cannot relax

between rapidly arriving stimuli. (17) _____ _____ _____ contract relatively

slowly and the intensity of the contraction is low, whereas (18) _____ _____

_____ contract relatively quickly and powerfully. Controlled contraction of the overall muscle results

from organized activation of (19) _____ _____.

Building Vocabulary

Using the definitions of the prefixes below, assign the appropriate prefix to the appropriate suffix for the
following:

Prefix	Meaning
sarco-	of or relating to flesh/muscle
myo-	of or relating to muscle

Suffix	Meaning
-mere	unit, part

	Prefix	Suffix	Definition
20.	_____	_____	The functional unit of a contractile element in a muscle cell
21.	_____	-fibril	The contractile element inside of a muscle cell
22.	_____	-globin	Oxygen-storing molecule in some muscle cells

Choice

For each of the following, choose the most appropriate type of filament from the list below.

A. Thick filament   B.   Thin filament

23. _____   Parallel bundles of myosin molecules

24. _____   Mostly composed of two linear chains of actin arranged in a double helix

Matching

Match each of the following structures with its correct definition.

25. ____   Skeletal muscle

A.   Connect to bones of the skeleton by tendons

26. ____   Myoglobin

B.   Muscle cell

27. ____   Neuromuscular junction

C.   Cylindrical contractile elements in a muscle cell

28. ____   Myofibrils

D.   The weak contraction of a muscle cell in response to a single action potential

29. ____   Muscle fibres

E.   Process in which there is relative movement of actin and myosin

30. ____   Muscle twitch

F.   Collection of muscle fibres controlled by branch of same neuron

31. ____   Tetanus

G.   Specialized junction between a neuron and a muscle cell

32. ____   Motor units

H.   Oxygen-storing protein in some muscle

33. ____   Sliding filament mechanism

I.   Continuous contraction of a muscle fibre

Labeling

Identify each numbered part of the following illustration.

34. _____

35. _____

36. _____

37. _____

38. _____

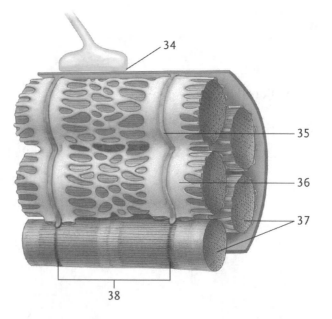

39. Describe how an action potential is propagated along a muscle fibre and initiates a muscle contraction.

_____

_____

40. Describe the role of calcium and ATP in muscle contraction and relaxation.

_____

_____

41. Summarize the events of the crossbridge cycle.

_____

_____

38.2 Skeletal Systems [pp. 949–952]

Section Review (Fill-in-the-Blanks)

A(n) (42) _____ _____ consists of muscles and fluid, with the fluid either within the muscle

or in compartments. A(n) (43) _____ is a rigid external covering that provides support, whereas a(n)

(44) _____ is made up of internal body structures that provide support such as bone. The skeleton of

vertebrates is organized into the (45) _____ _____ and the (46) _____

_____.

Short Answer

47. Describe the role of the skeletal system.

_____

_____

Choice

For each of the following descriptions, choose the most appropriate type of skeleton from the list below.

A. Axial skeleton   B.   Appendicular skeleton

48. _____   Contains skull and vertebral column

49. _____   Contains shoulders, hips, and limbs

38.3 Vertebrate Movement: The Interactions between Muscles and Bones [pp. 952–957]

Section Review (Fill-in-the-Blanks)

The bones of vertebrates are connected by three types of joints: (50) _____, (51) _____, and

(52) _____. A muscle that causes movement at a joint is a(n) (53) _____. Most bones are

moved by muscles in (54) _____ _____: (55) _____ _____, which extend

the joint, and (56) _____ _____, which retract the joint.

Choice

For each of the following descriptions, choose the most appropriate type of muscle from the list below.

A. Extensor muscle   B. Flexor muscle

57. _____   Retracts a joint

58. _____   Extends a joint

Matching

Match each of the following terms with its correct definition.

59.	_____	Agonist	A.	A muscle that causes movement in a joint when it contracts
60.	_____	Cartilaginous joint	B.	Arrangement of muscle groups in which one muscle has the opposite effect of the other
61.	_____	Fibrous joint	C.	Moveable joint enclosed by a fluid-filled capsule
62.	_____	Ligaments	D.	Moveable joint without a fluid-filled capsule
63.	_____	Antagonistic pair	E.	Joint connected by stiff connective tissue
64.	_____	Synovial joint	F.	Connective tissue that joins bones on either side of a joint

SELF-TEST

1. What does the sliding filament mechanism state? [pp. 941–943]

    a. Nebulin and titin filaments move relative to one another.

    b. Actin and myosin filaments become arranged perpendicular to one another.

    c. Actin and myosin filaments move relative to one another.

    d. The two actin chains unwind and dissociate into G-actin.

2. What are myofibrils composed of? [pp. 941–942]

    a. fibres

    b. myofibrils

    c. actin and myosin

    d. sarcoplasmic reticulum

3. What is the human skull part of? [p. 952]

   a. girdle
   b. axial skeleton
   c. atlas
   d. appendicular skeleton
   e. hydrostatic skeleton

4. Which of the following is part of the human axial skeleton? [p. 952]

   a. the ulna
   b. the shoulder blades
   c. the demur
   d. the sternum

5. What are the vertebrate appendages connected to? [p. 952]

   a. the cervical complex
   b. the atlas
   c. the appendicular skeleton
   d. the axial skeleton and girdles

6. In which animal group is a hydrostatic skeleton is NOT the primary means of support? [pp. 949–952]

   a. annelids
   b. cnidarians
   c. flatworms
   d. lobsters and crayfish

7. In which of the following do we find an internal skeleton? [pp. 949–952]

   a. annelids
   b. cnidarians
   c. echinoderms
   d. lobsters and crayfish

8. What is the primary neurotransmitter released at neuromuscular junctions in vertebrates? [p. 943]

   a. substance P
   b. inositol triphosphate
   c. epinephrine
   d. acetylcholine
   e. endorphin

9. What facilitates the diffusion of oxygen into tissues from blood and stores oxygen in tissues? [p. 947]

   a. myoglobin
   b. hemoglobin
   c. opsin
   d. bilirubin
   e. dystrophin

10. Which term refers to the connective tissue that joins bones together on either side of a joint? [p. 954]

   a. the periosteum
   b. the stratum corneum
   c. the tendons
   d. the ligaments
   e. the meninges

11. What controls the skeletal muscle contraction? [p. 941]

   a. the somatic system
   b. the sensory system
   c. the endocrine system
   d. the skeletal system

12. How are skeletal muscles attached to bones? [p. 941]

   a. through ligaments
   b. through tendons
   c. through Z-discs
   d. through troponin

13. What delimits a sarcomere? [pp. 942–943]

   a. A bands
   b. I bands
   c. two M lines
   d. two Z lines

14. What does ATP cause during the crossbridge cycle? [pp. 944–945]

   a. the detachment of myosin from actin
   b. the unbending of myosin crossbridges
   c. rigor mortis

15. Where is Ca^{2+} that is directly involved in muscle contraction? [pp. 944–945]

    a. in the tubules

    b. in the cytosol

    c. in the sarcoplasmic reticulum

    d. in the extracellular fluid

16. What statement is true about fast anaerobic muscle fibres? [pp. 947–948]

    a. They contain a high concentration of glycogen.

    b. They have many mitochondria.

    c. They have extensive vascularization.

    d. They are red in colour.

17. In skeletal muscles, how can the force of contraction be adjusted? [pp. 946–947]

    a. by controlling the recruitment of motor units

    b. by controlling the speed of contraction

    c. by contracting antagonist muscle pairs

    d. by tetanic contractions

18. Which of the following would have many motor units in a small area but with only a few myofibres in each unit? [pp. 946–947]

    a. abdominal muscles

    b. biceps

    c. fingers

    d. back muscles

19. What statement is true about the sliding filament mechanism? [pp. 941–943]

    a. It causes thick and thin filaments to slide toward the centre of the H band, bringing the Z lines closer together.

    b. It causes thick and thin filaments to slide toward the centre of the I band, bringing the M lines closer together.

    c. It causes thick and thin filaments to slide toward the centre of the M line, bringing the Z lines closer together.

    d. It causes thick and thin filaments to slide toward the centre of the A band, bringing the Z lines closer together.

20. Where is the compound chitin found? [pp. 950–951]

    a. in exoskeleton of vertebrates

    b. in exoskeleton of insects and lobsters

    c. in ligaments and tendons

    d. in lydrostatic skeletons

INTEGRATING AND APPLYING KEY CONCEPTS

1. *Insights from the Molecular Revolution*: Describe the factors that regulate gene expression and identify the possible targets of action for drugs aimed at increasing utropin content in the muscle cells of DMD patients.

2. Coordinated muscle contraction requires neuronal stimulation of motor units. Discuss the roles of calcium in neuromuscular function and the potential consequences of calcium deficiency. (Be sure to consider both the muscle cell and the nerve cell.)

39 Animal Behaviour

TOPIC MAP

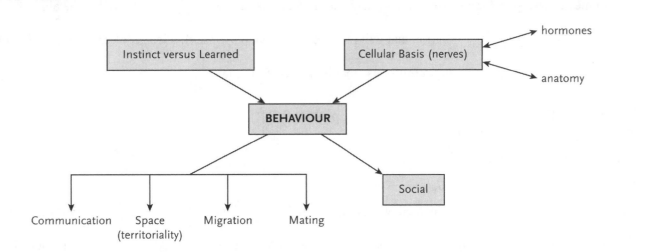

LEARNING OUTCOMES AND STUDY STRATEGIES

By the end of this chapter, you should be able to

- Differentiate between instinctive and learned behaviour

- Explain how hormones and anatomy each interact with nerves to produce a behaviour

- Describe how communication, space, migration, and mating patterns can increase an animal's fitness

- Differentiate between the different types of mating patterns

- Compare social behaviours among different species, explaining why some species work cooperatively in groups

- Calculate the relatedness between various family members

Study strategies for this chapter:

- First you need to be able to distinguish between the two very different components of animal behaviour, instinctive and learned.

- Since all behaviours are neural based, you need to understand how hormones and anatomy interact with an animal's nervous system.

- After studying the different behaviours, from communication to social behaviours, look at how a combination of behaviours can affect an animal's fitness, an important measure of how successful the animal will be in passing on its genes to the future generation.

- Note that the beginning of this chapter is devoted to how behaviour occurs and the end of the chapter addresses why different types of behaviour occur.

INTERACTIVE EXERCISES

Why It Matters [pp. 960–961]

Section Review (Fill-in-the-Blanks)

A reward, such as food, is often an incentive for an animal to change its (1) _____. In a changing

environment, new opportunities sometimes arise, and if an animal is (2) _____, it may be able to

develop a(n) (3) _____ action that will provide a positive response. If successful, an animal will then

have (4) _____ a behavioural response that it can continue to use.

39.1 Genes, Environment, and Behaviour [pp. 961–962]
39.2 Instinct [pp. 962–965]
39.3 Learning [pp. 965-966]

Section Review (Fill-in-the-Blanks)

Behavioural scientists have long debated whether an animal's behaviour is (5) _____, that is, innate

and performed correctly the first time it is used, or whether behaviour is (6) _____, that is, modified

by experience. Most attempts to answer this question involved experiments wherein animals were kept in

(7) _____ and not allowed exposure to experiences that could enable them to copy or learn a

behavioural response. The consensus today is that instinct and learning are both components of animal

behaviour, the result of complex (8) _____–_____ interactions.

Since instinctive behaviours are (9) _____ or developmentally programmed, they are often

performed in a rather invariant fashion, a(n) (10) _____ _____ pattern. Simple stimuli that

elicit these behaviours are called (11) _____ stimuli. On the other hand, learned behaviours are

(12) _____ variable than instinctive behaviours since they are modified by experiences. Many types

of learning have been identified, including (13) _____, in which an animal learns parents' and/or

species' identity when an appropriate stimulus is presented at a(n) (14) _____ period early in life;

(15) _____ _____, in which a previously neutral stimulus becomes associated with another

stimulus that causes a behavioural response; (16) _____ conditioning, where behaviour can be

modified by linking a stimulus with a positive result called a(n) (17) _____; (18) _____

learning, wherein the behavioural solution to a problem appears without trial and (19) _____; and

(20) _____, in which repeated, unreinforced stimuli are no longer responded to.

Matching

Match each of the following types of behaviour with the appropriate example.

21. _____ Conditioned stimulus

A. A cat comes running to cat food when it hears the sound of an electric can opener.

22. _____ Habituation

B. A chick follows a toy car after being exposed to it 24 hours after hatching.

23. _____ Imprinting

C. A chimp stacks two boxes in order to reach some bananas hanging beyond its reach, thereby solving the problem.

24. _____ Insight learning

D. A fish exhibits typical courtship behaviour despite being raised from a zygote isolated from other fishes.

25. _____ Instinct

E. A hungry mouse learns to press a bar (voluntary action) to get a food pellet (favourable consequence).

26. _____ Operant conditioning

F. A hydra stops contracting when the aquarium it lives in is continually tapped gently.

True/False

Mark if the statement is true (T) or false (F). If the statement is false, make it correct by changing the underlined word(s) and writing the correct word(s) in the lines blow each statment.

27. _____ In Pavlov's experiments, when dogs started salivating in response to a ringing bell, the food was the <u>conditioned</u> stimulus.

_____

_____

28. _____ When a mouse presses a bar to obtain food, the act of pressing on the bar is the <u>reinforcement</u>.

_____

_____

29. _____ A snail's lack of response to repeated light touches is <u>imprinting</u>.

_____

_____

30. _____ A fixed action pattern is a <u>stereotypical, instinctive</u> behaviour.

_____

_____

31. _____ Instinctive behavioural differences between animals of different species are a reflection of <u>environmental</u> differences.

_____

_____

32. _____ <u>Learned</u> behaviour is genetically or developmentally programmed in an animal.

_____

_____

39.4 Neurophysiology and Behaviour [pp. 966–967]
39.5 Hormones and Behaviour [pp. 967–968]
39.6 Neural Anatomy and Behaviour [pp. 969–971]

Section Review (Fill-in-the-Blanks)

Behaviour is a response to physiological activities resulting from (33) _____ cell biochemistry and

structure. Some behaviours are present at birth, as dictated by the animal's (34) _____ information

directing the development of its anatomy and physiology. These behaviours, as well as learned behaviours,

may be modified over time through the alteration of nerve cells as a response to an individual's

(35) _____ in its environment. Research has provided many examples of how a behavioural act has a

neural basis. For example, songbirds may use a distinctive song to help in defence of their

(36) _____ (an area of land defended by males or couples) or during (37) _____ , the time

period when an individual (usually male) tries to attract a mate. Proper development of a song, as well as

recognition that other species' songs are different, is controlled by specific nuclei in the (38) _____ .

Development of these nuclei to function correctly is usually regulated by (39) _____ .

Matching

Match the species with correct behavioural adaptation.

40. ____	Crickets	A.	Direction of visual stimuli (from above or below) results in different behaviours.
41. ____	Cichlids	B.	Estrogen production in males is greater than females, resulting in differences in their neural development.
42. ____	Fiddler crabs	C.	Increasing levels of a hormone cause changes in specific social tasks.

43. _____ Honeybees

44. _____ Bats

45. _____ Star-nosed moles

46. _____ Zebra Finches

D. Most of the cerebral cortex is devoted to processing information from the nose and forelimbs.

E. Ultrasonic vocalizations of predatory bats cause a neural response resulting in moving away from the source of the sound.

F. Comparison of cell and echo identifies the presence of potential prey.

G. Ownership of a territory stimulates the increased production of GnRH, resulting in sexual and aggressive behaviour.

39.7 Communication [pp. 971–975]

Section Review (Fill-in-the-Blanks)

Animals use many sensory "channels" or modalities to communicate. Specific sounds or vocalizations are examples of (47) _____ signalling, while movements that convey information are examples of (48) _____ signalling. The use of scents to communicate with others is an example of (49) _____ signalling, and the compounds used are referred to as (50) _____. (51) _____ signalling involves physical contact between individuals. Finally, some fishes use (52) _____ signalling because they live in murky waters that make other forms of signalling ineffective.

Choice

Choose one or more of the communication channels that would be most appropriate to the situation described.

A. Acoustical   B. Chemical   C. Electrical   D. Tactile   E. Visual

53. _____ Animals that live in a cluttered environment

54. _____ Animals that live in dimly lit areas

55. _____ Animals that live in open areas

56. _____ Animals that produce a pheromone to attract a mate

57. _____ Animals that sing to warn intruders entering their territory

58. _____ Animals that send out a mild charge as a threat to invaders

39.8 Space [pp. 975–977]

Section Review (Fill-in-the-Blanks)

No general principles for how animals select a(n) (59) _____ have been determined. One behavioural

response to environmental cues used by some animals to locate suitable habitat is (60)_____, which

involves a change in the rate of movement or frequency of turning. Another response that can be used, which

involves direct orientation toward or away from a stimulus, is called (61) _____. Often, after finding

a suitable habitat, animals will defend an area from other individuals of the same species, giving it exclusive

use of resources in that area, a behaviour known as (62) _____. Although protecting a territory can be

costly, primarily due to the (63) _____ that must be spent to patrol it, there are (64) _____,

such as having (65) _____ access to resources and increasing the likelihood of (66) _____

a mate.

Choice

Choose the type of behaviour appropriate to each description.

A. Kinesis   B. Taxis   C. Territoriality

67. _____   Male yellow-headed blackbirds defending an area against intrusion by other yellow-headed
blackbirds

68. _____   Moths flying directly toward a light

69. _____   Wood lice increasing their rate of locomotion in dry areas

70. _____   Cockroaches running to hide in spaces in the dark

39.9 Migration [pp. 977–981]

Section Review (Fill-in-the-Blanks)

The large-scale, predictable movement of animals that occurs on a seasonal basis is (71) _____.

There are a number of mechanisms that enable animals to find their way during these travels. One is

(72) _____ , in which animals use landmarks to guide them. Another method is (73) _____

_____ , in which animals use some environmental cue, such as the sun or stars, to enable them to

travel in a specific direction and often for a specific period of time. The most complex type of way-finding is

(74) _____ , which requires both a compass and a (75) "_____ map." The costs of

(76) _____ and energy incurred by migrating are offset by benefits such as leaving a northern winter,

which requires a(n) (77) _____ in metabolic rate and (78) _____ in food supply, and

returning when days are (79) _____, which provides more time for breeding.

Matching

Match each of the animals with the way-finding mechanism it uses for migration. You may choose more than one cue per animal.

80. _____ Digger wasps

81. _____ Homing pigeons

82. _____ Indigo buntings

83. _____ Salmon

84. _____ Monarch butterflies

85. _____ Grey whales

A. Piloting using visual cues

B. Using position of stars in the sky

C. Using sun as compass

D. Piloting using olfaction (smell)

39.10 Mates as Resources [pp. 981–982]
39.11 Sexual Selection [pp. 982–983]

Section Review (Fill-in-the-Blanks)

A special type of natural selection is called (86) _____ selection and involves both

(87) _____ for a mate, usually among rival males, and (88) _____ a mate, which tends to be

performed by the female since she often makes the greater (89) _____ in providing parental care.

These activities lead to physical and behavioural differences between males and females, called sexual

(90) _____. Elaborate ornamental structures often evolve in the male, which they display to either

attract the attention of females during a(n) (91) _____ ritual or, in some cases, to (92) _____

with other males for a female. Sometimes males of a species gather for competition in a common area known

as a(n) (93) _____. Females assess the quality of males and select one for mating. Successful males

may mate with numerous females, a mating system known as (94) _____. Other mating systems

include a single female having multiple male mates, called (95) _____ (rare), a single male pairing

with a single female, forming a (96) _____ relationship, and (97) _____, where both sexes

have multiple mates without any lasting pair bond forming between them.

Matching

Match the mating system with the correct life history pattern.

98.	_____	Monogamy	A.	Solitary species with little or no real social structure. Individuals encounter each other randomly.
99.	_____	Polyandry	B.	Species in which females are physically drained after egg laying, but resources are temporarily abundant, allowing them to recover quickly and mate with a second male while the first male incubates the eggs.
100.	_____	Polygyny	C.	Species in which resource availability is so poor that both parents are required to successfully rear offspring.
101.	_____	Promiscuity	D.	Territorial species in which the quality of territory is highly variable. High-quality territories provide abundant resources, so biparental care is unnecessary.

39.12 Social Behaviour [pp. 983–985]
39.13 Kin Selection and Altruism [pp. 985–987]
39.14 Eusocial Animals [pp. 987–988]
39.15 Human Social Behaviour [pp. 988–990]

Section Review (Fill-in-the-Blanks)

The interactions of animals with members of their own species describe their (102) _____

_____. Living in groups has costs as well as benefits associated with it. Often groups form a

pecking order known as a(n) (103) _____ _____. Subordinate individuals may stay in the

group despite their low status because survival is difficult for solitary individuals. Many social species exhibit

(104) _____, behaviours that help others while putting the performer at somewhat increased risk.

This seems to contradict the concept of selfishness inherent in Darwin's view of natural selection, but

William Hamilton demonstrated how, by helping relatives, these behaviours could evolve. His theory of

(105) _____ _____ shows how helping a relative can aid in passing on the family's genes into

the next generation. (106)_____, the unique genetics of sex determination in ants, bees, and wasps,

lends credence to Hamilton's hypothesis since members of any of these (107) _____ groups show

high relatedness and, not surprisingly, are highly cooperative. Under certain circumstances, altruistic

behaviour can evolve among nonrelated individuals if there is a good chance that the roles of helper and

helped may be reversed in the future. This form of cooperative behaviour is known as (108) _____

_____.

Short Answer

Calculate the degree of relatedness for each of the following pairs of individuals.

109. Full siblings

_____

_____

110. Parent and offspring

_____

_____

111. Uncle and full sibling

_____

_____

112. First cousins

_____

_____

Matching

Match each of the animals listed below with their social behaviours.

113. _____	Dolphin	A.	Dominants in the group must defend their status
114. _____	Bees	B.	Large brain size provides high social cognitive skill level
115. _____	Grey wolves	C.	A competitive altruist
116. _____	Humans	D.	Sex is determined by haplodiploidy in this eusocial animal

1. What is the difference between singing and song, according to Peter Marler's demonstrations of the White-crowned Sparrow? [pp. 961–962]

   a. singing is instinctive and song is instinctive
   b. singing is instinctive and song is learned
   c. singing is learned and song is instinctive
   d. singing is learned and song is learned

2. Which term refers to birds that lay their eggs in the nests of other species and whose young are raised by the "host" species? [pp. 962–963]

   a. brood parasites
   b. ectoparasites
   c. endoparasites
   d. parental hijackers

3. Which term refers to the cues that trigger fixed action patterns? [pp. 963–964]

   a. conditioned stimuli
   b. instinctive stimuli
   c. sign stimuli
   d. unconditioned stimulus

4. What did Stevan Arnold's experiments on newborn garter snakes and banana slugs demonstrate? [pp. 963–964]

   a. Banana slugs exhibit stereotyped avoidance behaviour when they detect a garter snake in their vicinity.
   b. Food preferences in garter snakes have a genetic component.
   c. Food preferences in garter snakes are learned.
   d. The coloration of banana slugs deters garter snakes from striking.

5. A rat presses a bar in its cage and receives a food pellet. Which of the following is a correct statement? [pp. 965–966]

   a. Insight learning has occurred.
   b. Pressing the bar in exchange for the food pellet is an example of classical conditioning.
   c. Pressing the bar is the operant; the food pellet is the reinforcement.
   d. Pressing the bar is the reinforcement; the food pellet is the operant.

6. Suppose that a Zebra Finch has learned to ignore the songs of neighbours that share his territory. Which term refers to the behaviour displayed by the finch? [pp. 965–966]

   a. classical conditioning
   b. operant conditioning
   c. habituation
   d. insight learning

7. Why can only male Zebra Finches sing? [pp. 967–968]

   a. Only males produce estrogen when their brains are developing.
   b. Only females produce octopamine when they are adults.
   c. Only males have vocal cords.
   d. Only females produce increasing concentrations of juvenile hormone as they age.

8. What causes changes in the types of behaviours honeybees perform as they get older? [pp. 967–968]

   a. changes in diet
   b. changes in hormone levels
   c. changes in photoperiod
   d. changes in their habitat

9. Crickets display evasive behaviour when they hear the ultrasonic sounds of a bat. What is this an example of? [pp. 969–970]

   a. habituation to bat vocalizations
   b. hardwiring between the sensory and motor systems
   c. hormonal control of behaviour
   d. imprinting on bat vocalizations during a critical period

10. Star-nosed moles live in dark tunnels and therefore vision is not a useful sensory modality. Which sense is most important to star-nosed moles? [pp. 970–971]

    a. hearing
    b. smell
    c. taste
    d. touch

11. What produces the acoustical signals that herrings use to communicate with each other? [pp. 971–972]

    a. striped colouring
    b. movement of fins
    c. little bursts of bodily gas
    d. release of pheromones

12. You place several planaria in a pan of water with one side covered so that it is dark, but the other side is open and well lit. You notice that their rate of movement slows on the dark side. What phenomenon have you observed? [pp. 975–976]

    a. compass orientation
    b. kinesis
    c. operant conditioning
    d. taxis

13. Which of the following describes the food preferences in Blue Tits and Coal Tits? [pp. 975–976]

    a. Food preferences for both species is for the same food.
    b. Food preferences for both species are innate.
    c. Food preferences for both species are learned.
    d. Food preferences for one species is innate and the other is learned.

14. Which situation would be an advantage for a low-testosterone spiny lizard male (low territoriality)? [pp. 975–976]

    a. an abundant localized food supply within his territory (low food supply in neighbouring territories)
    b. accessibility to females pursued by multiple males
    c. evenly distributed food supply throughout territory and surrounding area
    d. testosterone-enhanced males defending neighbouring territories

15. Which of the following is NOT one of the environmental cues used by migrating animals to reach their destination? [pp. 977–981]

    a. odours
    b. position of the stars
    c. position of the sun
    d. sounds

16. The most favourable reproductive strategies are often different for males and females of a species. What causes these differences? [pp. 981–982]

    a. body temperature
    b. emotional makeup
    c. parental investment
    d. sex ratio

17. What type of selection has resulted in the special ornaments or structures of males that increase the likelihood of attracting females? [pp. 982–983]

    a. artificial selection
    b. disruptive selection
    c. sexual selection
    d. stabilizing selection

18. Which term refers to a mating system in which one female has multiple male mates? [pp. 981–982]

   a. monogamy
   b. polyandry
   c. polygyny
   d. promiscuity

19. Which animal uses a behaviour that supports the idea of reciprocal altruism? [pp. 985–987]

   a. the honeybee
   b. the musk ox
   c. the naked mole rat
   d. the dolphin

20. In which type of relationship did Wilson and Daly find that criminal aggression by an adult toward a child was most common? [pp. 988–990]

   a. between adult and juvenile siblings
   b. between fathers and daughters
   c. between fathers and sons
   d. between stepparents and stepchildren

INTERACTIVE EXERCISES

1. Describe the behaviour an insectivorous bat displays to find its prey and a black field cricket uses to avoid being the prey.

2. Explain why a wandering raven uses the acoustical behaviour of yelling when it finds a carcass (instead of eating it in isolation).

3. Is a male lion who has taken over a pride altruistic? Explain your answer.

40 Plant and Animal Nutrition

TOPIC MAP

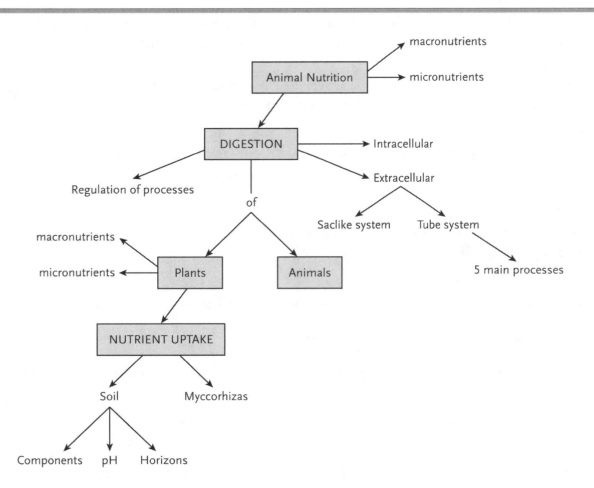

LEARNING OUTCOMES AND STUDY STRATEGIES

By the end of this chapter, you should be able to

- Differentiate between macronutrients and micronutrients in plants and animals, identifying those nutrients that tend to limit plant success

- Describe the characteristics and conditions of soil that affect plant nutrient uptake, including symbiotic relationships that increase uptake of specific nutrients

- Compare digestive systems of various animals, describing the structures, functions, and reactions occurring in the mammalian digestive system

- Describe how neuron networks and hormones regulate digestion in animals

Study strategies for this chapter:

- Remember that the goals of this chapter are to understand
  - What plants and animals need
  - How plants and animals obtain their nutrients from their environment
- First, focus on the mechanisms used by plants to acquire essential nutrients, and then shift your focus to animals and the various feeding mechanisms they use.
- Next, study the structures and processes used in the digestive process in humans, identifying the location and reactions involved in the breakdown of macromolecules and their absorption into the body.
- Make comparisons between the digestive system used by mammals and the various types of feeding, specializations, and nutritional requirements among other animals.

INTERACTIVE EXERCISES

Why It Matters [pp. 994–995]
40.1 Nutrition: Essential Materials [pp. 995–1003]
40.2 Soil [pp. 1003–1006]

Section Review (Fill-in-the-Blanks)

Plants are more than (1) _____% water, with the remainder composing the plant's (2) _____

_____, which is primarily composed of carbon, (3) _____, and oxygen elements.

(4) _____ is a technique whereby plants are grown in solutions containing measured amounts of

(5) _____, nutrients normally found in the soil. Plants receive most of their nutrients from the process

of (6) _____, although many are taken up by the roots (7) _____ (no energy required) with

the uptake of water from the soil. Since animals cannot photosynthesize, they acquire energy and nutrients

from other living organisms: from plants if they are (8) _____ consumers and from animals if they

are (9) _____ consumers (or higher level consumers).

(10) _____ elements are necessary for plants and animals to grow and reproduce. Out of

17 such elements, 9 are required in higher amounts and so are called (11) _____, while the remainder

are required in relatively small amounts and are known as (12) _____. Deficiency of one or more of

these elements in plants can lead to developmental or physiological problems, including (13) _____

growth and/or (14) _____ of the leaves. In animals, chronic malnutrition or (15) _____ often

results in weight (16) _____ since animals must use nutrients in their own bodies as fuel. Animals have the added requirement for (17) _____, organic molecules required in small quantities that they cannot synthesize for themselves. Often these molecules function as coenzymes, assisting (18) _____ in metabolic activities. In humans, there are (19) _____ known vitamins required to function normally, some of which are (20) _____-_____ since they are hydrophilic and others that are (21) _____-_____ since they are hydrophobic.

Soils are primarily composed of five components: (a) mineral particles, which determine size and the number of (22) _____ _____, characteristics that affect water and nutrient uptake; (b) decomposing dead plants and animals, called the (23) _____, which forms the organic component of the soil and helps in retaining (24) _____ in the ground; (c) living organisms, some of which burrow in the soil, thereby (25) _____ it, and others, such as saprophytic bacteria and fungi, which (26) _____ organic matter; (d) air, which is located in the pores and provides a source of (27) _____ to the plant roots; and (e) water, which is also located in pores and forms the (28) _____ _____ when mixed with dissolved substances. Minerals can be positively charged, called (29) _____, or negatively charged, called (30) _____. Positively charged minerals are less available to plant roots since they tend to bind tightly to (31) _____ charged soil particles but can be released by the (32) _____ _____ mechanism.

Matching

Match each of the following terms with its correct definition.

33. _____	Hydroponics	A.	Layer of soil with distinct texture and composition
34. _____	Essential elements	B.	Cleaning of contaminated soils using plants
35. _____	Macronutrients	C.	Yellowing of the plant tissue due to lack of chlorophyll
36. _____	Micronutrients	D.	Elements that are necessary for normal growth and reproduction of the plants
37. _____	Chlorosis	E.	Elements that are required in very small amounts
38. _____	Leaching	F.	Primarily eats plant material
39. _____	Cation exchange	G.	Primarily eats other animals

40. ____	Horizon	H.	Excessive intake of specific nutrients
41. ____	Primary consumer	I.	Drainage of nutrients from soil by excess water
42. ____	Overnutrition	J.	Growing plants in a solution with known solutes
43. ____	Phytoremediation	K.	Elements that are required in large amounts
44. ____	Secondary consumer	L.	Swap of one positively charged ion (usually H^+) for another

Choice

Choose the element(s) that can be found in each of the listed macromolecules. Elements can be used more than once.

45. ____	Carbohydrate	A.	Carbon
46. ____	Protein	B.	Hydrogen
47. ____	Lipid	C.	Nitrogen
48. ____	Nucleic acid	D.	Phosphorus
		E.	Sulfur
		F.	Oxygen

Complete the Table

49. Soil is a complex mix of important ingredients. Complete the following table by giving the role of each component of the soil.

Soil Ingredients	Value in Soil
Particles	A.
Humus	B.
Living organisms	C.
Minerals	D.

40.3 Obtaining and Absorbing Nutrients [pp. 1006–1010]

Section Review (Fill-in-the-Blanks)

Plants and animals are adapted to obtain the nutrients required for life. In plants, roots compose between

(50) _____ – _____% of plant dry weight, functioning to absorb water and minerals from soil. The greatest

absorption by plant roots occurs at root (51) _____, although the presence of root (52) _____

increases the surface area of roots, thereby increasing plant water and ion uptake dramatically. Furthermore,

cell membranes of some root cells contain (53) _____ - _____ transport proteins, providing

channels for the entrance of particular ions, such as potassium ions, into cells. Potassium, (54) _____,

and nitrogen tend to be the most limiting ions to plants. Symbiotic associations between plants and fungi,

called (55) _____, assist in nutrient uptake, since the fungi form a network of (56) _____

filaments, which increase surface area for absorption of water and ions. Nitrogen uptake is often limiting for

plants since (57) _____% of it is in its gaseous form and plants lack the (58) _____ to convert it into

nitrate and ammonium ions, forms that it can absorb. Various types of (59) _____ are found in the

soil that can convert different forms of nitrogen into (60) _____ and/or ammonium ions. Once plants

absorb these ions, they are all converted into (61) _____, which is then used to make

(62) _____ acids or other organic molecules.

Some (63) _____-fixing bacteria live in the soil, but others form a(n) (64) _____

association with the roots of legume plants, forming swellings in the plant roots called root

(65) _____. These bacteria enter roots through root hairs, attracted into roots by certain chemicals

belonging to the (66) _____. These bacteria then release proteins expressed by their

(67) _____ gene, some of which stimulate root cells to multiply and form root nodules and others

that produce the protein (68) _____, which provides necessary oxygen to the bacteria. Eventually, the

enclosed bacteria in a root nodule become larger and immobile, known as (69) _____, and they

produce the enzyme (70) _____, which converts nitrogen to ammonium.

Animals obtain their nutrients in different ways, depending on their (71) _____ to their

environments. There are (72) _____ basic groupings of how animals feed, each dependent on the

physical state of the food: (73) _____ feeders have mouthparts that allow animals to ingest foods that are liquid, (74) _____ feeders filter fluid entering the body such that trapped small organisms are

ingested, (75) _____ feeders take in solid material but digest only the edible particles in the sediment,

and (76) _____ feeders ingest relatively large pieces of food, which often requires chewing.

Matching

Match each of the following types of bacteria with their role in providing nitrogen to plants.

77. _____	Nitrogen-fixing bacteria	A.	Bacteria that are able to decompose dead organic matter in the soil to ammonium
78. _____	Ammonifying bacteria	B.	Bacteria that are able to convert atmospheric nitrogen to ammonium
79. _____	Nitrifying bacteria	C.	Bacteria that are able to convert ammonium to nitrates for plants to absorb
80. _____	Bacteroids	D.	Enlarged, immobile bacteria in the legume root nodules

Match each of the following terms with its correct definition.

81. _____	Root nodule	A.	Bacterial gene that makes proteins to help nitrogen-fixing bacteria enter plant roots
82. _____	Flavenoids	B.	Enzyme made by the bacteroids to convert atmospheric nitrogen to ammonium
83. _____	Nod gene	C.	A reddish, heme- and iron-containing protein that is produced by the root nodule cells to increase oxygen supply for the bacteria
84. _____	Leghemoglobin	D.	Chemicals released by plant roots to attract nitrogen-fixing bacteria
85. _____	Nitrogenase	E.	Swellings in the roots where nitrogen-fixing bacteria reside

Choice

Choose the type of feeding used by each of the animals listed.

86. _____	Alligator	A.	Suspension feeder
87. _____	Oyster	B.	Deposit feeder
88. _____	Aphid	C.	Fluid feeder
89. _____	Earthworm	D.	Bulk feeder
90. _____	Nectar-feeding butterfly		
91. _____	Cougar		

40.4 Digestive Processes in Animals [pp. 1010–1012]

Section Review (Fill-in-the-Blanks)

Digestion is the (92) _____ of larger particles into subunits that can be (93) _____ into body

fluids and cells. Many of the chemical bonds of larger particles are broken by (94) _____

_____. These enzymatic reactions are often very (95) _____, with a particular type of

enzyme breaking down a particular type of macromolecule. These digestive processes can occur within body

cells, (96) _____ digestion, or outside of body cells, (97) _____ digestion. In summary,

digestion requires (98) _____ main processes: (99) _____ _____, which involves

tearing large food particles into smaller particles; (100) _____ of enzymes and other substances,

which is required for the third process; (101) _____ _____, which involves the further

breakdown of food using enzymatic reactions; (102) _____ so that molecular subunits enter into

body fluids and cells; and (103) _____ to ensure that undigested food leaves the body.

Choice

For each of the following statements, choose the most appropriate enzyme from the list below.

A.   Lipases   B.   Amylases   C.   Nucleases   D.   Proteases

104. _____   Catalyzes the bonds within carbohydrates, such as starch

105. _____   Catalyzes the bonds between amino acids

106. _____   Catalyzes the bonds between glycerol and fatty acids

107. _____   Catalyzes the bonds within DNA or RNA

Short Answer

108.   Explain how endocytosis and exocytosis are involved in intracellular digestion.

_____

_____

109.   Explain how extracellular digestion is advantageous with respect to food source.

_____

_____

Choice

Choose the appropriate stage of digestion that occurs in each of the following anatomical locations. More than one stage can occur in the various locations.

110.	____	Long intestine of an annelid	A.	Mechanical processing
111.	____	Anus	B.	Secretion of digestive enzymes
112.	____	Gastric ceca of insects	C.	Enzymatic hydrolysis
113.	____	Gizzard	D.	Absorption
114.	____	Intestine	E.	Elimination
115.	____	Liver of bird		
116.	____	Proventriculus of bird		

40.5 Digestion in Mammals [pp. 1012–1021]

Section Review (Fill-in-the-Blanks)

The digestive process in mammals is very similar to other animals, also consisting of the (117) _____

steps of digestion. The mammalian digestive tract includes (in order) the mouth, pharynx,

(118) _____, stomach, small intestine, large intestine, (119) _____, and anus. The

(120) _____ and endocrine systems control digestion in all mammals; however, digestive systems in

herbivores are (121) _____ than in carnivores, due to the added digestion of (122) _____ in

plant cell walls.

Matching

Match each of the following structures/components of the digestive system with its correct description.

123.	____	Mucosa	A.	Found in the stomach; fibres are oriented in a diagonal direction
124.	____	Submucosa	B.	Wave of contraction from the circular and longitudinal muscles
125.	____	Muscularis	C.	Outermost layer of the gut; secretes a thin, slippery, lubricating fluid
126.	____	Serosa	D.	Smooth muscle rings that act as valves to ensure one-way flow
127.	____	Sphincter	E.	Muscle oriented perpendicular to the axis of the gut
128.	____	Peristalsis	F.	Innermost layer of the gut; absorption occurs in this layer

129.	____	Circular muscle	G.	Muscle oriented parallel to the axis of the gut
130.	____	Longitudinal muscle	H.	Major muscle coat of the gut—composed of 2–3 layers
131.	____	Oblique muscle	I.	Thick, connective tissue layer of the gut

Consecutive Order

Put the following structures or functions in the proper order, using numbers from 1 to 17.
Note: Number 1 has been provided.

132.	____	Gastroesophageal sphincter
133.	____	Esophagus
134.	____	Anal sphincter
135.	____	Large intestine
136.	____	Ileocecal sphincter
137.	____	Stomach
138.	____	Food passes the epiglottis
139.	____	Secretions of pancreas and liver added
140.	____	Pharynx
141.	____	Pyloric sphincter
142.	____	Rectum
143.	_1_	Mechanical processing in mouth
144.	____	Secretions of HCl and pepsinogen added
145.	____	Secretions from salivary glands added
146.	____	Anus
147.	____	Chyme enters small intestine
148.	____	Hydrolysis and absorption of nutrients completed

Matching

Match each of the secretions with the location in which it is produced.

149. _____ Pepsinogen   A.   Exocrine cells of pancreas

150. _____ Bile salts   B.   Parietal cells of gastric gland

151. _____ Aminopeptidase, dipeptidases, and mucus   C.   Salivary glands

152. _____ Alkaline mucus for stomach   D.   Chief cells of gastric gland

153. _____ HCl   E.   Microvilli

154. _____ Enzymes, such as trypsin, and bicarbonate ions   F.   Liver cells

155. _____ Amylase, lysozyme, mucus, and bicarbonate ions   G.   Mucus cells of gastric gland

40.6 Regulation of the Digestive Processes [pp. 1021–1023]

Matching

Match each of the hormones with its correct action during digestion.

156. _____ Gastrin   A.   Increases insulin release from the pancreas

157. _____ Cholecystokinin   B.   Inhibits additional HCl release from gastric glands and stimulates HCO_3^- release

158. _____ Secretin   C.   Stimulates secretion of HCl and pepsinogen and gastrointestinal tract motility

159. _____ Leptin   D.   Under control of hypothalamic neurons; thought to inhibit appetite

160. _____ Alpha-MSH   E.   Presence of fat stimulates release; inhibits gastric activity and increases pancreatic enzyme release

161. _____ GIP   F.   Increases when fat deposition increases, reduces appetite

True/False

Mark if the statement is true (T) or false (F). If the statement is false, make it correct by changing the underlined word(s) and writing the correct word(s) in the lines below each statement.

162. _____ Regulation and control of the digestive process are under local control by the <u>voluntary</u> nervous system.

_____

_____

163. _____ The presence of food in the gastrointestinal tract <u>initiates</u> secretion of mucus and digestive enzymes as well as motility.

_____

_____

164. _____ The neurons that make up the appetite centre are located in the <u>mucosa of the stomach</u>.

_____

_____

165. _____ <u>A decrease</u> in the blood level of leptin will stimulate or increase appetite.

_____

_____

40.7 Variations in Obtaining Nutrients [pp. 1023–1029]

Section Review (Fill-in-the-Blanks)

Different plants and animals have developed adaptations and specializations to assist in obtaining

(166) _____. Examples include plants that are (167) _____, stealing nutrients from the

tissues of other plants, to their detriment; plants that are (168) _____, growing on other plants but not

parasitizing them; animals that are ambushers, (169) _____ until prey is observed and then attacking

it; and animals that use (170) _____, something that attracts prey to the predator.

Matching

Match each of the following organisms with its specialization for obtaining nutrients.

171. ____	*M. termitophaga* flatworm	A.	Uses bioluminescent bacteria to lure prey
172. ____	Coralroot	B.	Uses roots to access vascular tissues and rob host plant of its nutrients
173. ____	Candiru	C.	Lies in wait on mound, uses eyes to detect movement, and then uses head to capture prey
174. ____	Dodders	D.	Uses its wide mouth to ingest food and its vertebrae as an egg-cracker during digestion
175. ____	Anglerfish	E.	Obtains carbon from other plants using shared mycorrhizal fungi
176. ____	*D. scabra* snake	F.	Attaches to gills of larger fish and feeds on its blood

1. Why were hydroponic techniques developed? [pp. 995–996]

    a. to study the roles of different minerals in growth of a plant
    b. to replace the agriculture industry
    c. to grow algae in water
    d. to multiply nitrogen-fixing bacteria

2. Which of these macronutrients is NOT found in proteins? [pp. 996–999]

    a. C
    b. N
    c. O
    d. K

3. The products of digestion are used for a fundamental process associated with life. Which is NOT considered part of this fundamental process ? [pp. 1000–1002]

    a. ATP production
    b. synthesis of biological molecules
    c. reproduction

4. Joe has been on antibiotics for six weeks due to an infection and is now finding he bleeds easily. What has been the long-term effect of Joe's antibiotic use? [pp. 1000–1002]

    a. a decrease in the bacteria that produce vitamin D
    b. a decrease in the bacteria that produce vitamin K
    c. an increase in the level of water-soluble vitamins

5. What adds organic chemicals to the soil? [pp. 1003–1006]

    a. soil particles
    b. humus
    c. live organisms
    d. minerals

6. What form of nitrogen is the one plants absorb most? [pp. 1007–1008]

    a. nitrogen gas
    b. ammonium
    c. nitrate
    d. amino acids

7. What form of nitrogen is the one plants use most? [pp. 1006–1008]

    a. nitrogen gas
    b. ammonium
    c. nitrate
    d. amino acids

8. A fertilizer bag is labelled 15-30-25. What sequence of minerals do these numbers represent? [p. 1000]

    a. carbon–hydrogen–oxygen
    b. carbon–nitrogen–oxygen
    c. nitrogen–phosphorus–potassium
    d. nitrogen–oxygen–phosphorus

9. What do nitrifying bacteria do? [pp. 1007–1008]

    a. convert atmospheric nitrogen into ammonium
    b. decompose organic chemicals to make ammonium
    c. convert ammonium into nitrates
    d. convert nitrates into ammonium

10. What are bacteroids? [pp. 1007–1008]

    a. bacteria that live in the soil
    b. bacteria that live in root nodules
    c. bacteria that live on dead organic matter
    d. bacteria that infect plants and parasitize them

11. What is the result of the expression of *nod* genes? [pp. 1007–1008]

    a. It allows plants to access more of the nitrogen in the soil.
    b. It stimulates plant cells to make leghemoglobin.
    c. It makes the enzyme for converting nitrogen to nitrates.

12. What type of feeder would an animal with teeth and claws most likely be? [pp. 1008–1010]

    a. a fluid feeder

    b. a suspension feeder

    c. a deposit feeder

    d. a bulk feeder

13. Which term refers to the digestive system of animals that intake food and remove waste through the same opening? [pp. 1010–1012]

    a. saclike

    b. tubelike

    c. filtering

14. Which structure is NOT typically involved with mechanical processing? [pp. 1010–1012]

    a. the gizzard

    b. the stomach

    c. the pancreas

    d. the crop

15. Which pair is NOT correctly matched? [pp. 1012–1020]

    a. giraffe—long intestinal tract

    b. tiger—short intestinal tract

    c. horse—long intestinal tract

    d. kangaroo—short intestinal tract

16. Where are villi located in mammals? [pp. 1017–1020]

    a. in the wall of the esophagus

    b. in the wall of the stomach

    c. in the wall of the small intestine

    d. in the wall of the large intestine

17. What statement about essential amino acids and vitamins is correct? [pp. 1012–1020]

    a. They are synthesized before any of the others.

    b. They are obtained in the diet.

    c. They are metabolized before others can be synthesized.

    d. They are obtained from a symbiotic relationship.

18. Suppose the pyloric sphincter were blocked. What would be true about the movement of chime? [pp. 1012–1020]

    a. It could not move from the esophagus to the stomach.

    b. It could not move from the large intestine to the rectum.

    c. It could not move from the stomach to the small intestine.

    d. It could not move from the oral cavity to the esophagus.

19. Suppose that one of the hormones produced by the intestine, secretin, was inactive. What effect would this have on the pH of the digestive secretions? [pp. 1021–1023]

    a. Secretions would be more acidic.

    b. Secretions would be more basic.

    c. Secretions would be neutralized.

20. Which term refers to an orchid that lives on the branch of a tree? [p. 1024]

    a. parasite

    b. omnivore

    c. carnivore

    d. epiphyte

INTERACTIVE EXERCISES

1. Describe differences between clay and sandy soils in terms of their limitations to plant nutrient uptake.

2. Why must vegetarians be careful about accessing eight of the essential amino acids?

3. For each of the four macromolecules, identify the enzymes that break down molecules in the small intestine, indicating the molecules that are being digested and the resulting molecules produced.

41 Gas Exchange: The Respiratory System

TOPIC MAP

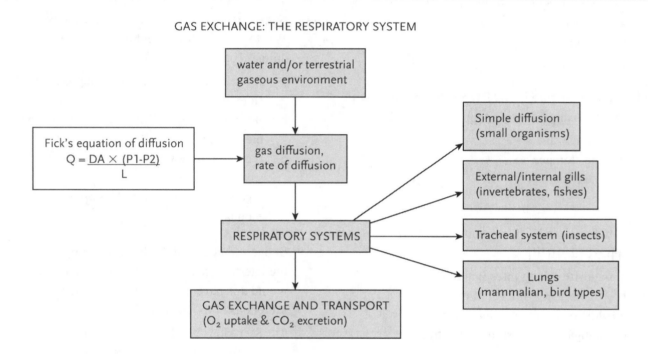

GAS EXCHANGE: THE RESPIRATORY SYSTEM

water and/or terrestrial gaseous environment

Fick's equation of diffusion
$$Q = \frac{DA \times (P1\text{-}P2)}{L}$$

gas diffusion, rate of diffusion

RESPIRATORY SYSTEMS

GAS EXCHANGE AND TRANSPORT (O_2 uptake & CO_2 excretion)

Simple diffusion (small organisms)

External/internal gills (invertebrates, fishes)

Tracheal system (insects)

Lungs (mammalian, bird types)

LEARNING OUTCOMES AND STUDY STRATEGIES

By the end of this chapter, you should be able to

- Describe the percent composition of air

- Calculate the partial pressure of gases under different atmospheric pressures

- Use Fick's equation of diffusion to explain the factors that influence the rate of gas diffusion across a respiratory surface

- Use Fick's equation of diffusion to explain adaptations for gas exchange in the water and terrestrial habitats

- Discuss the advantages of ventilation and perfusion for gas exchange

- List and explain the advantages and disadvantages of water and air as respiratory media

- Draw and label diagrams of the different respiratory systems: gills, tracheal system of insects, bird lungs, and mammalian lungs

- Compare gas exchange in fish, insects, birds, and mammals

- Draw and label a diagram of a hemoglobin–oxygen dissociation curve and use this diagram to explain oxygen exchange and transport in the blood and the factors that influence oxygen transport
- Explain the mechanisms of CO_2 transport and excretion

Study strategies for this chapter:

- The concepts of this chapter build on elements of diffusion developed earlier. You should briefly review these concepts to make sure that you understand them.
- This chapter contains a lot of new information and new terminology. DO NOT try to go through it all in one sitting. Take one section at a time. Start by skimming the section, writing down the boldface terms, and studying the figures, and then go back and read the text, followed by working through the companion section in the study guide. Repeat this process for each section of the textbook.
- Draw diagrams of the various respiratory systems, carefully labelling each component and noting its function.
- Try to relate Fick's equation of diffusion to make the link between gas exchange and the design of different respiratory systems for breathing in different types of environments.

INTERACTIVE EXERCISES

Why It Matters [pp. 1032–1033]

41.1 General Principles of Gas Exchange [pp. 1033–1035]

Section Review (Fill-in-the-Blanks)

Describe the gas composition of air: (1) _____% N_2; (2) _____% O_2; and (3) _____% CO_2.

If atmospheric pressure is the sum of the pressures of all of the gases in a mixture, what would be the partial pressures of N_2, O_2, and CO_2 at the following atmospheric pressures?

$P_{atm} = 760$ mm Hg (sea level) $\qquad P_{N_2} = $ ____ (4) $P_{O_2} = $ ____ (5) $P_{CO_2} = $ _____ (6)

$P_{atm} = 500$ mm Hg $\qquad P_{N_2} = $ ____ (7) $P_{O_2} = $ ____ (8) $P_{CO_2} = $ _____ (9)

$P_{atm} = 250$ mm Hg (top of Mt. Everest) $P_{N_2} = $ _____ (10) $P_{O_2} = $ ____ (11) $P_{CO_2} = $ _____ (12)

Short Answer

13. Describe the movement of gases.

_____

_____

14. Describe the factors that influence the rate of diffusion across a membrane.

_____

_____

Fill-in-the-Blanks

(15) _____ _____ is the process animals use to exchange gas with their surroundings. The source of O_2 and the "sink" for CO_2 in the environment is called the (16) _____ _____, which can be either air or water. (17) _____ is the exchange of gases with the respiratory medium. Gases move by simple diffusion across a(n) (18) _____ _____. The entire body serves as a respiratory surface in many small animals. Insects possess an extensive (19) _____ _____ to distribute air to internal organs. In larger animals, (20) _____ and (21) _____ are used for gas exchange with water and air, respectively.

Short Answer

22. What roles do ventilation and perfusion play in the rate of gas exchange? (Explain in terms of Fick's equation.)

_____

_____

Complete the Table

In the following table, list the advantages and disadvantages of water and air as respiratory media.

	Advantages	Disadvantages
Water	23.	24.
Air	25.	26.

41.2 Adaptations for Gas Exchange [pp. 1035–1040]

Section Review (Fill-in-the-Blanks)

Gills are evaginations of the body surface; (27) _____ _____ extend from the body and do

not have protective coverings, whereas (28) _____ _____ are located within chambers of the

body and have a protective cover. Many aquatic vertebrates maximize gas exchange with (29) _____

_____, a process whereby water flows over the gills in the opposite direction of the flow of blood

beneath the respiratory surface. Air enters and exits the tubes or (30) _____ of the unique respiratory

system of insects through (31) _____. In some air-breathing fish (e.g., lungfish) and amphibians, air

is gulped and forced into the lungs by a process called (32) _____ _____ breathing. Other

vertebrates, such as reptiles, birds, and mammals, use (33) _____ _____ breathing, in which

the air pressure in the lung is lowered by expanding the lung cavity through muscular contraction, resulting in

air being pulled inward. The mammalian lung consists of millions of tiny air pockets or (34) _____.

Birds possess nonrespiratory air sacs that ensure that all air in the lungs comes in contact with respiratory

surfaces and that create a(n) (35) _____-_____ flow of air that maximizes gas exchange via

cross-current exchange (i.e., air flows perpendicular to blood flow).

Building Vocabulary

Using the definitions of the prefixes below, assign the appropriate prefix to the appropriate suffix for the
following:

Prefix	Meaning
hyper-	over, above
hypo-	under, below
ventila-	to fan

Suffix	Meaning
-tion	the process of

	Prefix		Suffix	Definition
36.	_____		_____	The process of moving air or water across a respiratory surface
37.	_____	_____	_____	Excessively rapid breathing
38.	_____	_____	_____	Excessively slow breathing

Describe

39. Describe the process of countercurrent exchange in the gills of fish and its adaptive significance.

_____

_____

_____

_____

Complete the Table

Animal Group	Principal Respiratory Medium	Principal Respiratory Structure
Insects	40.	41.
Most fish	42.	43.
Reptiles	44.	45.
Mammals	46.	47.

Matching

Match each of the following structures with its correct definition.

48. _____	Breathing	A.	The exchange of gases with the respiratory medium
49. _____	Lungs	B.	The air tubes of the unique respiratory system of insects
50. _____	Alveoli	C.	Air hole on insect exoskeleton that controls air flow
51. _____	Tracheae	D.	Small air pocket of mammalian lung
52. _____	Tracheal system	E.	Process by which animals exchange gases with their environment
53. _____	Spiracles	F.	Respiratory structures that represent evaginations of the body
54. _____	Physiological respiration	G.	Respiratory structures that represent invaginations of the body
55. _____	Gills	H.	Extensive system of air tubes in insects

41.3 The Mammalian Respiratory System [pp. 1040–1043]

Section Review (Fill-in-the-Blanks)

Air enters the body through nasal passages and the mouth and enters the (56) _____, a common

pathway leading to the digestive tract and lungs. For respiration, air travels from the pharynx first into the

(57) _____ and then into the (58) _____, which branches into two (59) _____, one

leading to each lung. The terminal airways or (60) _____ in the lungs lead into cup-shaped pockets

called alveoli. The lungs are covered with (61) _____, a double layer of epithelial tissue. Inhalation

of the lung occurs by contraction of the (62) _____ and the (63) _____ _____

_____, actions that expand the thoracic cavity and reduce air pressure in the lung below atmospheric

pressure, thereby enabling the lungs to fill passively. Exhalation occurs by relaxation of these muscle groups.

With increased activity, air can be forcibly expelled from the lungs by contraction of the (64) _____

_____ _____. The volume of air entering and leaving the lung is the (65) _____

_____; the maximum such volume is the (66) _____ _____. A(n)

(67) _____ _____ of air is left in the lungs after exhalation. Respiration is controlled by the

medulla oblongata and the pons of the brain stem, which integrate chemosensory information about O_2 and

CO_2 levels centrally in the (68) _____ and peripherally from (69) _____ _____ and

(70) _____ _____.

Choice

For each of the following descriptions, choose the most appropriate type of adaptive immunity from the
list below.

A. Carotid bodies   B. Aortic bodies

71. _____ Chemoreceptors located in the aortic arch

72. _____ Chemoreceptors located in the carotid arteries

For each of the following descriptions, choose the most appropriate type of response from the list below.

A. Tidal volume   B. Vital capacity   C. Residual volume

73. _____ The maximum tidal volume of an individual

74. _____ The volume of air entering and leaving the lungs during inhalation and exhalation

75. _____ The volume of air left in the lungs after exhalation

Labelling

Identify each numbered part of the following illustration.

76. _____

77. _____

78. _____

79. _____

80. _____

81. _____

82. _____

83. _____

84. _____

85. _____

86. _____

87. _____

88. _____

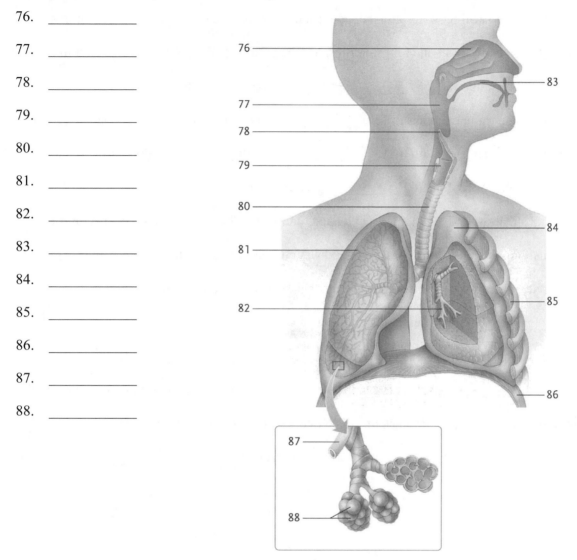

41.4 Mechanisms of Gas Transport [pp. 1043–1047]

Section Review (Fill-in-the-Blanks)

The (89) _____ of O_2 in clean, dry air at sea level is about 160 mmHg. The carrying capacity of O_2 in

the blood of vertebrates is increased by the presence of the respiratory pigment (90) _____. The

binding of O_2 to Hb, a protein with four subunits, can be described as a sigmoid (S)-shaped

(91) _____ _____ _____. The majority of CO_2 is transported in the plasma in the

form of bicarbonate (HCO_3^-) produced by the enzyme (92) _____ _____ in red blood cells

and represents an important (93) _____ to control blood pH.

94. What are the reasons for the shape of the hemoglobin–oxygen dissociation curve?

_____

_____

Short Answer and Label the Diagram

95. Using the following hemoglobin–oxygen dissociation curve, explain oxygen exchange and transport in the blood.

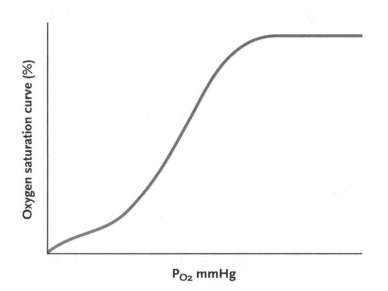

Locate on the diagram where you would expect the P_{O_2} of the blood to be (96) when blood is returning to the heart and (97 when blood has been oxygenated at the lungs.

98. Explain the effects of changes pH on the hemoglobin–oxygen saturation curve. On the diagram, draw the curve if the pH decreases (99). When would you expect this to occur (100)?

_____

_____

101. Explain the significance of the steep part of the curve.

_____

_____

102. List the different forms under which CO_2 is transported in the blood.

_____

_____

103. Explain the mechanisms of CO_2 transport in the blood and excretion at the lungs.

_____

_____

Choice

For each of the following descriptions, choose the most appropriate type of adaptive immunity from the list below.

A. Hemoglobin   B. Myoglobin

104. _____ Iron-containing respiratory pigment with four subunits

105. _____ Iron-containing respiratory pigment with one subunit and a very high affinity for O_2

Matching

Match each of the following terms with its correct definition.

106. ____	Buffers	A.	The pressure of an individual gas in a mixture
107. ____	Erythropoietin	B.	Resists changes in pH by accepting or donating electrons
108. ____	Partial pressure	C.	Protein hormone that stimulates RBC production
109. ____	Carbonic anhydrase	D.	Enzyme that catalyzes the reaction $CO_2 + H_2O \;\Xi\; [H_2CO_3] \;\Xi\; H^+ + HCO_3$

SELF-TEST

1. What is the normal composition of air? [pp. 1033–1034]

    a. 21 mm Hg O_2; 78 mm Hg N_2; 1 mm Hg CO_2
    b. 160 mm Hg O_2; 590 mm Hg N_2; 7.6 mm Hg CO_2
    c. 21% O_2; 78% N_2; 1% CO_2
    d. 16% O_2; 59% N_2; 7.6% CO_2

2. Which statement is NOT correct regarding Fick's equation of diffusion? [p. 1034]

    a. the larger the partial pressure difference, the lower the rate of diffusion
    b. the greater the surface area of exchange, the greater the rate of diffusion
    c. the shorter the length of the barrier, the higher the rate of diffusion
    d. the greater the solubility of a gas, the higher the rate of diffusion

3. Which of the following characterizes the tracheal system in insects? [pp. 1036–1037]
   a. closed tubes that circulate gases
   b. uncontrolled diffusion of gases between the atmosphere and the tissues
   c. the transport of respiratory gases directly to every cell
   d. countercurrent gas exchange

4. What statement about countercurrent gas exchange is correct? [p. 1038]
   a. It is described as the tidal flow of air in mammalian lungs.
   b. It results in the equilibration of partial pressure of gases along the respiratory surface during gas exchange.
   c. It allows establishment of a partial pressure difference that maintains gas exchange along the entire length of the respiratory surface.

5. Which characteristic is shared by all respiratory surfaces? [p. 1035]
   a. dryness
   b. thickness
   c. a large surface area
   d. the presence of alveoli

6. By what means does a cockroach obtain O_2 for its tissues? [pp. 1036–1037]
   a. internal gills
   b. pseudolungs
   c. countercurrent exchange
   d. a tracheal system

7. What is the normal path of air flow through a mammalian respiratory system? [pp. 1038–1040]
   a. trachea—larynx—pharynx—bronchus—bronchiole
   b. larynx—pharynx—trachea—bronchus—bronchiole
   c. pharynx—larynx—trachea—bronchus—bronchiole
   d. pharynx—trachea—larynx—bronchus—bronchiole

8. What statement is not consistent with the concept of countercurrent exchange? [p. 1038]
   a. It is used by bony fish.
   b. It maximizes gas exchange by maintaining diffusion gradient.
   c. It is described as the respiratory medium moving in the same direction as blood flow.
   d. It is described as the respiratory medium moving in the opposite direction of blood flow.

9. What detects O_2 levels in blood and provides information to the medulla oblongata? [p. 1043]
   a. macula densa
   b. islets of Langerhans
   c. carotid and aortic bodies
   d. nodes of Ranvier

10. What does not affect the ability of oxygen to bind to Hb? [pp. 1043–1047]
    a. P_{O_2} in respiratory medium
    b. pH
    c. salts
    d. P_{CO_2} in tissues

11. What is the definition of vital capacity? [pp. 1042–1043]
    a. the amount of air taken in the lungs at rest
    b. the maximum amount of air taken up by the lungs
    c. the amount of air remaining in the lungs following a forced exhalation
    d. the frequency of breathing during exercise

12. Which is true about negative pressure breathing? [pp. 1040–1043]
    a. the volume of the thoracic cavity increases
    b. the pressure of the thoracic cavity increases
    c. air is forced down the trachea by muscular contractions of the mouth and the pharynx

13. Which organism relies solely on simple diffusion for gas exchange? [pp. 1035–1040]

 a. a mammal
 b. a frog
 c. a flatworm
 d. a bird

14. What is true about the majority of CO_2 in the blood? [pp. 1045–1047]

 a. It is bound to hemoglobin.
 b. It is transported as HCO_3^-.
 c. It is dissolved as CO_2 in the plasma.
 d. It is dissolved as CO_2 in the red blood cells.

15. What does a hemoglobin–oxygen dissociation curve demonstrate? [pp. 1044–1047]

 a. the amount of O_2 bound to hemoglobin as a function of atmospheric pressure
 b. the amount of O_2 bound to hemoglobin as a function of oxygen partial pressure
 c. the amount of O_2 bound to hemoglobin as a function of pH
 d. the amount of CO_2 that binds hemoglobin when O_2 is delivered to the tissues

16. Suppose your pet dog lived at atmospheric P_{O_2} = 150 mm Hg and exhibited arterial P_{O_2} = 100 mm Hg and tissues P_{O_2} = 10 mm Hg. What would you expect the dog to do? [pp. 1043–1047]

 a. die
 b. accumulate CO_2
 c. have a serious but nonlethal O_2 deficit
 d. become dizzy from too much O_2
 e. function normally

17. As RBCs circulate into the region of actively metabolizing tissues (e.g., muscle), what would you expect to occur? [pp. 1043–1047]

 a. a decreased binding of CO_2 to Hb
 b. a decrease inreduced Hb
 c. an increase in bicarbonate ion concentration in plasma
 d. a movement of chloride out of RBC

18. Which terms refers to the process of bringing oxygenated water or air into contact with a gas exchange surface? [p. 1035]

 a. respiration
 b. inspiration
 c. exhalation
 d. ventilation

INTEGRATING AND APPLYING KEY CONCEPTS

1. Carbon monoxide is dangerous because it outcompetes O_2 for binding sites on Hb. The reaction between CO and Hb is reversible (like that between O_2 and Hb), whereas other pollutants, such as NO_x compounds, bind irreversibly to Hb. Discuss the differences in treatment strategies for individuals that you suspect to be suffering from CO and NO_x poisoning.

2. Using Fick's equation of diffusion, explain the adaptations that have allowed for life in water and terrestrial environments.

3. The oxygen partial pressure at sea level is approximately 160 mm Hg. At the top of Mount Everest, the oxygen partial pressure is approximately 53 mm Hg. Explain the challenges of breathing oxygen on top of Mount Everest. Why do some climbers use oxygen tanks to make their ascent? What type of acclimation would allow climbers to avoid the use of oxygen tanks? Explain.

42 Regulating the Internal Environment

TOPIC MAP

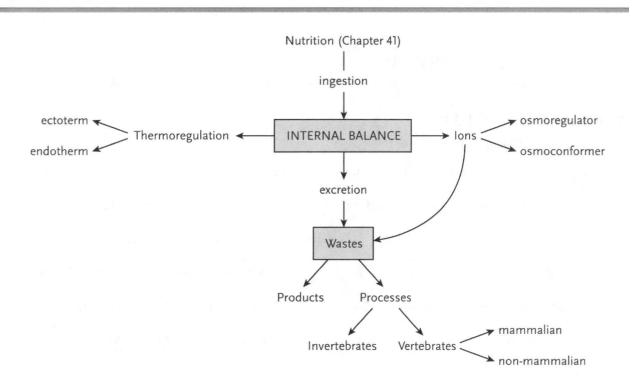

LEARNING OUTCOMES AND STUDY STRATEGIES

By the end of this chapter, you should be able to

- Define osmoregulation and thermoregulation, describing the importance of each to survival
- Differentiate between ammonia, urea, and uric acid excretory wastes, as well as describe the advantages and disadvantages of each
- Describe different excretory processes used by invertebrates and vertebrates
- Describe changes in blood and filtrate as molecules and ions are transported through the various structures within a nephron (mammalian)
- Compare mechanisms used by an ectotherm and an endotherm to regulate body temperature

Study strategies for this chapter:

- First, focus on concepts of osmoregulation and thermoregulation and how they help maintain an organism's internal environment.

- Examine the various types of osmoregulatory mechanisms in the animal kingdom, comparing the overall systems used by invertebrates, mammalian vertebrates, and nonmammalian vertebrates.

- Focus on the mammalian excretory system, both structure and function, making comparisons between mammals and other vertebrates.

- Evaluate thermoregulatory processes in the animal kingdom, with a focus on ectothermy and endothermy.

INTERACTIVE EXERCISES

Why It Matters [pp. 1050–1051]

Section Review (Fill-in-the-Blanks)

Organisms have mechanisms that assist them in maintaining their (1) _____, despite fluctuations in

the external environment. Terrestrial organisms are able to survive on land by conserving (2) _____

in their bodies so that all body (3) _____ systems are able to function to maintain life. For aquatic

organisms living in environments with (4) _____ concentrations greater than those found in body

cells, where the overall movement of water is (5) _____ the organism, physiological and

morphological adaptations counteract this movement and maintain a relatively constant (6) _____

environment.

42.1 Introduction to Osmoregulation and Excretion [pp. 1051–1054]

Section Review (Fill-in-the-Blanks)

(7) _____ is the process of water molecules moving from an area of (8) _____ concentration

(having a (9) _____ concentration of solutes) to an area of (10) _____ concentration (having

a (11) _____ concentration of solutes), through a(n) (12) _____ _____ membrane.

This type of movement is (13) _____ since no energy is required, where movement is down a(n)

(14) _____ gradient. The osmotic concentration in a solution is measured in (15) _____.

When the osmolality of two solutions is compared, specific terms are used: a(n) (16) _____ solution

has the same number of osmoles as the other solution, a(n) (17) _____ solution has more osmoles

than the other solution, and a(n) (18) _____ solution has fewer osmoles than the other solution. These terms only apply when comparing the osmoles between two solutions on either side of a selectively permeable membrane.

If an animal has control mechanisms that can maintain an internal osmolarity of its body fluids that is significantly different from the external environment, the animal is considered to be a(n) (19) _____. However, if osmoregulatory processes are lacking or adjust the internal environment to closely match the external environment, the animal is known as a(n) (20) _____. For animals to maintain the correct osmotic concentration, pH, and ionic balance, (21) _____ must be eliminated. Wastes produced from (22) _____ reactions, including the (23) _____ products from the digestion of proteins and nucleic acids, must also be eliminated. Many wastes are toxic to cells, especially when levels are elevated. The process of (24) _____ is the removal of metabolic wastes while maintaining water and ion (25) _____, thus allowing the animal to survive in its environment.

Matching

Match each of the following components of excretion or type of metabolic waste with its correct description.

26.	_____	Metabolic water	A.	Solution of relatively low osmolality
27.	_____	Urea	B.	Animal that maintains internal osmolality at the same level as its external environment
28.	_____	Hypoosmotic	C.	Highly toxic waste only excreted in dilute solutions
29.	_____	Osmoconformer	D.	Solution of relatively high osmolality
30.	_____	Ammonia	E.	Soluble waste that is relatively nontoxic
31.	_____	Hyperosmotic	F.	Solvent for excretion of waste products and other physiological processes
32.	_____	Uric acid	G.	Movement of water across a selectively permeable membrane down its concentration gradient
33.	_____	Osmosis	H.	Animal that maintains internal osmolality at different level than its external environment
34.	_____	Osmoregulator	I.	Nontoxic waste that forms crystals in water

42.2 Osmoregulation and Excretion in Invertebrates [pp. 1054–1057]

Section Review (Fill-in-the-Blanks)

(35) _____ invertebrates are (36) _____, since their internal osmolality matches the external environment, while freshwater and (37) _____ invertebrates are (38) _____. As osmoconformers, marine invertebrates use very little (39) _____ on regulating the osmotic concentrations of their body (40) _____. (41) _____ wastes, typically in the form of (42) _____, are directly released into the external environment. Freshwater and terrestrial invertebrates must expend (43) _____ to maintain an internal environment, which, in terms of osmolality, is (44) _____ to their external environment. The types of habitats these animals can inhabit are more (45) _____ than those of their osmoconformer counterparts.

Matching

Match each of the following types of excretory types with its correct definition.

46. ____	Protonephridia	A.	Closed tubule immersed in hemolymph
47. ____	Metanephridia	B.	Blind-ended tubule with a flame cell
48. ____	Malpighian tubules	C.	Funnel-shaped tubule with cilia

Match each of the following animals with the appropriate excretory system type.

49. ____	Insects	A.	Protonephridia
50. ____	Flatworms	B.	Metanephridia
51. ____	Earthworm	C.	Malpighian tubules
52. ____	Larval clam		
53. ____	Adult clam		

42.3 Osmoregulation and Excretion in Nonmammalian Vertebrates [pp. 1057–1059]

Section Review (Fill-in-the-Blanks)

In nonmammalian vertebrates, the environmental demands placed on the animal determine if (54) _____ (liquid) or (55) _____ (solid) are conserved or excreted. These vertebrates have a variety of mechanisms to maintain an internal environment that is compatible with life in their external environments. Marine teleosts live in a(n) (56) _____ environment; therefore, water must be (57) _____ and salts are (58) _____ for the animals to survive. Sharks and rays retain the metabolic waste (59) _____ and other (60) _____ wastes to maintain an internal body fluid that is (61) _____ to seawater. Freshwater fishes and aquatic amphibians maintain body fluids that

are (62) _____ to their environment by (63) _____ water and (64) _____ salts.

Terrestrial amphibians must (65) _____ both water and salts. Reptiles and birds conserve water by

excreting water-free (66) _____ _____ crystals. In addition to these mechanisms, these

animals have a variety of other (67) _____, some unique, that play a major role in conservation or

excretion of water and salts.

Choice

Choose organism(s) that use the water/salt conservation/excretion mechanisms listed. More than one choice can apply to a mechanism.

68.	_____	Rectal salt gland	A.	Reptiles and birds
69.	_____	Chloride cells	B.	Marine teleosts
70.	_____	Isoosmotic urine	C.	Freshwater fish and amphibians
71.	_____	Retain urea	D.	Sharks and rays
72.	_____	Hypoosmotic urine	E.	Terrestrial amphibians
73.	_____	Head salt glands		
74.	_____	Excrete uric acid crystals		
75.	_____	Excrete ammonia		
76.	_____	Active uptake of salts by gills		

42.4 Osmoregulation and Excretion in Mammals [pp. 1059–1065]

Section Review (Fill-in-the-Blanks)

The (77) _____ is the primary organ of excretion in mammals. The (78) _____ is the

structural and functional unit of the kidney. The outermost region of the kidney is the (79) _____,

while the innermost region is called the (80) _____. Some nephrons have long loops of Henle, called

(81) _____ nephrons, while the majority of nephrons have short loops, many of which do not cross

into the medulla; these are called (82) _____ nephrons. (83) _____ is the fluid produced in

the nephron that contains water, electrolytes, and (84) _____ products (by-products of metabolic

reactions). After leaving the collecting duct, urine is carried from the (85) _____ _____ of

the kidney to the (86) _____ _____ through a tube, the (87) _____. In terms of osmolality, mammalian kidneys produce (88) _____ urine compared to body fluids. The structure

and function of the nephrons, the (89) _____ _____ that surround the nephrons, and the

increasing (90) _____ of the kidney from the cortex to medulla all play significant roles in producing

a water-conserving, (91) _____ urine.

Sequence

A molecule of nitrogenous waste, in the form of urea, is in a human's afferent arteriole. Identify the pathway this molecule would take through the excretory system, starting with #1, before exiting from the body.

92. ____	Renal pelvis		98. ____	Proximal convoluted tubule
93. ____	Distal convoluted tubule		99. ____	Bowman's capsule
94. ____	Urethra		100. ____	Urinary bladder
95. _1_	Afferent arteriole		101. ____	Ureter
96. ____	Collecting duct		102. ____	Ascending loop of Henle
97. ____	Descending loop of Henle		103. ____	Glomerulus

Matching

Match each of the following regions of the nephron and associated area in the kidney with its primary characteristic. Multiple answers may occur.

104. ____	Glomerulus	A.	Region where some urea moves into interstitial fluid; permeable to water
105. ____	Proximal convoluted tubule	B.	Capillaries where filtration occurs
106. ____	Bowman's capsule	C.	Blood vessel that supplies the glomerulus
107. ____	Ascending segment of loop of Henle	D.	Portion of loop that takes filtrate toward the medullary region of the kidney
108. ____	Distal convoluted tubule	E.	Blood vessel that exits the glomerulus
109. ____	Peritubular capillaries	F.	Nephron portion of the filtration area
110. ____	Descending segment of loop of Henle	G.	Blood vessels that surround the convoluted tubule
111. ____	Afferent arteriole	H.	Region of the loop that is impermeable to water
112. ____	Efferent arteriole	I.	Region of the nephrons that reabsorbs electrolytes, nutrients, and 65% of water
113. ____	Collecting ducts	J.	Portion of the nephron located in the cortical region of the kidney where urine is isoosmotic to body fluids

True/False

Mark if the statement is true (T) or false (F). If the statement is false, make it correct by changing the underlined word(s) and writing the correct word(s) in the lines below each statement.

114. _____ Essentially all of nutrient molecules, including amino acids and glucose, are reabsorbed from the <u>proximal convoluted tubule</u>.

_____

_____

115. _____ Movement of water out of the distal convoluted tubule by osmosis is due to overall movement of ions <u>into</u> this structure.

_____

_____

116. _____ The large number of aquaporins in the wall of the <u>ascending</u> segment of the loop of Henle allows rapid reabsorption of water into interstitial fluid.

_____

_____

117. _____ The diameter of the afferent arteriole is <u>greater</u> than that of the efferent arteriole, increasing the pressure for movement of fluid into the Bowman's capsule.

_____

_____

118. _____ Sodium and chloride ions move <u>into</u> the ascending segment of the loop of Henle.

_____

_____

42.5 Introduction to Thermoregulation [pp. 1066–1068]
42.6 Ectothermy [pp. 1068–1070]
42.7 Endothermy [pp. 1070–1075]

Section Review (Fill-in-the-Blanks)

Temperature regulation is based on (119) _____ feedback mechanisms and (120) _____,

which detect changes from the internal (121) _____ _____. To accomplish these regulating

tasks, animals have both heat (122) _____ (when it is cool) and heat (123) _____ (when it

is hot) adaptations. There are two major strategies to maintain heat gain and loss. (124) _____ are

animals that produce heat internally primarily from physiological sources, while (125) _____ obtain

heat primarily from the external environment.

Ectotherms maintain an internal temperature that is close to the (126) _____ temperature. Most animals beside (127) _____ and (128) _____ are ectotherms. These animals typically use (129) _____ mechanisms to maintain their internal temperature. During seasonal changes, fish remain in (130) _____ water during the summer and move to the (131) _____ levels during the winter. Amphibians and reptiles utilize the warming rays from the sun to increase body temperature by (132) _____. In addition to behavioural mechanisms, these animals often have various physiological mechanisms or (133) _____ _____, which ensures survival. One such mechanism is multiple (134) _____ that can catalyze the same reaction. Each has a different optimal (135) _____ range of activity.

Endotherms use (136) _____ reactions and (137) _____ exchange with the environment to maintain body temperature around an optimal temperature, a(n) (138) _____ _____. This is (139) _____ expensive but allows these animals to be active over a(n) (140) _____ range of temperatures than ectotherms. In humans, thermoreceptors are located in the hypothalamus, spinal cord, and (141) _____. The latter assists in regulating temperature through various morphological and physiological adjustments, such as changing blood vessel diameter, (142) _____ the size to cool the body and (143) _____ it to raise body temperature; producing (144) _____ when the body is too hot; and coordinating small muscle contractions or (145) _____ when body temperature is too low.

Choice
Choose the term that describes or defines the situation.

A. Conduction   B. Convection   C. Radiation   D. Evaporation

146. An animal lying in the sun can either gain or lose heat by _____.

147. When you sweat, you are losing heat through _____.

148. A snake lying on a warm rock during the early morning is gaining heat through _____.

149. Standing in front of a fan allows heat to be lost by _____.

150. If you are naked standing on ice in the winter, you will lose heat through your feet by _____ and through your breath by _____.

Matching

Match the mechanisms with the primary function with respect to thermoregulation.

151. _____ Sweating

152. _____ Shivering

153. _____ Increased thyroid hormone

154. _____ Decreased epinephrine

155. _____ Vasodilation

156. _____ Increased blood flow to the skin

157. _____ Increased blood flow to the core

A. Heat-producing mechanism

B. Heat loss mechanism

True/False

Mark if the statement is true (T) or false (F). If the statement is false, make it correct by changing the underlined word(s) and writing the correct word(s) in the lines below each statement.

158. _____ If the external environment is cool, endotherms expend a <u>small</u> amount of energy for heat production.

_____

_____

159. _____ The period of torpor during <u>winter</u> is called estivation, while the period of torpor during <u>summer</u> is hibernation.

_____

_____

160. _____ Gills of fish and the ears of arctic animals have countercurrent exchanges between arterial and venous blood flow to <u>prevent</u> heat loss to the environment.

_____

_____

161. _____ Blubber prevents heat loss due to <u>radiation</u>.

_____

_____

162. _____ The <u>hypothalamus</u> is the primary thermoregulatory centre in birds and mammals.

_____

_____

1. Suppose John's body fluids has an osmolality of 0.5 osmoles/kg. What would be the equivalent to in mOsm/kg? [p. 1052]

   a. 0.0005
   b. 0.05
   c. 50
   d. 500
   e. 5000

2. Suppose that an animal secretes uric acid crystals. What type of environment could you conclude that this animal lives in? [pp. 1053–1054]

   a. freshwater
   b. marine
   c. terrestrial and very arid (dry)
   d. terrestrial and very wet

3. What statement about the removal of nitrogenous wastes in salmon at sea is correct? [pp. 1053–1054]

   a. It occurs by loss of uric acid crystals.
   b. It occurs by loss of urea.
   c. It occurs by loss of trimethylamine oxide.
   d. It occurs by loss of ammonia.

4. Which of the following describes an animal in which the osmolality of the intracellular fluids is maintained to be isoosmotic to the external environment? [pp. 1054–1059]

   a. an osmoregulator
   b. an osmoconformer
   c. an osmoequilibrator

5. What type of cells do animals living in freshwater tend to have? [p. 1058]

   a. hypoosmotic cells
   b. isoosmotic cells
   c. hypoosmotic cells

6. Invertebrates that excrete wastes using tubules with one open end that empties into a gut use which of the following structure? [pp. 1054–1057]

   a. protonephridia
   b. Malpighian tubules
   c. nephrons
   d. metanephridia

7. Which segment of the nephron lacks aquaporins? [pp. 1059–1064]

   a. the proximal convoluted tubule
   b. the descending segment of the loop of Henle
   c. the ascending segment of the loop of Henle

8. In mammals, what carries blood to the kidneys? [p. 1059]

   a. the renal arteries
   b. the renal pelvis
   c. the renal veins
   d. the ureters

9. What section of a nephron is involved in filtration? [p. 1060]

   a. the collecting duct
   b. Bowman's capsule
   c. the loop of Henle
   d. the proximal convoluted tubule

10. In which part of the kidney does the osmolality of the filtrate increases as it travels through it? [pp. 1061–1065]

    a. ascending segment of the loop of Henle
    b. descending segment of the loop of Henle
    c. bend at the bottom of the loop of Henle
    d. proximal convoluted tubule

11. What is the purpose of bicarbonate ions reabsorbtion into the peritubular capillaries? [pp. 1063–1065]

    a. to balance acidity in the filtrate
    b. to balance acidity in the blood
    d. to increase solute concentration in the interstitial fluid

12. What happens to substances that are NOT reabsorbed? [pp. 1063–1065]

    a. They are excreted from the body in urine.
    b. They remain in the nephron.
    c. They leave the kidney through the renal vein.
    d. They return to the glomerulus.

13. Which organism engages mechanisms in its body to maintain hyperosmotic body fluids? [pp. 1057–1059]

    a. an amphibian
    b. a marine fish
    c. a freshwater fish

14. What type of thermoregulation do boa constrictors exhibit when they wrap around their eggs and shiver ? [pp. 1066–1067]

    a. evaporation
    b. conduction
    c. convection
    d. radiation

15. Which organism would you expect to require a constant and high level of energy? [pp. 1066–1075]

    a. a rabbit
    b. a shark
    c. a lizard
    d. a frog

16. What statement about thermal acclimatization is correct?[pp. 1070]

    a. It involves regulation of body temperature in response to information provided by a thermoreceptor.
    b. It is the change in an animal's physiology that accompanies seasonal changes.
    c. It occurs when core body temperature is below normal for an extended period of time.
    d. It occurs when core body temperature is above normal for an extended period of time.

17. If the set point was increased, what would you expect to occur? [pp. 1066–1075]

    a. a decrease in epinephrine
    b. shivering
    c. vasodilation

18. Which term refers to the layer of the skin that contains sweat glands, thermoreceptors, blood vessels, and other thermoregulating structures? [p. 1071]

    a. hypodermis
    b. epidermis
    c. dermis

INTEGRATING AND APPLYING KEY CONCEPTS

1. Compare and contrast the structure and function of the various excretory systems of invertebrates with respect to habitat—marine, freshwater, and terrestrial.

2. Explain why osmolality in the filtrate increases as it travels down the descending segment of the loop of Henle.

3. Discuss the advantages and disadvantages of being either an ectotherm or an endotherm.

43 Defences against Disease

TOPIC MAP

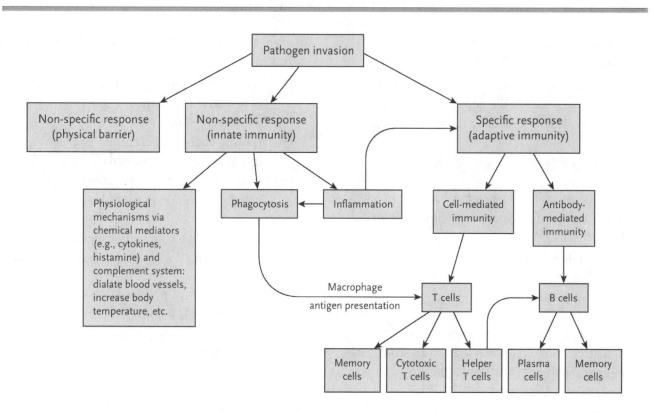

LEARNING OUTCOMES AND STUDY STRATEGIES

By the end of this chapter, you should be able to

- Differentiate between the three lines of defence used by vertebrates, identifying which is used by invertebrates and plants

- Describe the physical barriers to infection, as well as the different nonspecific responses provided by innate immunity

- Describe the process of both antibody-mediated immunity and cell-mediated immunity, identifying similarities and differences between them

- Explain how malfunction or failure of an immune response can result in disease, or worse

- Provide examples describing how some pathogens are able to overcome an organism's defences

Study strategies for this chapter:

- Be sure to review any concepts of cell biology from other chapters that you do not understand, such as phagocytosis, symbiosis, protein, cell signalling, etc.

- Since this chapter contains a lot of information and terminology and covers complex concepts, read only one section at a time and try not to go through the entire chapter in one sitting. You might want to start by skimming the section, writing down the boldface terms, and studying the figures before going back and reading the text.

- Drawing diagrams or flow charts of the various response pathways may be helpful.

INTERACTIVE EXERCISES

Why It Matters [pp. 1079–1080]
43.1 Three Lines of Defence Against Invasion [pp. 1080–1081]
43.2 Nonspecific Defences: Innate Immunity [pp. 1081–1086]

Section Review (Fill-in-the-Blanks)

The three lines of defence against invasion by foreign agents in humans and other vertebrates are physical

barriers; the (1) _____ _____ _____, a protection against any invading pathogen;

and the (2) _____ _____ _____, protection against specific pathogens. The

(3) _____ _____ is the defensive reaction of the immune system.

(4) _____ is a rapid response to injury that involves heat, pain, redness, and swelling.

(5) _____ are phagocytes that are usually the first to recognize pathogens, engulf them, and become

activated to secrete (6) _____, which recruit more cells to fight the pathogen. (7) _____

_____ also become activated by foreign substances and release histamine. (8) _____ are

attracted to an infection site by (9) _____, as are (10) _____ to help kill large pathogens.

The (11) _____ _____, a group of over 30 proteins, also become activated, and some of

these form (12) _____ _____ _____ on the surfaces of pathogens.

(13) _____, types of cytokines, are produced by viral-infected cells and initiate events that result in

RNA degradation and inhibition of protein synthesis in the infected cell. (14) _____ _____

cells destroy viral-infected cells often by triggering programmed cell death or (15) _____. NK cells

are a type of (16) _____, a type of leukocyte that carries out most of its actions in the lymphatic

system.

Choice

Choose the defence(s) that could be used by each of the organisms.

17. _____ Grasshopper   A. Body surface covering

18. _____ Corn plant   B. Adaptive immunity

19. _____ Giraffe   C. Innate immunity

20. _____ Mouse

For each of the following descriptions, choose the most appropriate type of defence from the list below.

A. Innate immunity   B. Adaptive immunity   C. Epithelial barrier

21. _____ Immediate, nonspecific response to an invading pathogen by recognizing its nonself molecular pattern

22. _____ Immediate, nonspecific response involving secretion of acid and digestive enzymes

23. _____ Specific response to a particular pathogen

24. _____ Nonspecific response to a pathogenic virus involving shutting down RNA and protein synthesis

Complete the Table

Type of Cell	Function
Macrophage	25.
26.	Releases histamine upon activation
Neutrophil	27.
28.	Type of leukocyte that helps kill large pathogens by secreting lysozmes and defensins
29.	Destroys viral-infected cells by perforating their plasma membrane

Matching

Match each of the following statements with the most appropriate type of chemical mediator.

A. Cytokines   B. Chemokines   C. Interferons

30. _____ Proteins produced by infected cells that initiate degradation of RNA and cessation of protein synthesis

31. _____ Released by activated macrophages and initiates heat, redness, and swelling of inflammation

32. _____ Released by activated macrophages and attracts neutrophils to infected site

Match each of the following terms with its correct definition.

33. ____ Apoptosis

A. The collection of defensive actions of the immune system

34. ____ Histamine

B. Rapid response that involves swelling

35. ____ Inflammation

C. Proteins that circulate in the blood and become activated by molecules on the surface of pathogens

36. ____ Complement system

D. Activated complement proteins that perforate cell membranes

37. ____ Lymphocyte

E. Type of leukocyte that carries out its actions in the lymphatic system

38. ____ Immune response

F. Programmed cell death

39. ____ Membrane attack complex

G. Causes dilation of blood vessels leading to the infected site

43.3 Specific Defences: Adaptive Immunity [pp. 1086–1097]

Section Review (Fill-in-the-Blanks)

A foreign molecule that triggers an adaptive immunity response is a(n) (40) _____. These molecules are recognized by (41) _____ _____, which are derived from and mature in bone marrow, and (42) _____ _____, which are derived from bone marrow and mature in the (43) _____ _____. The two types of adaptive immunity are (44) _____-_____ immunity, in which B cells differentiate into plasma cells that secrete (45) _____, and (46) _____-_____ immunity, in which a subclass of T cells become activated and, with other cells of the immune system, attach to foreign cells and destroy them. Some activated lymphocytes differentiate into (47) _____ cells that circulate and then initiate a rapid response upon re-exposure to the same (48) _____. B-cell receptors and (49) _____-_____ receptors bind to specific regions, or (50) _____, of an antigen molecule. Antibodies are a large class of proteins known as (51) _____. An individual protein of this class consists of four subunits: two identical (52) _____ _____, with one end embedded in the plasma membrane, and two identical (53) _____ _____. The protein has a(n) (54) _____ shape, with a(n) (55) _____-_____ site at the top end of each of the two arms.

Both types of adaptive immunity involve four basic steps. One or more lymphocytes must encounter, recognize, and then (56) _____ to an antigen. This interaction with the antigen causes the lymphocyte to become activated and undergo (57) _____ _____ to produce identical copies of itself, or (58) _____. These lymphocytes must then (59) _____ the host's body of all antigens. Lastly, some of the lymphocytes must differentiate into (60) _____ cells, which can provide a rapid response should this type of antigen appear in the body again. When exposed to a foreign antigen for the first time, a(n) (61) _____ immune response results, whereas when a foreign antigen enters the body for a second or subsequent time, a(n) (62) _____ immune response results. (63) _____ _____ is the production of antibodies in response to a foreign antigen, whereas (64) _____ _____ is the acquisition of antibodies by direct transfer from another individual.

Sequence

Identify the correct order of events during formation of helpter T cells in antibody-mediated immunity.
Note that number 1 is provided.

65. _____ CD4$^+$ T cell begins clonal expansion

66. _____ Lysosomes break down bacterial components

67. _____ CD4$^+$ T cell binds to antigen

68. _____ Infected cell is an antigen-presenting cell

69. _1_ Dendritic cell engulfs bacterium

70. _____ Clones differentiate into helper T cells

71. _____ CD4$^+$ T cell secretes cytokines

72. _____ Antigens bind to class II MHC

73. _____ CD4$^+$ T cell is activated

74. _____ APC secretes interleukin

Identify the correct order of events during B-cell activation in antibody-mediated immunity. Note that number 1 is provided.

75. _____ Helper T cell secretes interleukin

76. _____ B cell takes in bacterium and breaks it down

77. _____ B cell proliferates

78. _____ B cell activated

79. _____ Linkage between helper T cell and B cell

80. _____ Cloned B cells differentiate into plasma cells and memory cells

81. _____ Antigen binds to class II MHC

82. _1_ B cell binds to bacteria's antigen

83. _____ Plasma cells produce antibodies

84. _____ Antigen presented on cell surface (TCR and BCR for same antigen)

Choice

For each of the following descriptions, choose the most appropriate type of adaptive immunity from the list below.

A. Cell-mediated immunity   B. Antibody-mediated immunity

85. _____ Involves activation of T-cell derivatives, which then attach to foreign cells and kill them

86. _____ Involves production of specific proteins by B-cell derivatives that bind to foreign molecules

87. _____ Involves releasing perforin, which creates pores in membrane of infected cell

Short Answer

88. What is the major histocompatibility complex (MHC)?

_____

_____

89. Why is it important that B cells and cytotoxic T cells proliferate in antibody-mediated immunity and cell-mediated immunity, respectively?

_____

_____

Choice

For each of the following descriptions, choose the most appropriate type of response from the list below.

A.   Primary immune response   B.   Secondary immune response

90. _____   Response mounted by exposure to an antigen for the first time

91. _____   Response mounted by exposure to an antigen for a second or subsequent times

92. _____   Response occurs rapidly

93. _____   Production of a new type of memory B cell

For each of the following descriptions, choose the most appropriate type of immunity from the list below.

A.   Passive immunity   B.   Active immunity

94. _____   The production of antibodies in the body in response to exposure to a foreign antigen

95. _____   The acquisition of antibodies by direct transfer from another individual

96. _____   Blood transfusion between two individuals

97. _____   Resting in bed to recover from a virus

Complete the Table

Type of Cell	Function
B cell	98.
99.	Lymphocyte that differentiates from stem cells in bone marrow but matures in thymus gland
Plasma cell	100.
Memory cell	101.
Dendritic cell	102.
103.	Derived from activated CD4$^+$ cells and helps stimulate B cells
Helper T cell	104.
105.	A type of T cell that binds to an antigen-presenting cell via a CD8$^+$ receptor and leads to cell-mediated immunity
CD8$^+$ cytotoxic T cell	106.

Matching

Match each of the following structures with its correct definition.

107. ____	Thymus	A.	Organ of lymphatic system involved in maturation of T cells
108. ____	Antigen	B.	Protein that binds to antigens and marks them for elimination
109. ____	Antibodies	C.	Specific region of an antigen molecule
110. ____	Clonal expansion	D.	Family of proteins that serve as antibodies
111. ____	Clonal selection	E.	A cell that displays antigens on its surface
112. ____	Epitopes	F.	The proliferation of a particular clone of cells
113. ____	Immunoglobins	G.	The process by which a lymphocyte is specifically selected for cloning
114. ____	Antigen-presenting cell	H.	Ability to recognize previous antigens and foreign cells
115. ____	Immunological memory	I.	A foreign molecule that triggers an adaptive immunity response

43.4 Malfunctions and Failures of the Immune System [pp. 1097–1100]
43.5 Defences in Other Organisms [pp. 1101]
43.6 How Do Parasites and Pathogens Circumvent Host Responses? [pp. 1101–1103]

Section Review (Fill-in-the-Blanks)

(116) _____ _____ is a process in which a body's own molecules are protected from attack

by the immune system. Failure of this process can lead to a(n) (117) _____ _____ in

which (118) _____ antibodies are produced and they attack and eliminate specific body cells.

(119) _____ are a distinct class of antigen that initiate an allergic reaction. A severe reaction can

bring on (120) _____ _____, an inflammation that blocks airways and interferes with

breathing and that could lead to a quick death if a(n) (121) _____ injection is not administered.

Some pathogens are able to avoid elimination by using various techniques, such as hiding from a

host, infecting an area that has a(n) (122) _____ immune response, or manipulating a response. Some

pathogens can constantly change their surface coats, called (123) _____ _____. In certain

situations, a (124) _____ relationship between a pair of organisms, both benefiting from the association, allows them to infect a host and then feed and (125) _____ within the host, before leaving with their offspring to find a(n) (126) _____ host.

Invertebrates and plants do not have antibodies; they rely on their (127) _____ immune system to protect them from (128) _____.

Matching

Match each of the following with its correct definition.

129. _____	Allergen	A.	Protection of a body's own molecules from immune system attack
130. _____	Antigenic variation	B.	Production of antibodies against molecules of one's own body
131. _____	Immune tolerance	C.	Substance responsible for initiating an allergic reaction
132. _____	Anaphylactic shock	D.	Process that occurs in a host when first exposed to an allergen
133. _____	Autoimmune reaction	E.	Constant changing of the antigen's surface protein to evade a host
134. _____	Sensitization	F.	Extreme inflammatory response that can restrict air passages

SELF-TEST

1. How can an active immunity be artificially induced? [pp. 1079–1080]

   a. by transfusions
   b. by injecting vaccines
   c. by passing maternal antibodies to a fetus

2. Which of the following is a specific defence mechanism in vertebrates? [pp. 1086–1097]

   a. skin
   b. acid secretion
   c. inflammation
   d. phagocytosis by phagocytes
   e. antibody production

3. In terms of helping destroy pathogens, which of the following refers to complement? [pp. 1083–1085]

   a. It is a system of many proteins.
   b. It is an antibody.
   c. It is highly antigen specific.
   d. It is a system that assists in producing white blood cells.

4. What statement about natural killer (NK) cells is correct?[p. 1086]

   a. They secrete interleukin, which activates T cells.
   b. They are phagocytes.
   c. They are derived from plasma cells.
   d. They secrete perforins, which create pores in a cell membrane.
   e. They stimulate antibody production.

5. How does skin act as a defence? [p. 1080]

   a. It recognizes the molecular pattern on a pathogen and provides a response.
   b. It provides an inflammation response.
   c. It forms a physical barrier by connecting cells with tight junctions.
   d. It contains cells that have memory of the pathogen.

6. What part of the host organism recognizes the molecular pattern of a pathogen? [p. 1081]

   a. the pathogen-associated molecular pattern
   b. the pathogen effector molecule
   c. the PAMP
   d. the PRR

7. Why is defensin considered to be a highly conserved antimicrobial peptide? [pp. 1082–1083]

   a. because there is only one type of defensin
   b. because it is found only in mammals
   c. because it is found on all epithelial surfaces
   d. because it is found in a wide diversity of organisms, including invertebrates, plants, and vertebrates

8. Why are different mechanisms required to identify viral pathogens and bacterial pathogens? [pp. 1081–1082]

   a. because viruses are often found inside a host cell, hidden away from passing lymphocytes
   b. because there is little difference between viral-infected and normal cell surface molecules
   c. because cells become too large to be engulfed by the various leukocytes

9. During an inflammation response, a leukocyte is killed along with the pathogen, and pus forms at the infection site. Which leukocyte is killed? [pp. 1082–1083]

   a. the macrophage
   b. the neutrophil
   c. the eosinophil
   d. the cytokine

10. Which of the following cells are lymphocytes that target virus-infected hosts with low MHC protein concentrations? [p. 1086]

    a. macrophages
    b. eosinophils
    c. RNAi
    d. natural killer cells

11. What statement about the histocompatibility complex is correct? [p. 1091]

    a. It is found only in few cell nuclei.
    b. It is the same in each individual.
    c. It is derived from a large group of genes.

12. What statement about T cells is NOT correct? [pp. 1086–1097]

    a. They are lymphocytes.
    b. They are mature in the thymus gland.
    c. They are involved in adaptive immunity.
    d. They are neutrophils.

13. What statement is consistent with T-cell receptors? [pp. 1088–1089]

    a. They bind antigens.
    b. They have no known function.
    c. They are identical in all T cells.
    d. They stimulate antibody production.

14. Which site of the antibody determines the immunoglobulin it belongs to? [pp. 1089–1090]

    a. the conservative site
    b. the variable site
    c. the invariable site
    d. the recognition site

15. What causes the secondary immune response?[pp. 1094–1095]

    a. killer T cells
    b. memory cells
    c. plasma cells
    d. macrophages
    e. helper T cells

16. When does agglutination occur?
[pp. 1088–1095]

   a. when an antigen attaches to one of the arms of an antibody

   b. when each antigen binds to more than one antibody, forming a lattice

   c. when an antibody reproduces

   d. when an antigen is taken up by an antibody by phagocytosis

17. What method does the AIDS virus use to circumvent a host cell response?
[pp. 1099–1100]

   a. It interacts with a symbiont to enter the host cell.

   b. It implements antigenic variation.

   c. It induces the expression of inhibitors of apoptosis (IAPs).

18. What is the cause of watery eyes and runny nose resulting from an allergic reaction? [pp. 1098–1100]

   a. signals sent out by mast cells

   b. lack of histamine production

   c. production of IgM

   d. interaction with histocompatibility complex

19. When a nematode and bacteria work together to infect a host, what do the bacteria do to assist in the infection? [pp. 1101–1103]

   a. penetrate the host

   b. reproduce and inactivate the host's immune response

   c. encapsulate the host cells

   d. change physiology within the nematode to encapsulate the host cells

INTEGRATING AND APPLYING KEY CONCEPTS

1. Describe what happens during an inflammation response.

2. What is the function of cytotoxic T cells in adaptive immunity?

3. What occurs at the cellular level during an allergic reaction?

44 Population Ecology

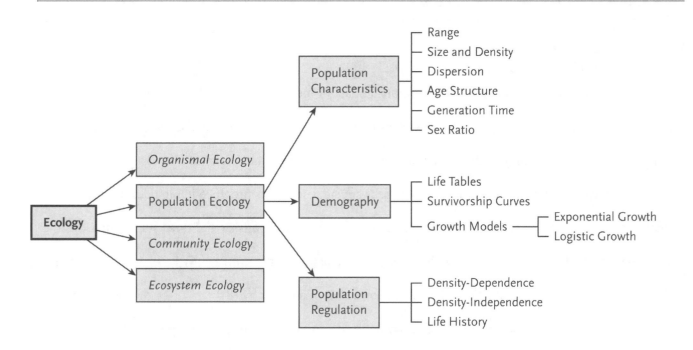

LEARNING OUTCOMES AND STUDY STRATEGIES

By the end of this chapter, you should be able to

- Explain how population characteristics affect population growth and size

- Use exponential and logistic growth curves to predict changes in population size

- Describe how population size and growth are regulated by density-dependent and density-independent factors

- Relate your knowledge of population ecology to human populations

Study strategies for this chapter:

- Review the hierarchy of biological investigation. This chapter concentrates on populations, but in upcoming chapters, you will need to know how populations relate to individuals, communities, ecosystems, and the biosphere. You will also need to know that each level of the hierarchy exhibits unique characteristics (emergent properties).

- Review the population concept, noting that interactions among members of a population are intraspecific.

- Be clear on the factors that regulate population growth and final population size.

- Keep in mind that many of the concepts presented in this chapter are presented in a somewhat simplified way to make them easy to understand. In reality, many factors interact with one another, sometimes producing unexpected results.

- Make a table showing the mechanisms that control population size in most organisms and how humans have circumvented those mechanisms.

INTERACTIVE EXERCISES

Why It Matters [pp. 1106–1107]
Section Review (Fill-in-the-Blanks)

Ecology provides an understanding of what controls the rate of increase and spread of a population. This applies to bacteria and (1) _____, as well as plants and animals, and hence has important applications in (2) _____, the study of the spread of disease. An example is the spread of a(n) (3) _____, or rabies, that has specific characteristics promoting its spread, such as its presence in high densities in an animal's (4) _____. The rabies eradication program in Ontario consisted of three stages: first was the development of the (5) _____; second was the vaccination of the primary (6) _____ of the rabies, (7) _____; and the third was the measurement of success by (8) _____ how many foxes were vaccinated. This successful rabies control program was designed to control population (9) _____ and spread using many different disciplines in biology, including population biology, (10) _____, immunology, and epidemiology, among others.

44.1 The Science of Ecology [pp. 1107–1108]
Section Review (Fill-in-the-Blanks)

Ecology can be studied on a number of hierarchical levels. (11) _____ ecology is the study of the various adaptations of individual organisms to the environment. The other levels include (12) _____ ecology, the study of groups of organisms of the same species living and interacting together; (13) _____ ecology, which focuses on sympatric populations of different species and their interactions; and (14) _____ ecology, the study of nutrient cycles and energy flow in the biotic and abiotic environments of the community. Ecologists can address questions at the various hierarchical levels using hypothetical (15) _____ that provide simulations of natural ecosystems but that should be followed up with exploratory (16) _____ work and controlled (17) _____ studies to test predictions generated by their hypotheses.

44.2 Population Characteristics [pp. 1108–1112]

Section Review (Fill-in-the-Blanks)

Populations have characteristics that make them unique, and population ecology focuses on those

characteristics. A fundamental characteristic is where you find the organisms, or the populations' geographic

(18) _____. More specifically, the biotic and abiotic features of a population's environment is its

(19) _____. Within a habitat, the population size is simply the number of individuals at any given

time, but when this is divided by the volume or area of the habitat, it is the population (20) _____.

Estimating population size is often difficult, and indirect methods are used, such as (21) _____–

_____–_____, which allows the calculation of population size using a simple ratio equation.

   Predicting population growth or decline requires estimates of other population characteristics that

relate to their potential for producing young. For example, an age structure that has many (22) _____

individuals is likely to grow in the near future as they age and reproduce, while populations with a majority of

(23) _____ individuals are likely to decline. Additionally, species with short delays between birth

and reproduction have short (24) _____ times and are capable of rapid population growth. Finally,

populations with few females and many males will have limited growth potential; thus, the

(25) _____ _____ of a population is of interest to population ecologists.

Complete the Table

Identify the most probable dispersal pattern for each described population.

Description of Population	Probable Dispersion Pattern
Redwing blackbirds, which defend areas of roughly equal size against entry by others	26.
Dandelions, a hardy species that develop from windblown seeds	27.
Herring off the west coast of Canada, which are found in large schools of tens of thousands of individuals	28.
Crickets, which have very specific habitat requirements and communicate effectively	29.
Marine blue mussels on the coast of Nova Scotia, which settle onto the ocean bottom after about a month of passive floating in the currents	30.

44.3 Demography [pp. 1112–1114]

Section Review (Fill-in-the-Blanks)

The movement of individuals into a preexisting population is called (31) _____, and the movement of individuals out of a population is referred to as (32) _____. Both types of movement can change a population's size and density. The process that drives changes in population size and density is a population's (33) _____, which can be summarized in a life table. A life table follows the lives of a single group of individuals of similar age, known as a(n) (34) _____, and tabulates age-specific death rates, referred to as (35) _____, and (36) _____. Of course, population size and density also depend on the number of offspring produced and when they are produced; thus, life tables also typically give age-specific (37) _____, the average number of offspring produced by females of a given age.

Calculations

Fill in the blanks in the following partial life table and then, using the information in the table, answer the question below.

Age Interval (Years)	Number Alive at the Start of the Interval	Number Dying during Interval	Age-Specific Mortality Rate	Age-Specific Survivorship Rate
0–2	1000	800	(38) _____	(39) _____
2–4	(40) _____	140	0.700	0.300
4–6	60	40	0.667	0.333
6–8	20	(41) _____	0.55	0.45
8–10	9	(42) _____	(43) _____	(44) _____
10–12	0	—	—	—

45. What type of survivorship curve does this population most closely resemble? Explain your answer.

   _____

   _____

Matching

Match each of the following populations with the survivorship curve below that best describes it.

46. _____ Humans. Infant survivorship is relatively high, and individuals surviving past their first 6 months typically survive for many years until mortality increases sharply in old individuals.

47. _____ Starfishes. A species with few predators whose numerous larvae are highly vulnerable and early mortality is high. Those that survive and metamorphose into adults typically live for a long time.

48. _____ *Hydra*. A small, stationary freshwater organism often eaten by larger organisms. The chances of being preyed upon are fairly constant throughout their life span.

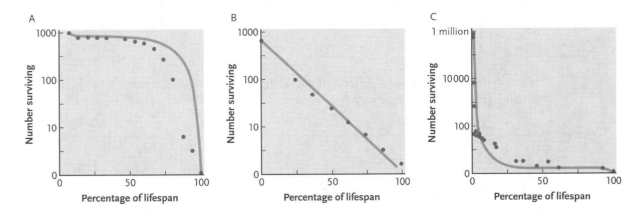

44.4 The Evolution of Life Histories [pp. 1114–1117]

Section Review (Fill-in-the-Blanks)

A life history is the lifetime pattern of an organism's (49) _____, or development; its

(50) _____, which occurs when it reaches reproductive age; and its (51) _____, or its ability

to produce offspring. An organism's life history is constrained by the total energy accumulated (referred to as

its (52) _____ _____), so organisms must make (53) _____ between the

components of their life history. The energetically expensive functions of most organisms can be placed into

three categories: the energy required for basic functioning, or (54) _____; the energy required to

increase body size, or (55) _____; and the energy needed to produce offspring through

(56) _____. There is a wide diversity in how species allocate their energy among these categories,

especially for reproduction: energy invested in young before birth or hatching is referred to as

(57) _____ parental care, while energy spent after birth or hatching to raise offspring is referred to as

(58) _____ parental care.

True/False

Mark if the statement is true (T) or false (F). If the statement is false, make it correct by changing the underlined word(s) and writing the correct word(s) in the lines below each statement.

59. _____ Generally, species that produce large numbers of relatively small offspring exhibit <u>active</u> parental care.

_____

_____

60. _____ In many organisms that get older and larger, their fecundity <u>increases</u>, and they may delay reproduction.

_____

_____

61. _____ If an organism has a low likelihood of surviving past reproduction (such as coho salmon), it will <u>likely reproduce many times</u>.

_____

_____

62. _____ <u>High</u> levels of predation may select for early reproduction.

_____

_____

63. _____ <u>Natural selection</u> probably impacts most species' life history strategies.

_____

_____

Choice

For each of the following population characteristics, choose the more likely time of reproduction.

64. _____ High survivorship among adults   A.   Early reproduction

65. _____ Long life span   B.   Delayed reproduction

66. _____ Low fecundity of larger individuals

67. _____ Size of individuals increases with age

44.5 Models of Population Growth [pp. 1117–1122]

Section Review (Fill-in-the-Blanks)

The (68) _____ _____ _____ _____, or "r," is an important component

of the two common models of population growth. The (69) _____ model of population growth results

in a population growing at an unrestricted and increasing rate over time. Under perfect conditions, r attains its

highest possible value and is referred to as r_{max}, or the population's (70) _____ _____

_____ _____. In the (71) _____ model of population growth, r becomes smaller as

the population approaches its (72) _____ _____, or "K," the number of individuals that the

environment can sustain indefinitely. This model takes into account the effect of (73) _____

competition, the competition for a limited resource by two or more members of the same species. One of the

flaws of this model is that it assumes that fecundity and survivorship respond immediately to changes in

population density. In reality, there is a delay or (74) _____ _____ involved.

Matching

Match the correct change to a population associated with the description of the identified model.

75. _____ N is small (logistic model)   A.   Population size will decrease

76. _____ $B = D$ (exponential model)   B.   Population size will remain constant

77. _____ $N > K$ (logistic model)   C.   Population size will increase exponentially

78. _____ $r > 0$ (exponential model)   D.   Population will go extinct

79. _____ $B = 0$ (exponential model)   E. r will approach r_{max}

True/False

Mark if the statement is true (T) or false (F). If the statement is false, make it correct by changing the underlined word(s) and writing the correct word(s) in the lines below each statement.

80. _____ In the logistic model of population growth, when $dN/dt = 0$, the population has gone extinct.

_____

_____

81. _____ Populations cannot exhibit exponential growth indefinitely.

_____

_____

82. _____ The logistic model of population growth predicts that r <u>decreases</u> with population size.

_____

_____

83. _____ The logistic model of population growth accounts for increasing <u>interspecific</u> competition as population size increases.

_____

_____

44.6 Population Regulation [pp. 1122–1127]

Section Review (Fill-in-the-Blanks)

As population density increases, it becomes easier for parasites to spread from host to host. This is an example

of a density- (84) _____ effect on population size. Natural disasters, on the other hand, kill a fixed

percentage of a population regardless of density. This is an example of a density- (85) _____ effect.

The type of population growth a species exhibits is often correlated with other life history strategies.

Species that show exponential growth when conditions are favourable are said to be (86) _____.

Species exhibiting logistic growth and utilizing density-dependent mechanisms to maintain population size

near carrying capacity are referred to as (87) _____; however, that distinction is relative, so it can be

difficult to unambiguously categorize a population. The difference between (88) _____ (internal) and

(89) _____ (external) control of population size is that the first depends primarily on changes in the

population or organisms, while the latter depends primarily on changes in the environment (including other

species). Furthermore, repeated population size increases followed by decreases, or (90) _____, may

be the result of (91) _____ _____ in the response of the population to changes in complex

interactions between the species and their environment.

Choice

For each of the following population characteristics, choose the most likely life history pattern.

92. _____   Small body size   A.   *r*-selected

93. _____   long life span   B.   *K*-selected

94. _____   Type III survivorship curve

95. _____   Repeated and frequent reproductive events in an individual's lifetime

96. _____   Substantial active parental care of offspring

True/False

Mark if the statement is true (T) or false (F). If the statement is false, make it correct by changing the underlined word(s) and writing the correct word(s) in the lines below each statement.

97. _____   Density-dependent factors will result in <u>decreased</u> body size as population density increases.

_____

_____

98. _____   Density-dependent factors will <u>increase</u> the probability of survival as population density increases.

_____

_____

99. _____   Density-independent factors will <u>reduce</u> reproductive success when population density is very low.

_____

_____

100. _____   Density-independent factors will <u>result in higher</u> predation mortality when prey population density is high.

_____

_____

44.7 Human Population Growth [pp. 1127–1131]
44.8 Sisyphean Problems in Population Biology [p. 1133]

Section Review (Fill-in-the-Blanks)

Over the last 200 years, human population growth has been (101) _____. Humans have avoided

limits to population growth in three ways: (i) humans have expanded their (102) _____

_____ and colonized virtually all terrestrial (103) _____, (ii) the shift from hunting and gathering has increased the (104) _____ _____ (_____) of human habitats, and (iii) modern medicine and improved hygiene have served to reduce the (105) _____ rate. The economic status of a country can have dramatic impacts on life history factors that drive population growth. A (106) _____ _____ model depicts the expected impact of preindustrial through postindustrial development on birth and death rates, ultimately determining expected population growth rates. Many countries with large and growing populations are attempting to control population growth through (107) _____ _____, although in some countries that is culturally unacceptable and even unlawful. Human populations of all sizes experience (108) _____ problems, often involving the regulation of a pest population. The pest species population size (109) _____, lowering when control measures are implemented and increasing when the controls are relaxed.

True/False

Mark if the statement is true (T) or false (F). If the statement is false, make it correct by changing the underlined word(s) and writing the correct word(s) in the lines below each statement.

110. _____ The preindustrial stage is characterized by <u>low</u> death rates and high birth rates.

_____

_____

111. _____ The postindustrial stage is characterized by birth rates <u>lower</u> than death rates and population decline.

_____

_____

112. _____ Women delaying having their first child will <u>increase</u> population growth.

_____

_____

113. _____ Mexico will have faster population growth than Canada because it has <u>fewer</u> prereproductive individuals.

_____

_____

114. _____ Bedbugs in North America are an example of a <u>Sisyphean</u> problem.

_____

_____

Matching

Match each description to the correct age structure pyramid in the figure below.

115. ____   A.   Many young males and females soon to reproduce: "population bomb"

116. ____   B.   Many older males and females: declining population numbers

117. ____   C.   Equal numbers of reproductive and prereproductive people: zero growth

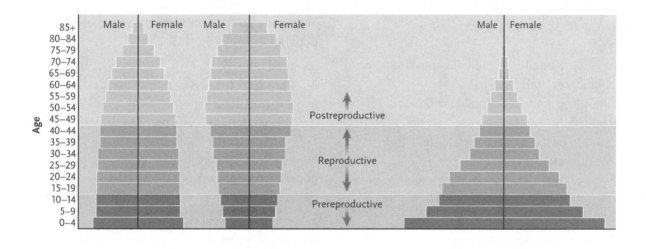

SELF-TEST

1. Which of the following is NOT a branch of the science of ecology? [p. 1108]

    a. abiotic ecology
    b. community ecology
    c. organismal ecology
    d. population ecology

2. Which dispersion pattern best describes the distribution of humans in Canada? [pp. 1109–1111]

    a. clumped
    b. even
    c. random
    d. uniform

3. Which term refers to the statistical study of the factors that affect population size and density? [p. 1112]

    a. biogeography
    b. demography
    c. organismal ecology
    d. logistics

4. Which pair of terms represents a tradeoff in life history strategies? [pp. 1115–1116]

    a. high fecundity — intense parental care
    b. geographic range — habitat
    c. intraspecific competition — population density
    d. long life span — metabolic rate

5. Why is the incidence of reproductive individuals particularly important for rare or endangered species? [p. 1112]

    a. because these species have a higher death rate

    b. because these species are more likely to emigrate

    c. because these species have the opportunity for rapid population growth

    d. because these species tend to be older individuals

6. Why is sex ratio a population characteristic that can affect population growth? [p. 1112]

    a. because a 50:50 sex ratio maximizes survivorship

    b. because low numbers of females can limit population growth

    c. because low numbers of males will block reproduction

    d. because high numbers of females lead to male emigration

7. What does the exponential model of population growth assume? [pp. 1118–1119]

    a. that birth rate is equal to death rate

    b. that density-dependent factors are involved

    c. that there are ideal conditions with no limits to growth

    d. that species are k-selected

8. Which of the following is a key component of the logistic model of population growth? [pp. 1120–1122]

    a. species range

    b. body size

    c. density-independent factors

    d. carrying capacity

9. Which of the following is NOT a density-dependent factor affecting population size? [pp. 1122–1124]

    a. crowding

    b. intraspecific competition

    c. nighttime air temperature

    d. spread of disease

10. What is the primary means by which the rabies virus extends its range? [pp. 1106–1107]

    a. by density-independent factors

    b. by transmission through biting

    c. by altering its dispersion pattern

    d. by insect carriers

11. What is the primary factor that determines a species' geographic range boundary? [p. 1108]

    a. K-selection

    b. the logistic growth curve

    c. birth rates versus death rates

    d. the availability of suitable habitat

12. What may be the cause of extrinsic cycles in population size? [pp. 1126]

    a. predation

    b. hormonal suppression of maturity

    c. large habitat size

    d. temperature tolerance

13. How many years did it take for the total human population to grow from 5 billion to 6 billion? [pp. 1127–1128]

    a. 1.5 million years

    b. 40 000 years

    c. 500 years

    d. 12 years

14. Which population characteristic would be most important in determining whether a community should spend money on schools or on nursing homes? [pp. 1128–1129]

    a. age structure

    b. carrying capacity

    c. population density

    d. sex ratio

15. If a population decreases from 500 individuals to 300 during the first year of life, what are the age 0–1 specific mortality and survivorship rates, respectively? [p. 1113]

    a. 0.530 and 0.470

    b. 0.600 and 0.400

    c. 0.375 and 0.625

    d. 0.400 and 0.600

16. If a population of salmon with fecundity that increases with age and body size experiences a change in the predation rate such that the salmon have a much higher survivorship late in life, what should happen to the age of first reproduction? [p. 1116]

   a. It will not change.
   b. It will increase.
   c. It will decrease.

17. What of the following will NOT result in differences in life history patterns among populations of a single species? [pp. 1115–1116]

   a. habitat differences
   b. natural selection
   c. change in the intrinsic rate of increase
   d. different predators

18. In the logistic model of population growth, what is expected to happen when $K > N$? [pp. 1120–1122]

   a. The population will decline.
   b. The population will continue to grow.
   c. The population will be eliminated.
   d. The population will expand its geographic range.

19. Which of the following is a likely population response to overcrowding? [pp. 1122–1123]

   a. increased mortality rate
   b. increased individual condition
   c. decreased emigration
   d. increased survival rates

20. What is juvenile survival expected to be in r-selected populations? [p. 1125]

   a. higher than in K-selected populations
   b. about the same as in K-selected populations
   c. lower than in K-selected populations

INTEGRATING AND APPLYING KEY CONCEPTS

1. Compare the impact of commercial fishing pressure on fish populations to the effect of pike cichlid predators on guppy populations in Trinidad. Explain similarities or differences you would expect. Would you expect similar impacts from the effect of pollutants on fish?

2. Some of the countries in the world with the worst overcrowding exhibit the fastest population growth, yet we know from our study of density-dependent factors that overcrowded populations usually suffer higher death rates and lower birth rates. Why are human populations not following that "rule"?

3. The Ontario rabies eradication program included three phases for ultimately eliminating rabies in southern Ontario, but despite success, rabies still persists at low levels. Using your knowledge of density-dependent factors that act on the rabies virus, explain why it would be very difficult to eradicate (eliminate) rabies from southern Ontario.

45 Population Interactions and Community Ecology

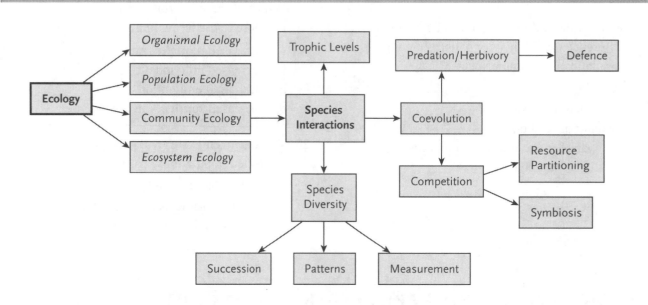

By the end of this chapter, you should be able to

- Explain how coevolution can ultimately shape species interactions in ecological communities
- Describe the various forms of species interactions that contribute to community characteristics
- List and provide examples of the types of defences that animals and plants use to avoid becoming prey
- Define, calculate, and interpret indices of species diversity and evenness
- Predict how competition may affect species diversity
- Explain trophic interactions and draw a simple food web
- Describe how the succession process determines the climax community
- Explain how the island theory of biogeography predicts species diversity in a variety of communities

Study strategies for this chapter:

- Since the emphasis of this chapter is on interactions among species and the effect of those interactions on populations and communities, be sure to become familiar with the various types of interactions as they may be confusing and then try describing the types of interactions in your own words.

- Next, review the variety of predation/herbivory defences that have evolved, noting which apply to plants and which to animals.

- Review interspecific competition in terms of mechanisms that maximize the likelihood of "winning" versus those that minimize competition.

- To become familiar with measurements of diversity, make up a data set of species numbers in a simple community (say five or six species), calculate Shannon indices of diversity (H') and evenness (E_H), and then change the numbers in the way you think will increase and/or decrease diversity. Did diversity change as you expected when you recalculated H'? Try this with E_H as well.

- After listing the various factors that are thought to affect climax community composition, think of examples where each factor may be in play.

INTERACTIVE EXERCISES

Why It Matters [pp. 1136–1137]

Section Review (Fill-in-the-Blanks)

The natural variation in the species composition and abundance in various ecosystems is apparent to even the

casual observer; however, the study of (1) _____ _____ seeks to explain differences and

patterns in species diversity and abundance. For example, the diet of tropical caterpillars is more

(2) _____ than the species found in temperate forests. This difference is thought to allow narrower

ecological (3) _____ for the caterpillars in the tropical forest and thus more "room" for species of

butterflies. One of the basic approaches in community ecology is to explain differences in ecological

community diversity through detailed study of species (4) _____.

45.1 Interspecific Interactions [pp. 1137–1138]

Section Review (Fill-in-the-Blanks)

Often species interactions affect one or more of the species involved positively or negatively. If a particular

interaction affects survival or reproduction in one of the species, then we expect (5) _____ through

natural selection. However, if two (or more) species are involved, both interacting species will experience

natural selection, thus potentially driving (6) _____, or genetically based reciprocal adaptation. A

simple example is predator–prey adaptation where, for example, the increased speed of the antelope prey forces the cheetah to adapt by evolving (7) _____ chasing speeds to survive. In reality, this

interaction is much more complex since the predators (cheetahs) pursue multiple potential (8) _____

and the prey (antelopes) have many potential (9) _____.

45.2 Getting Food [pp. 1138–1139]

Section Review (Fill-in-the-Blanks)

The process of gaining nutrients by consuming other organisms is herbivory if eating (10) _____ and

predation if eating (11) _____. Predators and herbivores have evolved effective mechanisms to locate

and feed upon their prey; for example, rattlesnakes use (12) _____ _____ found in pits on

their heads to detect warm bodies, while (13) _____ use chemical sensors on their legs to find food.

Predators also differ in the range of food they can tolerate; those with a broad range are (14) _____,

while those with specific needs are specialists. The choice of a predator's (or herbivore's) food is based on

maximizing the (15) _____ relative to the (16) _____, a ratio identified by the

(17) _____ _____ theory.

True/False

Mark if the statement is true (T) or false (F). If the statement is false, make it correct by changing the
underlined word(s) and writing the correct word(s) in the lines below each statment.

18. _____ Fish that feed on only one species of coral in tropical coral reef ecosystems are <u>generalist</u>
feeders.

_____

_____

19. _____ Optimal foraging theory predicts that predators choose prey that provide the <u>most</u> energy
for the least effort and risk.

_____

_____

20. _____ If the encounter rate for a specific type of prey is <u>low</u>, the predator will often concentrate
on that prey.

_____

_____

21. _____ Omnivores are very good examples of generalist feeders.

_____

_____

45.3 Defence [pp. 1139–1143]

Section Review (Fill-in-the-Blanks)

Most species are prey to another species, so prey species develop elaborate mechanisms of

(22) _____ to avoid being eaten. Some of these mechanisms are simple, such as having a

(23) _____ body size, which may make the prey not worth capturing, or (24) _____ body

size, which may make the prey difficult to capture and kill. Some prey defend against predators through

physiological and behavioural specializations, such as (25) _____ predators prior to attack and

preparing themselves (or running away), or through cryptic or (26) _____ colouration or behaviour to

hide from a predator. Alternatively, prey species can avoid attack through more aggressive means such as

defensive (27) _____ (as on a porcupine or some plants) or through (28) _____ defence

(e.g., a skunk or a rattlesnake). When an animal uses a chemical defence, it may advertise a warning through

bright colours or distinctive patterns; such species are referred to as (29) _____. However, this

elegant adaptation is used by other species that (30) _____ the well-defended species.

(31) _____ _____ is when a harmless species looks similar to the poisonous species, while

(32) _____ _____ is when two poisonous species resemble each other to increase the

likelihood that they will be recognized by predators.

Matching

Match the prey species on the left to the type of defence it would use on the right.

33. ____	Arrowhead frog	A.	Predator detection
34. ____	Leopard tortoise	B.	Chemical defence
35. ____	Meerkats	C.	Large size
36. ____	Cowhorn euphorb	D.	Armour defence
37. ____	Elephants	E.	Active defence (spines/thorns)

Choice

For most forms of prey defence, predators have developed mechanisms to overcome the defence. For each prey defence listed below, choose the best potential adaptation for the predator to overcome the defence. Choices may be used more than once.

38. ____   Evasive action   A.   Detect prey by characteristic smell

39. ____   Camouflage   B.   Capture prey by stealth or speed

40. ____   Vigilance   C.   Evolve resistance

41. ____   Poisonous   D.   Avoid defensive action

42. ____   Noxious chemical spray

45.4 Competition [pp. 1143–1151]

Section Review (Fill-in-the-Blanks)

Two or more individuals of competing species for the same limited resource are interacting by

(43) _____ competition. This phenomenon takes two forms: (44) _____ competition, in

which individuals interact directly and attempt to harm members of the other species; and (45) _____

competition, where use of the resource by one species reduces its availability to the other. The experiments of

G.F. Gause indicated that when two species are competing for the same limited resource in the same way, the

more efficient species eliminates the other from the system. Based on these results, he proposed the more

general (46) _____ _____ principle. Resource utilization and the environmental conditions

an organism requires are major components of an organism's ecological (47) _____. The fact that

two or more species use the same resource does not necessarily imply that competition is occurring since

(48) _____ _____ can minimize interspecific competition. Often closely related species

living in the same area will specialize on different resources and evolve structures to help them exploit the

specific resource, a phenomenon known as (49) _____ _____.

There are three main forms of symbiosis: (50) _____, where both species benefit from an

interaction; (51) _____, where one species benefits and the other is unaffected; and

(52) _____, where one species benefits and the other is harmed by the association. True parasites

usually do not kill their hosts. Since (53) _____ are animals that lay eggs within the larvae of host

insects, eventually consuming and killing their host, they lie somewhere between a parasite and a predator.

Choice

For the species interactions listed, choose the correct pair of effects for the two species involved. Answers may be used more than once.

54. _____ Commensalism

55. _____ Competition

56. _____ Herbivory

57. _____ Mutualism

58. _____ Parasitism

59. _____ Predation

A. Species A benefits; species B is harmed

B. Species A benefits; species B is unaffected

C. Both species benefit

D. Both species are harmed

45.5 The Nature of Ecological Communities [pp. 1151–1152]

Section Review (Fill-in-the-Blanks)

When studying food webs, a community is classified as being (60) _____ since one species is eating

another. This differs from the (61) _____ _____ interactions in a community. Work on both

plant–herbivore networks and pollinator networks has determined that structure of ecological interactions to

promote stability in these two networks (62) _____. Community stability was promoted by

pollination networks in which the components of the network were highly (63) _____ and nested,

whereas herbivore networks that showed compartmentalization and (64) _____ connections provided

a stable community. The transition zone between adjacent communities is a(n) (65) _____ and is

often characterized by elevated levels of species (66) _____.

True/False

Mark if the statement is true (T) or false (F). If the statement is false, make it correct by changing the underlined word(s) and writing the correct word(s) in the lines below each statement.

67. _____ Ecotones are <u>broad</u> when there is an abrupt change in critical resources.

_____

_____

68. _____ Ecotones generally have <u>high</u> species diversity because they include species from both bordering communities and species adapted to intermediate conditions.

_____

_____

69. _____ Studies by Elisa Thebault and Colin Fontaine indicate that the <u>interactive</u> hypothesis best describes species distribution within studied communities.

_____

_____

70. _____ Consumption in a community is associated with <u>mutually beneficial</u> interactions.

_____

_____

45.6 Community Characteristics [pp. 1152–1157]

Section Review (Fill-in-the-Blanks)

The number of species found in a community comprises that community's species (71) _____. The

relative commonness or rarity of a species in a community is its species (72) _____. Combining these

two community characteristics allows ecologists to objectively quantify the species (73) _____ of a

community.

All ecological communities have (74) _____ structure that includes all plant–herbivore,

prey–predator, and host– (75) _____ interactions. At the base of this hierarchy are photosynthetic

organisms or (76) _____ producers, which are photoautotrophs. Animals and other non-

photosynthesizing consumers are (77) _____. Herbivores occupy the second level and are called

(78) _____ consumers. Secondary consumers are carnivores that feed on the herbivores and occupy

the (79) _____ level in the trophic structure. Carnivores on the fourth level are called tertiary

consumers, and so on. Animals that feed on organisms from the first and higher trophic levels are called

(80) _____. Organisms that extract energy from dead animals or organic matter are called

(81) _____, while decomposers are smaller organisms such as (82) _____ and fungi.

The trophic structure of a community is often depicted in the form of a(n) (83) _____

_____, a simple, linear diagram. But a more realistic depiction is the (84) _____

_____ since it allows for organisms to feed on different foods and from different trophic levels.

Species diversity, (85) _____ complexity, and community (86) _____ are interlinked, such

that more links in the food web will increase community stability.

Complete the Table

In the table below, column 2 shows the species distribution for a simple community (Community 1). By performing the calculations and filling in the blanks, you will calculate Shannon's index of diversity (H'). First, calculate p_i (the proportion of each species to the total number of individuals) in the third column. Next, calculate the term $p_i(\ln(p_i))$ in column 4 using data from column 3. Calculate the sum of column 4 for the total.

Community 1	Number of Individuals	p_i	$p_i(\ln(p_i))$
Species A	6	(87) _____	(88) _____
Species B	10	0.22	−0.33
Species C	3	0.07	−0.18
Species D	1	(89) _____	−0.08
Species E	25	0.56	(90) _____
TOTALS	**45**	**1.00**	(91) _____

92. What is the Shannon's index of species diversity (H') for this community? Is this community more or less diverse than a community with $H' = 0.50$?

_____

_____

Choose

Using the information in the diagram below, provide the correct organism(s) for each of the terms.

93. _____ Autotroph   A.   Crabeater seal

94. _____ Carnivore   B.   Emperor penguin

95. _____ Herbivore   C.   Orca

96. _____ Primary consumer   D.   Phytoplankton

97. _____ Primary producer   E.   Zooplankton

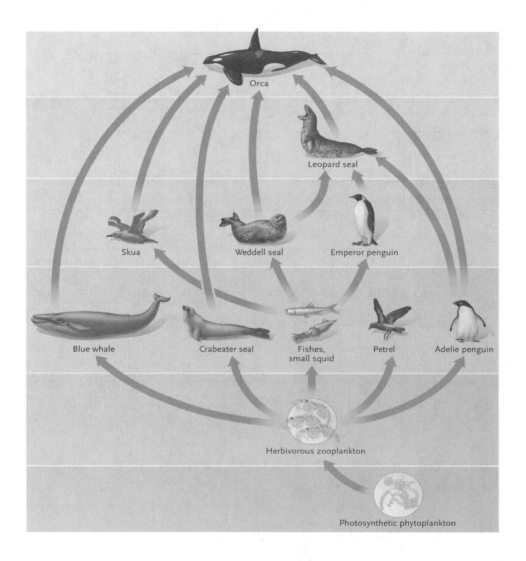

45.7 Effects of Population Interactions on Community Structure [p. 1158]

Section Review (Fill-in-the-Blanks)

Interspecific competition can limit species diversity since the inferior competitor may go locally

(98) _____, or competition may exclude new species from becoming established. Experiments

designed to test the effect of adding or removing species from a community have resulted in complex outcomes that are not completely understood by ecologists. However, in surveys of published competitive interactions, researchers have estimated that more than (99) _____ – _____ % of the species in ecological communities are sensitive to changes in competition. There is variation among species on the impact of competition, since ecologists working with plant or (100) _____ vertebrate species both conclude that competition is a critical factor in community structure, while insect ecologists working with (101) _____ species argue that competition is not a major factor. Interestingly, predators can act to (102) _____ species richness, as is the case for the marine mussel predator the sea star (*Pisaster*). When *Pisaster* is excluded, the marine mussel (*Mytilis*) dominates the near-shore community and species (103) _____ declines. Because of the wide range of ecological roles *Pisaster* plays in the marine near-shore community, it has been identified as a(n) (104) _____ species.

Matching

Match the appropriate type of interaction observed within a community to each of the listed species.

105. ____	*K*-selected species	A.	Relatively few competitive interactions
106. ____	Keystone species	B.	A dominant competitor
107. ____	*r*-selected species	C.	Many strong competitive interactions
108. ____	*Mytilis* mussel	D.	Larger impact on community than expected based on numbers

45.8 Effects of Disturbance on Community Characteristics [pp. 1158–1161]

Section Review (Fill-in-the-Blanks)

Recent work generally supports the individualistic view of community structure, where the species composition is not at (109) _____, because physical (110) _____ such as storms, floods, fires, etc., often eliminate some species, while making way for new ones. Based on analyses of long-term monitoring of coral reef communities, Joseph Connell hypothesized that communities that are subject to disturbances of moderate frequency and intensity show greater species diversity than those that are severely disturbed and/or with great frequency or those that are rarely disturbed. The (111) _____ _____ hypothesis predicts that communities experiencing moderate levels of disturbance will include both (112) _____ species that colonize the disturbed areas and (113) _____ species that remain in the undisturbed areas. Communities that have high species (114) _____ were proposed to be more stable over time, which is supported by a study of (115) _____ plots recovering from fire.

True/False

Mark if the statement is true (T) or false (F). If the statement is false, make it correct by changing the underlined word(s) and writing the correct word(s) in the lines below each statement.

116. _____ Frequent and very large storms can foster <u>very high</u> species diversity in coral reef communities.

_____

_____

117. _____ <u>Physical</u> disturbances include storms, fires, floods, avalanches, and earthquakes.

_____

_____

118. _____ <u>High</u> species diversity buffers change in future species composition.

_____

_____

119. _____ Recruitment is the growth and survival of <u>new individuals</u> arising from larvae that have settled in coral reefs.

_____

_____

120. _____ Oceanographic models are <u>not useful</u> for predicting the impact of disturbances on marine communities.

_____

_____

45.9 Succession [pp. 1161–1166]

Section Review (Fill-in-the-Blanks)

When a community is disturbed, it does not immediately return to its equilibrium state but rather goes through a sequence of changes known as (121) _____. If an area has never supported a community before, for example, a volcanic island, the sequence of changes is referred to as (122) _____ _____.

The final, relatively stable community in the sequence is the (123) _____ _____. Secondary succession is the (124) _____ of a community after it has been disturbed. The process of ecosystem development is not restricted to terrestrial communities. If the process occurs in a water body, such as a lake ecosystem, it is referred to as (125) _____ _____.

        Several hypotheses have been proposed to explain the mechanisms of ecological succession. The (126) _____ hypothesis states that earlier species alter conditions in ways that make it easier for later species to get established. The (127) _____ hypothesis is based on the notion that earlier communities resist colonization by new species, but disturbances and life span of species ultimately lead to changes in community structure. The (128) _____ hypothesis states that new species colonize according to their superior competitive ability and that the earlier species neither facilitate nor inhibit new species colonization. The three models are not mutually exclusive, and all three may play a role in succession. Sometimes biotic or abiotic disturbance disrupts succession from proceeding to a true climax community; the resulting community is a(n) (129) _____ community.

Choice

For each statement, choose the appropriate term from those listed below. Answers may be used more than once.

A.   Not predictable

B.   *K*-selected species

C.   Dispersal

D.   Primary succession

E.   Disturbance

130. The development of a new rocky habitat that alters the environment to allow subsequent colonizers is _____.

131. The final equilibrium community usually includes many _____.

132. A climax community includes both established and newly colonized species due to new, open habitat created by _____.

133. According to the inhibition hypothesis, the order of species colonization during succession is _____.

134. High species richness may be a result of succession coupled with moderate _____.

45.10 Variance in Species Richness among Communities [pp. 1167–1171]

Section Review (Fill-in-the-Blanks)

Community ecologists try to identify patterns in the variation in species richness among communities. Two large-scale patterns that have been documented are (135) _____ _____, which reflect community differences from the tropics to the polar regions, and (136) _____ _____, which occur in small isolated patches of habitat.

A number of hypotheses exist to explain the generally observed higher species richness in tropical communities. One possibility is that tropical ecosystems may have higher speciation rates due to a higher number of (137) _____ per year, the result of a benign climate, warmer temperatures, and a higher level of local isolation due to reduced (138) _____ in the stable climate of the tropics. Other hypotheses focus on the year-round availability of abundant resources that lead to feeding (139) _____ and hence high species richness.

MacArthur and Wilson's (140) _____ _____ of island biogeography predicts species richness on islands (or isolated habitats such as mountain tops and lakes) based on island size, distance from the mainland, and immigration and extinction rates. Under this theory, the mainland acts as a (141) _____ _____, providing colonizers for the islands, and islands closer to the mainland will receive more colonizers. In terms of size, (142) _____ islands receive more colonizers than (143) _____ islands. The combined rate of (144) _____ of new species will be balanced by the rate of species (145) _____ at equilibrium to produce a characteristic species richness that depends on a balance between the arrival of new species versus the loss of the existing species.

Matching

Match each island with the appropriate characteristics.

146. ____	Large, distant island	A.	High immigration rate, high extinction rate
147. ____	Large island, close to mainland	B.	High immigration rate, low extinction rate
148. ____	Small, distant island	C.	Low immigration rate, high extinction rate
149. ____	Small island, close to mainland	D.	Low immigration rate, low extinction rate

1. Which of the following is most likely a result of coevolution? [pp. 1137–1138]

   a. tolerating extremely low temperatures

   b. using mimicry to prevent predation

   c. presence of specialized digestive organs

   d. defending a territory from other individuals of the species

2. Which of the following is NOT a symbiosis? [pp. 1148–1150]

   a. commensalism

   b. intraspecific competition

   c. mutualism

   d. predation

3. Some toxins used for defence are synthesized by the user. Where else do toxins commonly come from? [p. 1141]

   a. other plants or animals

   b. photosynthesis

   c. the organism's mother

   d. water or air

4. What is interference competition characterized by? [p. 1143]

   a. One species benefits but the other is unaffected.

   b. Individuals directly harm their competitors.

   c. Individuals use the same limiting resource.

   d. Both species benefit.

5. What may occur when there is intense competition for the same resources? [p. 1148]

   a. a realized niche

   b. facilitation

   c. mimicry

   d. resource partitioning

6. Which correctly identifies commensalism? [p. 1148]

   a. Both species benefit.

   b. One species benefits and the other is unaffected.

   c. Both species are harmed.

   d. One species benefits and the other is harmed.

7. A parasitoid is an organism that parasitizes another individual. But, what makes a parasitoid different from a true parasite? [p. 1150]

   a. A parasitoid kills the host.

   b. A parasitoid benefits the host.

   c. A parasitoid has no effect on the host.

   d. A parasitoid does not have a host.

8. Which term refers to the transition zone between adjacent communities that often has a high species diversity? [p. 1152]

   a. climax community

   b. ecotone

   c. ecotype

   d. trophic zone

9. Which aspect of species diversity is Shannon's evenness index (E_H) designed to reflect? [p. 1154]

   a. species richness

   b. competition

   c. species number

   d. relative abundance

10. Which term refers to the classification of organisms that obtain the energy necessary for life by eating other organisms? [p. 1156]

    a. consumers

    b. decomposers

    c. detritivores

    d. producers

11. How are complex trophic relationships typically illustrated? [pp. 1155–1157]

    a. trophic levels

    b. diet diagrams

    c. food webs

    d. food chains

12. What characteristic did MacArthur propose for species-rich communities with complex food webs? [p. 1156]

    a. extinct

    b. a climax community

    c. stable

    d. unstable

13. Which of the following correctly describes changes found to coral colonies on Heron Island reefs due to physical disturbance? [pp. 1158–1161]

    a. greater loss of colonies in sheltered areas than in exposed pools of coral

    b. tendency for higher recruitment of new colonies in sheltered areas than in exposed areas.

    c. greater storm damage in sheltered areas than in exposed areas

14. What type of organism has a greater impact on community structure than its numbers might suggest? [p. 1158]

    a. keystone species

    b. Müllerian mimic

    c. mutualist

    d. primary producer

15. Which community characteristic would be predicted by the intermediate disturbance hypothesis? [p. 1161]

    a. a preponderance of K-selected species

    b. a preponderance of r-selected species

    c. an extreme sensitivity to slight disturbances

    d. a high species diversity

16. In which area would you most likely observe primary succession? [pp. 1161–1163]

    a. a clear-cut forest

    b. a prairie after a fire

    c. an abandoned farm

    d. some rocky outcrops created by a receding shore

17. Which hypothesis does NOT attempt to explain the processes that drive succession? [pp. 1163–1166]

    a. the island equilibrium hypothesis

    b. the facilitation hypothesis

    c. the inhibition hypothesis

    d. the tolerance hypothesis

18. What type of colonist tends to be favoured by disturbances in a climax community? [pp. 1161–1163]

    a. a K-selected species

    b. an aquatic species

    c. a generalist species

    d. an r-selected species

19. Which of the following statements correctly describes the global patterns in latitudinal clines of species diversity? [p. 1167]

    a. There are no species in the Arctic.

    b. There are fewer species with increasing latitude.

    c. There are more species with increasing latitude.

    d. There is greater evenness with increasing latitude.

20. Which assumption is necessary in MacArthur and Wilson's equilibrium theory of island biogeography? [pp. 1168–1169]

    a. Islands close to the mainland have relatively low immigration rates.

    b. Large islands have relatively low extinction rates.

    c. Large islands have relatively low immigration rates.

    d. Small islands have relatively low extinction rates.

INTEGRATING AND APPLYING KEY CONCEPTS

1. Imagine four species: A and B are Müllerian mimics, C is a noxious model, and D is its Batesian mimic. Do you think each of the following scenarios would be beneficial or detrimental to each species? (i) A greatly outnumbers B; (ii) C greatly outnumbers D; and (iii) D greatly outnumbers C. Explain your answer.

2. Why would K-selected species be more likely to show strong competitive interactions than r-selected species?

3. The equilibrium theory of biogeography was developed for true islands, but it also applies to "islands" of suitable habitat in a "sea" of unsuitable habitat. List three such scenarios, explain how they are "islands," and describe what you think the "mainland" sources of new species might be.

46 Ecosystems

TOPIC MAP

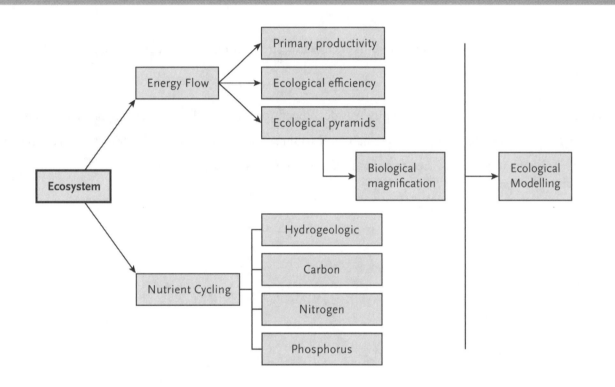

LEARNING OUTCOMES AND STUDY STRATEGIES

By the end of this chapter, you should be able to

- Define and describe the flow of energy through ecosystems, from solar radiation to top predators
- Define and estimate various types of efficiencies of energy transfer in an ecosystem
- Interpret ecological pyramids in terms of efficiencies and relative availability of energy at each level
- Describe hydrogeologic, carbon, nitrogen, and phosphorus cycles and draw schematic diagrams to illustrate the cycles
- Explain how ecosystem models are constructed and what they are used for

Study strategies for this chapter:

- It is important to understand that energy FLOWS THROUGH ecosystems, which can be tracked and quantified using food webs and ecological pyramids, whereas elements that make up the organisms in an ecosystem are in finite supply, so material CYCLES BETWEEN the living and nonliving parts of the system.

- Using this basic information, you can then interpret models that attempt to reduce a complex system to what is believed to be its most important components. It is important to realize that factors not incorporated into the model can have an impact.

INTERACTIVE EXERCISES

Why It Matters [pp. 1174–1175]

Section Review (Fill-in-the-Blanks)

(1) _____ ecosystems are the fastest growing habitat on Earth today. Such ecosystems are very

different from the way they were before human development; the runoff of (2) _____ over the

asphalt and concrete and the reflectance of energy from the (3) _____ by buildings fundamentally

change the nature of the ecosystem. These ecosystems are not recent; one of the earliest, Tell Brak, existed in

Syria about (4) _____ years ago. Although urban sprawl may not be new, it represents a serious

threat to the conservation of (5) _____.

46.1 Energy Flow and Ecosystem Energetics [pp. 1175–1184]

Section Review (Fill-in-the-Blanks)

The conversion of solar energy into chemical energy by autotrophs is known as the (6) _____ primary

productivity. Primary producers are, however, complex organisms, and the energy left after deducting the

amount spent on maintenance is the (7) _____ primary productivity. Generally, producers use between

(8) _____% and (9) _____% of the energy they capture for respiration. There are several ways to estimate

these different forms of energy. One is by measuring (10) _____, the dry weight of organic matter per

unit area or volume of a habitat. The (11) _____ _____ of biomass is the total amount of

organic matter in an area, which is not to be confused with the rate of (12) _____ (or production) of that

matter. Like all organisms, plants need a variety of materials to live and function. The element in shortest supply

is called a(n) (13) _____ nutrient because its scarcity determines productivity.

Heterotrophic organisms acquire some of the energy accumulated by autotrophs when they consume

the autotrophs. Any energy left over after consumer maintenance is stored as (14) _____

productivity. That energy is available to organisms at the next trophic level. The ratio of net productivity at

one trophic level to that of the level below it is known as (15) _____ efficiency, which is determined by the efficiency of three processes: (16) _____ efficiency (the ratio of the food energy available to the energy in the food actually consumed); (17) _____ efficiency (the ratio of the energy gained by consumption to the energy contained in the food consumed); and (18) _____ efficiency (the ratio of the energy content of new biomass produced to the energy gained by consumption). The flow of energy through a food web is often represented diagrammatically in the form of ecological (19) _____, of which there are three types. The (20) _____ _____ _____ depicts the amount of energy temporarily stored in a trophic level as dry weight. This pyramid is often inverted in aquatic systems if the producers reproduce rapidly; that is, they have high (21) _____ rates. The amount of energy at a trophic level often affects the population size of the organisms at the next higher level; thus, the (22) _____ _____ _____ uses the number of individuals at a particular trophic level to represent energy. The (23) _____ _____ _____ is the only one that actually measures energy flow, and the second law of thermodynamics dictates that it must show a reduction between each trophic level. Some interactions between two trophic levels have indirect impacts on lower trophic levels, a phenomenon known as a trophic (24) _____.

The interaction among trophic levels and the interconnectedness of organisms in an ecosystem is dramatically demonstrated when (25) _____ are introduced into the environment (e.g., DDT). The process whereby the concentration of the contaminant increases in higher trophic levels is (26) _____

_____.

Matching

Match each of the following ecological efficiencies with the correct definition.

27. _____   Assimilation efficiency   A.   Ratio of energy absorbed from food consumed to total energy content of food

28. _____   Harvesting efficiency   B.   Ratio of net productivity at one trophic level to the net productivity at the trophic level below

29. _____   Production efficiency   C.   Ratio of energy content of new tissue produced to energy assimilated from food

30. _____   Ecological efficiency   D.   Ratio of energy content of food consumed to energy content of available food

True/False

Mark if the statement is true (T) or false (F). If the statement is false, make it correct by changing the underlined word(s) and writing the correct word(s) in the lines below each statement.

31. _____ A pyramid of biomass is sometimes inverted because it <u>overestimates</u> the importance of high turnover rates.

_____

_____

32. _____ A pyramid of energy can never be inverted because the transfer of energy from one trophic level is always less than <u>100% efficient.</u>

_____

_____

33. _____ Individuals at the <u>top</u> of a pyramid of numbers are often of considerable conservation concern.

_____

_____

34. _____ Photosynthesis converts approximately <u>25%</u> of the solar energy hitting Earth's surface into chemical energy.

_____

_____

46.2 Nutrient Cycling in Ecosystems [pp. 1185–1195]
Section Review (Fill-in-the-Blanks)

The circulation of nutrients from the living to the nonliving part of an ecosystem and back again is referred to

as a(n) (35) _____ cycle. Unlike the flow of energy through an ecosystem, which is eventually lost,

matter is (36) _____ in the various cycles. The (37) _____ _____ model describes

nutrient cycling based on whether molecules and ions are available or unavailable for assimilation and

whether they are in organic or inorganic form.

Although not technically a nutrient, water cycles through ecosystems much as minerals do. This

cycling is referred to as the (38) _____ cycle. It is based on evaporation and (39) _____ of

water as rain or snow.

Carbon enters the food web when producers convert (40) _____ _____ into

carbohydrates. Although most carbon is stored as sedimentary rock, most (41) _____ carbon is present as bicarbonate ions in the ocean. Human activities, such as burning (42) _____

_____, are transferring carbon into the atmosphere at an unprecedented rate, causing a general

(43) _____ of the climate.

The (44) _____ cycle is primarily based on the activity of prokaryotic organisms since they

are the only organisms capable of converting atmospheric nitrogen (N_2) into an organic form that can be

utilized by eukaryotes, a process known as nitrogen (45) _____. The breakdown of organic nitrogen

in detritus into ammonia by various bacteria and fungi is (46) _____. This ammonia can be

assimilated by plants. The ammonia may also be converted to nitrites and nitrates by other bacteria in a

process called (47) _____. Still other bacteria convert unused nitrites and nitrates into N_2 through the

process of (48) _____. N_2 can also be fixed through an artificial process (the Haber–Bosch process),

which is how (49) _____ are produced.

Phosphorus compounds lack a(n) (50) _____ phase since the phosphorus cycle consists of

movement between the terrestrial and (51) _____ ecosystems in a(n) (52) _____ cycle.

Within a community, phosphorus cycles rapidly, with plants (53) _____ it and heterotrophs

(54) _____ it.

Choice

Choose the biogeochemical cycle associated with each item in the following list. Answers can be used more than once.

55. _____   Ammonification   A.   Carbon cycle

56. _____   Fixation into organic form mainly   B.   Hydrologic cycle
             by photosynthesis

57. _____   Fixation into organic form mainly   C.   Nitrogen cycle
             by prokaryotes

58. _____   Largest available reservoir is   D.   Phosphorus cycle
             bicarbonate ions in the oceans

59. _____   Largest available reservoir is the
             atmosphere

60. _____   Largest available reservoir is
             Earth's crust

61. _____   Largest available reservoir is
             Earth's oceans

46.3 Ecosystem Modelling [pp. 1196–1197]
46.4 Scale, Ecosystems, Species [pp. 1197–1199]

Section Review (Fill-in-the-Blanks)

Ecosystem modelling helps in the understanding of ecosystem dynamics. Conceptual models tend to be more

general in scope than (62) _____ models, which, if well constructed, can give precise answers to

specific questions about ecosystems without disturbing them. It can also be used to (63) _____ how

future disturbances (such as climate change) can affect ecosystem function. To develop a model,

(64) _____ must be collected to provide information about the ecosystem to be studied, such

as its (65) _____ (anywhere between millimetres and kilometres), species relationships, and the

impact of (66) _____ factors (e.g., climate). For example, a study on the influence of spawning

salmon on (67) _____ availability to streambed plant communities provided information to

develop a model for this ecosystem. A model based on well-defined ecological relationships and good

(68) _____ data can be used to (69) _____ how a future change can impact an ecosystem.

True/False

Mark if the statement is true (T) or false (F). If the statement is false, make it correct by changing the
underlined word(s) and writing the correct word(s) in thelines below each statement.

70. _____ Ecologists use ecosystem modelling to make predictions about how <u>a species</u> will
respond to specific changes in the environment.

_____

_____

71. _____ Ecosystem simulation models rely on detailed data concerning the interaction and
relationships in a <u>specific ecosystem</u>.

_____

_____

72. _____ Ecosystem modelling allows us to explore potential impacts of change <u>without</u>
environmentally damaging experimentation.

_____

_____

73. _____ Ecosystem models <u>do not</u> rely on assumption.

_____

_____

74. _____ The portfolio effect indicates that diversity provides <u>greater</u> stability in an ecosystem.

_____

_____

SELF-TEST

1. How are urban ecosystems similar to natural ecosystems? [pp. 1174–1175]

    a. Both have similar rainfall runoff patterns.
    b. Both have similar solar reflectance patterns.
    c. Both have similar biodiversity levels.
    d. Both have animal and plant communities.

2. Which two types of food webs does the energy in ecosystems usually flow through? [pp. 1175–1176]

    a. detrital food webs and decomposer food webs
    b. grazing food webs and detrital food webs
    c. predator food webs and prey food webs
    d. producer food webs and consumer food webs

3. What provides the greatest contribution to overall net primary productivity of an ecosystem? [p. 1178]

    a. the nitrogen cycle
    b. the phosphorous cycle
    c. the location of the ecosystem
    d. the size and/or productivity of the ecosystem

4. Which term refers to the rate of conversion of solar energy into chemical energy by autotrophs? [p. 1176]

    a. gross primary productivity
    b. net primary productivity
    c. respiration
    d. standing crop biomass

5. Which term refers to the element that is in shortest supply in an ecosystem? [pp. 1176–1177]

    a. essential nutrient
    b. primary nutrient
    c. basal nutrient
    d. limiting nutrient

6. Which of the following is NOT a form of new biomass? [pp. 1176–1177]

    a. growth of existing biomass
    b. reproduction to make new producers
    c. storage of carbohydrates
    d. intensity of sunlight

7. Which term refers to the energy that is stored by consumers, as it is transferred to them from producers? [p. 1178]

    a. gross primary productivity
    b. net primary productivity
    c. standing crop productivity
    d. secondary productivity

8. Which term refers to the ratio of net productivity at one trophic level to that at the trophic level below? [pp. 1178–1179]

    a. harvesting efficiency
    b. production efficiency
    c. ecological efficiency
    d. assimilation efficiency

9. How much more assimilated energy does an ectothermic animal convert into new biomass than an endothermic animal? [pp. 1178–1179]

    a. less than10%
    b. 20%
    c. 30%
    d. greater than 40%

10. Why do energy pyramids usually have very broad bases relative to the top of the pyramid? [pp. 1180–1181]

    a. It is due to low turnover rates.
    b. It is due to low ecological efficiency.
    c. It is due to reduced numbers of organisms.
    d. It is due to increasing biomass.

11. What are two types of nutrient cycles ? [p. 1185]

    a. atmospheric and sedimentary
    b. biotic and abiotic
    c. organic and inorganic
    d. terrestrial and aquatic

12. Which source of energy drives the hydrogeologic cycle? [p. 1186]

    a. photosynthesis
    b. hydrolysis
    c. solar
    d. hydrothermal

13. How does carbon enter the biotic (living) component of the ecosystem? [pp. 1186–1188]

    a. via ammonification
    b. via photosynthesis
    c. via precipitation
    d. via respiration

14. Which of the following would NOT cause levels of atmospheric carbon dioxide to rise? [pp. 1186–1189]

    a. burning fossil fuels
    b. destruction of terrestrial forests
    c. volcanic eruptions
    d. increased rates of photosynthesis

15. Which process returns N_2 to the atmosphere? [pp. 1188–1189, 1192]

    a. ammonification
    b. denitrification
    c. nitrification
    d. nitrogen fixation

16. Which of the following can convert N_2 into ammonium and nitrate ions? [pp. 1188–1189, 1192]

    a. nitrogen-fixing microorganisms
    b. denitrifying microorganisms
    c. nitrifying microorganisms
    d. photosynthesizing organisms

17. Which statement relating to the phosphorus cycle is correct? [pp. 1194–1195]

    a. Excess phosphorus from fertilizers is a pollutant of lakes and ponds.
    b. Phosphorus cycles slowly within terrestrial ecosystems.
    c. Phosphorus is made available to plants through fixation by prokaryotes.
    d. The atmosphere is the largest reservoir of phosphorus.

18. Why is the phosphorus cycle different from many of the other biogeochemical cycles? [pp. 1194–1195]

    a. because the phosphorus cycle includes artificial fertilizers
    b. because the phosphorus cycle includes freshwater and marine components
    c. because the phosphorus cycle does not include an atmospheric component
    d. because the phosphorus cycle has the atmosphere as the main reservoir

19. Which of the following does NOT correctly describe ecosystem modelling? [pp. 1196–1197]
    a. It attempts to identify the most important factors that are involved in ecosystem function.
    b. It describes ecosystem processes but has no predictive value.
    c. It simplifies events that occur in nature.
    d. It uses mathematical equations to define relationships between populations and the environment.

20. Which of the following would NOT likely be included in an ecosystem simulation model? [pp. 1196–1197]
    a. temperature
    b. limiting nutrient levels
    c. energy flow
    d. time of day

INTEGRATING AND APPLYING KEY CONCEPTS

1. This chapter is focused on two ecosystem processes: ecosystem energetics and nutrient cycles. What are the fundamental differences between these two processes, and how are they related?

2. Compare and contrast gross and net primary productivity. Explain how production efficiency plays a role in the determination of net primary productivity.

3. Describe how net primary productivity could vary depending on the ecosystem being considered. Give examples.

4. This chapter describes four biogeochemical cycles. Identify (a) which two rely on solar radiation to drive part of the cycle, (b) which cycle does not include the atmosphere as part of the cycle, and (c) where the main reservoirs for each cycle are located.

47 Conservation of Biodiversity

TOPIC MAP

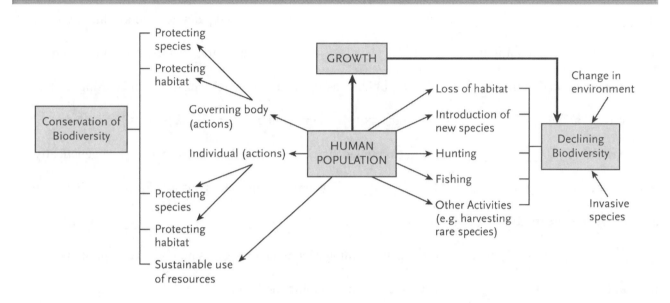

LEARNING OUTCOMES AND STUDY STRATEGIES

By the end of this chapter, you should be able to

■ Define and provide examples of species extinction

■ Discuss why species have become extinct or are threatened to become extinct

■ Explain how species are categorized by a governing body in terms of their status (number and distribution) in nature

■ Identify conservation efforts explaining why they have or have not been successful, especially in terms of the human population

Study strategies for this chapter:

■ After learning about the negative impact humans have had on populations, you can then look at what humans are doing to try to protect those species at risk.

■ Be sure to differentiate between the different governing bodies, as well as understand how these bodies determine which group of organisms should be protected.

■ You can now address the conflicting needs of humans versus nature, noting the challenges that must be addressed.

INTERACTIVE EXERCISES

Why It Matters [pp. 1201–1202]

Section Review (Fill-in-the-Blanks)

To maintain biodiversity, it will be necessary for humans to change their attitudes about nature from a

(1) _____-_____ view to a view in which each animal and plant, as well as other living

organisms, is as important in nature as (2) _____ believe that they are. Historically, some religious

beliefs have resulted in the (3) _____ of humans from nature, thereby justifying increasing

productivity, at the (4) _____ of biodiversity, to supply the needs of humans. This has included

development of (5) _____ farming (to produce large amounts of one food species) and genetically

modified organisms, increased use of (6) _____ to enhance the soil's nutrient level, as well as water

and energy to increase food production. It is hoped that the (7) _____ _____

_____ project will aid in identifying and naming species since species number is an important

indicator of (8) _____, a measure of ecosystem stability and productivity.

47.1 Extinction [pp. 1202–1204]

Section Review (Fill-in-the-Blanks)

It is expected that over time some species become extinct. This low rate of species loss is known as the

(9) _____ _____ rate, and it usually results from climate change and the inability of some

organisms to adapt. Consequently, there is a continual (10) _____, or loss and replacement, of

species living on earth over time. For species that are closely related, usually due to having a common

(11) _____, some (12) _____ may be found in more than one taxa, making it difficult to

differentiate between the taxa and therefore to determine if a particular species has become

(13) _____ (that no individuals of the species are alive). However, in many situations, it is clear

when a species has become extinct, although it can be difficult to ascertain why the species has become

extinct. For example, it is surmised that the demise of multituberculates in early Oligocene resulted from

being (14) _____ by rodent species, which were newly evolved due to (15) _____

_____; however, information from fossil records is limited.

There are at least (16) _____ times in history when mass extinctions have occurred. The cause of the mass extinction at the end of the Cretaceous period has provoked extensive debate. Although it is generally agreed that a(n) (17) _____ hit the Earth at that time, as evidenced by the presence of (18) _____ found in rocks from that time period (substance found in asteroids) and the 180 km diameter (19) _____ off a peninsula in Mexico, it is not clear if this event resulted in the mass extinction. It has been suggested that changes in the (20) _____ from the asteroid resulted in the extinction of many birds, mammals, and other organisms.

Choice

Choose the correct period for each of the events or results relating to a mass extinction.

21. ____	Glaciations due to formation of Pangea	A.	End of Ordovician
22. ____	Extinction of dinosaurs	B.	End of Devonian
23. ____	Asteroid hitting Earth	C.	End of Permian
24. ____	Extinction of trilobites and trees of coal swamp forests	D.	End of Triassic
25. ____	Human degradation of environment	E.	End of Cretaceous
26. ____	Most severe; > 85% of species became extinct	F.	Present day
27. ____	Glaciation from move of Gondwana toward South Pole		

47.2 The Impact of Humans [pp. 1204–1207]
47.3 Introduced and Invasive Species [pp. 1207–1210]
47.4 How We Got/Get There [pp. 1210–1213]

Section Review (Fill-in-the-Blanks)

Human actions have been responsible, whether directly or indirectly, for the (28) _____ in individual numbers of various species, sometimes resulting in the loss of the species, its (29) _____. These actions usually involve overharvesting the species, (30) _____ a new species to an area, or destroying a species' (31) _____ so that it can no longer access what it needs for survival. For example, the extinction of the Dodos on Mauritius Island around (32) _____ resulted from extensive hunting by new settlers and introduced (33) _____, such as dogs, cats, and rats, as well as from habitat loss due to the expanding settler population on the island. Many introduced or invasive species are not successful in their new environment; however, it has been found that invaders are usually more successful if the new habitat is (34) _____-_____, allowing the invader to use (35) _____ growth and reproduction rates to outcompete native species. Surprisingly, a recent study on plants indicated that even in nutrient-poor sites, invasive species had a higher (36) _____ _____ _____, assimilating more carbon (biomass) per unit of resource, which indicated that limited resources may not limit the success of invaders. Effects of human activities seldom affect a species in isolation since a species interacts with its environment at many levels, all the way up to the (37) _____ level. For example, it is hypothesized that the dramatic (38) _____ in bay scallops is not directly due to overfishing but rather is an indirect effect of overharvesting various species of (39) _____. Decreased numbers of these animals allowed their prey, skates and rays, to increase in numbers, and since they are (40) _____ of bay scallops, the number of bay scallops decreased.

Matching

Match the name of the invader with each of the species known to be negatively affected by its presence.

41. ____	Flatworms	A.	Flightless wrens
42. ____	Starlings	B.	Chestnut tree
43. ____	Zebra mussels	C.	Native bird species
44. ____	*Endothia parasitica*	D.	Earthworms
45. ____	Cats	E.	Eastern pond mussels

Choice

Choose the appropriate action by humans that has caused a large reduction in numbers of individuals belonging to each of the following organisms.

46. ____	Sea turtles	A.	Reduction in predator numbers (by humans)
47. ____	Cape buffalo	B.	Caught as bycatch by fishers
48. ____	Bay scallops	C.	Hunted and shot by trophy hunters
49. ____	Barndoor skate		
50. ____	African elephant		

Short Answer

51. How is the extinction of the Dodos, which occurred more than 300 years ago, related to the approaching extinction of the Mauritian calvaria tree?

_____

_____

52. What is it about the horns of black rhinos that has made this species so attractive to hunters, resulting in its dramatic drop in numbers?

_____

_____

47.5 Protecting Species [pp. 1213–1216]
47.6 Protecting What? [pp. 1216–1220]
47.7 The Downside of Being Rare [p. 1220]
47.8 Protecting Habitat [pp. 1220-1221]

Section Review (Fill-in-the-Blanks)

Before organisms can be protected, it is necessary to ascertain whether they are (53) _____ for

consideration, as regulated by a government agency. A group of organisms being considered must be

identified as one or more (54) _____ units, such as a species, population, ecosystem, etc. If this group

is identified as at risk, it must then be categorized using (55) _____-_____ criteria for

assessing the risk posed. These data include number of individuals, fecundity, (56) _____ (rate at

which they are dying), intrinsic rate of increase, and (57) _____ _____ (maximum number

of individuals in a population without negatively affecting their habitat). Based on the criteria and assessment

procedures identified by the International Union for the Conservation of Nature, a Canadian body called

(58) _____ (acronym) assesses the data collected and categorizes the group of organism as

(59) _____, if it no longer exists; (60) _____, if it no longer exists in a particular area but

does live elsewhere; (61) _____, if it is expected to become extinct or extirpated;

(62) _____, if it is expected to become endangered; of (63) _____ _____, if there

are threats or it has biological characteristics that indicate it may become threatened or endangered; or

(64) _____ _____, if there is insufficient information available to determine if it is eligible

and/or at risk. When some species are identified to be at risk, their value tends to (65) _____ due to competition to acquire the last individuals.

In some situations, identifying species at risk does not ensure (66) _____ of the group of organisms or its habitat. The expansion of (67) _____ population size and associated needs reduces the area available for the habitat and needs of other species.

Matching

Match each of the acronyms associated with conservation regulatory bodies to the description of its purpose.

68. _____	IUCN	A.	Categorizes potential species at risk in Canada based on data-based criteria
69. _____	CITES	B.	Developed criteria and assessment procedures for identifying species at risk at an international level
70. _____	COSEWIC	C.	Identifies animals or animal parts that should be banned from importation

Choice

Choose the correct category to which each of the animals belong. Choices can be used more than once.

71. _____	Chinese bahaba	A.	Extinct
72. _____	White-coloured moose	B.	Extirpated
73. _____	Banff Springs snail	C.	Endangered
74. _____	Pacific water shrew	D.	Threatened
		E.	Special concern
		F.	Not at risk

47.9 Effecting Conservation [pp. 1221–1224]
47.10 Taking Action [pp. 1224–1225]

Section Review (Fill-in-the-Blanks)

The root problem of declining biodiversity is the increasing (75) _____ _____, and if it continues to grow at its present rate, it will double in (76) _____ years. Although the human population growth rate is (77) _____ globally, some countries, such as Afghanistan, continue to maintain relatively high population growth rates. It is hoped that with continued education on family planning, more women will have the knowledge to control their own (78) _____.

It will be up to humans to take action to maintain global (79) _____. Both ecosystems and

biodiversity are very (80) _____ systems, and a disruption, such as a species going extinct or

introduction of a new species, tends to lead to (81) _____ biodiversity. If humans continue to try to

achieve (82) _____ use of resources, as well as taking action in (83) _____ species and

habitats locally, these conservation efforts could help maintain biodiversity.

True/False

Mark if the statement is true (T) or false (F). If the statement is false, make it correct by changing the underlined word(s) and writing the correct word(s) in the lines below each statement.

84. _____ Human population growth rate in Afghanistan is <u>less</u> than in Sri Lanka.

_____

_____

85. _____ Bird flu can spread from birds, such as chickens, to <u>humans</u>.

_____

_____

86. _____ Reducing the human growth rate requires empowering women to control <u>their own fertility</u>.

_____

_____

87. _____ <u>Mammals and birds</u> dominate the list of threatened species both internationally and in Canada.

_____

_____

1. What is the reason humans drive other species to extinction? [pp. 1201–1202]

    a. Humans feel that species facing extinction must be protected.
    b. Humans appreciate that organisms have medicinal or magical value.
    c. Humans harvest organisms for food and industrial development.
    d. Humans have a responsibility to maintain biodiversity.

2. What was the status of dinosaurs living during the Cretaceous period? [pp. 1203–1204]

    a. They were all large and dominating creatures.
    b. They were all small and delicate creatures.
    c. They were a mix of small to large in size but they were all dominating creatures in their communities.
    d. They were a mix of combinations of small to large size and delicate to dominating creatures in their communities.

3. What does background extinction rate measure? [p. 1203]

    a. the number of species becoming extinct due to human activities
    b. the number of species becoming extinct due to environmental change
    c. the number of species becoming extinct in terrestrial ecosystems only
    d. the number of species becoming extinct in aquatic ecosystems only

4. What has been suggested as the proportion of species that have ever lived which have gone extinct? [pp. 1203–1204]

    a. 10%
    b. 50%
    c. 85%
    d. 99.9%

5. What type of curve describes the survivorship of *Albertosaurus* species during its lifespan most closely? [pp. 1203–1204]

    a. Type I
    b. Type II
    c. Type III
    d. Type IV

6. In which geographical region is the cartwheel flower an introduced species? [pp. 1209–1210]

    a. the British Isles
    b. British Columbia
    c. Hawaii
    d. the Great Lakes

7. Which statement correctly describes ballast water? [pp. 1209–1210]

    a. It can contain many species of many different phyla.
    b. It is water that is taken in and released by ships in the same port.
    c. It used to ensure that species are not introduced to new areas.

8. Which of the following is an introduced species that is now established in Hawaii? [pp. 1209–1210]

    a. flatworms
    b. chestnut blight
    c. Monterey pine
    d. zebra mussels

9. Which RUE ($\mu mol\ CO_2 \bullet m^{-2} \bullet s^{-1}$) would provide an invading species with the greatest chance of success? [pp. 1209–1210]

    a. 1
    b. 5
    c. 10
    d. 15

10. Which species has been hunted to extinction? [pp. 1205–1206]

    a. black rhinos

    b. passenger pigeons

    c. starlings

    d. barndoor skates

11. Which characteristic would COSEWIC NOT consider in determining the status of a potential species at risk? [pp. 1213–1216]

    a. morphology of individuals

    b. population information

    c. generation time

    d. risks to species survival

12. How is the Bali starling categorized? [p. 1220]

    a. extinct species

    b. extirpated species

    c. endangered species

    d. threatened species

13. Why are some organisms that appear to be at risk not protected? [pp. 1216–1217]

    a. They are a subspecies of a not-at-risk species.

    b. They belong to a species that is at risk.

    c. They are morphologically distinct individuals that belong to a species at risk.

14. On what basis were killer whales on the west coast of Canada divided into four designatable units? [pp. 1216–1217]

    a. according to species

    b. according to subspecies

    c. according to behaviour and geography

    d. according to populations

15. Why is it difficult to protect the Chinese bahaba? [p. 1220]

    a. It is easy to catch.

    b. Its swim bladders have medicinal properties.

    c. Its fins have medicinal properties.

    d. It is valued as a pet.

16. Which level of organization could NOT be given consideration as being at risk? [pp. 1215–1221]

    a. organism

    b. ecosystem

    c. population

    d. community

17. What percentage of drylands are suffering from severe land degradation? [pp. 1221–1224]

    a. 1–5%

    b. 5–10%

    c. 10–20%

    d. 25–50%

18. What is the root problem of declining biodiversity? [pp. 1221–1224]

    a. introduced species

    b. human population growth

    c. trophy hunting

    d. changing climate

19. Historically, which of the following have humans NOT managed to achieve? [pp. 1221–1224]

    a. abolition of slavery

    b. emancipation of women

    c. maintenance of biodiversity

INTEGRATING AND APPLYING KEY CONCEPTS

1. If you had a time machine and travelled back to the end of the Cretaceous period, what animals would you expect to see and what would you expect to happen to life on earth after an imminent collision with a large asteroid occurred?

2. American ginseng is categorized as endangered, but it is difficult to protect. Explain why.

3. Why is the number of birds decreasing globally?

48 Putting Selection to Work

TOPIC MAP

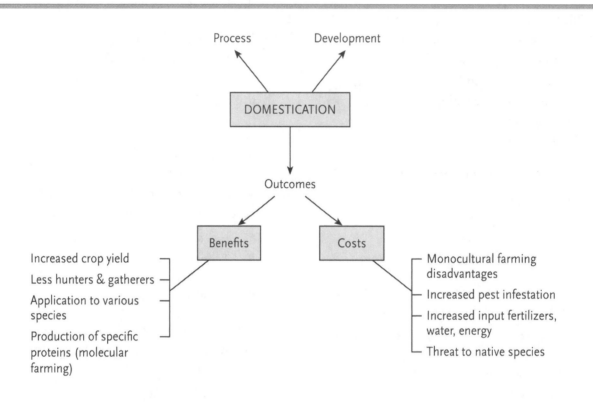

LEARNING OUTCOMES AND STUDY STRATEGIES

By the end of this chapter, you should be able to

- Define domestication and describe its development over time
- Provide examples of plants and animals that have been domesticated and identify their uses
- Describe the benefits and costs of advanced technology relating to domestication

Study strategies for this chapter:

- After noting the importance of domestication through history, focus on the costs and benefits of associated technological development.

INTERACTIVE EXERCISES

Why It Matters [pp. 1228–1229]

Section Review (Fill-in-the-Blanks)

Improvements in agricultural techniques, including combining new genetic strains, better (1) _____ (to promote plant growth), and more efficient harvesting and processing, have (2) _____ yields. The advent of chemical fertilizers and other agricultural techniques is known as "the (3) _____ _____." (4) _____ also plays an important role, as seen when comparing areas with different amounts of rainfall, such as Zimbabwe, Africa, with its (5) _____ annual precipitation relative to southwestern Ontario, Canada. Even with technological advancements, the food available for children to eat differs between countries, as indicated by the statistics that one in three children in Zimbabwe are (6) _____, whereas an increasing number of children in Ontario suffer from (7) _____. In the *homo* genus, changes in (8) _____, such as increasing the consumption of "brain" food made available by use of fire and tools, may have influenced the adaptive radiation of ancestors.

48.1 Domestication [pp. 1229–1234]

Section Review (Fill-in-the-Blanks)

Originally, humans acquired food by hunting and (9) _____ resources from the environment, but, over time, they progressed to (10) _____ seeds and growing their own plants, a process known as (11) _____. Eventually, humans began to selectively breed individuals of a species, or (12) _____ them, thereby promoting characteristics that benefited humans. Many species of (13) _____, yeast, and animals have been domesticated at different times and places throughout history. The use of (14) _____ and molecular genetics has provided evidence of the development of cultivation and domestication of many organisms. For example, genetic evidence indicates that the domestication of pigs occurred at (15) _____ different locations throughout Eurasia. Archaeological evidence of fires indicates the possible emergence of cultivation and domestication by humans as far back as (16) _____ years ago (in Mossel Bay, South Africa).

True/False

Mark if the statement is true (T) or false (F). If the statement is false, make it correct by changing the underlined word(s) and writing the correct word(s) in the lines below each statement.

17. _____ <u>Humans</u> are believed to be the first species to manipulate organisms for their own benefit.

_____

_____

18. _____ Parthenogenic figs can be domesticated <u>rapidly</u> due to their use of asexual reproduction.

_____

_____

19. _____ Early cultivation of rice in China required clearing of land using <u>fire</u>.

_____

_____

20. _____ The birth of <u>agriculture</u> arose from domestication.

_____

_____

21. _____ <u>Aquatic</u> species were the first organisms to be domesticated.

_____

_____

22. _____ The change from hunting and gathering to cultivation and domestication provides an opportunity for <u>increased</u> population size.

_____

_____

Short Answer

23. Explain how the appearance of indehiscent wheat grains promoted cultivation and domestication of wheat.

_____

_____

24. Why is fire indicative of cultivation?

_____

_____

48.2 Why Some Organisms Were Domesticated [pp. 1234–1242]

Section Review (Fill-in-the-Blanks)

Although the primary motivation for cultivation and domestication of plants and animals was to provide a

supply of (25) _____, they have provided many other uses.

Choice

For each domesticated organism, choose one or more ways that it is used.

26. ____	Corn	A.	Food or food source
27. ____	Grapes	B.	Making beer
28. ____	Honeybees	C.	Labour source
29. ____	Squash	D.	For pollination
30. ____	Yeast	E.	Making wine
31. ____	Cattle		
32. ____	Wheat		

Matching

Match each of the following organisms with the latest date at which domestication is believed to have occurred. Note that BP = before present.

33. ____	Cotton	A.	4400 years BP
34. ____	Dogs	B.	6000 years BP
35. ____	Cattle	C.	6250 years BP
36. ____	Squash	D.	9000 years BP
37. ____	Yeast	E.	10 000 years BP
38. ____	Corn	F.	14 500 years BP

48.3 Yields [pp. 1242–1246]
48.4 Complications [pp. 1246–1248]
48.5 Chemicals, Good and Bad [pp. 1248–1249]

Section Review (Fill-in-the-Blanks)

Farmers must consider many aspects of crop production when trying to determine which crop provides the

(39) _____ yield on a particular piece of land and, overall, which crop will bring in the

(40) _____ income, after (41) _____ all costs. Increasing yield is possible if the farmer is

able to take advantage of (42) _____, such as a tractor or bailer, or improve the land with the addition of (43) _____ (if low nutrient soil) or water (if little or seasonal rainfall), but all of these add to the

cost of producing the crop.

Choice

Choose whether each of the following conditions or practices will have a potential positive or negative impact on yield of a present-day farm.

44. _____	Milkweed mixed in with barley	A.	Positive
45. _____	Addition of manure to soil	B.	Negative
46. _____	Use of cisterns to capture rainwater		
47. _____	Presence of a fungus in a grain storage tank		
48. _____	Increase in fuel prices on farm with limited budget		
49. _____	Use of high technology farm equipment		
50. _____	Introduction of cats to control a rodent problem		

True/False

Mark if the statement is true (T) or false (F). If the statement is false, make it correct by changing the underlined word(s) and writing the correct word(s) in the lines below each statement.

51. _____ Ginseng is a <u>toxin</u> that stimulates the immune system.

_____

_____

52. _____ The yield on terrain that is terraced will be <u>lower</u> than on terrain that is flat.

_____

_____

53. _____ The domestication of cats is believed to have <u>occurred before</u> the development of agriculture.

_____

_____

54. _____ Around 2 CE, Rome was able to produce a <u>sufficient</u> amount of wheat to feed all of its people.

_____

_____

48.6 Molecular Farming [pp. 1249–1250]
48.7 The Future [p. 1250]

Section Review (Fill-in-the-Blanks)

The domestication of plants, along with the ability to (55) _____ modify plants, has provided the

opportunity to mass produce specific (56) _____ at a relatively low cost. This type of agriculture is

called (57) _____ _____. One example of this practice is the planting of tobacco plants that

contain the inserted human (58) _____ (acronym) gene. These plants produce the protein interleukin-

10, which, after harvest, can be used by humans to treat (59) _____ _____ disease.

Although there is concern that the products of these genetically modified plants might enter an ecosystem's

(60) _____ _____ and (61) _____ affect existing crops, tobacco is a(n)

(62) _____ plant, and research has indicated that the protein does not enter the soil or enter insects

that infect the plant.

Molecular farming, as well as other forms of domestication, is allowing us to (63) _____

other species. The (64) _____ for humans are many, including an increased food supply, labour

resource, production of chemicals and other materials, and pest control. With these benefits, there are costs, so

it is imperative that innovations are scrutinized to ensure that implementation of any development will result

in benefits that (65) _____ costs.

Matching

Match each of the following descriptions with how tobacco is, or has been, used in the past.

66. ____	In molecular farming	A.	Smoking a cigarette
67. ____	Traditional medicine	B.	Applied to plants to control or prevent pest infestation
68. ____	An insecticide	C.	Producing the protein that treats irritable bowel disease
69. ____	Recreational use	D.	Reducing the pain of childbirth

Short Answer

70. Explain why using corn to produce the biofuel ethanol is not environmentally friendly.

   _____

   _____

1. How was it possible for wheat to be domesticated? [pp. 1230–1232]
    a. through a mutation that resulted in the production of indehiscent wheat grains
    b. through a mutation that resulted in the production of dehiscent wheat grains
    c. through wheat's ability to asexually reproduce
    d. through wheat's ability to grow in marine environments

2. For how long has the domestication of freshwater animals, as well as marine plants and animals, been occurring? [p. 1230]
    a. 100 000 years
    b. 10 000 years
    c. 1000 years
    d. 100 years

3. Why is it sometimes difficult for archaeologists to determine when an organism has undergone domestication? [p. 1230–1232]
    a. The DNA has degraded over time.
    b. Domestication of some organisms originated from more than one location.
    c. It is difficult to distinguish between domestic and wild-type organisms using bone or plant material.

4. What is niche construction? [pp. 1233–1234]
    a. the ability of an organism to build its own shelter
    b. the destruction of habitat that occurs when an undomesticated animal moves to a new location
    c. the modification of the environment in preparation for domestication
    d. the breeding of a species for its specific characteristics

5. Which of the following did NOT assist in the emergence of domestication? [pp. 1230–1234]
    a. changes in climate
    b. changes in human behaviour
    c. changes in human settlement
    d. changes in human skills in hunting and gathering

6. Which of the following has NOT been domesticated? [p. 1242]
    a. mushrooms
    b. honeybees
    c. yeast
    d. Atlantic salmon

7. Which of the following domesticated plants originated in more than one location? [p. 1237]
    a. corn
    b. barley
    c. rice
    d. wheat

8. Which of the following used the formation of indehiscent reproductive structures to aid in its domestication? [pp. 1236–1237]
    a. rice
    b. cotton
    c. lentils
    d. eggplant

9. Which of these plants do NOT belong to the *Solonaceae* family? [pp. 1239–1241]
    a. tomatoes
    b. locoweed
    c. squash
    d. the *Capsicum* species of chili peppers

10. Some First Nations people believed that there were "three sisters" that needed to be present each year. Which three staple foods were they referring to? [pp. 1239–1241]

    a. tomatoes, potatoes, and corn

    b. potatoes, corn, and beans

    c. corn, beans, and squash

    d. beans, squash, and wheat

11. For which of the following are honeybees important pollinators? [p. 1235]

    a. wheat

    b. broccoli

    c. cotton

    d. rice

12. Which substance does NOT contain a phenolic compound? [pp. 1248–1249]

    a. cinnamon

    b. coffee

    c. nutmeg

    d. parsley

13. Which plant can contaminate crops and cause renal failure when eaten by humans? [p. 1248]

    a. milkweed

    b. *Aristolochea clematitis*

    c. *Panax quinquefolius*

    d. Queen Anne's lace

14. How many domestication events occurred during the domestication of cats? [pp. 1246–1247]

    a. one

    b. two

    c. four

    d. five or more

15. What effect does a genetically modified food organism have on other organisms? [p. 1249]

    a. They pose a serious risk to organisms that consume them.

    b. They do not provide a health benefit to organisms that consume them.

    c. They may pose a threat to wild-type organisms of the same species.

16. Which of the following statements refers to EROI? [p. 1250]

    a. It stands for "energy resistance of insects," relating ability of organisms to resists pathogens.

    b. It cannot be determined for plants grown in Roman times.

    c. It is a high value for corn-produced ethanol (~17:1).

    d. It stands for "energy return on investment," relating energy input to energy output.

17. Where does the *IL-10* gene that is inserted into *IL-10* protein-producing tobacco plants come from? [pp. 1249–1250]

    a. the mouse genome

    b. the human genome

    c. the tobacco genome

    d. the *Solonaceae* genome

18. Which of the following occurred as a result of from domestication in human societies? [p. 1250]

    a. There was less concern regarding exposure to diseases.

    b. There was reduced control and exploitation of other species.

    c. There was reduced access to food, medicinal chemicals, and labour.

    d. There was an increase in number of individuals who could contribute to society in ways not related to gathering and processing food.

INTEGRATING AND APPLYING KEY CONCEPTS

1. Differentiate between cultivation and domestication.

2. Describe the effect of cultivation on the Abu Hureyra settlement from 12 000 years BP to 9400 years BP.

3. To become domesticated, some species must undergo one or more specific genetic changes. Contrast the genetic changes required to promote domestication in lentils and in rice.

4. You have just inherited a 20-hectare parcel of agricultural land in central Canada. What do you need to consider if you want to be successful at farming?

Answers

Chapter 1   Light and Life

1.1 The Physical Nature of Light [pp. 2–4]

1. electromagnetic radiation; 2. wave; 3. photons; 4. electromagnetic; 5. higher; 6. see; 7. reflected; 8. transmitted; 9. absorbed; 10. energy; 11. information; 12. pigments; 13. C, B, D, A; 14. A – Photon, B – Electron at ground state, C – Electron at excited state, D – Low energy level, E – High energy level; 15. F – The energy of light is inversely related to its wavelength; 16. F – It is the result of the fusion of hydrogen nuclei into helium; 17. T; 18. F – Chlorophyll absorbs red and blue light meaning the differences are equal to the energy of red and blue wavelengths; 19. F – The electrons are delocalized so are free to interact with a photon of light; 20. D; 21. A; 22. B; 23. C.

1.2 Light as a Source of Energy [pp. 4–6]
1.3 Light as a Source of Information [pp. 6–10]

24. photosynthesis; 25. chlorophyll; 26. NADPH; 27. carbohydrates/sugars; 28. respiration; 29. ATP; 30. halobacteria; 31. bacteriorhodopsin; 32. ATP; 33. rhodopsin; 34. retinal; 35. ion; 36. eye spot; 37. swimming; 38. Phytochrome; 39. photomorphogenesis; 40. compound; 41. single-lens; 42. D; 43. C; 44. K; 45. G; 46. J; 47. A; 48. I; 49. F; 50. B; 51. E; 52. H; 53. A – Non-image-forming, senses light intensity and direction; B – Single lens, C – Arthropods such as insects and crustaceans; 54. Eyes contain the photoreceptors but also require a brain or simple nervous system to interpret and respond to the information, whereas eyespots trigger a change in flagellar movement through a simple signal transduction response; 55. They both allow the same type of response (movement in response to light); however, the ocellus transmits information via nerves to a cerebral ganglion; 56. The compound eye is extremely sensitive to movement; 57. Delocalized electrons are promoted to their excited states and this causes a conformational change in the pigment molecule; 58. F – The bacteriorhodopsin in the halobacteria generates a proton gradient that is used for the synthesis of ATP, not for the conversion of carbon dioxide to carbohydrates; 59. T.

1.4 The Uniqueness of Light [pp. 10–12]
1.5 Light Can Damage Biological Molecules [pp. 12–14]

60. visible; 61. absorbed; 62. water; 63. shorter; 64. Longer; 65. excite; 66. damage; 67. photosystems; 68. dimers; 69. bases; 70. mutations; 71. Melanin; 72. heat; 73. F – Light of wavelengths less than 400 nm (i.e., in the UV range) are referred to as ionizing radiation because their high energy levels breaks bonds, oxidizing molecules so that they release ions; 74. F – It absorbs the shorter wavelength UV light but not the longer wavelengths; 75. T.

1.6 Using Light to Tell Time [pp. 14–16]

76. 24 hours; 77. one year; 78. light; 79. diurnal; 80. circadian; 81. biological; 82. clock; 83. oscillate; 84. free-running; 85. jetlag; 86. synchronization; 87. photoperiod; 88. flowering; 89. A – Higher humidity prevents drying out/dessication,

B – Nighttime DNA replication protects against UV damage, C – Arctic fox; 90. T; 91. T; 92. F – They are triggered by changes in the photoperiod and are under control of the biological clock.

1.7 Role of Light in Ecology and Behaviour [pp. 17–20]

93. mates; 94. predators; 95. feathers; 96. oxygen; 97. health; 98. co-evolved; 99. visual; 100. light pollution; 101. nocturnal; 102. Hummingbirds but not bees can detect red, so hummingbirds are the dominant pollinators of red flowers. In contrast, bees and certain other insects can detect ultraviolet light, so they pollinate flowers that reflect UV light; 103. The Industrial Revolution caused an increase in air pollution and a darkening of the bark on the trees in their habitat, making the dominant light-coloured moths more visible to predators. The dark-coloured variants thus had a selective advantage and became more common.

1.8 Life in the Dark [pp. 20–21]
1.9 Organisms Making Their Own Light: Bioluminescence [pp. 21–23]

104. photons; 105. mole rat; 106. photoreceptors; 107. biological clock/circadian rhthym; 108. bioluminescence; 109. electron; 110. excited; 111. photon; 112. quorum; 113. alarm/self-defence; 114. predators; 115. T; 116. F – The term "milky sea" to describe this phenomenon has been used for hundreds of years and is mentioned in the classic story *Twenty Thousand Leagues Under the Sea*.

Self-Test

1. c [400 nm is in the blue region of the spectrum, closest to the UV region]
2. b [The colour corresponds to the wavelength(s) of transmitted light]
3. a [The energy of the photon must exactly match the energy difference between the ground and excited states of an electron in a conjugated system]
4. d [Chlorophyll pigments absorb blue and red light but not green, with the excited-state electrons being used for photosynthetic electron transport]
5. C [Photosynthetic organisms use the energy of sunlight to *synthesize* matter (NADPH, ATP, and carbohydrates from CO_2). Phototrophs are any organism that can extract energy from sunlight while all organisms perform cellular respiration]
6. d [Bacteriorhodopsin is a membrane-embedded light-activated proton pump that generates a proton gradient which is then used to make ATP but not carbohydrates from CO_2]
7. d [Retinal is the light-absorbing pigment in the light-driven proton pump bacteriorhodopsin, as well as rhodopsin]
8. c [The *C. reinhartii* eyespot responds directly to light and does not require the nervous system, which is an essential component of vision]
9. a [Phytochrome is the light-sensing photoreceptor in the cytoplasm of plants that is essential for the developmental changes associated with exposure of seedlings to light]
10. a [The single lens eye or camera eye of humans has a single lens that focuses the incoming light onto the photoreceptor cells of the retina]
11. d [Infrared light is absorbed by water vapour in Earth's atmosphere and by water in matter, whereas short wavelength UV light is absorbed by ozone. Long wavelength UV light reaches Earth's surface and can damage matter including DNA]
12. d [Light in the UV region of the spectrum has a shorter wavelength, higher energy and capable of removing an electron from an atom, creating an ion]
13. a [Exposure of skin to UV light is reduced by feathers, fur, or the skin pigment melanin. Melanin absorbs UV light and dissipates the energy as heat; however, in blocking the UV light, it also reduces vitamin D synthesis, which requires some exposure to UV light]
14. a [A critical characteristic of circadian rhythms is that they are not dependent on daily changes in exposure to light]
15. b [Biological clocks exist in all life forms and may regulate circadian or diurnal rhythms, or respond to changes in the photoperiod, thus regulating seasonal rhythms]
16. b [Melatonin, not melanin, is a hormone produced by the pineal gland as part of the human biological clock]
17. c [Plants have co-evolved with their pollinators so that flower colour, for example, has evolved to fit with the evolving visual systems of their pollinators]

18. b [The colour allows it to blend with the colour of trees in its normal habitat. Prior to the Industrial Revolution, light-coloured moths were more common than dark and they blended with light-coloured lichen on trees, but this changed as pollution levels rose and the lichen died from exposure to soot]
19. a [The eyes of mole rats have been overgrown by layers of tissue making them blind; however, their retinas can still respond to light and this is believed to regulate their biological clock]
20. a [Bioluminescence, as opposed to ecological light pollution, is light that is created biologically, serving a variety of roles including the quorum-sensing communication of bacteria]

INTEGRATING AND APPLYING KEY CONCEPTS

1. Read section 1.3d and the legend of Figure 1.15. Compare this information to the description of the life and evolution of the blind mole rat and Mexican cave fish (section 1.8).
2. Read the beginning of section 1.2; examine Figure 1.7 and its legend, as well as sections 1.3a and 1.3b.
3. a) Read the beginning of section 1.1a, section 1.2; examine Figure 1.7 and its legend.
   b) Read section 1.4 and the beginning of section 1.5b, examine Figure 1.16 and its legend.

Chapter 2   The Cell: An Overview

Why It Matters [pp. 25–26]
2.1 Basic Features of Cell Structure and Function [pp. 26–30]

1. cell; 2. microscopy; 3. organisms; 4. basic unit; 5. pre-existing; 6. mm; 7. electron; 8. prokaryotic; 9. eukaryotic; 10. DNA; 11. cytoplasm; 12. nucleus; 13. endomembrane; 14. C. 15. D; 16. G; 17. F; 18. B; 19. H; 20. A; 21. E; 22. A, C, B, D; 23. T; 24. F – It is now known that bacteria and archaea also have a cytoskeleton; 25. T; 26. F – An electron microscope gives higher magnification because the wavelength of a beam of electrons is less than visible light; the light microscope has lower resolution; 27. The cytoplasm contains the cytosol, organelles, and cytoskeleton, whereas the cytosol is the aqueous component of the cytoplasm; 28. The hydrophobic nature is responsible for the barrier function of plasma membrane as water-soluble molecules can only traverse the membrane through protein transporters; 29. As cells grow, the surface area increases at a lower rate than the volume so that eventually the rate of exchange of nutrients and waste across the plasma membrane cannot support the reactions occurring within the volume of the cell.

2.2 Prokaryotic Cells [pp. 30–31]
2.3 Eukaryotic Cells [pp. 31–43]

30. smaller; 31. circular; 32. nucleoid; 33. cell wall; 34. nucleus; 35. endoplasmic reticulum; 36. Golgi; 37. mitochondria; 38. one; 39. linear; 40. larger; 41. cytoplasm; 42. nuclear; 43. rough; 44. cytoskeleton; 45. chromosome; 46. division; 47. animal; 48. flagella; 49. pili; 50. cilia; 51. C; 52. E; 53. D; 54. A; 55. I; 56. J; 57. K; 58. B; 59. G; 60. F; 61. E; 62. pili; 63. plasma membrane; 64. cell wall; 65. capsule; 66. nucleoid; 67. cytoplasm; 68. ribosomes; 69. mitochondrion; 70. nuclear pore complex; 71. nucleolus; 72. rough ER; 73. smooth ER; 74. plasma membrane; 75. cytosol/cytoplasm; 76. Golgi complex; 77. vesicle; 78. microtubules; 79. lysosome; 80. centrioles; 81. C, A, E, B, F, D; 82. A – The fusion of a secretory vesicle with the plasma membrane, B – Endocytosis, C – Intermediate filaments, D – The smallest cytoskeleton element, made of actin protein and functions in maintaining cell structure and locomotion, E – Microtubules, F – Process used by some cells to engulf bacteria and cell debris, G – Proteins that generate movement by pushing or pulling against microtubules and microfilaments, H – Central barrel-shaped structures that give rise to flagella and cilia, 83. F – Animal cells do not have cell walls; 84. T; 85. F – Although analogous, these structures have evolved independently; 86. T; 87. T; 88. T; 89. They are identical in structure but cilia are shorter than flagella and move by beating. Flagella allow cells to move whereas cilia move fluids over the cell surface; 90. In prokaryotes it is the site of ATP synthesis from light or chemical energy. In eukaryotes, membrane proteins may mediate

the adhesion that generates tissues or serve as markers to the immune system; 91. The plasma membrane is a single lipid bilayer that contains the cytoplasm, whereas the nuclear envelope contains two membranes connected by large nucleoprotein complexes and contains the nucleoplasm; 92. Chromosomes are present in all types of cells and contain one complete DNA molecule with its associated proteins, whereas chromatin is a collection of eukaryotic chromosomes and their associated proteins.

2.4 Specialized Structures of Plant Cells [pp. 43–45]
2.5 The Animal Cell Surface [pp. 45–47]

93. lysosome; 94. chloroplast; 95. vacuole; 96. cell wall; 97. fungi; 98. algal; 99. carbohydrates; 100. central vacuole; 101. pressure; 102. growth; 103. storage; 104. adhesion; 105. tissues; 106. junctions; 107. junctions; 108. extracellular matrix; 109. protection; 110. G; 111. J. 112. A; 113. L; 114. H; 115. C; 116. K; 117. B; 118. D; 119. I; 120. F; 121. E; 122. A – Plasmodesmata, B – Tight connections made by fusion of membrane proteins of adjacent animal cells, C – Protein channels between adjacent animal cells allowing passage of ions and small molecules, D – anchoring junctions, 123. T; 124. T; 125. F – Collagen is a key component of the ECM. The consistency is determined by the cross-linking, water composition, and the presence of mineral crystals within the matrix; 126. It functions in structural support, cell growth, and storage; it concentrates the pigments that give flowers their colour, may contain hydrolytic enzymes like lysozymes, and may also contain defense molecules; 127. They are channels between adjacent plant and animal cells, respectively. The former is lined by the plasma membrane and allows the energy-dependent flow of proteins and nucleic acids, whereas gap junctions are formed by alignment of adjacent protein channels in the plasma membrane and only allow the flow of ions and small molecules; 128. It forms the mass of skin, bone, tendons, cornea, and the filtering networks of the kidneys; is involved in cell division, adhesion, motility, and embryonic development; and takes part in reactions to wounds and disease.

SELF-TEST

1. b [While this statement is true, it is not one of the three tenets of the cell theory as described in the middle of the 19th century, prior to the discovery of nucleic acids]
2. a [The previous domain "Prokaryota" is no longer used as a result of recent evidence indicating that, while structurally similar, the bacteria and archaea are not evolutionarily related]
3. d [Bacteria can be seen with the light microscope; however, subcellular structures and viruses are considerably smaller and require the superior magnification and resolution of electron microscopes]
4. c [As cells grow, the surface area increases as the square of the linear dimension, while the volume increases faster, as the cube of that linear dimension]
5. c [Organelles are defined structures with a specific cellular function; however, they are not necessarily bounded by a membrane]
6. c [While their ribosomes differ in size and their chromosomes differ in number, size, and shape, the basic distinction between the two cell types is the absence of a nucleus in prokaryotes]
7. a [Visualization of the nucleoid requires an electron microscope]
8. a [While capsule/slime serve other functions as well, they also help cells attach to surfaces and other cells, which is the basic function of pili]
9. c [The prokaryotic flagella differ structurally from those of eukaryotes but have the same function—to provide motility, moving cells through liquid]
10. a [The nuclear envelope is not called the "nuclear membrane" because of the fact it comprises two concentric membranes, which each have the typical lipid bilayer structure]
11. d [Prokaryotic cells generally have a smaller, single circular chromosome in the non-membrane-bound nucleoid area of the cell. The nucleolus is typical of eukaryotic cells and is probably visible due to the higher concentration of DNA and ribosomal RNA and protein genes in the eukaryotic nucleus]
12. c [Cristae are typical of mitochondria and are formed by the infolding of the internal mitochondrial membrane]

13. b [The Golgi is the site where proteins made on the RER are modified and is the major organelle for trafficking of intracellular macromolecules]
14. a [Exocytosis is the fusion of secretory vesicles made by the Golgi, with the plasma membrane]
15. b [Respiration involves the oxidation of food molecules for energy and generates most of the ATP in animal cells]
16. b [Collagen is the primary glycoprotein associated with the extracellular matrix of animal cells]
17. d [Intermediate filaments are a cytoskeleton element that is specifically found in multicellular organisms]
18. a [Amyloplasts are a type of plastid that specifically stores starch, as denoted by the prefix *amylo*]
19. c [The aqueous contents of the two types of storage plastid, the amyloplast and chromoplast, include starch and red/yellow pigments, respectively. Similarly, the aqueous contents of the central vacuole include flower pigments and sugars]
20. d [Gap junctions are typical of specific cells within multicellular animals, for example, heart muscle cells]
21. a [Both structures connect adjacent cells and allow the free passage of small molecules and ions]
22. c [Tight junctions, as the name implies, seal adjacent cells together, essentially fusing their plasma membranes. This makes these cell layers impermeable to even small ions and keeps the contents of body cavities from leaking into surrounding tissues]
23. a [Hair is made of proteins intead of collagen and other glycoproteins, and is specifically constructed from a type of intermediate filament]

INTEGRATING AND APPLYING KEY CONCEPTS

1. Reread the introductory part of section 2.1 and and sections 2.1c and 2.3 and re-examine the topic map at the beginning of this study guide chapter.

Chapter 3   Defining Life and its Origins

Why It Matters [pp. 50–51]
3.1 What Is Life? [pp. 51–52]
3.2 The Chemical Origins of Life [pp. 52–57]

1. atoms; 2. chemistry; 3. order; 4. energy; 5. stimuli; 6. development; 7. evolve; 8. 4.6; 9. 500; 10. CO_2, NH_3, CH_4, and H_2; 11. O_2; 12. Oparin–Haldane; 13. atmosphere; 14. Miller–Urey; 15. clay; 16. F – Although the meteorite has been dated at ~4.5 billion years old, the calculated age of Earth and the solar system, and may contain evidence of past life, it arrived on Earth only ~13 000 years ago, long after life began on Earth; 17. F – A reducing environment was critical to the abiotic synthesis of organics and the lack of oxygen in the atmosphere of early Earth meant no ozone was present to block ultraviolet light, the energy source for these synthetic reactions; 18. F – The term refers to something that is more complex than its individual components or more than the sum of its parts. Examples include the characteristics of life as well as the termites' cathedral; 19. T; 20. D; 21. C; 22. B; 23. E; 24. A; 25. D, A, B, C; 26. A – Displays order, B – Acquired from the environment and required to maintain order, C – Reproduction, D – Responds to stimuli, E – The ability to maintain constant internal conditions, F – The increase in size and number of cells and for some organisms, the change in form with time, G – Evolution; 27. Oxygen would have oxidized or removed electrons from electron-rich organic molecules, preventing their accumulation. Atmospheric oxygen means an ozone layer, which would have blocked UV light, an essential energy source for the formation of biological molecules; 28. Viruses contain nucleic acids, reproduce, and evolve; 29. They used a closed apparatus with an "atmospheric chamber" containing H_2, CH_4, NH_3, water vapour, and sparking electrodes and a cooling area where water condensed and the newly formed organic molecules accumulated.

3.3 From Macromolecules to Life [pp. 57–60]

30. membrane; 31. protobionts; 32. energy; 33. ribozymes; 34. RNA; 35. information; 36. catalyst; 37. proteins; 38. catalysts; 39. diversity; 40. selective; 41. DNA; 42. metabolism; 43. reduction; 44. processes/pathways; 45. It is the

flow of information in modern cells from DNA to RNA to protein. Enzymes are proteins required to synthesize DNA and RNA. Ribosomes contain catalytically active RNA, suggesting that an "RNA world" existed before the evolution of the central dogma; 46. Enzymes have far greater catalytic power; they are made from 20 building blocks instead of 4, producing far greater structural diversity; amino acids can interact with each other in more diverse ways than RNA bases, increasing structural diversity through complex folding; 47. DNA is double-stranded, contains the more stable sugar deoxyribose and includes thymine, whereas RNA is single-stranded and contains ribose and uracil in place of thymine; 48. They are lipid-enclosed vesicles containing abiotically formed organics. The first types may have been liposomes and clay would have accelerated their formation and been trapped inside, providing catalytically active surfaces for key reactions; 49. T; 50. T; 51. F – The first types of metabolic reactions probably involved oxidation of food molecules and direct, one-step transfers of the electrons in reduction (biosynthetic) reactions; 52. F – Cech discovered modern-day ribozymes. This discovery lead to the proposal that the earliest life forms lived in an "RNA world," where RNA was used for information storage and catalysis.

3.4 The Earliest Forms of Life [pp. 60–64]

53. stromatolites; 54. 3.5; 55. carbon; 56. 3.9; 57. Earth; 58. panspermia; 59. anaerobic; 60. oxygen; 61. oxygenic; 62. iron; 63. 2.5; 64. E; 65. F; 66. D; 67. B; 68. C; 69. A; 70. Organisms preferentially incorporate the ^{12}C isotope over other carbon isotopes, so demonstration of sedimentary rocks containing lower levels of other carbon isotopes (e.g., ^{13}C) is indicative of a biological source for the carbon; 71. The stromatolites in Shark Bay are approximately 2000 years old and are mineral deposits formed by cyanobacteria. Fossilized stromatolites are highly similar in structure but are ~3.5 billion years old and contain fossils that resemble modern-day cyanobacteria; 72. Panspermia proposes that life on Earth is extraterrestrial in origin, while astrobiology is a multidisciplinary scientific discipline that includes the search for extraterrestrial life; 73. It stands for "last unique common ancestor." The cell is the basic unit of all life and it has the same basic properties: a lipid bilayer and DNA for the genetic material; they all follow the central dogma, use the same translational apparatus, use proteins as primary catalysts, use ATP as the primary molecule of chemical energy, and use glycolysis to break down glucose; 74. F – These were probably preceded by anaerobic heterotrophs and anoxygenic phototrophs that used H_2S and Fe^{2+} as electron sources instead of water; 75. T; 76. T.

3.5 The Eukaryotic Cell and the Rise of Multicellularity [pp. 64–67]
3.6 The Search for Extraterrestrial Life [pp. 68–69]

77. nucleus; 78. membrane-enclosed; 79. mitochondrion/chloroplast; 80. chloroplast/mictochondrion; 81. endosymbiosis; 82. prokaryotic; 83. endosymbiont; 84. mitochondrion; 85. photosynthetic; 86. chloroplast; 87. infolding; 88. plasma; 89. energy; 90. multicellular; 91. extraterrestrial; 92. extrasolar; 93. habitable; 94. C; 95. D; 96. E; 97. A; 98. B; 99. They share common morphology, method of reproduction, circular chromosomes, transcription and translation machinery, and electron transport chains in inner membrane. Also, ribosomal RNA sequence analyses place both organelles in the bacterial domain of the tree of life; 100. Some non-essential genes were lost and others underwent horizontal gene transfer to the nuclear genome; 101. Eukaryotes are believed to have evolved from associations of prokaryotic cells; 102. F – Multicellularity is believed to have evolved more than once with the three multicellular lineages: the fungi, animals, and plants all arising from different multicellular lineages; 103. T; 104. F – Due to gene loss and horizontal gene transfer, these organelles are now essential parts of a single organism; 105. F – It is thought that the most important criterion is to be in a habitable zone relative to a sun. Over 1000 extrasolar planets have

been identified with over 400 belonging to systems with multiple planets, like our own solar system. Some of these may be in such a habitable zone; 106. Prokaryotic host cell; 107. Invaginating plasma membrane; 108. Aerobic heterotrophic bacteria; 109. Bacteria became mitochondria; 110. Horizontal gene transfer between protomitochondrion and nucleus; 111. Oxygenic photosynthetic bacteria; 112. Bacteria became chloroplasts; 113. Horizontal gene transfer from the protochloroplast and nucleus and protein import into protochloroplast of nuclear-encoded proteins; 114. Endocytosis of the plasma membrane could have given rise to the nuclear envelope and endoplasmic reticulum.

SELF-TEST

1. d [Viruses do not have energy transduction systems but must hijack the cellular machinery to replicate, transcribe, and translate the information in their nucleic acids, so are not considered to be life forms]
2. b [Cellular metabolisms emerges from the complex interactions of cellular molecules, proteins, and membranes]
3. b [Earth is approximately 4.6 billion years old, whereas chemical and fossil evidence supports the existence of the first life forms 4.0 and 3.5 billion years ago, respectively]
4. c [The absence of oxygen resulted in a reducing atmosphere that combined with the absence of ozone, allowing for the penetration of energetic UV light and the presence of water/water vapour, allowed for the spontaneous assembly of complex electron-rich molecules]
5. a [A reducing atmosphere, characterized by the lack of oxygen and the presence of electron and H-rich gases (such as H_2, CH_4, and NH_3), would have allowed for the formation of complex organic molecules]
6. d [They combined hydrogen, methane, ammonia, water vapour, and continuously sparking electrodes to synthesize organic molecules from spontaneous chemical reactions]
7. d [The clay hypothesis proposes that clay provided the adhesion forces and potential energy required for the first polymerization reactions]
8. b [In addition to their demonstrated ability to polymerize macromolecules, clay particles have been shown to accelerate the formation of protobionts]
9. b [Life is believed to have begun in an RNA world]
10. a [The limitation of ribozymes results from their relatively limited number of building blocks, intramolecular bonding, and their slow rate of catalysis]
11. b [The last step in its evolution, the evolution of DNA as the genetic material, would have reduced chemical damage, allowed for damage repair and a lower mutation rate]
12. c [Fossilized stromatolites dated at 3.5 billion years old resemble the modern stromatolites created by cyanobacteria]
13. c [Anaerobic heterotrophs, thought to have been the first life forms, use organics for energy (respiration) and do not require oxygen, which on primordial Earth was virtually absent]
14. a [Banded iron formations dated to 2.5 billion years ago contain iron oxides or rust, thought to result from the evolution of oxygenic photosynthetic bacteria]
15. d [Because of certain universally shared traits, all present day life is believed to have descended from LUCA, the last universal common ancestor. It is possible that other life forms also arose on Earth, however, but did not survive]
16. d [The oldest fossilized eukaryotes are 2.1 billion years old; however, chemical evidence points to the presence of eukaryotes 2.5 billion years ago]
17. b [Virtually all eukaryotic cells possess mitochondria, but only plants and algae possess both mitochondria and chloroplasts]
18. c [The ancestors of the mitochondrion and chloroplast are believed to have been an endosymbiotic aerobic heterotrophic bacterium and endosymbiotic oxygenic photosynthetic bacterium, respectively. In contrast, the endomembrane system (the nuclear membrane, the ER, and the Golgi complex) is believed to have developed from infolding of the plasma membrane]
19. a [Solving an energy crisis, thereby producing vastly higher levels of ATP, is thought to have allowed for the evolution of the eukaryotes]
20. b [Multicellularity allowed for the division of labour among the individual cells of the organism; it is thought to have arisen multiple times, giving rise to the fungal, animal, and plant lineages]

INTEGRATING AND APPLYING KEY CONCEPTS

1. Consider the by-product of this type of photosynthesis, the energetic advantages of aerobic respiration, as well as the fact that endosymbiosis must provide an advantage to the endosymbiont and the host. What does that suggest about the type of benefit(s) the endosymbiosis of an aerobically respiring bacterium provided to the host?

2. Read Box 3.2 to understand the goals of astrobiologists, make sure you understand what is meant by the term "habitable zone," then read section 3.6 and the legend for Figure 3.25.

Chapter 4   Energy and Enzymes

Why It Matters [pp. 71–72]
4.1 Energy and the Laws of Thermodynamics [pp. 72–75]

1. enzymes; 2. energy; 3. metabolic; 4. Energy; 5. kinetic; 6. potential; 7. Thermodynamics; 8. surroundings; 9. isolated; 10. energy; 11. closed; 12. energy; 13. open; 14. created/destroyed; 15. destroyed/created; 16. system; 17. entropy; 18. energy; 19. closed; 20. second; 21. disorder/entropy; 22. D; 23. G; 24. F; 25. H; 26. E; 27. A; 28. B; 29. C; 30. There is energy stored in the arrangement of atoms of the molecules making up the hamburger; 31. There is potential energy due to the position of the skier relative to Earth's gravitational field; 32. There is potential energy due to the position of the water relative to Earth's gravitational field; 33. A – Exchanges neither matter nor energy with its surroundings, B – Open, C – Exchanges energy and matter with its surroundings, D – Closed; E – Greenhouses, Earth; 34. Electrons; 35. Molecules; 36. Photons; 37. Photons.

4.2 Free Energy and Spontaneous Reactions [pp. 75–78]

Note that in section 4.2a of the textbook, the terms exothermic *and* endothermic *are used interchangeably with* exergonic *and* endergonic, *respectively. The terms* exothermic *and* endothermic *refer to reactions that release or absorb* **heat** *energy.* 38. energy; 39. free energy; 40. work; 41. enthalpy; 42. entropy; 43. $\Delta G = \Delta H - T\,\Delta S$; 44. spontaneously; 45. negative; 46. exergonic; 47. positive; 48. endergonic; 49. lower; 50. equilibrium; 51. equal; 52. metabolism; 53. catabolic; 54. anabolic; 55. I; 56. G; 57. H; 58. A; 59. J; 60. C; 61. E/F; 62. F/E; 63. B; 64. D; 65. F – It is catabolic because it involves the breakdown of large molecules into smaller ones and the release of energy; 66. T; 67. F – Water is more disordered than ice, so the ice melts spontaneously and the reaction is exergonic ($-$ve ΔG); 68. T; 69. One calculates using the formula $\Delta G = \Delta H - T\,\Delta S$. If ΔG is negative, the reaction will be spontaneous; 70. Catabolic pathways convert complex molecules with a high chemical potential energy (enthalpy) and low disorder (S) to smaller molecules with a lower chemical potential energy and higher disorder. Anabolic pathways do the reverse; 71. This is because living organisms are open systems, obtaining a constant supply of reactants from their surroundings but not generating an increase in products as these are consumed as reactants of other reactions.

4.3 Adenosine Triphosphate Is the Energy Currency of the Cell [pp. 79–81]

72. endergonic; 73. anabolic; 74. ADP + Pi; 75. endergonic; 76. energy coupling; 77. positive; 78. breakdown; 79. D; 80. E; 81. B; 82. A; 83. C; 84. It reduces intramolecular repulsion caused by the adjacent, negatively charged phosphate groups; it allows for greater hydration/solvation, which is energetically favoured; and the released Pi can exist in a greater number of resonance forms, which increases the entropy of the system; 85. Reactions for life require an input of energy, and this comes from, in the case of animals, the breakdown of food molecules. Energy coupling allows the energy to be transferred between these types of reactions; 86. While it is exergonic, it is a very slow process and if it happened without the involvement of enzymes (with water instead), it would result in the loss of energy as heat.

4.4 The Role of Enzymes in Biological Reactions [pp. 81–85]

86. activation; 87. transition; 88. unstable/strained; 89. enzymes; 90. lowering; 91. free energy; 92. free energy; 93. catalysts; 94. active; 95. substrate; 96. induced fit; 97. active sites; 98. reactants; 99. charge; 100. conformation/

shape; 101. transition; 102. E; 103. D; 104. F; 105. G; 106. A; 107. B; 108. C; 109. A – Enzymes bring reacting molecules together faster than they would through random motion, B – The active site may have charge/ionic groups that alter the substrate(s) to favour the formation of the transition state, C – Closing of the active site upon binding of the substrate(s) may cause a distortion of the bound molecule(s), making bonds easier to break; 110. T; 111. F – They lower the activation energy required to reach the transition state; 112. T; 113. Kinetic instability refers to the rate at which a reaction occurs: the higher the instability, the faster the reaction rate. Thermodynamic instability refers to the change in free energy of a reaction. The more thermodynamically unstable, the more negative the change and the more exergonic the reaction.

4.5 Conditions and Factors that Affect Enzyme Activity [pp. 85–90]

114. increases; 115. increases; 116. saturated; 117. inhibitors; 118. Competitive; 119. active site; 120. Allosteric; 121. conformation/shape; 122. allosteric; 123. decreased/increased; 124. increased/decreased; 125. end product; 126. covalent; 127. The inhibitor resembles the enzyme substrate, competing with the reactants for the active site; 128. The regulator binds to a site other than the active site of the enzyme—i.e., the allosteric site—causing a change in 3D structure of the enzyme; 129. The end product of a metabolic pathway inhibits the activity of the first enzyme in the pathway through allosteric binding; 130. Covalent attachment of a phosphate group, causing a conformational change of the enzyme; 131. Cleavage of the catalytically inactive form of the enzyme by a protease, resulting in release of the slightly shorter active form of the enzyme; 132. Increasing temperature increases the kinetic energy of the system and the catalytic rate, until the bonds within the enzyme start to break, causing the denaturation of the enzyme and the loss of catalytic activity; 133. Above and below the optimum pH for the enzyme, catalytic activity is reduced as changes in pH alter the structure and ionic environment within the active site; 134. T; 135. F – Protein kinases covalently modify enzymes by adding phosphate groups, thereby altering enzyme activity; 136. F – Allosteric inhibitors convert allosteric enzymes to the low-affinity conformation, whereas activators convert them to the high-affinity conformation.

SELF-TEST

1. c [Glucose is a source of chemical potential energy whereas heat, electricity, and light are examples of kinetic energy]
2. a [A hydroelectric plant, like cells and the ocean, exchanges energy and matter with its surroundings. It converts the kinetic energy of the falling water into other types of energy]
3. d [Entropy is given by S and is the measure of disorder in a system]
4. d [A living cell is an open system, exchanging energy and matter with its surroundings, in order to maintain a low entropy. When it dies, its spontaneous chemical reactions will reach equilibrium where $\Delta G = 0$]
5. c [Ice has low entropy as it has a highly ordered structure. As it absorbs enthalpy from its surroundings, it melts and its entropy increases]
6. c [The reaction would be exergonic; that is, the ΔG of the reaction would be negative]
7. b [Reactions are spontaneous if they have a negative ΔG, that is, the products have lower enthalpy and/or higher entropy (disorder) than the reactants]
8. a [Anabolism refers to metabolic pathways that involve the synthesis of cellular molecules and structures, whereas catabolism involves the breakdown of high-energy molecules (i.e., food). Each type of pathway may have endergonic or exergonic reactions; however, anabolism requires an input of free energy and catabolism releases free energy]
9. b [While kinetically slow, the hydrolysis of ATP in aqueous solution, or using energy coupling, releases a large amount of free energy]
10. a [Energy coupling allows an endergonic reaction to occur by coupling it with the exergonic, enzymatic breakdown of ATP, giving an overall exergonic (negative ΔG) reaction]
11. a [The activation energy is the energy required for the reactants of a spontaneous reaction to reach the transition state. It explains why reactions, in the absence of the enzyme catalyst, occur so slowly – this is a kinetic barrier]

12. d [Catalysts can be enzymes or, in a chemistry lab, heat from a bunson burner. They do not participate the reaction (they are not themselves altered), they just speed up the reaction]

13. d [An endergonic reaction will not proceed without an input of energy and this comes from energy coupling— i.e., linking an exergonic reaction with an endergonic one. Enzymes function by increasing the rate of spontaneous reactions through their temporary binding of the substrate(s) to help them attain the transition state]

14. c [A cofactor is inorganic, often a metal such as copper]

15. a [A coenzyme is organic, often derived from vitamins]

16. b [Because enzymes do not themselves participate in the reaction, as soon as the catalytic event is complete, the active site becomes free to immediately bind another substrate, and catalyze another reaction]

17. b [Enzymes help speed up the rate of spontaneous (ΔG is negative) reactions by helping the substrate(s) reach the transition state. In this state, the substrate has maximum enthalpy so is most thermodynamically unstable. Enzymes often require coenzymes which, in turn, may be derived from vitamins]

18. a [Competitive inhibitors are structurally similar to the substrate and work by competing for the active site of an enzyme, thereby preventing the natural substrate from binding]

19. d [Free energy is a characteristic of the reactants and products; enzymes do not participate in the reaction, so cannot contribute free energy]

20. b [The end products of the pathways are allosteric inhibitors of enzymes at the beginning of the pathway, binding to the allosteric sites on the enzymes and causing a conformational change from high affinity to low affinity]

21. a [Enzymes have a characteristic range of pH and temperature over which they will act, with an optimum pH and temperature being somewhere between the two extremes]

INTEGRATING AND APPLYING KEY CONCEPTS

1. Read section 4.3, consider the primary product of photosynthesis and respiration (Chapter 3), and examine the structure of ATP and ADP in Figure 4.10.

2. Read section 4.3b and examine Figure 4.11. Recognize that Figure 4.11c represents the net reaction but that, in the presence of the enzyme, there is no water-based hydrolysis, instead the phosphate group that is removed from ATP is temporarily transferred to glutamic acid.

Chapter 5   Cell Membranes and Signalling

Why It Matters [pp. 92–93]
5.1 An Overview of the Structure of Membranes [pp. 93–94]

1. transport; 2. Cl⁻; 3. selectively; 4. fluid mosaic; 5. lipid; 6. proteins; 7. proteins; 8. halves; 9. Using freeze fracture techniques with electron microscopy, the slicing/fracturing of the cells often splits the bilayer so one half of the membrane is visible as is the other, demonstrating asymmetrical distributions of proteins; 10. The membrane proteins of human and mouse cells were labelled with differently coloured dye molecules and then fused. Within less than 1h, the two different types of proteins were evenly distributed over the surface of the hybrid cells, providing a demonstration of the fluid nature of the membrane; 11. T; 12. F – It is extremely rare for them to flip-flop from one side of the bilayer to the other.

5.2 The Lipid Fabric of a Membrane [pp. 94–97]

13. Phospholipids; 14. hydrophilic; 15. hydrophobic; 16. amphipathic; 17. polar; 18. hydrophobic; 19. fatty acid; 20. saturated; 21. unsaturated; 22. carbon-carbon; 23. unsaturated; 24. ectotherms; 25. desaturase; 26. double; 27. C; 28. H; 29. F; 30. B; 31. G; 32. A; 33. D; 34. E; 35. T; 36. F – They remove a hydrogen atom from adjacent carbon atoms of the fatty acid chain, to generate a C-C double bond; 37. F – At high temperatures they help restrain movement between neighbouring fatty acid tails. At low temperatures they disrupt the interactions between neighbouring fatty acid tails, thus slowing the transition to the non-fluid gel state; 38. Double bonds introduce bends in the fatty acid chains meaning that the more double bonds within the fatty acid chain, the lower the degree of packing of the membrane and the higher the fluidity; 39. Sterols are associated with animal membranes and act to buffer the effects of changing

temperatures: with temperature increases they restrain the motion of the membrane lipids, effectively decreasing fluidity and with temperature decreases they disrupt the interactions between adjacent lipids, effectively increasing fluidity;
40. Low temperature causes gelling of the membrane so transport processes cannot occur. High temperature causes the membrane to become leaky, so the ion balance is destroyed and cells can rupture.

5.3 Membrane Proteins [pp. 97–100]

41. proteins; 42. Transport; 43. enzymatic; 44. electron; 45. signal transduction; 46. attachment; 47. recognition;
48. integral membrane; 49. transmembrane; 50. peripheral; 51. hydrogen/ionic; 52. ionic/hydrogen; 53. A – Containing a mixture of polar and non-polar amino acids and associated with one of the membrane surfaces through hydrogen or ionic bonding with lipid molecules or integral membrane proteins, B – Anchoring cytoskeleton and associated with respiratory or photosynthetic electron transport chains, C – Composed of domains of 17–20 non-polar/hydrophobic amino acids, giving rise to membrane-spanning alpha-helices, connected by flexible loops of hydrophilic/polar amino acids that are exposed to the aqueous environment on either side of the membrane, D – Transport proteins; 54. One examines the amino acid sequence for stretches of 17–20 hydrophobic/non-polar amino acids. There is often more than one domain within the protein, and in between will be stretches of primarily polar/charged amino acids; 55. A – Cholesterol, B – Integral protein (glycoprotein), C – Peripheral protein, D – Lipid bilayer, E – Polar (phosphate) head group.

5.4 Passive Membrane Transport [pp. 100–104]

56. hydrophobic; 57. high; 58. low; 59. diffusion; 60. size/charge; 61. charge/size; 62. non-polar; 63. hydrophobic;
64. facilitated; 65. channel; 66. carrier; 67. channels; 68. ions; 69. bind; 70. conformational; 71. solute; 72. osmosis;
73. aquaporins; 74. G; 75. D; 76. A; 77. B; 78. C; 79. F; 80. E; 81. F – Diffusion is entropy-driven with maximum entropy being attained at equilibrium; 82. T; 83. Both involve the movement of solutes from areas of high concentration to lower concentration without the expenditure of energy, but facilitated diffusion uses a transport protein specific for a particular type of substrate, has a faster initial rate, but displays saturation at high concentration of substrate molecules;
84. The channel contains positive charges that repel protons and has such a narrow diameter that water molecules must pass through single file; 85. In the absence of active transport of ions to balance the osmotic pressure, water would rush into the cells, causing them to swell and burst; 86. A – Simple diffusion, B – Facilitated diffusion, C – All transporters are occupied; 87. A – Membrane, B – Solute, C – Into the cell, D – Hypertonic, E – No net movement (equilibrium), F – Isotonic, G – Out of the cell, H – Hypotonic.

5.5 Active Membrane Transport [pp. 104–107]

88. energy; 89. binding; 90. conformational; 91. solute; 92. primary; 93. ATP; 94. gradients; 95. secondary; 96. sodium;
97. potassium; 98. potential; 99. ion; 100. symport; 101. antiport; 102. Both involve transport proteins that are substrate-specific, saturable, and undergo conformational changes to move the solute from one side of the membrane to the other;
103. There is a concentration gradient of the two chemicals on either side of the membrane and because the two different ions are not transported in equal numbers, there is also a charge or electrical gradient across the membrane; 104. Uptake of essential nutrients, removal of waste or secretory material, and maintenance of constant intracellular ion concentrations; 105. A – Transport requires an input of energy and involves moving materials across the membrane against a concentration gradient, B – Symport, C – Antiport.

5.6 Exocytosis and Endocytosis [pp. 107–109]

106. endocytosis; 107. exocytosis; 108. vesicle; 109. plasma membrane; 110. endocytosis; 111. endocytic vesicle; 112. bulk-transport; 113. receptor-mediated; 114. lysosomes; 115. transport; 116. membrane; 117. phagocytosis; 118. C; 119. A; 120. B; 121. A; 122. C; 123. All three are energy-dependent processes for moving materials across the plasma membrane; 124. The substance to be transported binds specifically to integral proteins in the plasma membrane and the complexes collect in a clathrin-coated pit within the plasma membrane. The pit deepens and pinches off as an endocytic vesicle; the clathrin molecules are lost, and the vesicle fuses with a lysosomal vesicle. If the digested contents are of value to the cell, the products are transported across the vesicle membrane into the cytoplasm.

5.7 Role of Membranes in Cell Signalling [pp. 109–112]

125. signals; 126. signal transduction; 127. signal transduction; 128. response; 129. molecule; 130. membrane; 131. activates; 132. phosphorylation; 133. kinases; 134. amplified; 135. phosphatases; 136. active; 137. A – Reception; B – Transduction; C – Response; D – Amplified; 138. The extracellular signal molecule binds the surface receptor, causing a conformational change that activates the cytoplasmic protein kinase domain. This autophosphorylates then transfers the phosphate group to the next protein in the cascade, ultimately leading to phosphorylation of the last component, which then initiates its cellular response activity; 139. The last component of the cascade may be a transcriptional regulator which, when phosphorylated, has altered transcriptional regulation of a suite of genes, generating the cellular response.

SELF-TEST

1. a [The term "mosaic" refers to the fact that membranes contain an assortment of asymmetrically distributed proteins]
2. c [eukaryotic membranes contain various sterols; however, cholesterol is specific to animal membranes]
3. b [the phosphate groups are hydrophilic whereas the fatty acid chains are hydrophobic, making the entire molecule amphipathic. In aqueous solution a bilayer forms so that the hydrophilic region of the molecules is facing the aqueous environment, while the hydrophobic regions are sequestered from water inside the bilayer. This is also called the hydrophobic effect]
4. b [Increased unsaturation increases the kinks in the fatty acid tails of adjacent lipids meaning they cannot pack as tightly. The expression of desaturases, the enzymes that introduce the carbon-carbon double bonds, is increased in order to increase unsaturation and lower gelling temperature]
5. a [Desaturases introduce the carbon-carbon double bonds in fatty acid tails by removing a hydrogen atom from adjacent carbons. They are more active at lower temperatures in order to maintain a fluid membrane through a lowed gelling temperature]
6. d [Membrane proteins function in transport, recognition/attachment, enzyme activity, and signal transduction. The phospholipid bilayer establishes the barrier function]
7. a [These are typical of integral membrane proteins only]
8. a [Polar head groups are associated with the phosphate portion of membrane phospholipids. Integral membrane proteins, once folded, have hydrophobic surface domains that associate with the hydrophobic interior of membranes and hydrophilic/polar surface domains that associate with the cytoplasm and exterior environment]
9. b [Only very small non-polar molecules such as O_2 and CO_2 can cross a membrane by simple diffusion. Larger solutes such as glucose and other sugars, and any ions, must be transported through transport mechanisms]
10. c [Diffusion stops when equal concentrations of solutes across the membrane are reached. At this point, the system has maximum entropy and while solutes continue to move in either direction, there is no NET movement of solutes]
11. d [Sodium is charged and, like all ions, must cross using a transport protein]
12. d [Aquaporins are extremely narrow channels that are filled with positive charges so that water passes through single file and other solutes are prevented from entering]
13. a [Voltage-gated channels are involved in facilitated diffusion]
14. c [The concentration of sucrose in B is higher than in A, so relative to A it is hypertonic]

15. b [Because the cellophane is only permeable to water, water would move by osmosis from an area of lesser solute concentration to one of higher solute concentration]

16. a [Water would move by osmosis from A, the area of lesser solute concentration to B, the area of higher solute concentration]

17. d [All ions are transported through primary active transport. Water is transported by simple diffusion through the lipid bilayer or aquaporins]

18. c [They are common in animal cells and are used to generate a membrane potential/electrochemical gradient across the plasma membrane]

19. c [ATP provides the energy for primary active transport and this may result in the generation of favourable ion gradients, which may provide the energy to drive secondary active transport]

20. a [The cytoplasmic side of the pits is coated and reinforced by clathrin proteins. These proteins are lost once the endocytic vesicle forms]

21. a [Pinocytosis is another name for bulk-phase endocytosis]

22. b [Surface receptors are integral membrane proteins that bind an extracellular environmental signal and undergo a conformational change that transduces the signal across the membrane, triggering activation of the cytoplasmic domain of the receptor. Diffusion across the membrane would circumvent these critical first steps]

INTEGRATING AND APPLYING KEY CONCEPTS

1. Read section 5.2 on membrane lipids and consider the differences between membrane structure, relevant enzyme(s), and transcription levels.

2. Read section 5.2c and 5.6 and think about where cholesterol is needed within cells and what process would likely allow the cholesterol to reach that destination. Given the size of the blood complex, and the fact that the lipoprotein complexes are accumulating in the extracellular environment, what process might be used to import a specific complex into the cell and what is the basis for the specificity of this process? So what might be defective in such individuals?

3. Read "Why It Matters" and sections 5.4c and 5.4d. Also examine Figures 5.14 and 5.16.

Chapter 6   Cellular Respiration

Why It Matters [pp. 115–116]
6.1 The Chemical Basis of Cellular Respiration [pp. 116–118]

1. respiration; 2. fuel; 3. photosynthesis; 4. sugar/organic; 5. electrons; 6. work; 7. oxidation; 8. removal/loss;

9. reduction; 10. redox; 11. ATP; 12. F; 13. A; 14. G; 15. C; 16. E; 17. B; 18. D; 19. A – Makes, B – Breaks,

C – Releases, D – Uses, E – Uses, F – Releases, G – Stores, H – Releases; 20. T; 21. F – As atoms move further from the

atom's nucleus, they gain energy; 22. F – Sometimes other molecules are used and sometimes molecules are only

partially oxidized or reduced; 23. Methane is partially reduced to carbon dioxide because the carbon electrons move from

being equally shared in the C-H bonds to being much closer to the electronegative oxygen; oxygen is partially reduced to

water because the electrons in the O-H bond of water are held closer to the oxygen atom than in the O_2 bonds.

6.2 Cellular Respiration: An Overview [pp. 118–119]
6.3 Glycolysis: The Splitting of Glucose [pp. 120–122]
6.4 Pyruvate Oxidation and the Citric Acid Cycle [pp. 122–123]

24. three; 25. glycolysis; 26. pyruvate; 27. citric acid; 28. CO_2; 29. substrate-level; 30. NADH/$FADH_2$; 31. electron

transport chain; 32. oxidative; 33. proton; 34. ATP; 35. mitochondrion; 36. C; 37. E; 38. A; 39. B; 40. F; 41. D; 42. F –

Organisms from all branches of the tree of life carry out this process; 43. F – Gycolysis occurs in the cytoplasm but

pyruvate oxidation occurs in the mitochondrial matrix; 44. F – Pyruvate crosses the outer mitochondrial membrane by

diffusion but must be transported across the inner mitochondrial membrane; 45. It is widespread among life forms, does

not require oxygen, which appeared later in the evolution of life and is a series of cytoplasmic enzymatic reactions

without the requirement of electron transport chains or organelles; 46. During the initial, energy investment phase, two molecules of ATP supply phosphate for two phosphorylation reactions; 47. Some of the potential energy present in glucose has been lost in the form of the high-energy molecules ATP and NADH; 48. A – Glycolysis, B – Glucose, C – 2 Pyruvate, 2ATP and 2 NADH, D – Pyruvate, E – Acetyl CoA, 1 CO_2, 1 NADH, F – Citric acid cycle, G – Acetyl CoA, H – CoA, 2 CO_2, 3 NADH, 1 $FADH_2$, 1 ATP.

6.5 Oxidative Phosphorylation: Electron Transport and Chemiosmosis [pp. 123–129]

49. NADH/$FADH_2$; 50. $FADH_2$/NADH; 51. complexes; 52. electron; 53. inner membrane; 54. exergonic; 55. spontaneous; 56. proton; 57. motive force; 58. chemiosmosis; 59. transport; 60. synthase; 61. down; 62. ADP/Pi; 63. Pi/ADP; 64. electron transport; 65. ionophores; 66. heat; 67. G; 68. A; 69. F; 70. E; 71. B; 72. C; 73. D; 74. The former uses the ATP synthase and inorganic phosphate for phosphorylation, whereas the latter uses soluble enzymes and other phosphorylated molecules as a donor for the phosphorylation reaction; 75. NADH and $FADH_2$ both possess free energy and this is extracted after they donate their electrons to the electron transport chain which converts the chemical energy to a proton motive force; 76. In eukaryotes it is in the inner membrane of the mitochondrion, whereas in the prokaryotes it is in the plasma membrane; 77. The exergonic electron flow through the electron transport chain is usually coupled with synthesis of ATP by oxidative phosphorylation. Uuncoupling proteins cause a loss of proton motive force and release of the energy from electron flow as heat. This is used to maintain body heat in hibernating animals and the newborn babies; 78. A – Outer membrane, B – Intermembrane space, C – Inner membrane, D – Matrix, E – Cytosol; 79. E; 80. D; 81. D; 82. C; 83. C; 84. C, D, A, B.

6.6 The Efficiency and Regulation of Cellular Respiration [pp. 129–132]

85. 10; 86. 3; 87. 3; 88. $FADH_2$; 89. 38; 90. 38; 91. fats/proteins/carbohydrates; 92. anabolic/biosynthetic; 93. supply; 94. demand; 95. phosphofructokinase; 96. AMP; 97. ATP; 98. citrate; 99. F – Some is made in the cytoplasm through glycolysis and substrate-level phosphorylation, while the rest is made in the mitochondrial matrix; 100. T; 101. F – This is true of eukaryotes but not bacteria, which do produce the maximum yield; 102. F – The inhibition is allosteric rather than competitive; 103. A – 2, B – 3, C – 6, D – 2, E – 6, F – 2, G – 2, H – 18, I – 4, J – 4; 104. Three reasons: 1) 2 molecules of ATP are used to transport 2 molecules of NADH into the mitochondrion, 2) The inner mitochondrial membrane is somewhat leaky to protons and this represents a reduction in the proton motive force used to make ATP, and 3) Some of the proton motive force is used for other energy-requiring reactions, such as transport of pyruvate into the mitochondrion; 105. Electron transport releases free energy that is used to create the proton motive force. This is, in turn, used by the membrane-bound ATP synthase to produce ATP.

6.7 Oxygen and Cellular Respiration [pp. 132–136]

106. ATP; 107. fermentation; 108. oxidative; 109. pyruvate; 110. NAD^+; 111. substrate-level; 112. anaerobic respiration; 113. ferric iron/Fe^{3+} or sulfate/ SO_4^{2-} or nitrate/NO_3^-; 114. aerobes; 115. facultative anaerobes; 116. anaerobes; 117. reactive oxygen intermediates; 118. C; 119. E; 120. F; 121. A; 122. B; 123. D; 124. The enzymes superoxide dismutase and catalase act together to convert superoxide then hydrogen peroxide to water by catalyzing their reduction. Molecules such as vitamins C and E do the same thing; 125. The reduction of oxygen to water requires four electrons. Cytochrome oxidase fills with all four electrons before simultaneously transferring all four to the electron acceptor; 126. A – Cytosol, 2, 2, 0, no, pyruvate, B – Cytosol, 0, 0, 0, no, lactic acid + NAD^+; 127. T; 128. F – It only occurs in certain bacteria and archaea; 129. T.

1. b [Their oxidation yields more energy than carbohydrates because they consist of predominantly carbon-hydrogen (C-H) bonds where the electron is shared equally and is therefore higher energy than in polar bonds such as the C-O bonds of carbohydrates]
2. d [Redox reactions may consist of complete reductions, complete oxidations, or reactions where the gain or loss of an electron is incomplete, as in the burning of natural gas/methane in air]
3. c [Dehydrogenases are the enzymes that transfer high-energy electrons removed in respiratory oxidation reactions, donating them to coenzymes NAD and FAD]
4. d [The energy released is in the form of heat]
5. a [It is reduced by dehydrogenases, accepting two electrons and one proton]
6. a [2 ATP molecules are consumed in phosphorylation reactions in the energy investment phase of glycolysis]
7. b [The 6-carbon glucose is oxidized to two 3-carbon molecules of pyruvate, which is oxidized prior to the citric acid cycle]
8. a [The end product, pyruvate, is then transported from the cytoplasm to the mitochondrial matrix]
9. b [Pyruvate oxidation yields 1 CO_2, 1 NADH, and 1 acetyl CoA but no ATP]
10. b [Energy was extracted during glycolysis, in the form of 2 ATP and 2 NADH]
11. c [Pyruvate is oxidized to acetyl CoA, and it is the latter that enters the citric acid cycle]
12. d [Electron transport chains generate a proton motive force, and this provides the energy to drive oxidative phosphorylation, where ATP is made by the membrane-bound ATP synthase through chemiosmosis]
13. c [Photosynthesis involves a photosynthetic electron transport chain, the energy from the sun used to drive electrons through the chain and the generated proton motive force converted to ATP by chemiosmosis using a membrane-bound ATP synthase]
14. a [He won the Nobel prize for his work determining that synthesis of ATP through oxidative phosphorylation was the result of chemiosmosis, a concept that was originally ridiculed]
15. a [Harnessing the energy in proton motive force to make ATP using an ATP synthase is fundamental to almost all forms of life and is therefore thought to have evolved very early]
16. c [They insert into the membrane, allowing protons to flow down their concentration gradient, effectively eliminating the proton motive force. However, electrons still flow through the electron transport chain, with the energy being released in the form of heat, as is seen in brown adipose fat cells]
17. d [When fire is used for combustion, all the energy is lost as heat, whereas cellular respiration uses energy to release the energy gradually, trapping it in forms that can be used to do work. The process is, however, not 100% efficient due to the factors identified in a, b, and c]
18. b [Intermediates of the respiratory pathways are also used in biosynthesis/anabolism, making the careful regulation by supply and demand extremely important]
19. b [Glycolysis produces ATP through substrate-level phosphorylation and is the only source of ATP in muscle cells starved for oxygen]
20. a [Glycolysis produces pyruvate, and this is not imported into the mitochondrion but is reduced in the cytoplasm, to regenerate the NAD required for continuing glycolysis]
21. d [The bacteria in yogurt perform lactic acid fermentation, producing lactic acid, the product that causes the thickening and souring of the milk used to make yogurt]
22. d [The yeast perform alcoholic fermentation which generates CO_2 and alcohol. The CO_2 causes the bread dough to rise and the alcohol is burned off during baking]
23. b [Some bacteria and archaea perform respiration but use a terminal acceptor other than O_2— for example, sulfate, nitrate, and ferric iron]
24. d [The enzyme is highly efficient, avoiding the production of ROIs by the simultaneous reduction of oxygen with four electrons; however, since oxygen was not present on primordial Earth, it likely evolved later]

INTEGRATING AND APPLYING KEY CONCEPTS

1. Read sections 6.3, 6.4, and 6.5 to determine the relative localization of the pathways and transfer reactions in the mitochondrion and aerobic bacteria. Where does respiration stop in fermentation? And what is the distinction between anaerobic and aerobic respiration (section 6.7)?
2. Read the section on the effect of uncouplers (section 6.5e) and reread the description of Luft syndrome in "Why It Matters." What are the similarities between the effects of uncouplers and the effects of the syndrome?
3. Read the section on the metabolic effects of anaerobic conditions (section 6.7) and the first paragraph in box 6.2, "Molecule behind Biology."

Chapter 7   Photosynthesis

Why It Matters [pp. 139–140]
7.1 Photosynthesis: An Overview [pp. 140–142]

1. photosynthetic; 2. aquatic; 3. CO_2; 4. autotrophs; 5. consumers; 6. producers; 7. light; 8. pigment; 9. ATP/NADPH;

10. NADPH/ATP; 11. Calvin; 12. carbohydrate; 13. organic; 14. chloroplasts; 15. plasma membrane; 16. A –

Chloroplast inner and outer membranes, B – Thylakoid/thylakoid membrane, C – Stroma, D – Thylakoid lumen; 17. B;

18. C; 19. T; 20. T; 21. F – Phototrophs can convert the energy of sunlight to chemical energy, so the halobacteria

(archaeons) are also photrophic although not photosynthetic/photoautotrophic; 22. C; 23. G; 24. I; 25. H; 26. A; 27. B;

28. J; 29. F; 30. E; 31. D; 32. A – makes, B – breaks, C – releases, D – uses, E – uses, F – releases, G – stores, H –

releases; 33. $6 CO_2 + 12 H_2O \rightarrow C_6H_{12}O_6 + 6 H_2O + 6 O_2$, the light-dependent reactions occur in the thylakoids and the

CO_2 is fixed in the stroma of the chloroplast; 34. Photosynthesis is the use of light energy to provide the high energy

molecules required for the Calvin cycle. Phototrophs include photosynthetic organisms as well as those that can convert

the energy of light to chemical energy but do not obtain their carbon from carbon dioxide (e.g., the halobacteria).

Chemoautotrophs obtain their energy from inorganic chemicals and use this to convert CO_2 to organics.

7.2 The Photosynthetic Apparatus [pp. 142–146]

35. pigment; 36. ground; 37. excited; 38. light; 39. resonance; 40. excited; 41. primary; 42. Chlorophylls;

43. photosystems; 44. thylakoid; 45. reaction; 46. antenna; 47. reaction; 48. primary; 49. P680*; 50. P680$^+$; 51. water;

52. oxygen; 53. F; 54. G; 55. A; 56. K; 57. H; 58. C; 59. E; 60. I; 61. L; 62. M; 63. D; 64. B; 65. J; 66. This phase traps

light energy and uses it to create the high-energy molecules NADPH and ATP. These are used convert CO_2 to

carbohydrates and other organic molecules for cell structures; 67. Upon absorption, the antenna chlorophyll molecules

transfer the absorbed energy to neighbouring molecules through inductive resonance, until the energy is funnelled to the

reaction centre chlorophyll; 68. P680 is the reaction centre chlorophyll of PSII at ground state, whereas P680* is the

molecule after absorbing a photon of light, with its excited state electron. P680$^+$ is the molecule after it has been oxidized

by the primary acceptor and before it has been reduced by the splitting of water; 69. F – This is the technique used to

measure the activity spectrum. The absorption spectrum is measured using a spectrophotometer which provides relative

units of absorption as a function of wavelength; 70. F – They are both chlorophyll a molecules. The difference in

absorbed wavelength is the result of the various molecules that surround them in their respective photosystems; 71. T.

7.3 The Light Reactions [pp. 146–149]

72. reaction centre; 73. photosynthetic; 74. linear; 75. oxidation; 76. electron; 77. NADP$^+$ reductase; 78. P680$^+$;

79. water; 80. oxygen-evolving; 81. proton motive force; 82. ATP synthase; 83. photophosphorylation; 84. cyclic;

85. ATP; 86. NADPH; 87. E; 88. G; 89. B; 90. A; 91. H; 92. I; 93. J; 94. F; 95. C; 96. D; 97. B, D, A, D, C; 98. F – It is

to augment the ATP production; 99. T; 100. T; 101. F – It is on the lumen side of the thylakoid membrane; 102. A – To

make ATP and NADPH, B – The reaction centre chlorophyll of PSII once excited by absorption of light, C – This is

where the photosystems and electron transport chains are located and where the ATP synthase is located, D – This is the

reaction centre chlorophyll of PSII after being oxidized by the primary acceptor; 103. The water-splitting complex is

associated with PSII, which is involved in linear electron flow, so that once oxidized, the P680 reaction centre

chlorophyll cannot undergo another oxidation reaction until it has been reduced. The electrons for that come from water;

104. The carbon fixation process requires 18 ATP for every molecule of glucose made and only 12 NADPH. Since limear electron flow makes one of each, the additional ATP required is supplied by cyclic flow, which only generates ATP; 105. To get one electron from H_2O/PSII to NADPH, two photons of light must be absorbed, one for each PS. Each water molecule releases two electrons when split and the formation of oxygen requires two oxygen atoms—i.e., two water molecules must be split. Therefore $2 \times 2 \times 2 = 8$ photons are required to generate 1 molecule of O_2.

7.4 The Calvin Cycle [pp. 149–152]

107. NADPH; 108. carbohydrates/sugar; 109. endergonic; 110. rubisco; 111. ribulose-1, 5-bisphophshate; 112. glyceraldehyde-3-phosphate; 113. 3; 114. glyceraldehyde-3-phosphate/G3P; 115. organic; 116. C; 117. D; 118. B; 119. A; 120. F – it produces 1 molecule of G3P for every 3 cycles and $2 \times$ G3P generate 1 molecule of glucose; 121. T; 122. F – The reason for its abundance is that it is catalytically very slow; 123. F – all photoautotrophs, including cyanobacteria, use the Calvin cycle; 124. Fixation, where the CO_2 is combined with RuBP to make 3PG, followed by reduction where NADPH and ATP generate G3P, and finally, regeneration, where 5 carbons from 2 molecules of G3P get rearranged to yield RuBP so the cycle can start over; 125. A – Acceptor molecule for CO_2 fixation by Calvin cycle, B – The product of the Calvin cycle which is then used as a building bock to make other organic molecules, C – The immediate product of CO_2 fixation in the Calvin cycle, D – The carboxylase enzyme of the Calvin cycle, E – The aqueous environment of the chloroplast in which the Calvin cycle occurs; 126. A – Thylakoid, produced, produced, produced, NA, NA, B – Stroma, used, used, NA, used, produced.

7.5 Photorespiration and CO_2-Concentrating Mechanisms [pp. 152–157]
7.6 Photosynthesis and Cellular Respiration Compared [p. 157]

127. oxygen; 128. active; 129. oxygenase; 130. photorespiration; 131. toxic; 132. CO_2; 133. CO_2; 134. HCO_3^-; 135. carbonic; 136. PEP carboxylase; 137. oxaloacetate; 138. CO_2; 139. mesophyll; 140. bundle sheath; 141. mesophyll; 142. PEP; 143. stomata; 144. Calvin cycle; 145. E; 146. K; 147. H; 148. C; 149. B; 150. D; 151. I; 152. A; 153. J; 154. F; 155. G; 156. F – The solubility of all gases decreases with increasing temperatures; 157. T; 158. T; 159. It likely evolved at a time when there was no oxygen in Earth's atmosphere so no problem with oxygen as a competitive inhibitor. Even in the presence of equal amounts of CO_2 and O_2, the enzyme uses CO_2 far more efficiently; however, the modern-day atmosphere consists of 21% O_2 and less than 1% CO_2; 160. Some algae actively pump HCO_3^- into the cell, enzymatically convert it to CO_2, which diffuses into the chloroplast where it is at much higher levels than O_2. C_4 plants use a supplemental enzyme for carbon fixation to oxaloacetate in the surface mesophyll cells, where O_2 concentrations are high. They convert this to malate which diffuses into the deeper bundle sheath cells, where O_2 is less concentrated, and in these cells, malate is hydrolyzed, releasing high quantities of CO_2 for the Calvin cycle; 161. Corn is a C_4 plant so it separates its two CO_2-fixing processes spatially, with the C_4 pathway occurring in mesophyll cells and the Calvin cycle occurring in the bundle sheath cells. Cacti are CAM plants so they separate the processes temporally. The C_4 pathway occurs in mesophyll cells at night, when the stomata are open, and during the day, the stomata are closed, and the Calvin cycle occurs in the mesophyll cells by hydrolyzing malate that had been stored in vacuoles, and releasing large amounts of CO_2; 162. A – Glucose & O_2, B – H_2O & CO_2, C – H_2O & CO_2, D – O_2 & sugars, E – G3P, F – Oxidative phosphorylation, G – Photophosphorylation, H – Mitochondria, I – All, J – Chloroplasts, K – Mesophyll.

1. c [Nutrients, in particular iron, are in poor supply nearer the equator but are in rich supply around the poles]
2. a [Photoautotrophs use the energy from sunlight to make the high-energy molecules that then allows them to fix carbon dioxide. Phototrophs, by contrast, do not necessarily use the energy from sunlight to fix carbon dioxide and autotrophs may use the energy from chemical fuel molecules instead of sunlight, to fix carbon dioxide]
3. b [These are archaea that can trap the energy of sunlight, but they do not use it to synthesize organics so they are not photosynthetic]
4. d [G3P is an intermediate in the Calvin cycle, the so-called "dark reactions"]
5. a [Cyanobacteria perform the same kind of oxygenic photosynthesis as eukaryotic photosynthetic organisms, and it is in part based on this that the cyanobacteria are thought to be the ancestors to the eukaryotic chloroplast]
6. d [The thylakoid membrane contains the photosynthetic apparatus, which includes the pigment-containing antenna and the reaction centre chlorophyll]
7. a [Absorption occurs when the photon carries the same energy as the energy difference between the ground state electron, which is located close to the nucleus, to an excited state, where it moves to an outer orbital]
8. c [Fungi are decomposers, that is, they are heterotrophic, using organics as their energy source]
9. b [An action spectrum measures the rate of oxygen production as a function of wavelength, which means that it is a measure of photosynthetic activity of the organism or cell. This would include involve the chlorophylls, which absorb in the blue and red regions of the spectrum and the carotenoids, which absorb in the intermediate regions of visible light]
10. c [Carotenoids and chlorophyll b may occur in the antennae but special chlorophyll a molecules, P680 and P700, are the reaction centre chlorophylls]
11. c [Inductive resonance allows the direct transfer of energy from one antenna pigment to the next until it reaches the reaction centre chlorophyll, which is the only one that undergoes an oxidation reaction, donating its excited state electron to the primary acceptor]
12. a [P680 is the PSII reaction centre chlorophyll and when oxidized, i.e., having lost an electron, is denoted as $P680^+$]
13. a [Linear electron flow involves the flow of electrons from water, through PSII to PSI and to the final electron acceptor, NADP. Due to the generation of proton motive force and chemiosmosis the products are NADPH and ATP in equal proportions]
14. b [Proton motive force is generated across the thylakoid membrane with the interior having the higher concentration of protons. As a result, protons flow out of the lumen through the ATP synthase, generating ATP at the stroma side of the ATP synthase, where it is then used for the Calvin cycle, which also occurs in the stroma]
15. d [One molecule of O_2 is generated from two molecules of water. One molecule of water, when split, yields four electrons so two molecules would yield eight electrons and one photon energizes one electron]
16. b [Cyclic electron flow only involves PSI, and the electrons from P700 flow through the photosynthetic electron transport chain, providing the energy for development of proton motive force. Once the energy in the electron is depleted, the electron reduces $P700^+$ rather than $NADP^+$. So ATP is the only product, made through chemiosmosis]
17. a [PEP is the acceptor of CO_2 in the C_4 cycle, whereas rubisco is the enzyme from the Calvin cycle that carboxylates RuBP, producing 3PG/3-phosphoglycerate]
18. d [Three rounds of the Calvin cycle are required to generate one surplus G3P and two G3P are required to combine to produce, ultimately, glucose, through a reversal of glycolysis]
19. a [G3P is produced in the Calvin cycle and some of it is retained by the cycle to help regenerate RuBP, the acceptor of CO_2 in the carboxylation activity catalyzed by rubisco]
20. c [Rubisco has a higher affinity for CO_2 than for O_2; however, since O_2 is present at higher levels (21%) in the atmosphere compared to CO_2 (0.04%) under normal atmospheric conditions and temperature, O_2 successfully competes for the active site ~25% of the time]
21. b [The algae reduce the rate of oxygenation reactions catalyzed by rubisco through a membrane-bound carbon pump that actively pumps inorganic carbon into the cell. This gives an intracellular CO_2 concentration higher than the surrounding waters, and reduces the ability of oxygen to compete for rubisco's active site]
22. a [C_3 plants perform only the Calvin cycle when fixing carbon dioxide—they have no way of helping concentrate CO_2 to levels higher than 0.04%, so they will undergo photorespiration as oxygen successfully competes for the rubisco active site]
23. c [The immediate product of C_4 metabolism, specifically the PEP carboxylase, is oxaloacetate, which is further converted to malate and this is hydrolyzed to provide high levels of CO_2, either in the bundle sheaths of C_4 plants or during the day in mesophyll cells of Cam plants]
24. b [CAM plants such as cacti and pineapples only open their stoma during the night when it is cool, and thus can avoid water loss but allow CO_2 to diffuse in. They fix this carbon using the C_4 pathway and store the product, malate, in vesicles. During the day the stoma are closed and the malate diffuses out of the vesicles, is hydrolyzed,

releasing large amounts of CO_2 which is then fixed using the Calvin cycle. The oxygen produced by the Calvin cycle is released the following night when the stomata reopen]

INTEGRATING AND APPLYING KEY CONCEPTS

1. Read sections 7.5c, d, and e, playing particular attention to Table 7.1 and Figure 7.20.
2. This question is, in part, asking you to be able to reproduce the information in Figure 7.11 without referring to the diagram for guidance. Having done that, if you are stuck with the cyanobacteria, reread section 7.1b.
3. Read sections 7.3e, 7.4a, and 7.4b. Remember that glucose is a 6-carbon molecule and that it is made from three molecules of G3P.

Chapter 8   Cell Cycles

Why It Matters [pp. 161–162]
8.1 The Cycle of Cell Growth and Division: An Overview [pp. 162–163]
8.2 Cell Division in Prokaryotic Organisms [pp. 163–164]

1. binary fission; 2. chromosome; 3. DNA replication; 4. origin; 5. origins; 6. Cytokinesis; 7. wall; 8. F – The mechanism of segregation of bacterial chromosomes is unknown; 9. This means the splitting or dividing into two parts and is the process by which prokaryotic cells undergo cell division.

8.3 Mitosis and the Eukaryotic Cell Cycle [pp. 164–171]

10. three; 11. DNA replication; 12. DNA; 13. cytokinesis; 14. daughter; 15. parental; 16. genetically; 17. mitosis; 18. chromosomes; 19. proteins; 20. chromosomes; 21. parent; 22. diploid; 23. haploid; 24. ploidy; 25. chromatids; 26. interphase; 27. mitosis; 28. G_1; 29. S; 30. G_2; 31. prophase; 32. condense; 33. centrosomes; 34. spindle; 35. prometaphase; 36. nuclear; 37. spindle; 38. spindle; 39. kinetochore; 40. metaphase; 41. spindle; 42. metaphase; 43. anaphase; 44. sister chromatids; 45. spindle; 46. segregation; 47. daughter; 48. telophase; 49. decondense; 50. spindle; 51. nuclear; 52. cytokinesis; 53. furrowing; 54. plate; 55. E; 56. F; 57. B; 58. G; 59. A; 60. C; 61. D; 62. T; 63. F – All of the cells that make up a multicellular organism arose by mitosis from a single cell, the zygote, so they all have the same genetic material; 64. M; 65. D; 66. E; 67. A; 68. B; 69. H; 70. L; 71. J; 72. K; 73. G; 74. I; 75. N; 76. F; 77. C; 78. F – DNA is synthesized during the S phase; 79. T; 80. F – They are synthesizing RNA and proteins in preparation for mitosis; 81. C – G_2, D – $4n$, E – Prophase, F – $4n$,G – Prometaphase, H – $4n$, I – Metaphase, J – $4n$, K – Anaphase, L – $4n$, M – Telophase, N – $4n$; O – G_1, P – $2n$; 82. By undergoing this transition, cells commit themselves to cell division. It is subject to molecule controls and loss of these controls is a hallmark of cancer; 83. Sister chromatids are the replicated chromosome pairs that exist in a cell prior to cytokinesis; 84. Cell furrowing is the process used by animals in cytokinesis and involves the formation of a band of microfilaments just inside the plasma membrane which gradually contracts. This gives rise to a furrow that expands until the daughter cells are separated. Cell plate formation is used by plants to separate the two daughter cells. It involves the vesicular deposition of cell wall material at the former spindle midpoint until the daughter cells are separated.

8.4 Formation and Action of the Mitotic Spindle [pp. 171–173]

85. mitotic spindle; 86. centrosome; 87. organizing; 88. microtubules; 89. nucleus; 90. kinetochores; 91. kinetochore; 92. nonkinetochore; 93. midpoint; 94. kinetochore; 95. disassembles; 96. nonkinetochore; 97. poles; 98. D; 99. C; 100. A; 101. B; 102. F – They are responsible for generating the microtubules for cilia and flagella; 103. T.

8.5 Cell Cycle Regulation [pp. 174–178]

104. checkpoints; 105. reactions; 106. cyclin; 107. cycle; 108. cyclin-dependent; 109. phosphorylation; 110. cycle; 111. cyclins; 112. surface receptors; 113. peptide; 114. growth; 115. contact; 116. phosphate; 117. contact inhibition; 118. dividing; 119. tumours; 120. metastasis; 121. body; 122. death; 123. apoptosis; 124. surplus; 125. infected; 126. caspases; 127. B; 128. F; 129. E; 130. G; 131. C; 132. D; 133. A; 134. F – The cyclin proteins vary with the cell cycle, rising in concentrations until a critical level where they are able to bind and activate their cognate CDK kinase activity. After that transition has passed, the cyclin is degraded; 135. T; 136. This is the loss of replicative ability in "older" cells and it is thought to be caused, at least in part, by progressive damage to DNA sequences and to the shortening of chromosomal telomeres; 137. Cancerous cells often have suffered mutations to genes that encode the proteins and molecules involved in the internal or external regulation of cell division. These mutated genes are called oncogenes.

SELF-TEST

1. b [Mitosis is the process by which eukaryotes grow, ensuring that the new cells are exactly the same as the parental cells]
2. a [G_1 is the most variable in length; cells make the transition to S only when they need to divide]
3. a [The envelope breaks down in prophase, the chromatids begin to condense, and the duplicated centrosomes begin to make the mitotic spindle. The nuclear envelope has disappeared by prometaphase]
4. c [G_o is the phase that some cells enter from G_1 and is a state of division arrest]
5. c [Each chromatid has a single kinetochore through which the molecule attaches to and eventually moves along a kinetochore microtubule]
6. c [Flowering plants and conifers lack a centrosome and instead have multiple MTOCs]
7. a [Cyclin B is the internal signal molecule that, at a critical concentration, binds to and activates CDK1, which in turn initiates a signal transduction pathway that causes the cell to enter the M phase]
8. b [Contact inhibition is a normal property of healthy eukaryotic cells but is lost in cancerous cells, allowing them to overgrow each other, forming dense masses of cells called tumours]
9. c [The method of segregation of the daughter chromosomes in prokaryotic cells is unknown]
10. b [Only prokaryotic cells, with their much smaller chromosomes, have an origin of replication, that is, a unique DNA sequence at which replication begins]
11. a [Apoptosis is a process of programmed cell death that in required for normal development of multicellualr organisms, whereas senescence is a process that is not understood but that leads to the gradual loss of replicative ability over time]
12. d [Cellular senescence was discovered by Hayflick and Moorrhead, and scientists have been unable to confirm the underlying explanation or "Hayflick factor," although shortening of the telomeres and accumulation of DNA damage are both strong possibilities]
13. d [This is the technique of growing living cells in the laboratory and can be done with many different types of prokaryotic or eukaryotic cell types, including various human cells in cancer-testing laboratories; this technique is not restricted to prokaryotic cells]
14. b [Karyotypes are done using fully condensed metaphase chromosomes]
15. c [Cancer is a disease of multicellular organisms that involves the loss of normal regulatory control of the cell cycle so that tumours develop]
16. b [Peptide hormones are signal molecules that bind to surface receptors on target cells and give rise to a cellular response that can modify the cyclin:CDK phosphorylation state]
17. b [Although exhibiting similarities with the process of division in bacteria, the process in yeast is believed to have evolved separately from that of animals and higher plants]
18. a [In plants, the layer of microtubules that persists at the spindle midpoint serves as an organizing centre for vesicles derived from the ER and Golgi and that gradually coalesces to give cytokinesis and a new cell wall—the cell plate]
19. c [Eukaryotes cannot replicate the linear ends of their chromosomes, so during replication they employ this enzyme to enzymatically add repetitive DNA sequences, or telomeres, to the ends; however, as cells "age" this enzyme does not maintain the length of the ends, resulting in shortening of these sequences and possibly contributing to senescence]
20. d [Cancer cell lines are, by their nature, naturally immortal]

1. Read the section on cell division in prokaryotes and pay particular attention to the description of the genome in prokaryotic cells.
2. Remember that all cells in a multicellular organism are derived by mitosis from a single parental cell, the zygote. Pay attention to the descriptions in this chapter of external factors that control the cell cycle, the resulting intracellular processes, and take note of the fact that the blastema is described as being a temporary structure. Once regenerated, are the cells likely to continue growing and dividing?
3. After rereading the relevant sections, think about the reasons for a cell entering each of these three phases, what is happening or not happening in cells in each of the three phases/states, and the end result for each.

Chapter 9 Genetic Recombination

Why It Matters [pp. 181–182]
9.1 Mechanism of Genetic Recombination [pp. 182–183]

1. sameness; 2. genetically; 3. population; 4. selection; 5. different; 6. heritable; 7. mutation; 8. recombination; 9. meiosis; 10. differ; 11. proximity; 12. backbones; 13. exchange; 14. paste; 15. Homologous; 16. line up; 17. backbone; 18. exchanged; 19. four; 20. four; 21. single; 22. circular; 23. fusing; 24. C; 25. D; 26. A; 27. B; 28. A single crossover event between two molecules involves cutting the two backbones of each molecule, then joining the cut ends from one molecule to the other. If the two molecules are circular, then the result is fusion of the two together to give a single recombinant molecule, whereas with two linear molecules, the cut ends are "swapped," giving two recombinant linear molecules.

9.2 Genetic Recombination in Bacteria [pp. 183-190]

29. recombination; 30. organisms; 31. offspring; 32. *E. coli*; 33. conjugation; 34. donor; 35. pilus; 36. F plasmid; 37. F$^+$; 38. integrated; 39. Hfr ; 40. chromosomal; 41. plasmid; 42. nutritional; 43. entry/transfer; 44. map; 45. dead; 46. transformation; 47. transformed; 48. genetic; 49. transduction; 50. bacteriophages; 51. host; 52. lytic; 53. random; 54. generalized; 55. specialized; 56. λ; 57. lysogenic; 58. E; 59. C; 60. A; 61. F; 62. B; 63. D; 64. J; 65. D; 66. E; 67. G; 68. K; 69. B; 70. C; 71. F; 72. O; 73. I; 74. M; 75. A; 76. N; 77. H; 78. L; 79. A – The absorption of free DNA across the plasma membrane, B – The one-way transfer of DNA, usually a conjugative plasmid, through a pilus from a donor cell. When the plasmid integrates into the chromosome, conjugation results in transfer of chromosomal genes, C – Occurs when a virus accidentally packages host DNA then transfers that DNA when it infects the next host cell; 80. A – The bacteriophage injects its DNA, the DNA is transcribed, viral products are translated, viral particles assemble and are released by rupture or lysis of the host cell, and the cycle is therefore called a lytic life cycle, B – The bacteriophage injects its DNA and the DNA becomes integrated into the host's chromosome where it is replicated as part of the host's DNA. If conditions within the cell change the virus can excise from the host's chromosome, and revert to a lytic life cycle; 81. T; 82. F – Only certain species are able to undergo transformation unless "forced" in the lab; 83. F – It depends upon whether the donor is F$^+$, in which case the recipient will become F$^+$, but if the donor is an Hfr, then the entire F sequence will not get transferred so the recipient remains F$^-$; 84. T; 85. P22 encodes an enzyme that degrades the host DNA into short fragments that can become integrated in a random fashion when the phage particles assemble; in bacteriophage λ, the phage chromosome becomes integrated into a specific region of the host's chromosome; when triggered to excise the phage may accidentally remove a host gene on either side of the prophage (*gal* or *bio*); 86. A bacteriophage is the infectious form of a virus, whereas a prophage is the form when the phage DNA is integrated into the host's chromosome.

9.3 Genetic Recombination in Eukaryotes: Meiosis [pp. 191–201]

87. meiosis; 88. half; 89. recombination; 90. three; 91. haploid; 92. diploid; 93. mitotic; 94. diploid; 95. gametes; 96. mitosis; 97. fertilization; 98. meiosis; 99. four; 100. haploid; 101. different; 102. interphase; 103. I; 104. prophase I; 105. chromatids; 106. synapsis; 107. recombination; 108. prometaphase I; 109. kinetochore; 110. opposite; 111. I; 112. metaphase; 113. anaphase I; 114. haploid; 115. disassembly; 116. decondensation; 117. prophase II; 118. prometaphase II; 119. each; 120. metaphase II; 121. anaphase II; 122. telophase II; 123. reproductive; 124. gametes; 125. zygote; 126. I; 127. I; 128. maternal; 129. paternal; 130. recombinant; 131. fertilization; 132. A; 133. A; 134. B; 135. A; 136. B; 137. A; 138. C; 139. D; 140. A; 141. E; 142. B; 143. A, E, D, F, C, B; 144. It is a condition that results from nondisjunction of chromosome 21 so that babies are born with three copies of this chromosome instead of two; 145. It is the brief interlude between meiosis I and II during which no DNA replication occurs; 146. Tetrads are the homologous pairs of sister chromatids that form through the process of synapsis; 147. F – It is a rare event and generally zygotes that form from cells that have suffered nondisjunction rarely survive; 148. T; 149. A – 2, diploid, B – Occurred, C – Crossovers, D – Homologous chromosomes, random, no, E – Sister chromatids, haploid; 150. i – E, F, ii – D, iii – B, iv – C, v – G, vi – A.

9.4 Mobile Elements [pp. 201–206]

151. transposable elements; 152. transposition; 153. transposase; 154. pasting; 155. replicating; 156. inactivate; 157. expression; 158. cancer; 159. mutagens; 160. insertion sequences; 161. transposons; 162. transposase; 163. resistance; 164. F plasmid; 165. conjugative; 166. retrotransposons; 167. retroviruses; 168. RNA; 169. transcribing; 170. gametes; 171. I; 172. C; 173. E; 174. F; 175. A; 176. B; 177. D; 178. G; 179. H; 180. F – Insertion sequences are short sequences with usually only the gene for the transposases; transposons carry extra genes; 181. T; 182. The different colours in the kernels are the result of the movement of transposons into and out of genes controlling pigment production; 183. Plasticity refers to changes in the genome, the raw material for evolution. Stability refers to the fact that genetic change must occur at very low levels and that as the organism grows and develops and the somatic cells are replicated, the daughter cells that are produced must be genetically identical to the parental cell.

SELF-TEST

1. a [Binary fission is the method of cell division and growth, and since bacteria are haploid, there are no homologous alleles to undergo recombination]
2. d [Auxotrophs are nutritional mutants that arise from exposure to mutagens such as X-rays and UV]
3. c [A sex pilus is a tube-like structure that connects the cytoplasm of donor cell to recipient cell]
4. c [Hfr stands for high frequency recombination, so named because the F plasmid has been integrated into the chromosome resulting in the transfer of chromosomal genes to recipient cells and the generatin recombinants]
5. a [In an Hfr, the F plasmid is integrated into the chromosome and transfer originates from a gene in the middle of the plasmid so that chromosomal genes are transferred but the entire plasmid sequence does not get transferred because mating pairs are unstable. Those genes that are transferred make the recipient a partial diploid and the new sequences can undergo homologous recombination with the recipient cell's DNA]
6. b [This can happen through generalized or specialized transduction and involves the transfer of chromosomal DNA from one host cell to the next via a phage head containing host DNA]
7. b [Lysogenic bacteriophage insert their chromosome into the host's chromosome and reside there until conditions change and they excise from the chromosome and revert to the lytic life cycle]
8. a [In the lytic life cycle, bacteriophage particles are released by rupturing or lysis of the host cell]
9. c [Bacteriophage λ in *E. coli* and retroviruses in humans both integrate their chromosomes into the host chromosome]
10. d [The transfer of DNA segments from one bacterial cell to another occurs by conjugation]

11. b [In a diploid organism, i.e., *2n*, the haploid number is *n*. So $2 \times n = 16$, $n = 8$ chromosomes of maternal origin and 8 of paternal origin]

12. c [Alleles are variants of a particular gene and depending upon the alleles in the mother and father and whether these particular genes were recombined during formation of the two gametes giving rise to the individual, they could be different or the same]

13. a [Never – After replicating the chromosomes in the S phase, the sister chromatids enter meiosis I where they undergo synapsis and are separated in anaphase I, so that at the end, there are two haploid daughter cells which then go on to meiosis II, during which the sister chromatids are separated]

14. a [Anaphase I is the phase of meiosis I where the homologous pairs are separated; during anaphase II the sister chromatids are separated to give, by the end, four haploid daughter cells]

15. d [In nondisjunction, a homologous pair fails to separate and moves to one pole of the cell so that if the the diploid number is six then there are three homologous pairs, and after nondisjunction one cell will be missing one of the homologous chromosomes and the other will have both]

16. b [Females are XX and males are XY and during meiosis, the X and Y chromosomes in the male behave as a homologous pair so gametes are either X or Y]

17. a [Crossovers do not alter the amount of DNA unless nondisjunction happens. So if the diploid number is *x,* then when homologous pairs are separated during meiosis I, the haploid pair will be half of that, 0.5*x*]

18. d [Asexual reproduction does not contribute to genetic variability]

19. c [Crossovers during meiosis I followed by random segregation of homologous pairs and recombinant chromatids all give rise to genetic diversity so that the gametes are not alike, nor are they the same as the parental cell]

20. c [Retroviruses are animal viruses]

INTEGRATING AND APPLYING KEY CONCEPTS

1. Remember the purposes of meiosis: to reduce the diploid number to haploid by separating the homologous pairs of chromosomes and generating genetic variability through recombination of homologous sequences. Think about what role synapsis plays in both of these.

2. The textbook starts and ends with a discussion of the tension between having to replicate cells of the individual without introducing change vs. the needs of the population for genetic variability in order for evolution to function. These needs must be met through introducing change in the DNA in the gametes.

3. Think about what "homologous" means and the consequences of nondisjunction, which might be analogous to this hypothetical situation.

4. This question may seem complicated, but simply requires rereading the section on bacterial conjugation and paying attention to the details and the figures. In terms of the control(s), you want to be able to ensure that the clones you had growing on your "diagnostic" media were the results of recombination and not mutation of the parent's mutant allele back to functional. In terms of the units of measurement, it may help to know the alternate name for this type of experiment: "time-of-entry" experiments.

Chapter 10   Mendel, Genes, and Inheritance

Why It Matters [pp. 211–212]
10.1 The Beginnings of Genetics: Mendel's Garden Peas [pp. 212–223]

1. Gregor Mendel; 2. blending; 3. generation; 4. garden pea; 5. true; 6. pollination; 7. self-fertilized; 8. alleles; 9. P;

10. F_1; 11. self; 12. F_2; 13. meiosis; 14. characters; 15. phenotype; 16. genotype; 17. monohybrid; 18. pairs;

19. dominant; 20. separately; 21. segregation; 22. testcrosses; 23. true-; 24. genotype; 25. dihybrid; 26. independently;

27. assortment; 28. inheritance; 29. F; 30. K; 31. D; 32. H; 33. G; 34. A; 35. L; 36. B; 37. E; 38. M; 39. I; 40. C; 41. J;

42. A; 43. B; 44. B; 45. A; 46. A; 47. A – 2, B – R, C – r, D – T, E – T, F – R, G – r, H – 4, I – T, J – t, K – R, L – r;

48. A – Rr, B – Red, C – Phenotype, D – Tall, E – Red, F – TT, G – Rr, H – rr, I – tt, J – Dominant, K – Recessive,

L – Testcross; 49. This refers to the fact that two alleles for a given character will segregate or separate and enter the

gametes singly; 50. This refers to the fact that during gamete formation, the alleles for two different traits segregate

independently from each other; 51. A testcross is performed to determine if a phenotype is the product of a homozygous

genotype or a heterozygous dominant genotype. To do the test you cross your organism of interest with a true-breeding homozygous recessive parent and examine the F_1 progeny. They will have a specific ratio of phenotypes depending upon the genotype of the organism in question; 52. Genes and their alleles are carried on chromosomes; 53. A – Tt, tt, B – ½ Tt, ½ tt, C – ½ tall, ½ dwarf, D – A testcross because a monohybrid cross involves crossing two individuals that are heterozygous for the same pair of alleles (e.g., Tt × Tt); 54. A – TS, TS, TS, TS and ts, ts, ts, ts, B – 1 TtSs, C – 1 tall, strong, D – 1/16 TTSS, 2/16 TTSs, 2/16 TtSS, 4/16 TtSs, 2/16 Ttss, 1/16 ttSS, 2/16 ttSs, 1/16 ttss, 1/16 TTss, E – 9/16 tall strong, 3/16 tall weak, 3/16 dwarf strong, 1/16 dwarf weak.

10.2 Later Modifications and Additions to Mendel's Hypotheses [pp. 223–230]

55. dominant; 56. recessive; 57. incomplete; 58. pink; 59. sickle cell anemia; 60. co- ; 61. MN; 62. allele; 63. organ; 64. epistasis; 65. deposition; 66. deposition; 67. polygenic; 68. continuous; 69. polygenic; 70. bell; 71. pleiotropy; 72. P could be a true dominant, masking the recessive p allele, or P and p could be co-dominant so that the effect(s) of P and p would both be visible, or P might be incompletely dominant in that the effect(s) of p are not completely masked so if they represented two colours the heterozygote would be a blended colour; 73. In the case of a pleiotropic character, a single gene would give rise to multiple traits, whereas in polygenic inheritance and single character (e.g., the height of a human adult) is determined by the combined effects of multiple genes.

SELF-TEST

1. a [Meiosis is the process of segregating the maternal and paternal chromosomes so that haploid gametes are formed. The separation of any pair of homologous chromosomes is independent of the separation of any other two pairs]
2. a [The phenotype is the expression, i.e., blood type, and can arise, in the case of dominance and multiple alleles, from different possible genotypes in the parental cross, for example, $I^A i$ or $I^A I^A$. If either or both of the parents was heterozygous, then the children would have a different blood type, i.e., ii or type O]
3. c [The alleles segregate or assort independently so the Aa pair would give gametes of A and a; the BB pair would only give gametes that are B. Then the various possible combinations for these are: AB and aB]
4. a [A cross of this type would generate all heterozygote offspring so in the case of complete dominant, they should all look like the AA parent. Since they don't look like either, there is one possible explanation based on the choices—A is not completely dominant over a, so that the heterozygote has a blended phenotype]
5. c [Bb × bb yields the F_1 offspring 50% Bb and 50% bb. Since B is dominant, the heterozygotes would be blue and the homozygous recessive would be white]
6. c [Bb × bb yields the F_1 offspring 50% Bb and 50% bb]
7. b [Type A blood (father) can result from either $I^A I^A$ or $I^A i$; Type B blood (mother) results from either $I^B I^B$ or $I^B i$. So if both parents were homozygous, the offspring would have type AB blood (which results from $I^A I^B$ only) with no other possibilities; if the father was heterozygous but the mother was homozygous, the offspring would either have AB or B type blood; if the father was homozygous and the mother was heterozygous, then the offspring would have either AB or A type blood; finally if both parents were heterozygous, the offspring would have either A, B, or O type blood (which results from ii only)]
8. a [codominance occurs when neither allele dominates; this is the case with the AB blood type $I^A I^B$; however, the i allele is a normal recessive allele as it is masked by either of the other two alleles]
9. a [Yellow Labs are the result of a homozygous recessive epistasis allele (ee) which prevents the pigment or product of the B allele from being deposited. So it doesn't matter if the parents were BB (black) or Bb (black) it only matters that each had one e allele (if either had had two e alleles, they would have been yellow rather than black]
10. c [The E gene is epistatic, that is, it has an effect on another trait: colour (B); the determination of colour is not just dependent upon the ability to synthesize the colour but the ability to then deposit it in the hair. Retrievers that are homozygous for the recessive allele e are yellow regardless of how much pigment they produce]
11. b [Adult human height is a polygenic trait or the product of multiple genes so that one sees a continuous gradient of height distribution in the population]
12. d [Sickle cell disease results from a single mutation in the gene for a hemoglobin subunit and this mutation has multiple effects, as depicted in Figure 10.18]
13. c [Codominance means that neither allele is dominant over the other AND they are both expressed, whereas in incomplete dominance neither allele is dominant; however, one is able to mask the expression of the other to a limited degree]

14. b [Looking at the product of the first cross, the offspring would all be heterozygous and therefore have a single phenotype of Tt; with the second cross there would be two possible genotypes in the offspring: TT and Tt, which are the same phenotypes]
15. b [Looking at the product of the first cross, the offspring would all be heterozygous and therefore have a single blended phenotype of Tt; with the second cross there would be two possible genotypes in the offspring: TT and Tt, where the first would display the pure phenotype of T, while the Tt offspring would have a blended phenotype]
16. c [Cystic Fibrosis is a genetic disorder that is the result of a mutation in a single membrane transporter]
17. a [Although the result of a single genetic mutation, individuals who are heterozygous for this mutation display a milder form of the disease as a result of incomplete dominance]

Integrating and Applying Key Concepts

1. Assume complete dominance (given the good health of the heterozygous individuals) and use a Punnett square to determine the genotypes of the F_1 offspring. Now assuming you could do this with multiple lines of mice (to prevent inbreeding), which offspring would you mate?
2. Read the section on codominance and take note of the description of the antigens that each blood type has on the surface—which of these would match Suzie and her two parents? Keep in mind that the basis of rejection or adverse reactions is based on antibody recognition of "non-self" antigens.
3. Read the section on codominance and take note of the description of the antigens that each blood type has on the surface. Now design a Punnett square for the mother's blood type alleles and Joe's. Examine the offspring for the AB blood type.

Chapter 11   Genes, Chromosomes, and Human Genetics

Why It Matters [pp. 234–235]
11.1 Genetic Linkage and Recombination [pp. 235–240]

1. linked; 2. chromosomes; 3. independently; 4. linked; 5. recombination; 6. recombination; 7. crossover; 8. homologous; 9. proportional; 10. frequency; 11. map unit; 12. each other; 13. map; 14. frequencies; 15. relative; 16. *AaBb*; 17. aabb; 18. unlinked; 19. double; 20. not linked; 21. D; 22. E; 23. G; 24. A; 25. C; 26. B; 27. The number of recombinants over the total number of progeny multiplied by 100 ; 28. In the cross *TtRr* × *ttrr*, based on the principle of independent assortment of two unlinked genes, the expected progeny would be 4 *TtRr*, 4 *Ttrr*, 4 *ttRr*, and 4 *ttrr* that is a ratio of 1:1:1:1 . If the *T* and *R* genes are linked, then the ratio you actually obtain would differ from that; 29. F – The genes for flower colour and seed colour are on the same chromosome; however, they are so far apart they behave as if they were not linked; 30. T.

11.2 Sex-Linked Genes [pp. 240–245]

31. pairs ; 32. sex chromosomes; 33. autosomal chromosomes; 34. fruit flies; 35. X; 36. Y; 37. inheritance; 38. reciprocal; 39. X-linked; 40. parents; 41. sex; 42. X-linked; 43. inactivation; 44. condensation; 45. Barr body; 46. E; 47. F; 48. A; 49. G; 50. B; 51. C; 52. D; 53. F – It is an X-linked trait, so mothers are generally carriers and male offspring that inherit the recessive gene will have the disease; 54. T; 55. F – Inactivation of one of the X-chromosomes occurs in cells of the developing multicellular embryo, and inactivation is random so that all decendants of a given cell (for example, in a particular developing tissue type) will have the same chromosome inactivated, but this is independent of which chromosome is inactivated in another cell; 56. If she was homozygous recessive, she would display the trait; 57. The SRY gene is a Y-linked gene that is the master switch for sex determination. In its absence, the fetus will develop female physical features and sexual organs but will be genetically male; 58. There is a small region of homology between the X and Y chromosomes, so that in males these two chromosomes pair during meiosis I; 59. If the mutation is recessive and mothers are healthy then they must be carriers, in which case their father may have had the disease. There

is a 50% chance that any male offspring of the carrier mother would acquire the defective allele and exhibit the same disease their grandfather had; 60. A – Suzie would be a heterozygous carrier but phenotypically normal due to the dominant wild type allele, B – There would be a 50% chance that a male child will be phenotypically and genotypically SQ; however, any female offspring would be phenotypically normal, with a 50% chance that they will be heterozygous carriers, C – $X^{SQ}Y$ and $X^+ Y$, D – $X^+ X^{SQ}$ and $X^+ X^+$.

11.3 Chromosomal Alterations that Affect Inheritance [pp. 245–249]
11.4 Human Genetics and Genetic Counselling [pp. 249–252]

61. inheritance; 62. radiation; 63. viruses; 64. duplications, deletions, inversions; 65. translocations; 66. homologous; 67. evolution; 68. germ; 69. nondisjunction; 70. homologous; 71. sister chromatids; 72. polyploid; 73. mitosis; 74. three; 75. autosomal; 76. carriers; 77. unaffected; 78. dominant; 79. recessive; 80. X-linked; 81. heterozygous; 82. counsellors; 83. pedigree; 84. offspring; 85. F; 86. D; 87. A; 88. I; 89. B; 90. H; 91. E; 92. G; 93. C; 94. T; 95. F – In plants it can give rise to hardier plants with increased growth and production; 96. For an autosomal recessive trait, both male and female heterozygous individuals are healthy carriers but homozygous recessive individuals exhibit the trait. It is the opposite for autosomal dominant defects, where heterozygous and homozygous dominant individuals are both affected but homozygous recessive individuals are not.

11.5 Nontraditional Patterns of Inheritance [pp. 253–254]

97. Cytoplasmic; 98. imprinting; 99. mitochondrial; 100. maternal; 101. energy generation; 102. silenced; 103. imprinting; 104. methylation; 105. gametes; 106. imprinted; 107. imprint; 108. imprinting; 109. gene; 110. F – Loss of imprinting means that an allele that should be silenced by methylation, i.e. imprinted, is not. As a result, the individual has an effective gene dosage twice what it should be; 111. This term is used to describe the phenomenon where all of the progeny, regardless of sex, inherit the genotype of one of the parents. It is usually the result of cytoplasmic inheritance; 112. This would indicate that a trait is cytoplasmically inherited, that is, associated with the maternal mitochondria.

S E L F - T E S T

1. b [If the two genes are tightly linked then they will behave as if they were a single gene and be inherited together]
2. a [Since both parents share the same phenotype, 50% of the male offspring vary from the phenotype while all of the females have the same phenotype as the parents one can conclude that the parents are X^+X^- and X^+Y where X^+ represents the X-linked gene dominant gene for short wings and X^- represents the recessive gene for long wings]
3. b [Red-green colour blindness is an X-linked recessive trait and so a carrier would have two copies, one normal and one defective and would therefore have to be female (XX)]
4. c [Barr bodies are the condensed, inactivated second X chromosome that forms in females in order to reduce the X-linked gene dosage to one, as it is in males (XY)]
5. d [the sequence GFED is an inversion from the normal sequence and appears twice before it appears that the rest of the normal sequence reappears]
6. d [assuming the normal diploid chromosome content is 50, if there was a failure of the spindle during mitosis of a germ line cell, giving rise to 100 chromosomes (4n) and this was followed by meiosis, the content would be reduced to 2n rather than the normal 1n; fertilization with a normal gamete would give 3n that is a triploid individual]
7. b [A karyotype would clearly demonstrate three copies of chromosome 21 (and two of every other homologous pair)]
8. a [failure of chromosome 21 homologous pairs during meiosis I or of the sister chromoatids during meiosis II would both lead to a single extra copy of the chromosome in one gamete (i.e. 2) and a missing copy in another gamete. Upon fertilization those numbers would increase by 1]
9. c [since 50% of the offspring would be expected to be male one can conclude this is not X-linked (i.e. sex-linked). If the trait were autosomal dominant and if the parents were Aa and Aa and one assumed the A allele is dominant,

conferring the disease, the offspring would be Aa, Aa, Aa, aa and only the aa individual (25%) would not exhibit the disease]

10. b [PKU is an enzymatic deficiency that can be assayed following birth. When identified early, diet modification will prevent the development of symptoms]
11. b [SRY is the master switch that controls the sex of an individual and it is located on the Y chromosome]
12. c [it is due to inactivation of one of the X chromosomes in the female]
13. c [The calico colour is the result of epistasis, X-linkage and inactivation of one of the X-chromosomes in females]
14. d [Sharks, which evolved earlier than humans, only have one gene for hemoglobin; however, humans have a few suggesting that these arose subsequently by duplication]
15. b [Aneuploidy is usual fatal and may be responsible for ~ 70% of miscarriages]
16. a [Cystic is a genetic disease caused by a gene that encodes a mutant transport protein. Only individuals that are homozygous for this trait will develop the disease]
17. a [either amniocentesis or chorionic villus sampling would provide the cells of the embryo which could then be screened by karyotyping for trisomy of chromosome 21]
18. c [if a mother has the trait and it is cytoplasmically-inherited then all offspring will also have the trait because of the much greater volume of cytoplasm in the female egg than the sperm that fertilizes it]
19. c [Although the ratio suggest the genes are not linked and assort independently, when genes are linked but separated by a wide distance on the chromosome they beahev as if they were not linked]
20. c [Determining the distance from one outside gene to one in the middle and then from the other outside gene to that same one in the middle will allow you to add up the two measurements to get the distance between the two outside genes]

INTEGRATING AND APPLYING KEY CONCEPTS

1. Use the topic map at the beginning of this study guide chapter and incorporate the concepts and ideas from the textbook. Or start from scratch and focus on heredity patterns and chromosomal alterations.
2. Think about the differences in complexity and developmental requirements.
3. Read the section on aneuploids and study Table 11.1.
4. Study Figure 11.8.

Chapter 12   DNA Structure, Replication, and Organization

Why It Matters [pp. 257–258]
12.1 Establishing DNA as the Hereditary Molecule [pp. 258–261]

1. *Streptococcus pneumonia*; 2. smooth; 3. nonvirulent; 4. transformed; 5. transforming; 6. culture tubes;

7. macromolecules; 8. transforming; 9. (bacterio)phages/viruses; 10. protein; 11. life; 12. aDNA; 13. past; 14. E; 15. A;

16. D; 17. F; 18. C; 19. B; 20. F – DNA contains phosphorus but not sulfur, and some amino acids contain sulfur, but

none contain phosphorus; 21. If the labelled protein coat had entered the cell, there would have been no clear evidence

that the protein coat was not somehow involved in determining the life cycle of the virus. That fact that only the labelled

DNA was proven to enter the cell provided clear evidence for DNA as the genetic/hereditary material.

12.2 DNA Structure [pp. 261–264]

22. double helical; 23. X-ray; 24. Chargaff's; 25. thymines; 26. guanines; 27. right-hand; 28. antiparallel; 29. base;

30. pyrimidine; 31. deoxyribose; 32. phosphate; 33. sugar; 34. phosphate; 35. phosphodiester; 36. hydrogen; 37. T;

38. G; 39. 10; 40. E; 41. F; 42. B; 43. A; 44. D; 45. C; 46. F – The AT base pairs are held together by two hydrogen

bonds while the CG pairs are held together by three hydrogen bonds; 47. Based on the definition of a molecule being a

single chemical species with the component atoms held together by covalent bonds, each chain of the double helix

would then represent two molecules held together by non-covalent hydrogen bonding; 48. A – 5′ end, B – 5′ carbon,

C – 4′ carbon, D – 3′ carbon, E – 1′ carbon, F – 2′ carbon, G – Phosphate, H – Deoxyribose sugar, I – 3′ hydroxyl,

J – 3′ end.

12.3 DNA Replication [pp. 264–276]

49. semiconservative; 50. template; 51. complementary; 52. helicase; 53. origins; 54. RNA primer; 55. primase; 56. DNA polymerase; 57. 3′; 58. 3′ → 5′; 59. 5′ → 3′; 60. origin; 61. leading; 62. lagging strand; 63. RNA; 64. ligase; 65. 5′ → 3′; 66. 5′; 67. shortening; 68. telomeres; 69. shorter; 70. death; 71. telomerases; 72. B; 73. E; 74. C; 75. D; 76. F; 77. A; 78. E; 79. D; 80. F; 81. A; 82. B; 83. C; 84. F – The 5′ end of the oldest part of a newly replicated chain because of the fact DNA polymerase can only polymerize DNA in the 5′ → 3′ direction, incorporating new bases by covalent attachment to the 3′ OH; 85. T; 86. F – Although the enzyme works more slowly, replication begins from many, sometimes hundreds of origins of replication, instead of the single *ori* in *E. coli*; 87. T; 88. A – Leading strand, B – Lagging strand; 89. The leading strand (A) has continuous replication because the DNA polymerase is synthesizing the DNA in the 5′ to 3′ direction, the only direction it can move in, and this is following immediately behind the helicase and the direction of unwinding. The lagging strand has discontinuous replication because of the antiparallel nature of the DNA strands: the orientation of the template strand is such that the polymerase on the lagging strand template cannot following behind the helicase while polymerizing in the 5′ to 3′ direction; 90. With conservative, there would be two bands (^{15}N–^{15}N heavy DNA and ^{14}N–^{14}N light DNA), with semiconservative, there would be two (^{15}N–^{14}N hybrid DNA and ^{14}N–^{14}N light DNA), and with dispersive there would be only one: ^{15}N–^{14}N hybrid DNA.

12.4 Mechanisms that Correct Replication Errors [pp. 276–277]

91. mismatches; 92. proofreading; 93. mismatched; 94. 3′ → 5′; 95. distortion; 96. mismatch; 97. mismatched; 98. DNA polymerase; 99. ligase; 100. mutations; 101. evolutionary; 102. DNA alterations can lead to mutations if the alteration is not repaired by the time the cell divides. At that point, it is an inherited change from the parental sequence, so is a mutation.

12.5 DNA Organization in Eukaryotic versus Prokaryotic Cells [pp. 277–280]

103. histones; 104. positively; 105. phosphate; 106. nucleosome; 107. H2A, H2B; 108. linker; 109. 10 nm chromatin; 110. H1; 111. 30 nm chromatin; 112. euchromatin; 113. heterochromatin; 114. turned off; 115. nonhistone; 116. gene expression; 117. circular; 118. plasmids; 119. loops; 120. positively; 121. nucleoid; 122. H; 123. G; 124. F; 125. B; 126. A; 127. C; 128. D; 129. E; 130. A – DNA double helix, B – Nucleosome, C – Linker, D – H1, E – 30 nm chromatin/solenoid; 131. Bacterial chromosomes are replicated bidirectionally from a single origin of replication and are complete when the replication forks meet at a point opposite the origin replication. When plasmid conjugation is occurring, one strand of the plasmid breaks and enters the recipient cell, being displaced as the advancing polymerase replicates continuously, using the remaining strand and a rolling circle process of replication. In the recipient, the newly acquired single-stranded plasmid is replicated in a discontinuous fashion; 132. Histones H2A, H2B, H3 and H4 form the nucleosome core particle around which the DNA wraps to give the 10nm chromatin fibre. Histone H1 binds in the linker region of the DNA as well as to the nucleosomes forming the 30nm chromatin fibre or solenoid. DNA is further compacted into euchromatin and, at its most condensed, into heterochromatin.

Self-Test

1. c [The smooth strains were virulent but when heat-killed and mixed with the avirulent rough strains, were found to transfer a mystery material that transformed the *R* strains into *S* strains which were then able to cause pneumonia in mice]

2. c [They grew *R* and *S* strains in culture tubes, heat-killed the *S* strains, purified the DNA and showed that it alone transformed the *R* strains into the smooth type characteristic of virulent *S. pneumonia*]
3. a [DNA contains phosphorus but amino acids do not, while certain amino acids contain sulfur and DNA does not. They were therefore able to distinguish between DNA and protein, the only two components of bacteriophage T2, by radioactively labelling the DNA with ^{32}P and the protein coat of the bacteriophage with ^{35}S]
4. a [Rosalind Franklin correctly interpreted her X-ray diffraction results as resulting from a helical structure in DNA; however, she did not determine that DNA was a double-helix. That was one of the predictions of Watson and Crick]
5. d [There are three phosphates covalently attached via the 5′ carbon of deoxyribose and upon DNA polymerization, the first one attached to the 5′ participates in phosphodiester bond formation to give the backbone of the DNA strand, while the pyrophosphate is released]
6. b [Wilkins and Franklin had produced the X-ray diffraction studies while Chargaff had determined that the number of As = Ts and the number of Cs = Gs. They were able to explain both through their double-helical model of DNA with AT and CG hydrogen-bonded base-pairs connecting the two strands]
7. a [Purines (A and G) base-pair with pyrimidines (T and C, respectively) through hydrogen bonds in the middle of the double helix. AT pairs have two H bonds and CG pairs have three. The result is a right-handed double-helix with a regular structure of 3.4 nm for one full twist and a constant distance between the two strands of 2 nm]
8. d [Rolling circle is seen in the replication of bacterial plasmids during conjugation. The three other mechanisms were all thought possible until Meselson and Stahl proved that replication results in new DNA molecules with one parental strand and one newly replicated daughter strand, that is, it was semiconservative]
9. a [Prior to replication in the ^{14}N-containing medium, the chromosomes would have been uniformly labelled with the heavy isotope (^{15}N). After one round of replication in the ^{14}N-containing medium, each parental strand (heavy) would be base-paired with a newly formed daughter strand (light) giving a single type of DNA that contained one strand of each]
10. c [The polymerase catalyzes the formation of a phosphodiester linkage between the phosphate group attached to the 5′ carbon of the deoxyribose and the hydroxyl attached to the 3′ carbon of the previously-incorporated deoxyribonucleotide. Hydrolysis of the pyrophosphate generates the energy required for the polymerization reaction]
11. c [DNA polymerase 1 removes the bases in the primer one-by-one using its 5′ → 3′ exonuclease activity, replacing each base with a deoxyribonucleotide, using its 5′ → 3′ polymerase activity]
12. b [Because of the antiparallel nature of DNA and the fact polymerases can only work in the 5′ → 3′ direction, the polymerase replicates discontinuously on the lagging strand, using all of the same replication machinery, but generating Okazaki fragments that need to be "stitched together" as replicatin proceeds]
13. a [Ligase "stitches" DNA fragments together on the lagging strand, after the primers on the Okazaki fragments have been removed and replaced with DNA]
14. d [Like prokaryotic chromosomal replication, replication proceeds bidirectionally from an origin of replication. Although eukaryotic chromosomes are much longer than prokaryotic chromosomes, and the eukaryotic polymerase is slower than the prokaryotic polymerase, eukaryotic chromosomes are often replicated faster because replication is initiated from many, sometimes hundreds of origins of replication]
15. d [They are buffers of non-essential repeat sequences at the ends of eukaryotic chromosomes, functioning to prevent loss of essential genes when the RNA primer at the ends is removed and DNA polymerase is unable to replace the deleted sequences. Eventually, however, because most cells lack telomerase to increase the length of the ever-shortening telomeres, the last sequences of the telomeres is lost and ensuing replication eventually results in deletion of essential functions, leading to cell death]
16. a [Telomerase, present in early embryo, germ and cancer cells, has, like other DNA polymerase, 5′ → 3′ activity. However, in order to extend the length of telomeres, it carries its own RNA, which is complementary to the repeat within the telomere and base pairs with the end repeat. The polymerization activity of the enzyme then uses the 3′ hydroxyl at the end of the telomere and the internal RNA template to extend the telomere sequence of the chromosome]
17. b [Proofreading occurs immediately after a base has been incorporated by the polymerase. It detects distortions where the last base was incorporated and, if distorted, backs up, removing the base with its 3′ → 5′ exonuclease activity, replacing the base with the correct base]
18. a [Between the proofreading ability of DNA polymerase and the mismatch repair system that functions immediately after replication, errors are reduced to one-in-a-million]
19. d [Eukaryotic DNA is compacted into the 10 nm chromatin fibre which is, in turn, compacted into the 30 nm chromatin fibre and this is further compacted either loosely, into transcriptionally active euchromatin or tightly, into transcriptionally inactive heterochromatin]

20. b [Although prokaryotic chromosomes are not organized in the same fashion, they are condensed using histone-like proteins which are positively charged and bind the DNA through ionic bonding with the negatively charged phosphate groups of the DNA]

21. a [Rolling circle replication occurs when conjugative plasmids are transferred to a recipient bacterial cell. One strand of the plasmid is cut and the 3′ hydroxyl of the cut strand primes unidirectional replication as the other end of the cut strand is transferred into the recipient cell, being displaced by the advancing replication fork]

INTEGRATING AND APPLYING KEY CONCEPTS

1. Begin by drawing a circular double-stranded molecule as depicted in Figure 12.22 (including a single replication bubble). Arbitrarily assign one parental strand as having a 5′ to 3′ direction in the clockwise direction and the other parental strand being antiparallel. Now remember the antiparallel nature of the DNA double helix to determine the orientation of the newly replicated DNA and whether this follows the direction of the advancing replication forks.

2. Reread section 12.5a paying attention to specific role of H1, the manner in which it binds DNA and the effect of its binding, in normal cells, on chromosomal structure, gene expression and sensitivity to DNA damaging agents.

3. Read "Molecule Behind Biology," box 12.1, to understand how drug therapy requires a compound that is selectively toxic to abnormal cells or cell functions. The reread the sections on the effects of telomere shortening, and the mechanism by which telomerase functions (section 12.3h).

Chapter 13   Gene Structure and Expression

Why It Matters [pp. 283–284]
13.1 The Connection between DNA, RNA, and Protein [pp. 284–289]

1. keratin; 2. adhesive; 3. ribosomes; 4. DNA; 5. enzymes; 6. auxotrophic; 7. enzyme; 8. polypeptide; 9. Dogma; 10. transcription; 11. mRNA; 12. translated; 13. polypeptide; 14. codon; 15. redundant/degenerate; 16. codon; 17. codon; 18. reading; 19. C; 20. E; 21. G; 22. J; 23. M. 24. K; 25. A; 26. L; 27. F; 28. B; 29. D; 30. I; 31. H; 32. A – Transcription, B – Processing, C – Translation; 33. F – Some proteins comprise multiple subunits or polypeptides; 34. T; 35. This is a heritable defect in a metabolic pathway; 36. Uracil is a nucleotide that replaces thymine in RNA; 37. In prokaryotic cells the two processes happen in the same cellular compartment, the cytosol, so translation occurs simultaneously with transcription.

13.2 Transcription: DNA-Directed RNA Synthesis [pp. 289–291]

38. RNA polymerase; 39. 3′ → 5′; 40. 5′ → 3′; 41. promoter; 42. TATA; 43. 30; 44. transcription; 45. terminators; 46. transcript; 47. DNA; 48. II; 49. tRNA/rRNA; 50. rRNA/tRNA; 51. I and III; 52. C; 53. F; 54. B; 55. H; 56. A; 57. K; 58. J; 59. D; 60. E; 61. I; 62. G; 63. A, H, B, E, G, D, C, F; 64. A – DNA: C-G, A-T, Transcription: C-G, A-U, B – DNA: 2, Transcription: 1, C – DNA: chromosome, Transcription: gene, D – DNA: DNA polymerase, Transcription: RNA polymerase, E – DNA: helicase, Transcription: RNA polymerase; 65. A – Prokaryotic Cells: RNA polymerase, Eukaryotes: RNA polymerases I, II and III, B – Prokaryotic Cells: Direct binding, Eukaryotes: Requires transcription factors, C – Prokaryotic Cells: Requires transcription of terminator sequences, Eukaryotes: Does not involve "terminator sequences," D – Prokaryotic Cells: RNA polymerase, Eukaryotes: RNA polymerase I and III; 66. Prokaryotes have one type of RNA polymerase that transcribes all types of genes, and is directed to specific promoters by a protein factor that dissociates once transcription has initiated. Eukaryotic cells have three RNA polymerases: RNA polymerase I and III transcribe non-protein-encoding genes, while RNA polymerase II transcribes protein-encoding genes; 67. It is a sequence found in the eukaryotic promoter that is recognized by transcription factors. These bind to the sequence then recruit the appropriate polymerase; 68. More RNA polymerases are following along immediately behind; 69. T; 70. T; 71. F – This is only true of prokaryotes. In eukaryotes, transcription requires processing of the 3′ UTR.

13.3 Processing of mRNAs in Eukaryotes [pp. 291–294]

72. processed; 73. nucleus; 74. guanine; 75. guanine; 76. degradation; 77. ribosome; 78. polyadenylation; 79. terminate; 80. poly(A) polymerase; 81. poly(A); 82. degradation; 83. introns; 84. splicing; 85. snRNPs; 86. intron-exon; 87. introns; 88. intron-exon; 89. exons; 90. alternate; 91. gene; 92. exon shuffling; 93. K; 94. M; 95. A; 96. G; 97. F; 98. J; 99. D; 100. L; 101. C; 102. E; 103. H; 104. I; 105. B; 106. T; 107. F – The process is highly accurate although different intron/exon splicing may generate different proteins from the same gene; 108. F – It is the diversity of proteins that is the key determinant and in eukaryotes this arises from the different genes as well as alternate splicing of the pre-mRNAs; 109. Through alternate splicing, it provides the ability to make more functionally distinct proteins without having to increase the size of the genome and through exon shuffling it provides a mechanism for evolving new proteins; 110. The genes of both have promoters, although only eukaryotic promoters have TATA boxes. Both transcripts have 5′ and 3′ UTRs; however, only eukaryotes have a polyadenylation signal in the 3′ UTR and introns are far more common in eukaryotic genes; 111. A – promoter, B – RNA coding sequence, C – 5′ UTR, D – Exon, E – Intron, F – Polyadenylation signal, G – Cap, H – Cleavage site; 112. A – Contains polyadenylation signal which directs cleavage of transcript just downstream and subsequent polyadenylation by poly(A) polymerase, Role: The first activity causes termination of transcription and the second protects the tmRNA from degradation, B – Capping enzyme and GTP, Role: Provides a site for the ribosome to first bind and protects mRNA from degradation, C – Part of snRNP complex, this is a ribozyme that cleaves at the intron-exon junction and joins exons together, Role: Function is to mediate correct splicing through sequence-specific base pairing, D – Contains TATA box, Role: Bound by transcription factors that recruit and bind polymerase to form the initiation complex.

13.4 Translation: mRNA-Directed Polypeptide Synthesis [pp. 294–305]

113. amino acid; 114. cytoplasm; 115. chloroplast; 116. tRNA; 117. aminoacyl-tRNA; 118. anticodon; 119. codon; 120. mRNA; 121. Met-tRNA; 122. P; 123. elongation; 124. A; 125. polypeptide; 126. peptidyl transferase; 127. GTP; 128. E; 129. P; 130. stop; 131. A; 132. release; 133. processing; 134. amino acids; 135. organic; 136. chaperones/ chaperonins; 137. signal; 138. N; 139. DNA; 140. missense; 141. nonsense; 142. termination; 143. frameshift; 144. reading frame; 145. silent; 146. redundancy/degeneracy; 147. C; 148. G; 149. A; 150. K; 151. B; 152. O; 153. D; 154. P; 155. E; 156. F; 157. H; 158. I; 159. N; 160. J; 161. M; 162. L; 163. T; 164. F – They are protein factors that successfully compete for the A site when there is no tRNA that can fill that site, specifically when there is a stop codon in the A site; 165. T; 166. T; 167. A – Mutation where a nucleotide is replaced by another type of nucleotide but there is no corresponding amino acid change, B – Missense mutation, C – Nonsense mutation, D – Mutation where a base pair is deleted or added, causing a change in the reading frame downstream for the mutation so that all the codons on mRNA change and the resulting protein is generally non-functional; 168. A – This is part of the endomembrane system so requires an N-terminal signal sequence, a signal recognition particle, signal peptidase in the RER membrane, possibly an additional sorting tag, added in the lumen of the ER or in the Golgi, B – Cytoplasm, C – N-terminal transit sequence, specifically a nuclear localization signal, a cytosolic transport protein, and nuclear pore complex, D – Mitochondrion, chloroplast, or eukaryotic microbody (e.g., peroxisome), E – N-terminal signal peptide, signal recognition particle, signal peptidase, F – N-terminal signal peptide, possible additional sorting signal dictating plasma membrane final destination; 169. The advantage is that prokaryotes can respond much more quickly to changes in their environment, altering gene protein expression. This is not possible in eukaryotes because transcription and translation occur in different cellular

compartments and eukaryotic mRNA requires processing; 170. Prokaryotic polysomes, like eukaryotic ones, include mRNA covered with actively translating ribosomes; however, they also include multiple mRNA molecules in the process of being transcribed by the RNA polymerase; 171. The bond linking the amino acid to the tRNA contains a lot of energy, and that energy ultimately came from the hydrolysis of ATP by the aminoacyl-tRNA synthetases; 172. In prokaryotes, the small subunit of the ribosome, the Met-tRNA (initiator tRNA) and GTP bind to the start codon and, via complementary base-pairing of a small subunit rRNA, to a ribosome-binding sequence immediately upstream from the start codon. In eukaryotes, the small subunit of the ribosome, the initiator tRNA and GTP bind to the 5′-guanine cap and the complex scans along the message until the AUG start codon arrives at the P site; 173. A – E, P, A sites (from l to r), B – Anticodon, C – Aminoacyl tRNA, D – Peptide chain, E – Released/uncharged tRNA, F – 5′ end of the mRNA, G – 3′ end of mRNA, H – codon, I – elongation factors (EF), GTP, and peptidyl transferase in ribosome.

SELF-TEST

1. c [Using *arg* mutants of the haploid fungus *Neurospora crassa*, they were able to correlate mutations to enzymes in the biosynthetic pathway for arginine, concluding that one gene encoded one enzyme]
2. a [The "one gene–one enzyme" hypothesis had to be modified when it became clear that a polypeptide, the translated product of a single gene, may not be functional unless associated with one or more other polypeptide chains, to give the functional protein]
3. d [the number is determined by the formula 4^3, which is derived from the fact that there are four different bases and they are combined in a three-base code]
4. b [RNA polymerase uses ribonucleotide triphosphates as building blocks, progresses in a $3′ \rightarrow 5′$ direction on the DNA template, polymerizing like all polymerases, in the $5′ \rightarrow 3′$ direction. Unlike DNA, RNA molecules contain the pyrimidine uracil in place of thymine]
5. a [The TATA box is a sequence typical of eukaryotic promoters. In prokaryotes, the RNA polymerase binds directly to the promoter using a protein factor that directs it to the promoter then diffuses away]
6. d [In prokaryotes, transcription is terminated after the RNA polymerase transcribes one of two terminator sequences. One type of terminator forms a hairpin structure through complementary base pairing of sequences at the 3′ end of the transcript, causing the polymerase to be released]
7. c [Eukaryotes, unlike prokaryotes, use different RNA polymerases for differnet types of genes. RNA polymerase II is the polymerase specifically used for protein-encoding sequences]
8. c [Eukaryotic mRNA is generally made as a larger pre-mRNA, which is then processed by modification of the 5′ and 3′ untranslated sequences and splicing out the introns]
9. a [Introns are removed by the snRNPs so that the final transcript has the 5′ cap, 3′ poly (A) tail, and the sequence comprises the exons only]
10. a [The process requires the activity of snRNAs, ribozymes within snRNPs and, through alternate splicing, creates a much higher protein-coding capacity than the number of genes in the cell]
11. b [Each boundary sequence is recognized through complementary base pairing of an snRNA within a snRNP]
12. b [Alternative splicing allows for alterations in the way introns are spliced out of the pre-mRNA; exon shuffling is believed to be a method of creating or evolving new proteins; however, it is likely not a routine method of mRNA processing]
13. d [The prokaryotic ribosome forms the initation complex through base pairing of a small subunit RNA with an initation sequence upstream of the start codon. Because of the absence of a nucleus, transcription and translation happen throughout the cell and occur simultaneously]
14. c [A modified base, inosine, in the first position of the anticodon, increases the "wobble" at that position, allowing tRNAs with that base to pair with 3 different bases in the 3' position of the codon]
15. c [The anticodon is the complementary sequence to the codon(s) for whichever amino acid is carried by the tRNA]
16. d [The hypothesis explains how there are 20 different tRNAs, one for each amino acid, but there is a total of 61 amino acid-encoding codons. Specifically, the base pairing of the particular tRNA for a particular amino acid "wobbles" generally in the third position so that one tRNA can base pair with any of the codons that encodes their particular amino acid]
17. a [The aminoacyl transferases hydrolyse ATP, using the energy from that to drive formation of the energy-containing bond linking the amino acid to the tRNA. During translation, energy from that bond therefore ultimately from ATP, is used to drive the formation of the peptide bond between amino acids]

18. a [Both have a similar function, consist of a small and large subunit with similar organization; however, the prokaryotic ribosome is smaller, largely because of differing ribosomal proteins, and this difference is exploited with certain antibiotics that specifically target bacterial ribosomes]
19. c [AUG is the universal start codon, encoding methionine; the uracil is the base in RNA that replaces the thymine base in the DNA]
20. a [The A stands for aminoacyl and is the site where the charged tRNA binds. The exception is the initiator tRNA carrying methionine; this binds the P site]
21. c [Initiation and elongation of translation both use GTP as an energy source]
22. d [The peptidyl transferase activity of all ribosomes is associated with a catalytic rRNA molecule, i.e., a ribozyme, in the large ribosomal subunit]
23. b [In all organisms, when a stop codon enters the A site, protein release factors enter because there is no corresponding tRNA for the codon. These release factors cause the peptidyl transferase to cleave the bond linking the peptide chain to the tRNA in the P site, releasing the polypeptide and causing the ribosome and mRNA to dissociate]
24. b [Because nuclear proteins need to re-enter the nucleus after completion of the cell cycle, their trafficking/localization signal is not cleaved when it is transported through the nuclear pore complex]
25. c [Frameshift mutations result when a base is inserted or deleted so that from the point of insertion/deletion, the reading frame of the protein is altered, the amino acid sequence of the remaining polypeptide chain is altered and the structure and function of the protein is lost]

INTEGRATING AND APPLYING KEY CONCEPTS

1. Reread section 13.3b describing the highly accurate nature of snRNP activity. Remember that the genetic code is a triplet code and that the reading frame is established by the presence of the start codon with no subsequent "commas" in the sequence.
2. Reread sections 13.1b and 13.3c. Think about the structure of a simple protein vs. a complex protein like hemoglobin and about the processing that eukaryotic pre-mRNA must undergo to generate the translatable mRNA.
3. Reread section 13.4h paying attention to the comment regarding breakdown of the nuclear membrane during cell division cycles. Also pay attention to the discussion of why protein sorting is believed to be a very ancient mechanism.

Chapter 14   Control of Gene Expression

Why It Matters [pp. 308–309]
14.1 Regulation of Gene Expression in Prokaryotic Cells [pp. 309–314]

1. genes; 2. expression; 3. Housekeeping; 4. transcription; 5. simultaneously; 6. operons; 7. transcriptional; 8. operator; 9. operon; 10. repressor; 11. inducer; 12. repressor; 13. activator; 14. on; 15. negative; 16. co-repressor; 17. operator; 18. C; 19. F; 20. G; 21. A; 22. J; 23. K; 24. H; 25. L; 26. B; 27. I; 28. D; 29. E; 30. N; 31. M; 32. A – An operon that is normally repressed and is turned on or induced when a molecule—i.e., the inducer—binds and inactivates the repressor, B – An operon that is normally on—e.g., a biosynthetic operon—and is turned off when a corepressor, usually the end product of the biosynthetic pathway, complexes with the repressor protein to give the active repressor, C – Negative gene regulation involves *reduction* of gene expression through binding of a regulatory protein, D – Positive gene regulation is the opposite of negative gene regulation—that is, expression is *increased* through binding of a regulatory protein; 33. The *lac* genes would be expressed; 34. The strain would be unable to make a functional activator complex so would only give low levels of transcription of the *lac* operon in the presence of lactose, even when glucose is absent; 35. The *trp* operon would be expressed regardless of whether tryptophan was present; 36. T; 37. F – Like mRNA, the proteins also have a short half-life; 38. A – *lacI*, B – promoter, C – Lac repressor, D – β-galactosidase, E – *lacY*, F – *lacA*, G – CAP sequence.

14.2 Regulation of Transcription in Eukaryotes [pp. 315–322]

39. operons; 40. short; 41. long; 42. transcriptional; 43. transcriptional; 44. translational; 45. transcription; 46. II; 47. proximal; 48. enhancer; 49. coactivator; 50. repressor; 51. proximal; 52. enhancer; 53. combinations; 54. regulator;

55. sequences; 56. chromatin; 57. chromatin; 58. histone; 59. silencing; 60. cytosine; 61. imprinting; 62. C; 63. E; 64. D; 65. A; 66. B; 67. N; 68. H; 69. F; 70. J; 71. M; 72. L; 73. G; 74. I; 75. K; 76. A – The condensed structure of chromatin is loosened around the promoter region either through binding of an activator protein upstream of the promoter, and the subsequent recruitment of remodelling proteins that displace the nucleosome or the recruitment of acetylation enzymes that acetylate the histone proteins, causing them to loosen their interaction with the chromosome, B – The use of different combinations of regulators for different genes, as dictated by the specific combination of regulatory sequences associated with that gene, C – All genes that respond to the same signals have the same regulatory sequences, D – In gene silencing, methylation of whole chromosomes or segments of chromosomes completely inactivates that region/ chromosome. In genomic imprinting, methylation of specific alleles during gametogenesis inactivates them and is an inherited change; 77. T; 78. T; 79. F – Methylation of histones gives highly condensed, transcriptionally inactive heterochromatin. Euchromatin is more loosely condensed and is transcriptionally active; 80. This alters the degree of binding to DNA, altering gene expression. Acetylation, or phosphorylation of histone tails gives them a negative charge so the histone is less attracted to the negatively charged DNA, whereas methylation of histones is associated with the highly condensed heterochromatin, causing gene inactivation; 81. Housekeeping genes are ones that need to be expressed in all types of cells, for example, those involved in glucose metabolism. They have promoter proximal sequences recognized by activators present in all cell types. Hormone-regulated genes are found in specific cell types and have an identical hormone response element that binds the hormone–hormone receptor complex; 82. This is a multiprotein complex that hydrolyzes ATP to slide the nucleosome along the DNA, exposing the promoter; 83. A – gene, B – RNA polymerase II, C – promoter, D – promoter proximal element, E – general transcription factors, F – coactivator, G – activator proteins, H – enhancer.

14.3 Posttranscriptional, Translational, and Posttranslational Regulation [pp. 322–326]

84. pre-mRNA; 85. translation; 86. degradation; 87. alternate splicing; 88. exons; 89. masking; 90. eggs; 91. microRNA; 92. hormones; 93. UTR; 94. cleavage; 95. modifications; 96. cleavage; 97. ubiquitin; 98. H; 99. D; 100. A; 101. E; 102. G; 103. B; 104. F; 105. C; 106. A – Alternative splicing generates different proteins through different combinations of exons, masking proteins combine with the mRNA to block translation, different 5′ UTR sequences change the rate of mRNA degradation, and RNA interference involves short, complementary RNA sequences that block translation or trigger mRNA cleavage, B – Alterations to the 3′ poly(A) tail length , C – Reversible chemical modification of proteins, e.g., acetylation or phosphorylation, processing of preproteins, ubiquitin-mediated proteolysis; 107. T; 108. F – The 5′ UTR seems to be involved in determining the half-life of the mRNA molecule; 109. Researchers are able to synthesize double-stranded RNA molecules of a particular sequence that can be targeted by Dicer and the other proteins of the RNA interference pathway and then base-pair with the mRNA of a gene being studied to silence the gene. This may help elucidate the function of unknown genes; 110. Through an unknown mechanism, the 5′ UTR affects the half-life of mRNA. mRNA can also be degraded by the miRISC. Proteins can be targeted for proteolytic degradation with the ubiquitin "doom tag."

14.4 The Loss of Regulatory Controls in Cancer [pp. 326–329]

111. dedifferentiated; 112. Malignant; 113. proto-oncogenes; 114. tumour; 115. oncogene; 116. suppress/inhibit; 117. inhibitory; 118. increase; 119. decrease; 120. multistep; 121. C; 122. D; 123. B; 124. G; 125. I; 126. H; 127. E; 128. A; 129. F; 130. A – Both arise from cells displaying uncontrolled growth and division; however, only malignant tumours invade and disrupt surrounding tissue and may metasize, B – Proto-oncogenes are normal genes that encode

functions that promote cell division, whereas oncogenes are mutant versions of these where they cause cells to progress unregulated through the cell cycle, C – Differentiation is the process whereby cells become specialized with some genes being turned on and others being turned off and is usually accompanied by a slowing or cessation of cell growth. Dedifferentiation occurs when differentiated cells become cancerous and the genes that were turned off are turned back on, the cell reverts partially or completely to the embryonic state, and the cell starts growing rapidly. D – Tumour-suppressor genes are normal cellular genes that encode proteins that inhibit cell growth and division. *TP53* is a tumour-suppressor gene that is found to be mutant in many different types of cancer; 131. Spontaneous mutations in the promoter or other regulatory sequence, making the gene abnormally active, spontaneous mutations within the coding portion of the gene to give an abnormally active protein, translocations of the gene to another chromosome so gene expression is under the control of different promoters, alteration of gene sequences or regulatory sequences by insertion of viral DNA; 132. People who inherit mutant copy of a tumour-suppressor gene then only need to suffer a mutation to the other allele of that gene to develop cancer. Normally a person has to suffer mutations in both alleles for inhibitory activity of the gene product to be lost.

SELF-TEST

1. c [An operon is the name proposed by Jacob and Monod when studying the cluster of genes for lactose metabolism in *E. coli*]
2. b [In prokaryotes, the RNA polymerase can bind directly to the promoter in order to transcribe a gene or operon]
3. d [An inducer is a molecule that interacts with a repressor to cause the repressor to become inactivated, relieving repression of the gene or operon]
4. d [*LacI* is the repressor for the *lac* operon. The operon is part of a regulon of operons regulated in response to glucose levels, through the binding of the cAMP-catabolite activator protein complex]
5. b [The *trp* operon is under negative control with a repressor that is produced in an inactive form; when tryptophan, the end product of the pathway, accumulates, it acts as a corepressor, binding to the repressor protein to make a functional repressor]
6. d [Prokaryotes are single-celled organisms that lack a nuclear membrane and perform transcription and translation simultaneously. They are therefore able to adapt quickly to their rapidly changing environment, such as the intestinal bacterium *E. coli*. Eukaryotes have a histone-condensed chromatin surrounded by a nuclear membrane and, in the case of multicellular organisms, undergo differentiation.]
7. d [Transcription factors are required to bind the TATA box of the promoter and recruit one of the RNA polymerases. Activators bind promoter proximal elements and enhancers and the combination of specific activators and repressors allows the coordinate regulation of genes without the genes being organized in operons]
8. a [Although regulation if gene expression in eukaryotes is far more complex and occurs at many different levels, regulation of transcription is the most important and is also the prevalent method of regulation in prokaryotes]
9. c [Prokaryotes do not have a nuclear membrane so perform simultaneous transcription and translation. So translation begins on an mRNA before transcription is complete. No pre-mRNA is made so no processing is required]
10. a [Repressors and activators both bind to the promoter proximal and enhancer sequences. The coactivators bridge the proteins at the enhancer with those at the promoter proximal elements. The RNA polymerase is bound to promoters via transcription factors]
11. b [A masking protein associates with certain mRNAs, such as those in animal eggs prior to fertilization. The binding blocks translation of the mRNA]
12. a [Methyl groups are added to cytosines to inactivate whole regions of a chromosome or whole chromosomes to "silence" the genes within that region or, in the case of the Barr body, the whole chromosome. They can also be added to the cytosines in a particular gene, to silence just that gene, as is the case with genomic imprinting]
13. d [Epigenetics is the alteration of gene expression without a change in the DNA sequence. This is accomplished by methylation of cytosines and underlies inactivation of the X chromosome as a Barr body, genomic imprinting, and gene silencing. Acetylation of histone tails is associated with the phenomenon of chromatin remodelling]
14. c [Methylation of cytosines is the basis for the phenomenon of epigenetics. Chromatin remodelling is initiated by binding of an activator that may recruit proteins to form the nucleosome remodelling complex which uses ATP hydrolysis to shift the nucleosome or may instead recruit acetylases to acetylate histone tails, causing a loosening of the chromatin]

15. a [Masking proteins are used as a method of posttranscriptional regulation, binding to the mRNA and preventing the ribosomes from gaining access to translate the message. When eggs are fertilized, these proteins are displaced, allowing translation to occur]

16. a [RNAi in animals typically involves imperfect base pairing of the miRNA in the miRISC to the target, blocking translation. In plants, it typically involves perfect base pairing of the miRNA to the target mRNA, resulting in cleavage of the message by an enzyme in the miRISC]

17. b [miRNA or microRNA molecules are short single stranded RNA molecules that are generated from a double-stranded precursor by the Dicer enzyme to then take part in the posttranscriptional regulation of gene expression through complementary base pairing to the sequences in the 3′ UTRs of target mRNAs]

18. c [Specific characteristics of the 5′ UTR sequences determine the half-life of their associated mRNAs]

19. b [Ubiquitin, also called the "doom tag," is attached to proteins such as transcipritonal regulators that are rapidly degraded in the cell. The tag is recognized by the proteasome, the cytoplasmic multiprotein complex that degrades the protein to its component amino acids]

20. b [Although benign tumours are also composed of dedifferentiated cells like malignant tumours, in contrast to malignant tumours, they do not invade or metastasize and are not cancerous]

21. d [*TP53* is a tumour suppressor gene that is often associated with cancers once mutated]

INTEGRATING AND APPLYING KEY CONCEPTS

1. Read sections 14.1c and the section in 14.2b that describes coordinated transcriptional regulation, paying attention to the regulatory molecules, whether a partner is required in both cases, the scope of the gene(s) that are targeted, the mechanism of regulation (negative or positive? transcriptional or translational?) and what determines which genes are subject to this regulation. Identify as many similarities as possible and critical differences.

2. Remember that blood cells and every other cell in the body are derived from the zygote and think about whether regulation of the relevant genes would require short-term or long-term regulation.

3. Read the section in 14.3a on regulation of gene expression by small RNAs. While reading this section, pay attention to the specific types of genes that are regulated by miRNA and think about the structural/physiological differences between worms and humans.

Chapter 15   DNA Technologies and Genomics

Why It Matters [pp. 332–333]
15.1 DNA Cloning [pp. 333–341]

1. cloning; 2. function; 3. Restriction; 4. vector; 5. ligase; 6. recombinant; 7. transformed; 8. replicated; 9. labelled; 10. hybridization; 11. library; 12. library; 13. expressed; 14. mRNA; 15. DNA; 16. transcriptase; 17. polymerase chain reaction; 18. primers; 19. DNA polymerase; 20. denaturing; 21. annealing; 22. extending; 23. doubles; 24. metagenomics; 25. microbial; 26. cultured; 27. C; 28. K; 29. P; 30. A; 31. G; 32. D; 33. M; 34. B; 35. H; 36. E; 37. O; 38. J; 39. F; 40. I; 41. N; 42. L; 43. Restriction enzymes recognize and cut specific sequences, which facilitates the precise cleavage of vector and insert DNA. Some generate single-stranded "sticky" ends that base-pair with any other DNA molecule that has the same ends; 44. A cDNA library provides a clone base of all genes that were expressed by the organism or cell type under a single set of conditions; 45. DNA hybridization is a technique used to identify the presence of DNA sequences of interest based on complementary base pairing to a labelled nucleic acid primer; 46. In order to perform PCR one must have the sequence information that allows for the synthesis of the two primers that will be complementary to and hybridize to either end of the gene or sequence of interest; 47. T; 48. F – They methylate the enzyme's recognition sequence within their own DNA; 49. T; 50. C, E, A, D, B.

15.2 Applications of DNA Technologies [pp. 341–352]

51. DNA; 52. genetic/inherited; 53. restriction; 54. length polymorphisms; 55. alleles; 56. electrophoresis; 57. blot analysis; 58. PCR; 59. fingerprints; 60. PCR; 61. short tandem repeats; 62. identical twins; 63. engineering; 64. crops; 65. animals; 66. proteins; 67. genetic; 68. engineering; 69. genetically modified organisms; 70. I; 71. D; 72. H; 73. J;

74. A; 75. B; 76. F; 77. E; 78. C; 79. G; 80. The genetic material is isolated and digested with a restriction enzyme that gives different-sized restriction fragments depending on whether the allele is normal or mutant. The restriction digest fragments are separated by gel electrophoresis, then DNA hybridization is performed using a labelled nucleic acid probe for the gene. If a person has sickle cell trait then they will have both the normal allele and the mutant allele; 81. This terms denotes an organism that contains, in its genome, a gene or genes from another species; 82. One can make a cDNA library and identify using hybridization the clone containing the gene. If the cloning vector is an expression vector for protein expression in bacteria, then the gene will be transcribed and translated; 83. Embryonic stem cells are undifferentiated and have the capacity to differentiate into any cell type. Adult stem cells are more differentiated and are used to replace specialized tissue and organ cells; 84. F – In order for the change to be heritable, it must be made to the germ-line or a fertilized egg; 85. T; 86. F – Although it has been used successfully with animals, it is illegal with humans, to use germ-line gene therapy; 87. T; 88. T.

15.3 Genome Analysis [pp. 353–361]

89. structural; 90. functional; 91. dideoxy; 92. replication; 93. dideoxyribonucleotides; 94. termination; 95. dideoxyribonucleotide; 96. shotgun; 97. fragments; 98. cloned; 99. sequences; 100. algorithms; 101. protein; 102. reading; 103. three; 104. start codon; 105. Comparative; 106. 95; 107. chimpanzess; 108. homologous; 109. homologues; 110. Functional; 111. microarrays; 112. microarrays; 113. proteomics; 114. proteins; 115. T; 116. F – It was predicted to have that many genes based on the number of different human proteins, however, it has only about 20 000 such genes; 117. F – The field uses genomic approaches, proteomics, and a variety of other techniques including complex quantitative techniques to develop models for all of the interactions within an organism; 118. It is an in vitro DNA replication technique that uses a specific DNA primer, template, DNA polymerase, dNTPS, as well as the four bases modified to lack the essential 3′ hydroxyl of the ribose and with each base also modified to carry a unique fluorescent dye. During replication, there is a random chance that with each base incorporated, a dideoxy base will be incorporated, causing termination of chain elongation with that molecule. Separation of the labelled molecules identifies the sizes of each and, for each, the fluorescent dye identifies the base at the 3′ end of the chain, thus giving, collectively, the sequence of the template DNA that was replicated; 119. This is a field of science that combines biology, mathematics, and computer science to analyze the vast amounts of biological data using computer algorithms and databases; 120. This uses a computer algorithm to search sequence databases for sequence similarities either at the nucleotide or amino acid level. This may provide some information on possible gene function of a newly sequenced gene; 121. Gene knock-outs mutate a gene so that it is not functional, whereas gene knock-downs use the phenomenon of RNAi to degrade the mRNA, lowering translation of a normal gene. Both may be used to assign function to a particular gene based on identification of the resulting phenotype.

Self-Test

1. c [Metagenomics determines the DNA sequence of the "metagenome"; that, is all of the DNA in a particular environmental sample. It provides a way to access the genetics of the largely uncultured microbial world]
2. c [While this would be one type of biotechnology, this is specifically a genetically engineered organism, whereas biotechnology does not necessarily use DNA technology and genetic engineering to produce a specific product, for example, using yeast to brew beer]
3. b [In order to produce a recombinant DNA molecule, the cloning vector as well as the DNA to be cloned both need to be digested with the same restriction enzyme, in order to recombine them into a single new molecule]

4. a [The restriction enzymes that make staggered cuts within the restriction site, such as *Eco*R1, generate single-stranded ends that will base-pair with the ends of any molecule cut with the same enzyme. They are therefore referred to as "sticky"]

5. a [Just as in DNA replication in vivo, ligase seals the nicks between two adjacent DNA strands, catalyzing the formation of a phoshpodiester bond between the 5′ phosphate of one strand and the 3′ hydroxyl of the adjacent DNA strand. In cloning, it covalently attaches the cloned insert and the vector sequences]

6. d [X-gal is a substrate for the β-galactosidase enzyme produced by the *lacZ* gene that is often included in cloning vectors. The X-gal is incorporated into the bacterial growth medium to allow blue-white selection of recombinants]

7. a [DNA containing a sequence of interest can be identified by using a labelled, single-stranded DNA or RNA oligonucleotide probe complementary to a region of the sequence of interest. The probe will base pair or *hybridize* with the sequence wherever it exists on a filter paper or in a Southern blot]

8. a [mRNA is reverse transcribed by reverse transcriptase, making a complementary DNA molecule, which can then be cloned, sequenced, or amplified in a PCR reaction]

9. c [Kary Mullis worked for a biotechnology company and won the Nobel Prize for his role in developing the technique]

10. d [cDNA is reverse transcribed from mRNA so a clone library containing cDNA from a tissue or organism contains only the sequences of the genes that were active at the time the mRNA was purified. It does not contain all of the noncoding and inactive genes]

11. a [Both utilize DNA polymerase enzymes and these always polymerize in only one direcrtion: 5′ → 3′. In fact, it is the use of a forward and reverse primer, combined with the directionality of the polymerization reaction, that allows the PCR reaction to amplify only the target sequence]

12. b [You have to know the sequence of your target in order to design forward and reverse primers for the PCR amplification of the sequence]

13. a [Agarose gel electrophoresis is commonly used to separate DNA molecules based on charge, shape, and size. In contrast, the identification of bacterial clones using a labelled probe merely uses the probe and a filter paper imprint of the colonies on a culture plate]

14. b [RFLP stands for restriction fragment length polymorphism and is a technique that detects sequence variations between different alleles of a gene by looking for resulting changes to the restriction fragments generated by digesting those alleles]

15. c [Everyone has alleles within their genome containing short tandem repeats. These are noncoding sequences that are unique to the individual, much like a fingerprint]

16. d [A transgenic organism is one that contains a foreign gene, for example, a bacterial strain containing the (human) insulin gene]

17. a [Knock-out mice have had the paternal and maternal alleles of a gene "knocked out" or mutated to facilitate study of the normal function of that gene]

18. c [For ethical reasons, germ-line gene therapy is not permitted in humans]

19. d [There are numerous examples of transgenic animals including any used for pharming projects]

20. b [One example of a successful pharming project was the generation of a transgenic sheep that produced human blood clotting factor in its milk. This pharmaceutical product is then easily purified from the milk without causing any harm to the sheep]

21. a [A diploid (somatic) mammary cell was used as the source of nucleus in an enucleated unfertilized egg cell]

22. d [The Ti plasmid of this organism is genetically modified and used to introduce foreign DNA into plant cells; however, this organism is not itself used nor does the recombinant DNA molecule cause tumour/gall formation, unlike the pathogenic bacterium]

23. a [The use of two primers in an in vitro DNA replication reaction is specific to the polymerase chain reaction. Sanger sequencing uses a single primer]

24. c [Computer programs are used to detect the overlapping sequences of individual DNA sequences, which allows assembly of the DNA sequence of the contiguous genome. Once this is done, the genome can be annotated, using various bioinformatic tools to characterize the genes and other specific sequences within the genome]

25. b [Suprisingly, simpler organisms can have bigger genomes and more complex genomes than larger more complex organisms, and in eukaryotes, the number of genes is less than the total number of proteins, as a result of alternate splicing and protein processing reactions]

26. a [The human genome encodes ~100 000 proteins but contains only ~20 000 genes. This represents a small proportion of the entire genome]

27. c [Protein microarrays are a tool of proteomics, whereas function genomics, which attempts to understand the functions encoded by a genome, identifies these function using homology searches with BLAST algorithms, microarrays, and the phenotypes resulting from gene knockdown experiments]

1. Remember that insulin is a human protein hormone. Since the human genome has been sequenced, you have the sequence information for generating PCR primers. Remember that eukaryotic genes cannot be cloned directly into bacteria because of the lack of introns in bacteria (read section 15.1c). From the cDNA, PCR can be used to specifically amplify the insulin gene (section 15.1d). Then follow the steps depicted in Figures 15.3, 15.4, and 15.10.

2. Read the relevant subsections of 15.2c then section 15.2d to review the discussion of genetically modified organisms, the concerns, possible problems, and oversight governing GMO production and commercialization.

3. Reread the section on the features of the human genome sequences and, if necessary, the relevant sections in 14.3a and 14.3b on processing of eukaryotic mRNA and proteins. To answer how the specific number of 100 000 different proteins being the total proteome of humans, read the section on tools used in proteomics, 15.3e.

Chapter 16   Microevolution: Genetic Changes within Populations

Why It Matters [pp. 364–365]

1. Penicillin; 2. resistant; 3. microevolution; 4. species.

16.1 Variation in Natural Populations [pp. 365–368]

5. phenotypic; 6. quantitative; 7. qualitative; 8. bar; 9. curve; 10. variation; 11. polymorphic; 12. frequency;

13. Phenotypic variation can result from genetic variation (mutation that produces new allele) or rearrangement of alleles, from an environmental cause (greater plant growth due to increased sunlight), or a combination of both factors;

14. Variation resulting from a genetic difference will be passed to the offspring and therefore evolution can act to select for or against the trait, whereas variation resulting from an environmental factor will not be passed on and therefore cannot result in evolutionary change; 15. Changes in the codons for a particular amino acid may not change the amino acid encoded due to the redundancy of the genetic code (there are generally multiple codons that will specify the same amino acid); 16. Researchers investigating the basis for increased wheel running behaviour and increased running speed in certain house mice, were able to show, by selective breeding, that the trait had a genetic basis; 17. If the height of a population of people were plotted on a graph against the number of people at each height, depending upon the size of the population, a bar graph showing a bell curve or a bell curve will result, indicating that differences between individuals are small and continuous, i.e., showing quantitative variation (textbook example, others possible); 18. The existence of discrete variants of a character (e.g., Mendel's garden pea flower colours); 19. This is a heritable change in the genetics of a population; 20. Gel electrophoresis; 21. All members of the same species that live together in the same place and time.

16.2 Population Genetics [pp. 368–370]

22. F; 23. D; 24. A; 25. E; 26. I; 27. J; 28. C; 29. B; 30. H; 31. G; 32. No mutations are occurring; 33. The population is closed to migration of individuals of other populations (gene flow); 34. The population is infinite in size; 35. All genotypes in the population survive and reproduce equally well; 36. Individuals within the population mate randomly with respect to genotype.

16.3 The Agents of Microevolution [pp. 370–378]

37. microevolution; 38. mutation; 39. gene flow; 40. genetic drift; 41. variability; 42. bottlenecks; 43. founder; 44. allele; 45. endangered; 46. population; 47. breeding; 48. heritable; 49. fitness; 50. B; 51. D; 52. A; 53. C; 54. E; 55. A; 56. D; 57. E; 58. C; 59. D; 60. B; 61. A.

16.4 Maintain Genetic and Phenotypic Variation [pp. 378–381]
16.5 Adaptation and Evolutionary Constraints [pp. 381–383]

62. genetic; 63. phenotypic; 64. diploid; 65. heterozygous; 66. polymorphism; 67. fitness; 68. heterozygote advantage; 69. alleles; 70. fitness; 71. neutral variation; 72. natural selection; 73. selectively neutral; 74. bottleneck; 75. adaptive; 76. adaptation; 77. changing; 78. existing; 79. F; 80. E; 81. D; 82. A; 83. C; 84. B.

SELF-TEST

1. b [A recessive trait is, by definition, masked in heterozygotes, so natural selection cannot act on these individuals. In the case of an undesirable allele, this means that it will not be eliminated from the population]
2. d [In the case of coloration, for example, genetic factors may determine the colour (e.g., Mendel's garden peas) and environmental factors may be involved, as is the case with hydrangeas and the determination of flower colour based on soil pH]
3. c [For example, crops that grow quickly and taller may do so because of genetic traits, and these can be selected for in selective breeding programs to be passed onto the next generation and potentially changing allele frequencies (evolutionary change)]
4. a [Alleles are different variants of a genetic trait and so changes arise by changes in the DNA sequence, i.e., mutations]
5. b [Genetic drift is the change in allele frequencies due to chance events, and it can be seen in a population that has undergone a population bottleneck, where there has been a massive die-off within a population and alleles are lost]
6. d [This is a measure of reproductive success, which is the essence of natural selection]
7. b [The rate of loss of a lethal allele decreases as an increasing number of these alleles are found in heterozygous individuals]
8. c [Stabilizing selection is seen when individuals expressing intermediate traits have the highest relative fitness; this therefore eliminates phenotypic extremes]
9. c [This is specifically the result of intersexual selection where extreme traits in males help attract mates and therefore results in a higher relative fitness]
10. a [Some mutations may have no measureable fitness consequences; selection does not produce perfect organisms regardless of human intervention; many traits that evolved for one purpose in an ancestor get co-opted for other purposes in descendants]
11. c [Sexual reproduction only shuffles existing alleles into new combinations]
12. b [The bacterial population is genetically diverse and exposure to antibiotics represents a selective pressure. Within the population will be individuals with varying levels of resistance, and those with the highest level of resistance will have the greatest relative fitness]
13. b [Because of the redundancy of the genetic code, some base changes will not cause a change in the amino acid sequence of the encoded protein]
14. a [The use of antibiotics is a selective pressure that selects for individuals within a population that have a greater relative fitness. It does not alter the genes]
15. a [The gene pool is dangerously low in populations that have undergone a population bottleneck or in cases where a small number of individuals have created a new population—for example, in the case of endangered species and captive breeding programs. This has undesired effects]
16. b [As in the case of the sickle cell trait where the heterozygotes have greater relative fitness in areas where malaria is endemic. The result is the maintenance of an otherwise harmful trait, so that both the normal and mutant allele are maintained in those populations]
17. a [Quantitative traits are those that give rise to a continuum of variation rather than having discrete phenotypes]
18. c [Dwarfism is the result of a mutation so is not represented by a continuum of phenotypes but rather numbers/frequencies of affected individuals]
19. a [Population bottlenecks are an example of genetic drift where there is a high rate of mortality among individuals of a small population; this can eliminate certain alleles or reduce genetic variation with the loss of so many individuals. It is not, however, stabilizing selection because the individuals that succumb are not being selected based on a genotype or phenotype]
20. c [Organisms that have inherent adaptive traits to their environments will benefit but note that organisms cannot cause these benefits to arise from their environmental conditions]

INTEGRATING AND APPLYING KEY CONCEPTS

1. Given the relative differences in life-span, think about the relative differences in the reproductive periods of each. Reread section 16.1c.

2. Reread section 16.2b and determine what experimental methods would be used to test each of the five criteria for satisfying the Hardy–Weinberg principle. Reading sections 16.1 again may also help.

3. Reread sections 16.1 and 16.2a.

Chapter 17   Darwin, Fossils, and Developmental Biology

Why It Matters [pp. 385–387]

1. erosion; 2. fossils; 3. living; 4. changes; 5. Charles Darwin.

17.1 Recognition of Evolutionary Change [pp. 387–388]
17.2 Changes in Earth [p. 388]
17.3 Charles Darwin [pp. 388–391]

6. Aristotle; 7. God; 8. change; 9. natural selection; 10. naturalist; 11. Galapagos Islands; 12. artificial selection; 13. Thomas Malthus; 14. Charles Lyell; 15. population; 16. reproduce; 17. generations; 18. Alfred Russell Wallace; 19. *On the Origin of Species by Means of Natural Selection*; 20. Thomas Malthus, 21. *Essay on the Principles of Population*; 22. Uniformitarianism; 23. Alfred Russell Wallace; 24. Jean Baptiste de Lamarck; 25. Gradualism; 26. Suggested that Earth changed slowly during its history; 27. Le Comte de Buffon; 28. Vestigial; 29. Aristotle; 30. Catastrophism; 31. Catastrophies are responsible for the layers of different fossils in strata; 32. A&B; 33. A; 34. B; 35. A; 36. A&B.

17.4 Evidence for Evolution: The Fossil Record [pp. 391–393]

37. Paleontology; 38. oxygen; 39. acidity; 40. teeth; 41. leaves; 42. minerals; 43. moulds; 44. decomposition; 45. fossilization; 46. deeper/lower; 47. higher; 48. radiometric dating; 49. half-life; 50. $^{14}C:^{12}C$; 51. F – They do not form in mountain forests as they require flowing water, including rain or run-off that carries fine rocks or soil downstream to a swamp, lake, or the sea whereupon the particles settle as sediments; 52. F – Because many types of structures or organisms are soft-bodied and normally do not form fossils, and because fossil formation requires specific conditions and only occurs in some areas, the fossil record is significantly incomplete; 53. T; 54. Soft-bodied organisms generally undergo microbial decay when they die; however, this requires the presence of oxygen, which is not present in peat bogs, tar pits, and glaciers; 55. Amber is the fossilized resin of coniferous trees and upon formation, it can trap insects, tiny lizards, and frogs; these do not decay because of the lack of oxygen.

17.5 Earth History, Biogeography, and Convergent Evolution [pp. 393–396]

56. plate tectonics; 57. mantle; 58. continental drift; 59. environment; 60. asteroids; 61. Biogeography; 62. continuous; 63. disjunct; 64. dispersal; 65. vicariance; 66. Pangaea; 67. realms; 68. biota; 69. morphological; 70. convergent; 71. D; 72. E; 73. B; 74. F; 75. C; 76. A; 77. T; 78. T; 79. T; 80. T; 81. F – continuous; 82. F – different biotas; 83. F – convergent.

17.6 Interpreting Evolutionary Lineages [pp. 396–402]
17.7 Macroevolutionary Trends in Morphology [pp. 402–404]

84. linear; 85. extinct; 86. anagenesis; 87. cladogenesis; 88. gradualist 89. punctuated equilibrium; 90. cladogenesis; 91. fossil; 92. complexity; 93. structures; 94. preadaptation; 95. Allometric growth; 96. heterochrony; 97. neoteny; 98. pedomorphosis; 99. reproduce; 100. juvenile features; 101. pedo; 102. hetero; 103. allo; 104. clado; 105. D; 106. E; 107. B; 108. F; 109. A; 110. C; 111. T.

17.8 Evolutionary Developmental Biology [pp. 404–409]
17.9 Evolutionary Biology since Darwin [p. 409]

112. Evolutionary developmental; 113. genetic tool-kit; 114. homeotic; 115. transcription factors; 116. activate; 117. repress; 118. *Hox;* 119. head-to-tail; 120. levels; 121. times; 122. switch; 123. allometric growth; 124. heterochrony; 125. C; 126. E; 127. A; 128. D; 129. F; 130. B; 131. F – It regulates genes that control the development of spines on the pelvic fins of sticklebacks; 132. T; 133. F – Tool-kit genes have been preserved for at least hundreds of millions of years, and differ in their activities and time of activation to give rise to substantial differences in body form; 134. Evo-devo is the study of the effects of changes in genes regulating embryonic development. These studies are revealing that such changes often result in changes in body plans which may give rise to adaptive radiations if the new body plan allows the organism to move into a new adaptive zone; 135. Marine populations of three-spined sticklebacks have bony armour along their sides and prominent spines, whereas the freshwater descendants of this fish have greatly reduced armour and may lack pelvic spines altogether. In the latter, deactivation of the homeotic gene *Ptx1* during embryonic development of fin buds provides the explanation. This change in expression appears to have been maintained through natural selection because the lack of long spines helps protect the freshwater fish from attack by dragonfly larvae. The gene is active in other areas of the developing fish, suggesting an unidentified mutation is specifically blocking expression of the gene in the fin buds; 136. When fruit flies were genetically engineered to express the *pax-6* gene of a squid or a mouse, its eyes developed normally, indicating that the gene has been maintained unchanged since the three lineages leading to squid, mice, and fruit flies diverged.

SELF-TEST

1. a [By the 14th century, Europeans had merged Aristotle's classification with the biblical account of creation, and sought to name and catalogue all of God's creations]
2. c [He proposed that organisms were conceived by Nature and produced by Time]
3. a [Georges Cuvier proposed that abruptly changing strata were the result of a dramatic shift in ancient environments and that the fossils within those strata were ones that died in a local catastrophe, such as a flood]
4. b [Although he proposed the idea of use and disuse, the idea behind this was that organisms change in response to their environment, an underpinning for Darwin's theory of natural selection]
5. c [Malthus wrote "Essays on the Principles of Population" that discussed the fact that the rate of increase in the England's population was outpacing its agricultural capacity and predicted that with limiting food some people would inevitably starve]
6. c [The first two are inferences he made based on observations, while the last is his hypothesis of evolutionary change based on natural selection]
7. b [Fossils are associated primarily with sedimentary rock, formed when fine rocks and sediment are carried by rain or run-off into lakes, rivers, bogs, or oceans, where they settle and gradually get buried by the increasing deposition of sediment. They do not form in the presence of oxygen as decomposition is increased with exposure to air, especially for soft-bodied organisms. Geological processes such as volcanic eruptions cause erosion and tend to destroy fossils]
8. a [Radioactive isotopes are unsteady and decay at a fixed rate that is characteristic of the particular isotope; therefore, the amount of a particular isotope in a stratum gives a measure of the age of the stratum and the fossils within that stratum. The amount of carbon 14 is constant while an organism is living but starts to decrease once it dies. Therefore the ratio of $^{14}C:^{12}C$ gives a measure of the age of a fossil as long as there is still organic material associated with it]
9. a [Earth's mantle is semisolid and flows in currents, causing the large rigid plates of Earth's crust and the continents embedded in them, to drift]
10. d [This kind of distribution is characterized by the existence of widely separated populations and is explained by the fact that the populations were previously part of one big land mass, e.g., Pangaea, which then separated, separating with them, the population]
11. c [For example, many of the species on the continent of Australia, which has been geographically isolated for approximately 55 million years]

12. b [Their lineages arose independently long after their respective continents had separated]
13. d [The other realms are the Nearctic, Palearctic, and Oriental]
14. c [Another term to describe adaptive radiation is diversification]
15. a [This process is the evolutionary transformation of an existing species so does not give rise to an increase in the number of species; however, if morphological changes are large, the organisms may be given different names at different times in their history]
16. d [This hypothesis suggests that most species experience long periods of stasis or morphological equilibrium punctuated by brief periods of rapid cladogenesis]
17. c [This observation is most applicable with vertebrates which concomitantly show an increase in morphological complexity]
18. b [In humans, the head, torso, and limbs all grow at a different rates]
19. a [The slower development time of *D. nudicaule* flowers results in a more closed flower, so hummingbirds will pollinate it]
20. c [For example, the *Hox* genes are universal among animals and are responsible for the development of the body form]

INTEGRATING AND APPLYING KEY CONCEPTS

1. Study Fig. 17.21 and reread section 17.8a.
2. Reread sections 17.5a and 17.5b.
3. Reread section 17.8a, paying particular attention to the experiments with genetically engineered fruit flies.

Chapter 18   Classification, Evolution, and Phylogeny

Why It Matters [pp. 412–415]
18.1 The Significance of Similarities and Differences [pp. 415–417]

1. conditions; 2. evolutionary; 3. parallel; 4. convergent; 5. deadly; 6. E; 7. D; 8. B; 9. A; 10. C.

18.2 Systematic Biology: An Overview [p. 417]
18.3 The Linnaean System of Classification [p. 418]
18.4 From Classification to Phylogeny [p. 418]

11. Linnaean; 12. taxonomic; 13. taxon; 14. domain; 15. morphological; 16. subcellular; 17. sequences; 18. behaviour; 19. taxonomy; 20. systematics; 21. phylogeny; 22.phylogenetic trees; 23. independently; 24. E; 25. G; 26. B; 27. H; 28. D; 29. A; 30. C; 31. F; 32. H; 33. E; 34. I; 35.C; 36. F; 37. A; 38. D; 39. B; 40. G; 41. F – Life on Earth is classified into three domains: Archaea, Bacteria, and Eukarya; 42. T.

18.5 Evaluating Systematic Characters [pp. 418–420]
18.6 Phylogenetic Inference and Classification [pp. 420–423]

43. genetic; 44. independent; 45. Homologous; 46. genetic; 47. analogous; 48. mosaic; 49. ancestral; 50. derived; 51. lineage; 52. characters; 53. evolutionary; 54. morphological; 55. cladistics; 56. clade; 57. parsimony; 58. cladogram; 59. evolutionary; 60. G; 61. K; 62. M; 63. A; 64. C; 65. J; 66. D; 67. E; 68. L; 69. N; 70. H; 71. B; 72. I; 73. F; 74. F – It considers only those traits that are shared among the group of organisms, i.e., derived traits. Traditional evolutionary systematics is based on shared ancestral and derived traits; 75. T; 76. F – Parallel evolution occurred between vertebrates, and convergent evolution occurred between insects and vertebrates, since the former are more closely related to each other than the latter; 77. F – It does not use taxonomic groups since classification is based solely on clades; 78. Homologous characters emerge from comparable embryonic structures and grow in similar ways during development, presumably because evolution has conserved the pattern of embryonic development; 79. Derived traits are those that are new and are heritable, and therefore shared by all subsequent descendants so they serve as markers for

entire evolutionary lineages, whereas ancestral traits do not provide this kind of information unless one were to move backward in evolutionary time and determine at which point that particular trait evolved, thus determining when it was "derived"; 80. ancestral; 81. derived; 82. ancestral; 83. ancestral; 84. insects.

18.7 Molecular Data [pp. 423–427]
18.8 Clarifications from Molecular Phylogenetics [p. 428]
18.9 Phylogeny: Contributions from Bayesian, Bootstrap, and Parsimony Analysis [pp. 428–430]

85. protein; 86. characters; 87. shared; 88. environmental; 89. quickly; 90. slowly; 91. mosaic; 92. constant; 93. molecular clock; 94. distant; 95. recent; 96. align; 97. phylogenetic trees; 98. maximum likelihood; 99. derived; 100. four; 101. B; 102. B; 103. B; 104. A&C; 105. B; 106. C; 107. D; 108. A; 109. E; 110. B; 111. F – These sequences evolve quickly so are more useful for determining evolutionary divergence that has arisen in the last few million years; 112. F – The molecular data indicated that organisms should be classified into three domains; 113. F – While the prokaryotes were assigned to a polyphyletic kingdom (Monera), this problem was not recognized at the time. It was, however, always recognized that the kingdom Protista was polyphyletic; 114. Genetic distance is a measure of the amount of divergence between species, i.e., species with very similar DNA sequences have a small genetic distance, whereas the maximum likelihood methods is a set of statistical tests to determine the most likely phylogenetic tree; 115. This refers to differences in DNA sequences that provide a time of evolutionary divergence.

18.10 The Evolution of Humans [pp. 430–437]

116. hominids; 117. erect/upright; 118. lumbar; 119. hands; 120. derived; 121. African emergence; 122. multiregional; 123. mitochondrial DNA; 124. oldest; 125. Y chromosome; 126. E; 127. A; 128. F; 129. C; 130. B; 131. D.

SELF-TEST

1. b [While this fossil had a flattened vertebral tail, the skull is quite distinct from that of the Canadian beaver, suggesting that the name and flattened tail notwith (most specific) is: Domain, Kingdom, Phylum, Class, Order, Family, Genus, Species. The molecular analyses of Carol Woese revealed that the prokaryotes are subdivided into two domains: Bacteria and Archaea]
2. a [The two major goals of systematics is to determine the phylogeny (i.e., evolutionary relatedness of organisms) and to identify and name organisms so that they can be placed within a classification scheme]
3. c [The taxon above the species level is Genus, which is more inclusive than species but less inclusive than the next higher level, Family]
4. c
5. d [Analogous characters would be such things as wings, which have evolved four separate times, with bats, birds, insects, and pterosaurs]
6. c [The stapes of the inner ear of four-legged vertebrates evolved from the hyomandibula, a bone that supports the jaw joint of most fishes]
7. c [Homologous characters are those shared traits that indicate a common genetic basis, inherited from a common ancestor and generally evident during embryonic development due to the conservation, by evolution, of embryonic developmental patterns. Since these have a genetic basis, they are not subject to variation based on environmental conditions]
8. a [Fossil evidence indicates that the earliest animals lacked backbones, which makes the vertebral column a derived character; whereas all other characters are derived characters within the organism groups indicated]
9. d [A monophyletic taxon is one that includes an ancestral species and all of its descendants]
10. c [A paraphyletic taxon is one that includes the ancestral species and some but not all of its descendants]
11. a [The node where the two lineages branch towards A and B represents the common ancestor]
12. d [Species I is the most distantly related so would be the best choice for the outgroup, sharing only ancestral characters]

13. c [Cladistic phylogenies are based only on evolutionary relatedness, not morphological divergence, therefore, contains only monophyletic clades. Some scientists that are supporters of cladistics maintain that we should dispense with traditional nomenclature and use a PhyloCode, which is based strictly on clades]

14. a [This is based on the Principle of Parsimony, that is, the least evolutionary changes to give rise to a particular lineage is the most likely explanation]

15. b [Traditional phylogeny as been criticized as lacking clarity because it classifies based on two separate phenomena: branching evoluation and morphological divergence. Cladistics is a more recent approach for classification that is based solely on evolutionary relationships, using derived characters as a basis for classification]

16. b [If comparing gene X from two organisms, if the base at position 200 is the same between the two organisms and a third presumed outgroup, based on that alone, one cannot determine if the change represents a shared derived trait or if it evolved separately as there are only four possible bases that could occupy that position, meaning that the chances are high for independent evolution of the same change]

17. d [molecular systematists use different types of molecules (DNA, RNA, and/or proteins) to build phylogenetic trees, but not morphological information]

18. c [The traditional tree of life consisted of five kingdoms: Monera (thought to be a monophyletic taxon containing the bacteria), Animalia, Fungi, Plantae, and Protista (known to be polyphyletic), whereas the tree of life determined by Carl Woese using rRNA sequence data consisted of three domains: Bacteria, Archaea, and Eukarya, with the latter containing monophyletic branches for the animals, plants, fungi and a variety of new lineages representing organisms that had previously been characterized as Protista]

19. b [Although humans belonged to the same evolutionary lineage as apes more than 6 million years ago, since then ape and humans have diverged and followed different evolutionary lines]

20. c [All genera listed are humans or their bipedal ancestors]

INTEGRATING AND APPLYING KEY CONCEPTS

1. Think about the morphological characteristics of prokaryotes compared to plants, animals and even fungi. If this doesn't help, reread section 18.8 and think about how phylogenetic classifications were determined from the time of Linnaeus to the time of Carol Woese.

2. Think about the requirements of a molecular clock, the intricacies of translation and the source of, and variation of mRNA (especially among eukaryotes). You might also think about the nature of the genetic code (how many codons are there compared to how many amino acids?) You may need to reread section 18.7 and even sections 13.3 and 13.4.

3. Reread the section on p. 424 about *Constructing a Cladogram*. You may also need to refresh your memory on what an outgroup is (p. 420) and the differences between ancestral and derived traits between a specific group of organisms (p. 420).

Chapter 19   Species

Why It Matters [pp. 441–442]
19.1 What's in a Name? [pp. 442–443]
19.2 Definition of *Species* [pp. 443–444]

1. genetic; 2. intraspecific; 3. subspecies; 4. naming; 5. species; 6. signals; 7. taxonomic; 8. Biological; 9. fertile;

10. asexually; 11. hybrid; 12. hermaphrodites; 13. Gynogenetic; 14. stimulated; 15. Recombination; 16. mutation; 17. C;

18. A; 19. B; 20. F – Although bacteria and archaea reproduce asexually, they are given species names; this is critical when distinguishing between pathogenic and nonpathogenic species; 21. T; 22. F – They can interbreed; however, their offspring are sterile; 23. Hybridization occurs when members of different species mate and produce fertile offspring;

24. This refers to hybrid offspring that are not only fertile but strong competitors of the original species (their relative fitness is high).

19.3 One Size Does Not Fit All [pp. 444–446]
19.4 Gene Flow: Four Examples [pp. 446–448]

25. organisms; 26. evolution; 27. static; 28. flow; 29. cohesive; 30. isolated; 31. distinct; 32. flow; 33. cohesive;

34. DNA; 35. distribution; 36. genetic; 37. Morphological; 38. morphological; 39. fossil; 40. B; 41. E; 42. A; 43. D;

44. C; 45. Geographic separation prevents gene flow, while an increase in habitat continuity allows an increase in gene flow which may then result in a reduction if biodiversity; 46. In the case of house mice, males are less easily assimilated into another population, limiting gene flow. However, females are readily assimilated and can interbreed with males of other populations; 47. Gene flow between discontinuous habitats can be accomplished if one organism can travel with/on another, for example, hitchhiking on migrating birds.

19.5 Geographic Variation [pp. 448–449]

48. phenotypic; 49. subspecies; 50. cultivar; 51. overlap; 52. intermediate; 53. gene flow; 54. ring; 55. cline; 56. different; 57. When an uninhabitable region is surrounded by members of a particular species, they may diverge into subspecies with individuals readily interbreeding in the zones of overlap to give hybrids of intermediate phenotypes. If a ring does not completely close, then the subspecies at each end may diverge to the extent that they are no longer able to interbreed; 58. Clinal variation arises when there is continuous variation in environmental conditions over a geographic gradient. These changing environmental conditions select for differing alleles and phenotypes which also show a gradual but continuous change over the geographic gradient; 59. They exist as different subspecies based on obvious phenotypic differences between geographically isolated habitats.

19.6 Reproductive Isolation [pp. 450–452]

60. Reproductive isolating; 61. prezygotic; 62. postzygotic; 63. five; 64. interspecific; 65. intraspecific; 66. A – Ecological isolation, B – Hybrid sterility, C – When reproductive structures are incompatible, D – Postzygotic, E – The offspring of the hybrids have reduced viability due to the accumulation of chromosomal abnormalities or genetic recombinations, F – Hybrid inviability, G – Prezygotic, H – Different species recognize appropriate mates based on species-specific courtship displays, I – Gametic isolation, J – Prezygotic, K – Prezygotic, L – Mating times differ, for example, if one species mates during a different month than another or at a different time of day; 67. F – Sympatric species are ones that occupy the same geographic area but are reproductively isolated; 68. T; 69. F – Since a horse and a donkey produces gametes with 32 and 31 chromosomes respectively, hybrid sterility prevents the resulting mule from producing gametes (chromosomes cannot pair during meiosis); 70. T; 71. This is thought to arise through mate choice by females and sexual selection so that they do not mate with and raise offspring that will be inviable, sterile, or exhibit hybrid breakdown. This would therefore be the product of natural selection, so that the relative fitness of the females is maximized; 72. This arises when the male gamete must recognize and bind to a specific receptor molecule on the surface of the female gamete prior to fertilization. Incompatible gametes are unable to do this due to the presence of molecularly distinct gamete receptors; 73. Mechanical isolation in flowers may physically prevent access by inappropriate pollinators or may have colours that are not recognized by inappropriate pollinators.

19.7 Geography of Speciation [pp. 452–457]
19.8 Genetic Mechanisms of Speciation [pp. 457–461]
19.9 Back to the Species Concept in Biology [pp. 461–462]

74. allopatric; 75. secondary; 76. hybrid; 77. reinforcement; 78. Parapatric; 79. alleles; 80. Sympatric; 81. host; 82. host; 83. flow; 84. genetic; 85. contact; 86. inviability; 87. reinforce; 88. mechanical; 89. plants; 90. polyploidy; 91. meiosis; 92. autopolyploidy; 93. tetraploids; 94. reproductively; 95. sterile; 96. allopolyploidy; 97. double; 98. diploid; 99. tetraploid; 100. species; 101. para; 102. auto; 103. allo; 104. sym; 105. allo; 106. F – Natural selection cannot select

for reproductive isolation between allopatric populations as they must be able to together in the same location to allow interbreeding and selection to select against hybrid offspring and select for mechanisms that prevent fertilization. Selection will therefore occur upon secondary contact; 107. T; 108. Genetic changes such as inversions may cause speciation because of failure of chromosomes to pair (e.g., if the region that suffered the inversion includes the centromere); 109. Species clusters occur when founding populations from the same parent species repeatedly colonize an isolated land mass (e.g., an island) and each evolves reproductive isolation mechanisms to give discrete, but closely related species; 110. A tetraploid organism will produce $2n$ gametes, while a normal diploid organism will produce haploid gametes. When the gametes from these two organisms fuse, the zygote will be $3n$ and while mitosis of somatic cells may occur normally, meiosis cannot reduce $3n$ germ-line cells: there will be an odd number of chromosomes.

SELF-TEST

1. a [The biological species concept is based on an individual's ability to interbreed in nature; the morphological species concept is based on anatomical traits; the phylogenetic species concept is based on analysis of a phylogenetic tree]
2. b [The morphological species concept is based on anatomical, i.e., morphological traits and although an old concept, is still used by biologists in the field and by paleontologists]
3. c [Subspecies can be used to describe plant or animal species that interbreed where their distributions overlap; cultivars refers to plants only]
4. a [This is a pattern of smooth variation along a geographic gradient]
5. c [Examples are the vocalizations, colour, and behaviour used by song birds to attract females of their species]
6. d [Another example would be the opposite coiling of some species of snails, preventing them from getting close enough to mate]
7. a [A prezygotic isolating mechanism would prevent fertilization of the egg]
8. a [Allopatric speciation requires geographical isolation of populations. The other choices do not]
9. d [Sympatric populations are those found in the same geographic area; because polyploidy results in the reproductive isolation of the organism (usually a plant), they can mate by self-fertilization or with other plants of the same ploidy number]
10. a [b, c, and d are true. Autopolyploidy is rare in animals because most animals are incapable of self-fertilization]
11. d [Interbreeding between conspecifics in a population acts as "glue," maintaining gene flow within a population. Habitat can be discontinuous and interfere with gene flow; as would a new geographic barrier within a population or the lack of interaction between individuals from distant populations of a ring species]
12. b [A cline is a smooth variation in a particular trait such as the length of appendages, as a result of a gradual variation in some environmental condition (such as average temperature)]
13. c [An example of this situation is seen with the different subspecies of the salamander *Ensatina eschscholtzi* that surround California's Central Valley]
14. a [A cline is a smooth variation in a particular trait such as the length of appendages, as a result of a gradual variation in some environmental condition (such as average temperature)]
15. a [An example of this would be the various closely related species of duck where they can breed and give fertile, viable hybrids, but in the wild sexual selection has given rise to morphologically distinct males and females breed exclusively with males of their own species, exhibiting behavioural isolation]
16. b [Polyploid plants often display hybrid vigour and can be created through the use of chemicals by plant breeders]
17. c [The use of Giemsa stain revealed chromosomal alterations between humans, chimps, orangutans, and gorillas with inversions and chromosomal fusions but with preservation of nearly all of the 1000 different chromosomal bands in each]
18. a [Giemsa stains reveal distinctive banding patterns that are reflective of chromosomal structures, as in the case of the comparison of chromosomal similarities and alterations between humans, chimps, gorillas, and orangutans. Chromosomal inversions seem to correlate with increased divergence in the genes within the inverted region compared to those outside of the inversion—these can trigger speciation. Although humans and chimps share approximately 99% genetic similarity, the phenotypic/physiological differences between them greatly exceeds the 1% genetic difference between them]
19. a [Sterile hybrids often are more robust than their parent strains, growing faster and taller. They do not, however, have a higher relative fitness than their parents: if they are sterile, they have a relative fitness (which is a measure of their ability to produce healthy, viable offspring) of zero. Coffee, plantains, cotton, potatoes, sugar cane, tobacco,

and wheat are all polyploid crop plants. The wheat strain used for bread may have evolved by hybridization and allopolyploidy of three ancestral wild wheat species thousands of years ago]

20. b [Autopolyploidy and allopolyploidy can result in speciation very rapidly and without the requirement of geographic isolation. In addition, chromosomal alterations such as those seen among the primates can cause speciation without geographic isolation]

INTEGRATING AND APPLYING KEY CONCEPTS

1. Reread section 19.7 and make sure you are clear on the underlying mechanisms of prezygotic and postzygotic isolation; also reread section 19.9. Think about what kind(s) of technique(s) you would need to use to identify genetic differences between two species and how you would determine if the reproductive isolation was prezygotic vs. postzygotic.

2. Reread the section on allopatric speciation (19.8a) and examine Figure 19.20, then reread the section on genetic divergence (19.9a). Again, be aware of the molecular or physical basis of prezygotic isolating mechanisms and what sexual selection generates.

3. Based on the biological species concept, distinct species are able to breed with members of their own species to give fertile and viable offspring. Although there are many examples of organisms that do not exactly match these criteria (e.g., gynogenetic organisms) think about what conclusions you would draw if: a) the different populations were able to give fertile fully viable hybrids, and b) if they were not?

Chapter 20   Bacteria and Archaea

Why It Matters [pp. 465–466]
20.1 The Full Extent of the Diversity of Bacteria and Archaea Is Unknown [p. 466]
20.2 Prokaryotic Structure and Function [pp. 466–475]

1. animals; 2. vitamin K; 3. domains; 4. diverse; 5. cultured; 6. circular; 7. nucleoid; 8. plasmid; 9. horizontal/lateral;

10. resistance; 11. cell wall; 12. Gram; 13. Gram; 14. peptidoglycan; 15. Gram-positive; 16. Gram-negative; 17. outer;

18. capsule; 19. energy; 20. heterotrophs; 21. phototrophs; 22. chemoautotrophs/lithotrophs; 23. photoheterotrophs;

24. requirement; 25. respiration; 26. respiration; 27. fermentation; 28. biogeochemical; 29. fixation; 30. ammonia;

31. binary; 32. pathogenic; 33. exotoxins; 34. endotoxin; 35. H; 36. A; 37. D; 38. E; 39. G; 40. I; 41. B; 42. F; 43. P;

44. J; 45. L; 46. C; 47. O; 48. K; 49. Q; 50. M; 51.N; 52. A – Chemoautotroph/Lithotroph, B – Obtain energy by

oxidizing organic molecules and use already prepared organic chemicals as their carbon source, C – Use light as their

energy source and CO_2 as their carbon source, D – Photoheterotrophs, E – Facultative anaerobes, F – Obligate anaerobes,

G – Use oxygen as the electron acceptor for cellular respiration and cannot grow in its absence; 53. T; 54. T; 55. F –

Gram-positive cells stain purple and Gram-negative cells, which have a thin peptidoglycan layer surrounded by an outer

membrane, stain pink; 56. F – It is largely due to their extremely rapid ability to multiply (asexually) which is, in turn,

largely due to their small genome sizes and simple structures; 57. T; 58. The prokaryotes existed on Earth for 3 billion

years before the eukaryotes evolved; 59. It protects against the entry of certain toxic chemicals such as the penicillins and

detergents; 60. They can be used for bioremediation and sewage treatment, but they may also be detrimental to human

health such as the biofilms that form on teeth as plaque or on pacemakers and artificial joints; 61. They may experience a

mutation so that the antibiotic no longer binds and inhibits its target; they may actively pump the antibiotic out of the cell

or they may enzymatically alter the structure of the antibiotic so that it loses its effect; 62. Instead of using oxygen as the

terminal electron acceptor with their respiratory electron transport chains, they use an alternative molecule such as nitrate

or sulfate; 63. A – flagellum, B – plasmid, C – pili, D – nucleoid, E – peptidoglycan layer, F – outer membrane,

G – capsule, H – cell wall.

20.3 The Domain Bacteria [pp. 476–479]
20.4 The Domain Archaea [pp. 479–482]

64. branches; 65. proteobacteria; 66. photosynthetic; 67. pathogens; 68. photoheterotrophs; 69. green bacteria;

70. photoheterotrophs; 71. cyanobacteria; 72. oxygen; 73. Gram-positive; 74. *Lactobacillus*; 75. peptidoglycan;

76. parasites; 77. spirochetes; 78. cultured; 79. eukaryotes; 80. lipids; 81. molecular; 82. Korarchaeota;

83. Euryarchaeota; 84. halophiles; 85. thermophiles; 86. thermophiles; 87. Crenarchaeota; 88. psychrophiles; 89. C;

90. A; 91. F; 92. D; 93. B; 94. E; 95. F-They have a different kind of photosynthetic pigment than plants and do not

produce oxygen. Some of them are even photoheterotrophs; 96. F – It is a spiral-shaped bacterium that causes syphilis;

97. T; 98. T; 99. F – The ancestor to the mitochondrion was believed to have been an ancient proteobacterium; however,

the chloroplast's ancestor was believed to have been a cyanobacterium; 100. They are classified based on sequence

differences in the ribosomal RNA genes; 101. The myxobacteria are members of the proteobacteria that produce a slime

that can trap and degrade bacterial prey and, under certain conditions, may form differentiated multicellular structures.

Mycoplasmas are Gram-positive bacteria based on molecular phylogeny but have no cell wall. They are among the

smallest cells on Earth.

SELF-TEST

1. a [The vast majority of prokaryotes are essential components of the ecosystem but cannot be grown using currently available laboratory conditions. In addition, prokaryotes constitute the majority of biomass in the world's oceans, which represents approximately 70% of the Earth's surface and much of this is inaccessible]
2. c [Prokaryotes existed for approximately 3 billion years before the appearance of the eukaryotes]
3. d [The chromosome is condensed in the region known as the nucleoid but with one apparent exception, they do not have any internal, membrane bound organelles]
4. c [Plasmids generally contain useful but not essential genes, antibiotic resistance plasmids being an example. These are only essential if the bacteria are exposed to that antibiotic]
5. d [Using the Gram staining technique, Gram-negative bacteria stain with the second stain, that is they stain pink or red]
6. b [The capsule is a polysaccharide layer that may surround some strains of bacteria and archaea and which may help in pathogenesis or protect against dessication, bacterial viruses, or the penetration of antibiotics. Movement along a surface is effected by flagella]
7. a [Prokaryotic flagella are made of a helical arrangement of a protein called flagellin and they move by rotation, much like a propeller. In contrast, eukaryotic flagella differ structurall and move through a whipping motion]
8. d [Sex pili facilitate horizontal transfer of plasmids and are also important in attachment, either during biofilm formation or to host cells. The electricity-conduction nanotubes of *Geobacter* are pili but movement along a surface is facilitated by flagella]
9. a [Lithotrophs (chemoautotrophs) translates as "rock-eaters." They obtain their energy from molecules such as ammonium and their carbon from CO_2]
10. d [For example, some of the green bacteria and the purple proteobacteria obtain their energy from sunlight but their carbon from organic molecules instead of from CO_2]
11. a [Facultative anaerobes may function aerobically when oxygen is present, but if it is not, they generate energy anaerobically using either anaerobic respiration or fermentation]
12. a [It is a biological process that is strictly limited to small numbers of prokaryotic species and is an essential component of the biogeochemical cycling of nitrogen in the environment. The process is the conversion of atmospheric nitrogen gas to ammonia, which, upon conversion to nitrate by nitrying bacteria and archaea, provides bioavailable nitrogen for all other organisms on Earth]
13. c [They possess very small genomes and divide simply by binary fission so have an extremely high reproductive rate combined with an very high mutation rate. Horizontal gene transfer also provides for the spread of genetic/functional diversity; however, their ability to colonize virtually every niche on the planet is the *result* of their vast genetic diversity compared to other life forms]
14. c [LPS or lipopolysaccharide is the molecule of the Gram-negative outer membrane that contains endotoxin. Specifically, the lipid A portion of the LPS of some species causes severe symptoms when the lipid is exposed to human immune cells, giving rise to an overwhelming immune response that can be deadly]

15. b [Bacteria have evolved multiple ways to resist the effects of antibiotics, some of which are encoded by genes on conjugative or transmissible plasmids. The overuse or inappropriate use of antibiotics provides increasing selective pressure for the growth and spread of resistant bacteria but does not cause the resistance]
16. a [Bacteria in biofilms are up to 1000 times more resistant to antibiotics than the same bacteria growing in liquid culture]
17. a [*Lactobacillus*, the bacteria used to make yogurts, pickles, and sauerkraut, are Gram-positive bacteria]
18. a [The early cyanobacteria evolved the ability to perform photosynthesis using water as an electron donor, producing oxygen as a by-product. The ancestor of the chloroplast was likely a cyanobacterium]
19. c [They may be pathogenic or non-pathogenic, are named for their spiral shape; however, it is the cyanobacteria that form a symbiotic relationship with fungi to give rise to lichens]
20. b [The Korarchaeota have not yet been cultured in the lab]
21. b [Halophiles are associated with places like Great Salt Lake, in Utah, and the Dead Sea. They can grow in fully saturated salt solutions]
22. d [The Euryarchaeota contains the halophiles, some of the thermophiles, and all of the methanogens, anaerobic organisms that produce methane]
23. c [The crenarchaea contain most of the extreme thermophiles as well as all of the psychrophilic ("cold loving") archaea and the more recently discovered mesophilic archaea, which grow in cool marine waters and serve as food for many of the higher marine organisms]

INTEGRATING AND APPLYING KEY CONCEPTS

1. Think about the relationship between the size of an organism's genome and its coding capacity. If these organisms evolved to live permanently associated with animal hosts, knowing that prokaryotes have a very high mutation rate, what kinds of mutations might have occurred that would have very little impact given the niche these bacteria occupy? Would there have been a benefit to undergoing such mutations?
2. Remembering that most microbes live in moist environments and looking at the cyanobacteria depicted in Figure 20.17, would organisms that do not produce oxygen and are photosynthetic be likely to require oxygen? If not, relative to the cyanobacteria in this figure, where might purple and green bacteria live so that there is minimal oxygen, water and but would still be exposed to some level of sunlight?
3. Think about the cell wall structure of bacteria, especially Gram-positive bacteria such as *Streptococcus pneumonia*. This cell wall is critical to the survival of these bacteria. Now think about the cellular structure of animal (human) cells. Check Table 20.2 and reread the section on internal bacterial structures in section 20.2a if the answer is still not clear. If this antibiotic is lethal to *Streptococcus* and other Gram-positive bacteria, how might this be an advantage to other microorganisms in nature, such as specific fungi or antibiotic-producing bacterial species?

Chapter 21 Viruses, Viroids, and Prions: Infectious Biological Particles

Why It Matters [pp. 484–485]
21.1 What Is a Virus? Characteristics of Viruses [pp. 485–487]
21.2 Viruses Infect Bacterial, Animal, and Plant Cells by Similar Pathways [pp. 487–492]

1. nucleic acid; 2. capsid; 3. envelope; 4. living; 5. RNA/DNA; 6. DNA/RNA; 7. single/double; 8. double/single; 9. receptor; 10. surface; 11. identified; 12. ecosystems; 13. pathway; 14. infects; 15. machinery; 16. particles; 17. bacteria; 18. virulent; 19. temperate; 20. daughter; 21. lysing; 22. latent; 23. E; 24. O; 25. F; 26. A; 27. K; 28. B; 29. P; 30. L; 31. N; 32. Q; 33. C; 34. H; 35. G; 36. D; 37. M; 38. J; 39. I; 40. T; 41. T; 42. F – The virus acquires the envelope from the host's plasma membrane when it buds through the membrane during the release phase of the infectious cycle; 43. F – Bacteriophages largely inject their chromosomes into the host cell, leaving the capsid behind. Animal viruses enter through endocytosis or fusion of their envelope with the host's plasma membrane. Plant viruses may enter via the pollen or through lesions or biting insects. Once they are in the plant, they spread to neighbouring cells through plasmodesmata and to the next generation through the seeds; 44. T; 45. F – They may cause symptoms through direct lysis of infected cells, causing massive cell death, or by causing, upon cell breakdown, the release of cellular materials that cause symptoms such as fever and inflammation. Alternatively, they may insert into the host chromosome, causing altered gene expression, which may lead to cancer; 46. Generalized transduction is done by bacteriophages that

are lytic viruses; they sometimes randomly incorporate pieces of the host's chromosome when they assemble and are released by lysis. Specialized transduction is done by certain bacteriophages that have a lysogenic life cycle; they become incorporated into the host's chromosome at a specific locus and when they excise in order to revert to the lytic life cycle, the excision may be imprecise so that the virus incorporates one or two genes from either side of the site of insertion; 47. They are agents of mortality, controlling the numbers of bacteriophages and thereby affecting nutrient cycling by bacteria and archaea. They are also a natural means of pest control, killing, for example, spruce budworm. Finally, in the case of certain cyanobacterial phages, they encode photosystem proteins allowing photosynthesis to continue during the infection, until the point when the bacteriophages are released; 48. Both have complex morphology with a head and tail fibres; however, T4 is a lytic bacteriophage while λ is a lysogenic temperate bacteriophage; 49. Animal viruses are often enveloped and their method of entry into host cells may be through fusion of the envelope with the host cell membrane, or through endocytosis. Plant viruses are either rod-shaped (helical) or polyhedral, not enveloped, and enter cells initially through sites of mechanical damage or biting insects, then spreading to other cells through the plasmodesmata; 50. A – head, B – tail, C – DNA chromosome, D – protein coat/capsid, E – T-even bacteriophages or λ .

21.3 It Is Typically Difficult to Treat and Prevent Viral Infections [pp. 492–493]
21.4 Viruses May Have Evolved from Fragments of Cellular DNA or RNA [p. 493]

51. antibiotics; 52. hidden; 53. machinery; 54. antiviral; 55. serious; 56. anti-influenza; 57. vaccines; 58. chromosomes; 59. mutation; 60. HIV; 61. animals; 62. ancestor; 63. cells; 64. nucleic acid fragments; 65. cell; 66. nucleus; 67. F – It appears that the viral polymerase had specific sequence changes that may have made it more efficient at replicating the viral chromosomes; 68. F – Antibiotics target specific bacterial structures or processes so are ineffective against viruses. Antiviral drugs target specific virus structures or processes; 69. A large, double-stranded DNA virus; 70. The virus has eight chromosomes and when an animal host is infected by more than one strain, the chromosomes may randomly assort into new strains with new combinations of the parental chromosomes. In addition, they have a very high rate of mutation so that, between the two processes, their coat proteins vary and look different to the human immune system; 71. Animal viruses may mutate to cross the species barrier, infecting humans, as happened with HIV. In addition, as humans encroach on wildlife habitats, they increase the chances of this happening, and with the ease of global travel, these new viruses may spread rapidly to non-immune populations.

21.5 Viroids and Prions Are Infective Agents Even Simpler in Structure than Viruses [pp. 494–495]

72. RNA; 73. crop; 74. proteins; 75. spongiform encephalopathies; 76. BSE; 77. scrapie; 78. Creutzfeldt-Jakob disease; 79. misfolding; 80. neural; 81. cells; 82. A – Nucleic acid may be RNA, DNA, single-stranded or double-stranded, Proteins form the capsid structure, There may or may not be a lipid envelope, B – Single-stranded RNA, No protein, No envelope, C – No genetic material, Single, misfolded protein, No envelope; 83. BSE arose in cattle, possibly through the consumption of scrapie-contaminated rendered cattle feed. vCJD arose in humans through the consumption of BSE-contaminated beef.

Sᴇʟғ-Tᴇsᴛ

1. d [All strains of influenza cause a respiratory illness, including one of the most deadly, the Spanish flu of 1918]
2. a [Viruses contain protein coats, genetic material, and may be surrounded by an envelope, but they do not contain any of the structures typical of cells, like the ribosomes that are used for protein synthesis]

3. d [Viruses evolved separately on more than one occasion so do not have an evolutionary or phylogenetic tree, although they do have a system of classification. Enveloped viruses acquire their envelope by budding through the host's plasma membrane; however, the membrane is modified by virus-encoded membrane proteins]

4. b [Bacteria and archaea are central to nutrient cycling in the environment and because bacteriophages kill bacteria and archaea in massive numbers and are species specific, they have a direct impact on the nutrient cycling in the environment. Although some cyanobacterial phages carry with them the gene for a photosystem protein, this simply allows the host cell to continue photosynthesis while the virus is replicating inside the cell: viruses themselves have no metabolic abilities]

5. b [They are virulent, infecting *E. coli,* and emerging by lysis. They do not have an envelope and they do not have a lysogenic phase]

6. a [Certain lytic viruses, but not the T-even bacteriophages, may accidentally package a random fragment of the host's chromosome and transfer the genes from the first host cell to the next host cell]

7. c [Bacteriophage lambda inserts into a specific site on the *E. coli* chromosome and occasionally excises inaccurately so that it packages a host gene located on one side or the other of the site of insertion, taking that gene from the original host to the next host cell]

8. c [It is an enveloped virus that enters the host through fusion with the membrane and leaves by budding through the host's membrane, thus acquiring its envelope. Although symptoms of the active phase of infection are typified by skin lesions, these arise indirectly through massive budding of the viral particles, causing damage to, and breakdown of, the host's membrane]

9. a [Viruses with an inactive phase equivalent to the lysogenic phase of bacteriophages like lambda, are called latent viruses. Depending on the virus they may reside during the latent phase in the cytoplasm, as is the case with herpesvirus]

10. a [So far, there are no known enveloped plant viruses]

11. c [zanamavir is an anti-flu antiviral drug that is commercially available]

12. c [Viruses have been suggested by some researchers to have infected the ancestor to the eukaryotic cells to give rise the eukaryotic nucleus; however, the theory that speculates on the origin of viruses after the appearance of the first cells proposes that viruses evolved from nucleic acid fragments that "escaped" from cells]

13. d [They are single-stranded RNA particles and have no associated proteins]

14. b [Variant CJD or vCJD arises from consumption of contaminated meat but based on another human SE disease, kuru, may take decades to give rise to symptoms]

15. b [Cows had been fed meal from rendered cow and sheep carcasses for many years; however, changes in the rendering process, reducing the heating time, is thought to have allowed for entry of active prion proteins into the cows' food supply from scrapie-infected sheep carcasses]

16. c [The "normal" prion protein is found in neural membranes of the brain and is caused to convert to the wrong folding pattern through exposure to the infectious prion proteins. This then causes the accumulation of fibrils and apoptosis of brain cells, leading to the spongiform appearance of affected brains]

INTEGRATING AND APPLYING KEY CONCEPTS

1. Reread the section on "Infection of Animal Cells."
2. Reread the section on "Infection of Animal Cells."
3. Think about the structures of animal viruses and compare this to bacterial cells. Are there any obvious shared structures? If you are thinking possibly a DNA chromosome or a membrane, think about the nature of the host cell structures.
4. Reread section 21.3. and the section that describes the Spanish flu pandemic of 1918 in "Why it Matters."

Chapter 22   Protists

Why It Matters [pp. 498–499]
22.1 The Evolution of Protists Involved Endosymbiosis [p. 500]
22.2 Characteristics of Protists [pp. 500–501]
22.3 Protists' Diversity Is Reflected in Their Metabolism, Reproduction, Structure, and Habitat [pp. 501–503]

1. *Giardia lamblia*; 2. Protista; 3. ancestor; 4. symbiosis; 5. mitochondrion; 6. chloroplasts; 7. symbiotic; 8. animals,

plants, and fungi; 9. fungi; 10. cellulose; 11. stem, leaves, and roots; 12. unicellular; 13. photoautotrophs; 14. terrestrial;

15. host; 16. intracellular; 17. flagella; 18. pseudopodia; 19. mitotic; 20. meiosis; 21. F; 22. E; 23. A; 24. B; 25. G; 26. D;

27. C; 28. A – Aquatic or moist terrestrial environments or inside host organisms, B – Flagella, cilia or pseudopodia, C – heterotrophic, photoautotrophic, or a combination of both, D – Asexual or sexual; 29. T; 30. F – Many are multicellular or have a multicellular stage and some of these may be extremely large, for example, the giant kelp; 31. Sea weeds to not have leaves, stems, roots, and seeds.

22.4 The Protist Groups [pp. 503–520]

31. mitochondria; 32. feeding; 33. diplomonads; 34. heterotrophic; 35. cristae; 36 *Trypanosoma brucei*; 37. photosynthetic; 38. alveoli; 39. ciliates; 40. dinoflagellates; 41. flagella; 42. apicomplexans; 43. nuclei; 44. flagella; 45. Oomycota; 46. degradative enzymes; 47. hyphae; 48. diatmos; 49. silica; 50. golden; 51. brown; 52. kelp; 53. pseudopods; 54. axopods; 55. shells; 56. capture; 57. pseudopodia; 58. fresh water; 59. amoebae; 60. slime moulds; 61. pseudopods; 62. slime; 63. cellular; 64. cells; 65. plasmodial; 66. plasmodium; 67. cytoplasm; 68. algae; 69. Plantae; 70. algae; 71. marine; 72. green algae; 73. land plants; 74. flagellum; 75. collar; 76. flagellum; 77. animals; 78. D; 79. I; 80. A; 81. L; 82. B; 83. G; 84. O; 85. P; 86. K; 87. N; 88. C; 89. F; 90. E; 91. J; 92. H; 93. M; 94. A – *Trypanosoma brucei*, B – Causes Beaver Fever, C – Sexually transmitted diseases that are asymptomatic in men but if untreated may cause infertility in women, D – Cause malaria, E – *Toxoplasma,* F – *Entamoeba histolytica*; G – *Phytophthora infestansansi;* 95. The rock forming the cliffs is sedimentary rock made white by the high composition of ancient foram shells, which are made of calcium carbonate; 96. The coral contain endosymbiotic dinoflagellates, photosynthetic protists. When the corals are stressed, they eject their endosymbionts and take on a bleached look because they are no longer coloured by their endosymbionts; 97. Diplo-; 98. Proto-; 99. Dino-; 100. Hetero- ; 101. Foramin-; 102. Rhodo-; 103. Chloro-; 104. Opistho-; 105. Choano-.

22.5 Some Protist Groups Arose from Primary Endosymbiosis and Others from Secondary Endosymbiosis [pp. 520–522]

106. algae; 107. cyanobacterium; 108. euglenoids; 109. dinoflagellates; 110. heterokonts; 111. eukaryote; 112. additional; 113. food vacuole.

Self-Test

1. d [The term "Protists" is a catch-all term used to identify those eukaryotes that are neither animal, plant, nor fungi and does not denote a single common ancestor]
2. b [The protists share certain typical eukaryotic cell structural features; however, unlike the fungi, some are photosynthetic and those with cell walls do not have cell walls of chitin but of cellulose (or other materials)]
3. a [Some protists, but not all, are multicellular and some protists have lost their mitochondria. The multicellular protists have differentiated structures. Some corals are photosynthetic because of photosynthetic protest endosymbionts; the coral animals themselves do not have chloroplasts]
4. c [The photosynthetic protists do not form stems, roots, leaves, or seeds, nor do they use starch for a storage reserve]
5. b [The contractile vacuole is found in protists like *Paramecium* that live in dilute environments. They do not have cell walls so the excess water is retained in the contractile vacuole, and when it swells to a certain size it is expelled to the outside through the movement of the vacuole to the plasma membrane and its contraction]
6. c [The excavates lack typical mitochondria and are restricted to making ATP through the anaerobic process of glycolysis]
7. a [The name *Euglena* roughly translates as "eyeball organism"]
8. d [A typical example is *Paramecium*: these have cilia that they use for swimming, to guide prey into their mouth-like gullet, and they have one macronucleus and one or more micronuclei that contain the diploid genome]
9. a [They are a major primary producer in the world's oceans, i.e., they are a major component of the phytoplankton]
10. c [They are all nonmotile]
11. c [They were originally thought to be fungi because they grow by forming hyphae and mycelia; however, molecular data indicates they are not part of the fungi]

12. a [They are all unicellular with intricately formed silica cell walls in two sections that enclose the organism like two halves of a Petri dish]
13. b [Fucoxanthin is the accessory pigment in brown and golden algae that masks the colour of the chlorophyll]
14. b [This is an extract from red algae. All of the other structures are associated with the kelps formed by many of the brown algae]
15. b [The amoeba in this group form rigid pseudopods, for example, the radiolarians and forams, the latter being a major component of the White Cliff of Dover; when they die their hard shells eventually become part of the sedimentary rock]
16. a [The water moulds, or oomycetes (which form hyphae and mycelia) are not related to the slime moulds and plasmodial slime moulds, which, in addition to the amoebas that are part of this group, are "shape-shifters" that use flexible pseudopods for feeding and locomotion, for at least part of their life cycle]
17. d [The ability of the cellular slime moulds as well as the plasmodial slime moulds, both members of the group Amoebozoa, to differentiate into stalks and fruiting bodies under certain environmental conditions has been extensively studied. The organism *Dictyostelium discoideum* has been a particularly valuable model system]
18. a [The phycobilins are the accessory pigments that mask the colour of the chlorophyll in these photosynthetic organisms]
19. b [This group includes the green algae, the red algae, and the land plants that evolved from the green algae]
20. a [This group includes choanoflagellates, believed to be the ancestor to the animals and fungi]
21. b [The ancestor of the chloroplast in these organisms is related to the modern-day cyanobacteria]
22. d [A green algae was swallowed up by a heterotrophic eukaryote to give rise to the Euglenoids. The chloroplasts in these organisms have additional membranes derived from the new host]

INTEGRATING AND APPLYING KEY CONCEPTS

1. Think about how classifications have traditionally been done using basic morphological and metabolic similarities and differences. Also remember from Chapter 20 how, until the advent of molecular phylogeny, the prokaryotes were thought to all be one domain/Kingdom, based on a similar structure. Now think about the diversities you have seen among the protists as well as the similarities between some of the protists and other life forms (kelps and plants, slime moulds, and fungi) as well as the complex evolutionary tree depicted in Figure 22.2.
2. Review section 22.3, looking for examples where members of different groups of protists have similar morphological, metabolic, or life style features (e.g., pseudopodia, undulating membrane). Are there any examples of protists that bear a strong similarity with animals, plants, or fungi? Prior to the advent of molecular phylogeny, characteristics such as morphology/structural features, life style, metabolism etc. were the criteria used to determine taxonomy and relatedness.
3. Reread section 22.5 and pay particular attention to Figure 22.31.

Chapter 23   Fungi

Why It Matters [pp. 524–525]
23.1 General Characteristics of Fungi [pp. 526–528]

1. saprotrophs; 2. symbionts; 3. recycling; 4. mutualistic; 5. parasites; 6. yeasts; 7. hyphae; 8. chitin; 9. septa;

10. organelles; 11. degradative; 12. transporting; 13. tips; 14. spores; 15. plasmogamy; 16. karyogamy; 17. diploid;

18. haploid; 19. F; 20. M; 21. N; 22. C; 23. G; 24. O; 25. L; 26. E; 27. B; 28. A; 29. D; 30. H; 31. I; 32. K; 33. J; 34.

A – Organisms that live on the organic material of dead matter, producing degradative enzymes to break them down,

B – Organisms that live on another living organism (the host), causing harm to the host, C – A symbiotic relationship

where both partners derive benefit; 35. A – Eukaryotic heterotrophs, B – Chitin, C – Unicellular/yeasts or multicellular

hyphae/mycelia, D – Absorptive nutrition, involving secreted degradative enzymes from the growing hyphal tips,

transport of the smaller breakdown products, and disseminated to the rest of the organism by cytoplasmic streaming,

E – Sexual or asexual involves fusion of spores or hyphae, with plasmogamy, karyogamy (sometimes delayed leading to

a dikaryon stage), and meiosis; 36. F – It is a symbiotic bacterium growing in crypts on the surface of the ants that

produces the antibiotics; 37. T; 38. T; 39. They are used to produce cheeses, wine, and therapeutic drugs including

antibiotics and steroids; 40. These are metabolites or cellular products that are not required for the day-to-day survival of the organism but which do provide some benefit to the organism; 41. Studies with the yeast *Saccharomyces cerevisiae* and the mould *Neurospora crassa* have helped elucidate the structure and function of DNA and have been instrumental in the development of genetic engineering techniques.

23.2 Evolution and Diversity of Fungi [pp. 528–539]

42. five; 43. Deuteromycota; 44. flagellated; 45. aquatic; 46. rhizoids; 47. sporangium; 48. aseptate; 49. sporangia; 50. hyphae; 51. gametangia; 52. zygospore; 53. dormant; 54. sporangium; 55. meiosis; 56. aseptate; 57. hypha; 58. spore; 59. arbuscular; 60. roots; 61. conidia; 62. plasmogamy; 63. dikaryotic; 64. karyogamy; 65. asci; 66. ascospores; 67. ascocarp; 68. budding; 69. basidiocarps; 70. basidiospore; 71. Plasmogamy; 72. karyogamy; 73. dikaryon; 74. favourable; 75. basidiospores; 76. basidia; 77. O; 78. E; 79. G; 80. H; 81. P; 82. K; 83. B; 84. D; 85. L; 86. N; 87. C; 88. A; 89. F; 90. I; 91. J; 92. M; 93. A – Some are yeasts, reproducing by binary fission or budding. Others form chains of haploid spores called conidia during asexual reproduction and in sexual reproduction, form haploid ascospores inside eongated sacs called asci which may be housed inside fruiting bodies, often cup-shaped, called ascocarps, B – Forms aseptate hyphae, asexual reproduction by spores formed in sporangia, sexual reproduction involves gametangia forming at the end of specialized + and – hyphae which fuse, and the nuclei then fuse, functioning as gametes to give rise to a thick-walled zygospore which may remain dormant for years. When conditions improve, these germinate with a sporangium emerging from the zygospore to release haploid spores of the two mating types, C – Some are yeasts, reproducing by budding. The majority reproduce primarily sexually through the formation of a large, club-shaped fruiting body called a basidiocarp (mushroom), which has a stalk and a cap. The underside of the cap has club-shaped basidia inside of which are haploid basidiospores, which may be dispersed and germinate to form haploid mycelia. D –These produce flagellated spores and generally live as unicellular organisms; however, they may form chains of cells and rhizoids that anchor them to a surface. They are normally haploid and most species reproduce asexually, forming sporangia from which emerge the spores. E – These form the arbuscular mycorrhizae and reproduce asexually by walling off a fragment of hypha to form a spore; 94. A – *Saccharomyces cerevisiae*—brewer's and bread-maker's yeast, *Candida albicans* causes thrush in humans, B – These are the moulds that grow on breads, and rot fruits, vegetables, and grains, C – Smuts and rusts cause blights of many crops and other plants; they are also the mushrooms, both edible and poisonous, D – Symbionts of cows and other herbivores, it is these fungi that break down the cellulose in the animal's diet, they also cause chytridomycosis, a fungal disease that is contributing to the worldwide die-off of amphibians, E – These are most important as mycorrhyzae, they are the only kind of fungus to form arbuscular mycorrhizae; 95. T; 96. F – The close biochemical relationship between fungi and animals may explain why these infections are so difficult to treat ; 97. T; 98. T; 99. F – They are believed to be the most ancient group, retaining certain aspects of an aquatic lifestyle, namely flagellated spores; 100. This ascomycete spoils grains and produces ergot, consumption of which causes the intoxication ergotism, characterized by vomiting and hallucinations. This has been implicated in the hysteria that resulted in the Salem witch hunts; 101. Two of the phyla, the Chytridiomycota and the Zygomycota, are paraphyletic, containing species that do not share a common ancestor. In addition, the Basidiomycota is not a true phylum but a "holding pen" for species of unknown taxonomy, largely because of the inability to identify a sexual reproduction phase; 102. The Ascomycota and the Basidiomycota include species that prey on various animals, obtaining, in particular, molecular nitrogen from the enzymatic breakdown of their prey; 103. A – flagellated spores, B – sporangium, C – rhizoids, D – Chytidiomycota; E – zygospore, F – spores, G – sporangium, H – Zygomycota, I – arbuscule, J – fungal

hyphae, K – spore, L – Glomeromycota, M – ascocarp, N – ascus, O – ascospore, P – Ascomycota, Q – basidiocarp, R – basidium, S – basidiospore, T – Basidiomycota, U – The Deuteromycota is missing because they are a group of unrelated fungi for which no sexual reproductive phase has been observed. It is largely the distinctive sexual reproductive structures that are used to identify the fungal phylum.

23.3 Fungal Lifestyles [pp. 539–544]

104. saprotrophs; 105. symbiotic; 106. ecosystems; 107. drywall; 108. structural; 109. health; 110. Lichens; 111. mycobiont; 112. photobiont; 113. ascomycete; 114. green algae; 115. cyanobacteria; 116. thallus; 117. carbohydrates; 118. Glomeromycota; 119. roots; 120. carbon; 121. phosphorus and nitrogen; 122. arbuscular; 123. abundant; 124. colonization of land; 125. ectomycorrhizas; 126. Endophytic; 127. toxins; 128. H; 129. A; 130. J; 131. F; 132. I; 133. C; 134. D; 135. B; 136. E; 137. G; 138. T; 139. F – Certain endophytic fungi have been found to produce chemicals of medicinal value, such as the taxol used to treat certain cancers; 140. Arbuscular mycorrhizas are formed by the Glomerulomycota, are the most prevalent, and are associated with a wide range of plants including most flowering plants. The fungal hypha penetrates the cell wall, forming a highly branched structure, which is in direct contact with the plant cell's plasma membrane. The ectomycorrhizas are formed by some species of Ascomycota and Basidiomycota and are associated with a variety of trees including the conifers of Canada's boreal forests and coastal rain forests. The fungus does NOT penetrate the plant cell wall but forms a sheath or mantle around the plant root and may grow between plant cells; 141. Fossil evidence reveals that arbuscular mycorrhyzae were common with ancient land plants and are thought to have played a critical role in facilitating the colonization of land by plants by enhancing transport of water and minerals from the nutrient-poor soil of early Earth.

Self-Test

1. d [They are eukaryotic heterotrophs that obtain their nutrients by absorptive nutrition and have cell walls of chitin]
2. b [The hyphae may have septa or cross walls, but even if they have septa, the septa have pores that allow materials including organelles to flow between cell-like compartments of the hyphae]
3. d [Only the hyphal tips may acquire nutrients, through absorption. These are then spread to the non-absorptive structures of the mycelium by cytoplasmic streaming]
4. a [Sequence analyses indicate that the common ancestor of the animals and fungi likely diverged between 760 million and 1 billion years ago]
5. c [The existence of arbuscules in fossilized early land plants suggests they were already present at that time and essential to the colonization of land by the land plants. However, the chytrids appear to be the oldest lineage of the fungi and because of their flagellated spores and their sequence similarity to the Choanoflagellates, they are believed to have had an aquatic origin]
6. d [These two lineages are not monophyletic as they contain subgroups that are not all descended from a common ancestor]
7. a [The Chytridiomycota appears to be the oldest fungal lineage and is the only one that produces flagellated spores. This fact, combined with molecular data, suggest that the first fungi evolved from aquatic, flagellated protists related to the Choanoflagellates]
8. c [The Zygomycota may also be used commercially for their products (secondary metabolites); however, they are well known spoilage organisms for fruits, vegetables, and grains]
9. a [The two oldest lineages within the fungal kingdom produce these very simple structures for disseminating spores. As the fungi evolved, their reproductive structures became larger and more elaborate]
10. e [The Glomeromycota are the most widespread of the mycrorrhiza-producing fungi and are older than the ectomycorrhyza-producing fungi (the Ascomycota and Basidiomycota)]
11. b [Although the Zygomycota may be parasites of insects (living in or on them but not first killing them), only the Ascomycota and the Basidiomycota include species that specifically trap their prey either through the use of hyphal nooses, in the case of the ascomycetes, or produce paralyzing toxins or gluey substances that immobilize their prey, as seen with the basidiomycetes]

12. b [These edible delicacies are the ascocarps or fruiting bodies of the fungal species]

13. c [This ascomycete produces a psychrotropic toxin called ergot, from which LSD is made. It is thought to be the explanation for the bizarre "bewitched" behaviour of young girls and cows documented during the Salem Witch Trials]

14. a [These fungi take their name from the sac-like structures or asci in which the sexual spores form]

15. c [The name basidium means "club," and is given to these fungi due to the shape of the cup-shaped cels in which the sexual spores are produced. The basidia are contained in basidiocarps, which include the fruiting bodies known as mushrooms, as well as puffballs, smuts and rusts, bracket fungi, and stinkhorns]

16. d [The Glomeromycota seems to only contain the species that form arbuscular mycorrhizas]

17. a [The Chytridiomycota largely reproduce asexually via flagellated spores. The well-known yeasts *Saccharomyces cerevisiae* and *Candida albicans* are ascomycetes and the human pathogen *Cryptococcus* is a basidiomycetes yeast]

18. d [As a result of this prolonged stage, hyphal growth continues, then when karyogamy is triggered, many more basidiocarps and haploid spores are made than if there was not this prolonged delay. The advantage is demonstrated by the existence of a basidiomycete individual in Oregon that may be the largest, heaviest, and oldest organism on Earth]

19. b [The Ascomycota form ascocarps as part of their sexual reproductive cycle. These are easily recognized and give the group their common name "cup fungi"]

20. a [Although the mycobiont consumes as much as 80% of the phycobiont's carbohydrates, and the phycobiont grows very slowly, it also is able to grow in environments where, on its own, it would not grow. So the relationship is mutualistic with the fungal partner providing nutrients that it absorbs through its absorptive feeding ability, in some cases even extracting nutrients from rocks]

21. c [The Deuteromycota is a temporary grouping for organisms that have not yet been determined to have a sexual reproductive cycle and for which molecular data does not allow classification to any of the five evolutionary lineages. The members of this group are therefore not evolutionarily related]

22. c [These are the reproductive structures and are clusters of the algae or cyanobacteria wrapped up in fungal hyphae. These are the means of dispersal for the lichen]

23. d [Ectomycorrhiza evolved more recently than the arbuscular mycorrhiza so are associated with the more recently evolved ascomycetes and basidiomycetes]

24. d [Endophytes are localized to above-ground plant structures, the leaves and shoots. Although it is not known exactly what the nature of the endophytic relationship is, in at least a few cases it seems to be mutualistic. The anticancer drug Taxol is produced by endophytes]

INTEGRATING AND APPLYING KEY CONCEPTS

1. Reread section 23.3a to clarify the importance of this process and section 23.1to clarify the nature of nutrient acquisition. Finally, reread the section on the impressive degradative abilities of the basidiomycetes.

2. Reread section 23.1 but also try to find the information on the dispersive abilities of spores of *Rhizopus* and the basidiomycetes, which have a prolonged dikaryon stage and a somewhat bizarre, very large, fruiting body.

3. Reread section 23.2a.

Chapter 24   Plants

Why It Matters [pp. 547–548]
24.1 Defining Characteristics of Land Plants [p. 548]

1. cellulose; 2. photoautotrophs; 3. chlorophyll; 4. heterotroph; 5. roots; 6. generations; 7. dominant; 8. sporophyte; 9. meiosis; 10. mitosis; 11. gametes; 12. fertilization; 13. sporophyte; 14. gametophyte; 15. A – Having a single set of chromosomes, B – Having two sets of chromosomes, one from each gamete/parent, C – The multicellular structure that gives rise to the spores, D – The multicellular structure that gives rise to the gametes, E – Fusion of the female gamete by the male gamete, F – Haploid cells that arise by the process of meiosis in the sporophyte, G – Haploid cells arising by mitosis in the gametophyte, H – The immediate product of fertilization; 16. T; 17. Plants alternate between the diploid sporophyte and the haploid gametophyte stages.

24.2 The Transition to Life on Land [pp. 548–557]

18. charophyte; 19. bryophytes; 20. poikilohydric; 21. diffusion; 22. cuticle; 23. stomata; 24. vascular; 25. xylem

26. phloem; 27. sunlight; 28. lignin; 29. apical meristems; 30. Roots; 31. mycorrhizae; 32. nutrients; 33. symbiotic;

34. sporophyte; 35. sporangia; 36. meiosis; 37. homosporous; 38. gametophyte; 39. heterosporous; 40. male; 41. female;

42. sporophyte; 43. gametangia; 44. sporangium; 45. gametophyte; 46. sporophyte; 47. homosporous; 48. heterosporous;

49. N; 50. O; 51. J; 52. A; 53. M; 54. B; 55. D; 56. C; 57. F; 58. E; 59. I; 60. G; 61. K; 62. L; 63. H.

24.3 Bryophytes: Nonvascular Land Plants [pp. 557–560]
24.4 Seedless Vascular Plants [pp. 561–566]

64. bryophytes; 65. roots; 66. liverworts; 67. hornworts; 68. mosses; 69. gametophyte; 70. gametangium;

71. archegonium; 72. antheridium; 73. fertilization; 74. germinates; 75. protonema; 76. gametophytes; 77. rhizoids;

78. antheridia; 79. archegonia; 80. archegonium; 81. egg; 82. sporophyte; 83. sporangium; 84. water; 85. sugar;

86. phloem; 87. seeds; 88. lycophytes; 89. ferns; 90. swimming; 91. vascular; 92. leaves; 93. sporophyte; 94. sporangia;

95. gametophytes; 96. archegonium; 97. antheridium; 98. sporophyte; 99. nutritionally; 100. heterosporous; 101. male;

102. megaspores; 103. F; 104. H; 105. J; 106. G; 107. I; 108. A; 109. D; 110. B; 111. E; 112. C; 113. A – Often poikilohydric, gametophyte dominant, motile sperm, B – Sporophyte dominant, motile sperm, vascular tissues, root and shoot system/apical meristem, C – Sporophytes retained attached to tips of gametophytes, spores are released and once they land and germinate they give rise to a protonema from which eventually arise the male and female gametophytes, D – Sporangia form on the underside of fern leaves (sorus), homosporous (only one type of spore). Male and female gametophytes form on the underside of the sporangium leaves, male and female on the same leaf, after fertilization, the embryo gives rise to the sporopophyte which remains attached to the gametophyte until it becomes nutritionally independent, at which point the gametophyte dies; 114. T; 115. T; 116. F – The various bryophyte lineages evolved separately in parallel with vascular plants; 117. If a bisexual gametophyte is surrounded by mainly male gametophytes and many of these are from other spores, this increases the chances that the eggs will be fertilized by the sperm of other plants, increasing genetic diversity; 118. They lack vascular tissue and they did not evolve from the same structures as leaves and stems did.

24.5 Gymnosperms: The First Seed Plants [pp. 566–570]
24.6 Angiosperms: Flowering Plants [pp. 570–575]

119. Gymnosperms; 120. angiosperms; 121. pollination; 122. seed; 123. naked; 124. male; 125. female; 126. pollen;

127. megagametophyte; 128. pollen tube; 129. egg; 130. zygote; 131. pine nut; 132. cycads; 133. Gingkophyta;

134. gnetophytes; 135. angiosperms; 136. vascular; 137. ovary; 138. endosperm; 139. pollinators; 140. fruits;

141. Anthophyta; 142. monocots; 143. eudicots; 144. gametophyte; 145. endosperm; 146. fruit; 147. dispersal; 148. G;

149. J; 150. F; 151. K; 152. M; 153. C; 154. A; 155. O; 156. E; 157. B; 158. D; 159. N; 160. I; 161. L; 162. H; 163. A – Confined to subtropics and tropics, look like small palm trees, may have giant cones, B – Gingkophta, C – Generally form woody cones in which the gametangia form, are evergreen with needlelike leaves and thick cuticle, fibrous epidermis and sunken stomata for moisture retention, D – Gnetophytes, E – Lilies, grasses, and orchids, F – Most flowering shrubs and trees, herbs, and cacti; 164. F – The coconut is the fruit of an angiosperm, whereas the pine nut is the seed of a gymnosperm; 165. F – It is a mix of organic compounds that are a by-product of metabolism. It flows in resin ducts and serves as a deterrent to wood-boring insects and certain microbes; 166. T; 167. The ovule represents the

female gametophyte, which develops inside the megaspore wall inside the megasporangium, remaining physically attached to the sporophyte. These multiple layers and physical attachment means the female gamete is protected from predation and environmental conditions and once fertilized, this becomes the seed; 168. This forms in heterosporous plants from the microspore. In these plants the male gametophyte develops inside the microspore wall and is very much smaller than non-seed plants, comprising only a few cells: this is the pollen. The result is a structure that is extremely lightweight and is easily carried by air currents and does not require water; 169. The evolution of flowers with their distinctive shapes, colours, nectar, and odours evolved in parallel with the animal pollinators (e.g., insects, birds, and bats) to maximize attraction of the appropriate pollinators and efficient transfer of the male pollen to the female reproductive parts.

SELF-TEST

1. a [The sporophyte generation is the diploid generation in the alternation of generations typical of plants. It ultimately gives rise to haploid spores through meiosis, which give rise to gametophytes. Both sporophyte and gametophyte generations are multicellular]
2. a [The charophytes are a lineage of green algae and they share a number of characteristics (ancestral traits) with the least evolved of the land plants, the liverwort lineage of the bryophytes]
3. c [Organisms cannot acquire or develop a trait, it must be present in the organism already thereby giving it an advantage in the environment]
4. b [The movement to land required plants to develop traits allowing them to live in a dry environment (they were already living in a wet environment)]
5. b [Spores form in a sporangium from meiosis. The sporangium is part of the sporophyte—the diploid structure/generation]
6. d [To grow up and away from the ground, plants needed strengthening tissue, lignin, an internal water and sugar circulating system (xylem and phloem), and an anchoring structure (roots). Producing two types of spores (heterospory) does not promote vertical growth]
7. b [Mosses cannot regulate their water content so they must tolerate desiccation, which is different from gymnosperms, angiosperms, and ferns, which are able to avoid desiccation]
8. c [Apical meristems are constantly dividing, undifferentiated cells at the growth sites of roots and shoots. They give rise to all of the tissues of the plant body and are present in vascular plants only]
9. c [Mycorrhizas are fungal symbionts that are associated with the root systems of most land plants. Fungi provide plants with nutrients and plant provides fungi with carbon]
10. b
11. d [The antheridia is the name given to a particular type of male gametangium. It is a multicellular structure made of haploid cells and gives rise to sperm in the bryophytes and seedless vascular plants]
12. b [Rhizomes are horizontal, modified stems that have the ability to penetrate substrates, providing support for plants. They do not absorb nutrients so they are not homologous with roots, are not part of a vascular system and since they do not absorb water and nutrients, they do not form symbiotic relationships with mycorrhizas]
13. c [The strobilus is a structure that is associated with the sporophyte generation (2n) of lycophytes or club mosses. It is a cone-like cluster of sporophylls, which are the specialized leaves that give rise to the sporangia]
14. c [The sorus is the name for the cluster of sporangia that forms on the underside of the leaves of the fern (sporophyte or diploid generation). The fiddlehead is the newly growing sporophyte generation that is generated by fertilization of the gametes]
15. c [Resin production is important for protection against infecting insects and microbes]
16. a [Double fertilization is associated with the angiosperms and is what gives rise to the fruit]
17. c [Angiosperms appear suddenly in the fossil record without a fossil sequence that links them to any other plant group]
18. a [This is a process unique to angiosperms. Two sperm are delivered to the ovule, one fertilizing the egg and the other fertilizing the endosperm-forming cell to give rise to a binucleate cell which gives rise to a 3n endosperm, which eventually forms part of the fruit]
19. c [Many floral features correlate with the morphology and behaviour of certain animal pollinators that coevolved with the flowers. For example, the bats pollinate intensely sweet-smelling flowers with white or pale petals which are easier to see at night than coloured petals]

20. d [Angiosperms evolved more a more efficient vascular system, their embryos are in seeds which are protected and dispersed by fruits. Pollen grains are dispersed by specific animal pollinators, not water]

INTEGRATING AND APPLYING KEY CONCEPTS

1. Think about what challenges faced early plants as they colonized land then reread the section that describes how the evolution of pollen, pollination, ovules and seeds provided an adaptive advantage (section 24.5a). Then think about the further evolutionary changes in the angiosperms (compared to the gymnosperms)—section 25.6 and how the diversity of the flowering plants compares to that of the gymnosperms.

2. Reread the introductory section of section 24.2, the discussions of Figures 24.6, 24.9, and section 24.6a. pay attention to the description of Fig. 24.9: is there agreement and confidence in the relationships presented? What kind of role has molecular data played in determining relationships? Are all of the genomes sequenced? Are there questions remaining that might be answered using molecular data?

3. Have a look at the topic map at the beginning of this chapter and see if all of the major points make sense to you. Can you identify the most ancient lineage and derive a timeline starting through the various lineages?

Chapter 25   Diversity of Animals 1: Sponges, Radiata, Platyhelminthes, and Protostomes

Why It Matters [pp. 578–579]

1. Cambrian; 2. species; 3. mudslide; 4. Burgess Shale; 5. sponges; 6. extinct.

25.1 What Is an Animal? [pp. 579–580]
25.2 Key Innovations in Animal Evolution [pp. 580–584]

7. monophyletic; 8. eukaryotic; 9. lack; 10. energy; 11. animals; 12. heterotrophs; 13. motile; 14. sessile; 15. sexual;

16. sperm; 17. asexual; 18. body; 19. metazoans; 20. diploblastic; 21. ectoderm; 22. endoderm; 23. germ; 24. mesoderm;

25. asymmetrical; 26. bilateral; 27. radial; 28. central; 29. acoelomate; 30. pseudocoelomate; 31. mesoderm; 32. coelomate;

33. K; 34. G; 35. M; 36. N; 37. H; 38. A; 39. O; 40. B; 41. F; 42. C; 43. P; 44. L; 45. D; 46. J; 47. E; 48. I.

25.3 An Overview of Animal Phylogeny and Classification [pp. 584–585]

49. morphology; 50. embryology; 51. molecular; 52. nucleotide; 53. mitochondrial; 54. genes; 55. lineages; 56. Radiata;

57. three; 58. phylogenetic.

25.4 Phylum Porifera [pp. 585–587]
25.5 Metazoans with Radial Symmetry [pp. 587–591]

59. Porifera; 60. Metazoan; 61. filter; 62. pores; 63. Sessile; 64. larvae; 65. Cnidaria; 66. Ctenophora; 67. two;

68. gastrovascular; 69. mouth; 70. polyp; 71. medusa; 72. cnidocytes; 73. nematocysts; 74. sticky; 75. cilia; 76. B; 77. B, C; 78. B; 79. A; 80. C; 81. B; 82. A, B; 83. A, B, C; 84. A; 85. B, C; 86. A; 87. B, C; 88. B; 89. A; 90. C.

25.6 Lophotrochozoan Protostomes [pp. 592–604]

91. bilateral; 92. two; 93. Lophotrochozoan; 94. Ecdysozoan; 95. three; 96. lophophore; 97. capture; 98. gas; 99. Ectoprocta;

100. Brachiopoda; 101. calcium; 102. Phoronida; 103. Platyhelminthes; 104. flatworms; 105. digestive; 106. nervous;

107. ganglion; 108. reproductive; 109. excretory; 110. flame; 111. four; 112. Turbellaria; 113. parasitic; 114. Rotifera;

115. cilia; 116. parthenogenesis;117. unfertilized; 118. complete; 119. mouth; 120. anus; 121. proboscis; 122. everted;

123. three; 124. visceral mass; 125. head-foot; 126. mantle; 127. eight; 128. Gastropoda; 129. Cephalopoda; 130. Annelida;

131. three; 132. segments; 133. septa; 134. metanephridia; 135. setae; 136. Polychaeta; 137. Oligochaeta; 138. Hirudinea;

139. P; 140. B; 141. O; 142. H; 143. N; 144. D; 145. K; 146. J; 147. L; 148. M; 149. C; 150. A; 151. I; 152. E; 153. G;

154. F; 155. Platyhelminthes; 156. Ribbon worm; 157. Annelida; 158. Brachiopoda; 159. Rotifer; 160. Mollusca.

25.7 Ecdysozoan Protostomes [pp. 604–614]

161. exoskeleton; 162. three; 163. Ecdysozoan; 164. Nematoda; 165. parasites; 166. Onychophora; 167. southern; 168. Arthropoda; 169. three-quarters; 170. ecdysis; 171. grows; 172. three; 173. abdomen; 174. cephalothorax. 175. A significant disadvantage of shedding the exoskeleton is loss of protection and support of the exoskeleton. An animal is extremely vulnerable to predation during this molting period; 176. Nematodes can reproduce sexually (as well as by parthenogensis). The large number of eggs a fertilized female produces, as well as the short gestation period, plays a major role in the success of these worms; 177. B; 178. G; 179. E; 180. F; 181. A; 182. H; 183. D; 184. C; 185. C; 186. B; 187. C; 188. B; 189. B, E; 190. D; 191. B, E.

Self-Test

1. c [Other selections are associated with plants; being heterotrophic is most unique to animals]
2. d [Platyhelminthes do not have a body cavity, they are Acoelomates]
3. b [The origin of mesoderm is different between protostomes and deuterostomes]
4. a [These are characteristics that are associated with protostomes]
5. a [Blastophore is an opening linking the gut to the environment and becomes a mouth in protostomes]
6. b [The innermost tissue, the endoderm, forms the lining of the gut in animals]
7. c [Cephalization is the formation of a head end, which can only occur for organisms that are bilaterally symmetrical]
8. c [The acoeomate body form was not ancestral, and therefore schizocoelom was lost by some phyla]
9. b [When one individual can produce both eggs and sperm, it is monoecious]
10. b [Nematocyst and polyp apply to Cnidarians and a porocyte is a cell lining the pore of a sponge; gemmule is a cluster of cells awaiting appropriate conditions to germinate]
11. d [*Obelia* metamorphose from a polyp to a medusa, and sponges and coral metamorphose from ciliated larvae to adult forms; only *Hydra* does not change its form during its life]
12. a [A radula is a scraping device, mollusks typically have a radula and are often bottom- or rock-dwelling animals]
13. b [Cephalopods move rapidly and require a high level of oxygen to support the increased mobility, thus a closed circulatory system will increase delivery of oxygen delivery to tissues]
14. c [Organisms of Phylum Rotifera have a corona and a mastax]
15. d [Rotifers make up a large portion of fresh water zooplankton]
16. b [Selection a is an incorrect statement, and selections c and d are associated with insects]
17. b [Animals with repeating units of internal systems are typically in Phylum Annelida, the segmented worms]
18. c [Centipedes do not have a thorax and shrimps and spiders have a cephalothorax]
19. c [Occupying different habitats and eating different food make insects that undergo complete metamorphosis very successful]

Integrating and Applying Key Concepts

1. An organism is an animal if it is eukaryotic and multicellular, with plasma membranes of neighbouring cells in contact with each other. All animals are heterotrophs, feeding on other living organisms, as well as being motile at some time during their life cycle. They reproduce either sexually or asexually.
2. Tapeworms, round worms, and earthworms are classified in three different phyla because, although they each are commonly called "worms," this is a generic term and is not based on phylogenetic characteristics. Earthworms and tapeworms have characteristics that makes them Lophotrochozoans, but within this group, earthworms belong in the Phylum Annelida because they produce trochophore larvae, whereas tapeworms belong in the Phylum Platyhelminthes because they do not produce trochophore larvae and they have no coelom. Round worms have a cuticle that they shed (ecdysis), so they belong in the group Ecdysozoa (not Lophotrochozoa) and since they are not segmented, they belong to the Phylum Nematoda.
3. Segmentation is found in animals in the Phyla Annelida, Onychophora, and Arthropoda within the protostomes. Since Phylum Annelida is in a separate and independent lineage from the other two phyla, segmentation must be a result of convergent evolution in response to environmental conditions (not from a common ancestor).

Chapter 26   Diversity of Animals 2: Deuterostomes: Vertebrates and Their Closest Relatives

Why It Matters [pp. 617–619]

1. molecular data; 2. classification; 3. phylogenetic; 4. morphology; 5. molecular; 6. *Xenoturbella*; 7. genetic; 8. mollusc; 9. phylum.

26.1 Deuterostomes [pp. 619–620]
26.2 Phylum Echinodermata [pp. 620–623]
26.3 Phylum Hemichordata [pp. 623–624]

10. anus; 11. blastopore; 12. mouth; 13. mouth; 14. arms; 15. cord; 16. adult; 17. bilaterally; 18. radially; 19. five; 20. water; 21. tube; 22. Hemichordata; 23. acorn; 24. proboscis; 25. pharynx; 26. cilia; 27. digestive; 28. gill slits; 29. C; 30. E; 31. A; 32. B; 33. D; 34. D; 35. K; 36. B; 37. J; 38. H; 39. C; 40. E; 41. G; 42. F; 43. A; 44. I; 45. Their arms are easily broken, a characteristic that helps them elude predators with minimal damage.

26.4 Phylum Chordata [pp. 624–626]
26.5 The Origin and Diversification of Vertebrates [pp. 626–628]

46. gill slits; 47. nerve; 48. segmented; 49. notochord; 50. skeleton; 51. invertebrates; 52. spinal; 53. cartilaginous; 54. backbone; 55. bone; 56. cranium; 57. neural; 58. duplications; 59. *Hox*; 60. complex; 61. location; 62. shape; 63. complexity; 64. C; 65. H; 66. G; 67. D; 68. E; 69. A; 70. I; 71. B; 72. F; 73. B; 74. D; 75. A; 76. B; 77. C; 78. A; 79. B; 80. A; 81. A; 82. B; 83. D; 84. F – They are present during embryonic development or in larvae; 85. T; 86. F – During metamorphosis they lose the notochord, dorsal nerve chord, and gill slits; 87. F – In the urochordates, water is expelled through the atrial siphon, and in the cephalochordates, it is expelled through the atrial pore; 88. The ganglion is the anterior concentration of nervous system tissue equivalent to the brain of vertebrates; 89. They do not have a skeleton made of bone but of cartilage, apparently a derived trait; 90. The axial skeleton includes the cranium, backbone/vertebral column, ribs, and sternum.

26.6 Agnathans: Hagfishes and Lampreys, Conodonts, and Ostracoderms [pp. 628–630]
26.7 Jawed Fishes: Jaws Expanded the Feeding Opportunities for Vertebrates [pp. 630–635]

91. Agnathans; 92. pharynx; 93. gills; 94. hagfishes; 95. lampreys; 96. oral/sucking; 97. arches; 98. larger; 99. Chondrichthyes; 100. dorsoventrally; 101. sharks; 102. Elasmobranchii; 103. bony; 104. endoskeleton; 105. scales; 106. mucus; 107. ray-finned; 108. fleshy-finned; 109. Teleosteii; 110. operculum; 111. lateral; 112. vibrations; 113. G; 114. H; 115. M; 116. F; 117. J; 118. K; 119. L; 120. A; 121. C; 122. D; 123. E; 124. B; 125. N; 126. I; 127. F – The life cycle of the hagfish lacks a larval stage, however, that of the lampreys has a larval stage that can last up to seven years; 128. T; 129. T; 130. F – Although they possess cartilaginous skeletons, they are agnathans, two of the earliest groups of verebrates; 131. They are used by some species to also groom, for defence, to construct nests and to transport young; 132. They have flexible fins, lightweight skeletons, streamlined bodies that lack heavy body armour and some have squalene in their livers: this is an oil that is lighter than water so increases their buoyancy; 133. It protects against bacterial growth and reduces water's drag on the surface of the fish; 134. Ray-finned have thin, bony, flexible rays supporting their fins, whereas the fins of the fleshy-finned fishes are supported by muscles and an internal bony skeleton.

26.8 Early Tetrapods and Modern Amphibians [pp. 635–638]

135. air; 136. skeletal; 137. pectoral; 138. tympanum; 139. sound; 140. gas; 141. moist; 142. lungs; 143. larval; 144. aquatic; 145. both; 146. Anura; 147. toads; 148. Urodela; 149. Gymnophonia; 150. E; 151. G; 152. A; 153. H; 154. B; 155. D; 156. C; 157. F.

26.9 The Origin and Mesozoic Radiations of Amniotes [pp. 638–643]

158. sac; 159. embryo; 160. amnion; 161. terrestrial/dry; 162. skin; 163. keratin; 164. waterproof; 165. shell; 166. membranes; 167. dessication; 168. gases; 169. yolk; 170. albumin; 171. urea; 172. ammonium; 173. temporal; 174. anapsids; 175. synapsids;176. diapsids; 177. F; 178. D; 179. G; 180. A; 181. C; 182. E; 183. B.

26.10 Subclass Testudines: Turtles and Tortoises [pp. 643–644]
26.11 Living Diapsids: Sphenodontids, Squamates, and Crocodilians [pp. 644–645]
26.12 Aves: Birds [pp. 645–650]

184. anapsids; 185. shell; 186. ribs; 187. retract; 188. two; 189. Lepidosaurs; 190. Archosaurs; 191. Squamata; 192. snakes; 193. Crocodylia; 194. crocodiles; 195. Aves; 196. keeled sternum; 197. furculum; 198. uncinate; 199. hollow; 200. bill; 201. wing; 202. feet; 203. D; 204. B; 205. E; 206. B; 207. E; 208. C; 209. A; 210. B; 211. A; 212. F – They generally lack the keeled sternum and also the furculum but retain the uncinate processes; 213. T; 214. T; 215. The keel on the sternum anchors the flight muscles and the furcuum acts like a spring to aid in wing movement.

26.13 Mammalia: Monotremes, Marsupials, and Placentals [pp. 650–653]
26.14 Evolutionary Convergence and Mammalian Diversity: Tails to Teeth [pp. 653–658]

216. synapsid; 217. temporal; 218. furry; 219. homeothermic; 220. diaphragm; 221. occipital; 222. palate; 223. cortex; 224. heterodont; 225. diphyodont; 226. milk/deciduous; 227. adult; 228. milk; 229. reproduction; 230. monotremes; 231. placental; 232. marsupials; 233. teat; 234. marsupium; 235. H; 236. F; 237. E; 238. G; 239. K; 240. A; 241. J; 242. D; 243. C; 244. B; 245. I.

SELF-TEST

1. a [The prefix "deutero" means two and refers not to a form of symmetry but to the embryological development of the mouth and anus]
2. c [The larvae are bilaterally symmetrical while the adults are radially symmetrical. Sexual reproduction is external so the presence of tube feet with their specific function, is the only correct characteristic]
3. b [The bilaterally symmetrical larval form is characteristic of the phylum Echinodermata, pedicellariae are found in the asteroidea or sea stars/starfish]
4. d [Only echinoderms have a water vascular system for movement. The proboscis is typical of hemichordates, while gill slits and a notochord are typical of chordates]
5. c [Pearl fish live in the tubes of other animals, including sea cucumbers. This group of echinoderms has five rows of tube feet and, like all echinoderms, have bilaterally symmetrical larvae]
6. c [This is the description is a tunicate, which belongs to the Urochordata phylum]
7. d [Seahorses are teleosts, a more complex and diverse group of fish, and therefore expected to have the greatest number of *Hox* gene complexes]
8. b [class Chondrichthyes includes sharks, rays, and chimeras, all of which have a cartilaginous skeleton]
9. a [Based on embryological evidence, one pair of gill arches gave rise to the upper and lower jaw bones while a second pair gave rise to the hyomandibular bones that brace the jaw against the cranium]
10. d [All except for d are Agnathans, lacking jaws]
11. d [The swim bladder is a hydrostatic organ which increases buoyancy; if destroyed, the fish would not be as buoyant]
12. a [Of the selections, dehydration is the only problem associated with moving from an aquatic to a terrestrial environment]

13. b [Gas exchange occurs across the skin, so blood vessels must carry oxygen and carbon dioxide to it and the skin must be well-supplied with blood vessels]
14. a [Of the selections, only keratin and lipid in skin will be advantageous to terrestrial life]
15. b [Turtles are anapsids. Of the remaining choices, all diapsids, a 4-chambered heart is a striking adaptation of crocodiles and is homologous to the bird heart and analogous to the mammalian heart]
16. c [Hollow limb bones significantly reduces the weight of the skeleton of birds]
17. e [The flicking tongue carries airborne molecules that are captured by the tongue , to the mouth where they are identified by receptors in the roof of the snake's mouth]
18. d [The prototheria are egg-laying mammals, also called monotremes. These include the duck-billed platypus. In contrast, birds (Aves) lay eggs but are NOT mammals]
19. a [Teeth are an example of diversity while only birds evolved feathers and only vertebrates evolved bone. The flattened tail is an example of convergence, having evolved separately in a Mesozoic mammal, the duck-billed platypus, which is a monotreme, and in beavers, which are mammals]
20. c [Mammals can replace their teeth once (milk teeth replaced by adult teeth]

INTEGRATING AND APPLYING KEY CONCEPTS

1. Both echinoderms and humans are deuterostomes because during embryonic development the blastopore forms an anus. However, in terms of other characteristics, individuals within the deuterstomes can vary greatly. An adult echinoderm has no "head," no excretory system, no respiratory system, and only a minimal circulatory system, whereas a human is cephalized (has a head), as well as having a complete excretory system, respiratory system, and circulatory system.
2. Movement from an aquatic to a terrestrial environment was possible with the evolution of four limbs for locomotion, lungs to breathe atmospheric oxygen, and specialized eggs that had coverings to protect them from dehydration.
3. Some echinoderms can regenerate body parts lost to predators, and most have movable spines with poison glands (e.g., sea urchins), hagfishes produce a sticky noxious slime when threatened which they remove once the threat is gone by tying themselves in a knot, jawed animals may use their jaws for defence, especially if they also have sharp teeth, turtles and tortoises withdraw into their hard shells, rattle snakes have a venomous bite, procupines have sbodies covered with harp spines.

Chapter 27   The Plant Body

Why It Matters [pp. 662–663]

1. root; 2. water; 3. shoot; 4. bark; 5. roots; 6. leaves; 7. outcompete.

27.1 Plant Structure and Growth: An Overview [pp. 663–668]

8. angiosperms; 9. shoot; 10. cells; 11. chloroplasts; 12. vacuoles; 13. cell walls; 14. lignin; 15. P; 16. A; 17. A; 18. P;

19. P; 20. P; 21. A; 22.F – Able; 23. T; 24. F – Shoot apical meristem; 25. F – Secondary; 26. T; 27. Multiples of 3;

28. Arranged randomly; 29. Network; 30. Taproot; 31. Perennial; 32. Woody; 33. Monocot; 34. Biennial; 35. Dicot.

27.2 The Three Plant Tissue Systems [pp. 668–672]

36. ground tissue system; 37. vascular tissue system; 38. dermal tissue system; 39. parenchyma; 40. collenchyma;

41. sclerenchyma; 42. Parenchyma, collenchyma, and sclerenchyma tissues are all simple tissues (primarily composed of one type of cell), but they differ since parenchyma tissue contains cells with thin primary cell walls that are permeable to water (many of which contain chloroplasts) and has large spaces between its cells, collenchyma tissue contains elongating cells with primary cell walls composed of alternating layers of cellulose and pectin, and sclerenchyma tissue contains cells (in shape of sclereids or fibres) with thick lignified secondary cell walls and pits that allow water movement between cells; 43. Structurally, tracheids and vessel members are found in the xylem and are composed of cells with secondary cell walls, but whereas tracheids are composed of tapering cells with pits and overlapping ends, vessel members are shorter and wider cells with pits and perforations at each end. Functionally, tracheids and vessel

members work separately or in combination to transport water and dissolved minerals upwards in plants, but whereas tracheids transport more slowly (uses pits) than vessel members (uses perforations), they are less likely to experience air bubble buildup and blockage than vessel members; 44. G; 45. F; 46. A; 47. E; 48. C; 49. D; 50. B; 51. A; 52. B; 53. A; 54. C, E; 55. B; 56. C, D; 57. A.

27.3 Primary Shoot Systems [pp. 672–677]

58. petiole; 59. node; 60. internode; 61. terminal buds; 62. lateral buds; 63. apical dominance; 64. primary meristems; 65. protoderm; 66. ground meristem; 67. procambium; 68. leaf primordia; 69. mesophyll; 70. veins; 71. B; 72. I; 73. G; 74. A; 75. E; 76. H; 77. F; 78. C; 79. D; 80. A leaf vein is a vascular bundle (primarily xylem and phloem tissues), which therefore functions in the transport of water and minerals (xylem) and sugars (phloem); 81. In most eudicot stems, vascular bundles are arranged in a circle, separating the outer ground tissue (cortex) and inner ground tissue (pith), whereas in monocots, vascular bundles are scattered throughout the ground tissue.

27.5 Secondary Growth [pp.681–685]

82. taproot; 83. lateral roots; 84. fibrous root; 85. adventitious; 86. apical meristems; 87. vascular cambium; 88. cork cambium; 89. girth; 90. xylem; 91. phloem; 92. growth rings; 93. spring wood; 94. summer wood; 95. bark; 96. elongation; 97. cell division; 98. differentiating; 99. maturation; 100. dividing; 101. apical meristem; 102. F – Zone of maturation; 103. T; 104. F – Endodermis; 105. T; 106. F –Are not; 107. T; 108. T; 109. F – Cork.

SELF-TEST

1. c [Morphology is defined as an organism's external form]
2. d [Plasmadesmata allow cytoplasm to flow between adjacent cells]
3. b [Primary cell wall acts as a semipermeable mesh that allows some substances to pass through]
4. b [Secondary cell wall is laid down <u>inside</u> the primary wall]
5. c [It is constantly undergoing cell division]
6. a [Apical meristems are responsible for growth in length]
7. b [Lilies are monocots]
8. b [Parenchyma cells have the greatest number of chloroplasts]
9. b [Sclerenchyma cells produce thick secondary cell walls]
10. b [Perforations at ends of vessel members allow greater water transport than tracheid pits]
11. a [Companion cells assist in providing sugars to sieve tube member cells]
12. b [Leave attach to the stem at the node. The distance between two nodes in the internode]
13. a [Meristematic tissue contains rapidly dividing cells]
14. d [Vascular cambium functions in secondary growth]
15. b [Bamboo is a hard-walled monocot plant that develops a hollow stem]
16. a [Stinging nettles contain needle-like protrusions that contain a stinging chemical]
17. c [Palisade mesophyll cells contain the greatest number of chloroplasts]
18. b [The zone of cell division produces new cells, so needs protection during primary root growth]
19. d [Xylem cells are larger in the spring than summer so reflect light differently to produce rings]
20. b [Size of tree rings indicates amount of growth; narrow rings means little growth]

INTEGRATING AND APPLYING KEY CONCEPTS

1. The term dendritic refers to having a spreading or branching form. Plant shoot systems need to have a branched form for leaves to be spread out to reduce shading, thereby maximizing the light absorbed by the plant and optimizing photosynthesis for energy (sugar) production. Plant root systems also need to be dendritic so that soil water and mineral access and absorption can be maximized.
2. Within a vegetative bud, cells must differentiate to form each of the necessary plant tissue systems. Identify what tissue system that each of the primary meristems develops into and give their resulting functions. Within an apical meristem (bud), three primary meristems develop: protoderm, procambium, and ground meristem. Over time, the

protoderm will develop into the plant epidermis, which is a tissue of the dermal tissue system. This tissue system functions in protection of the internal parts of the plant. The procambium develops into primary vascular tissues (primary xylem and primary phloem), which are the main components of the vascular tissue system. This system functions in transport of water and solutes throughout the plant. Lastly, the ground meristem will form the ground tissue system (parenchyma, collenchyma, and sclerenchyma tissues), which make up the majority of the plant body. This tissue system has many functions within a plant including storage, secretion, photosynthesis, flexibility, support, and protection.

3. You planted a red oak tree in your backyard three years ago. Explain how growth this summer will be different from the growth occurred in the tree's first summer. During the first year of the tree's (seedling's) growth, only primary growth (from apical meristems) would have occurred to increase the tree's length. In the third year of growth (this summer), both primary and secondary growth will occur. Apical meristems in the shoot (terminal and lateral buds) and root systems (root tips) will occur resulting in a further increase in tree length, but there will also be growth in girth as the vascular cambium (lateral meristem) produces secondary xylem and secondary phloem cells. The secondary xylem tissue produced this summer will appear as a ring in the tree's wood (if it is cut down).

Chapter 28   Transport in Plants

Why It Matters [pp. 688–689]

1. water; 2. pump; 3. cohesion; 4. evaporation; 5. gravity.

28.1 Principles of Water and Solute Movement in Plants [pp. 689–692]

6. roots; 7. xylem; 8. leaves; 9. phloem; 10. short-distance; 11. passive transport; 12. active transport; 13. transport;

14. osmosis; 15. water potential; 16. zero; 17. solution potential; 18. into; 19. turgor pressure; 20. pressure potential;

21. zero; 22. turgid; 23. central vacuole; 24. tonoplast; 25. aquaporins; 26. wilt; 27. T; 28. F – Decrease; 29. T; 30. T;

31. B; 32. A; 33. D; 34. C; 35. B; 36. C; 37. B; 38. A.

28.2 Uptake and Transport of Water and Solutes by Roots [pp. 692–694]
28.3 Long-Distance Transport of Water and Minerals in the Xylem [pp. 694–701]

39. apoplast pathway; 40. symplast pathway; 41. plasmodesmata; 42. endodermis; 43. radially; 44. casparian strip;

45. cohesion-tension; 46. cohesion; 47. adhesion; 48. transpiration; 49. stomata; 50. guard cells; 51. root pressure;

52. endodermis; 53. guttation; 54. crassulacean acid metabolism (CAM); 55. evening; 56. day; 57. G; 58. E; 59. A;

60. B; 61. H; 62. F; 63. C; 64. D.

28.4 Transport of Organic Substances in the Phloem [pp. 702–705]

65. translocation; 66. phloem sap; 67. source; 68. sink; 69. pressure flow; 70. pressure; 71. decreases ; 72. osmosis;

73. bulk flow; 74. transfer cells; 75. F—sucrose; 76. F—in any direction; 77. T; 78. T; 79. F – Only at the end of.

SELF-TEST

1. a
2. c [Symplast and apoplast carry water and minerals to the endodermis using extracellular and intracellular pathways respectively]
3. c
4. b [Water potential is the sum of the solute and pressure potentials]
5. d
6. d
7. c [Soil water does not enter cortical cells in the apoplastic pathway]
8. b
9. c [Sieve tube member cells are alive even though they do not contain a nucleus]
10. c

11. c [Cohesion is the attraction of water molecules to each other. Viscosity is the friction of liquid molecules as the flow past each other or over a solid surface]
12. b
13. c
14. a [When expanded, the inner walls of the guard cells do not expand as much as the outer cells, resulting in formation of a pore (stoma) between them]
15. c [low CO_2 concentration, daylight, and moist soil all encourage stomata to open]
16. c [CAM photosynthesis occurs most often in hot, dry habitats like those where *Sedum* is found]
17. d [Phloem sap is primarily composed of sugars but other solutes, including amino acids and fatty acids, are present as well]
18. c [It was phloem sap pressure that caused the phloem sap to travel through the gut and out the anus of an aphid]
19. b [As long as a pressure gradient exists, phloem sap will move toward the region of lower pressure]
20. a [Only in the early spring, before leaves are functional, are roots, buds, and bulbs acting as sources]

INTEGRATING AND APPLYING KEY CONCEPTS

1. For a stoma to open, first H^+ must be actively transported out of the two surrounding guard cells. As the H^+ move back down the concentration gradient, energy is released and used to actively transport K^+ into the guard cells. The higher solute concentration in the guard cells causes water to enter by osmosis, which results in guard cells expanding and bending away from each other, resulting in the opening of the central pore (stoma).
2. Transport in xylem is unidirectional since water and minerals are taken up in the roots only and therefore can only move upward in the plant (by cohesion-tension model and/or root pressure model mechanisms). However, the organic solutes that enter the phloem from all different areas of the shoot system may be needed in any region of a plant (roots or shoots) and therefore travel upward, downward, or sideways in phloem tissue.
3. Adaptations in root systems could include:
   1) increased length of roots to access greater soil water resources
   2) increased root hair production to increase surface area for water uptake
   Adaptations in shoot systems could include:
   1) decreased leaf surface area (e.g., spines) (to reduce water loss from surface of epidermis and stomata)
   2) decreased number of stomata (less water loss due to transpiration when stomata open)
   3) greater number of stomata on underside of leaf (reduces temperature and relative humidity conditions that promotes water loss during carbon dioxide uptake)
   4) recessed stomata or trichomes around stomata (reduces air movement in area of stomata so reduces water loss)
   5) CAM (stomata open at night when less water loss due to temperature, humidity, etc.)
   Note that there are many other examples.

Chapter 29   Reproduction and Development in Flowering Plants

TOPIC MAP

1. dedifferentiation; 2. differentiation; 3. maturation; 4. meiosis; 5. meiosis; 6. pollination; 7. double fertilization;

8. mitosis; 9. germination; 10. maturation.

Why It Matters [pp. 708–709]

11. flowers; 12. pollination; 13. bees; 14. colony collapse disorder; 15. fruits.

29.1 Overview of Flowering Plant Reproduction [pp. 709–711]
29.2 Flower Structure and Formation of Gametes [pp. 711–714]

16. sporophyte; 17. haploid; 18. pollen grain; 19. embryo sac; 20. gametes; 21. diploid; 22. mitosis; 23. floral shoot;

24. influorescence; 25. sepals; 26. petals; 27. stamen; 28. filament; 29. anther; 30. pollen; 31. carpels; 32. ovary;

33. style; 34. stigma; 35. microsporocyte; 36. microspores; 37. pollen grains; 38. sperm; 39. pollen tube; 40. ovary;

41. megasporocyte; 42. one; 43. embryo; 44. one; 45. two; 46. one; 47. central; 48. micropyle; 49. E; 50. C; 51. D; 52. F;

53. A; 54. G; 55. B; 56. H; 57. E; 58. A; 59. G; 60. B; 61. I; 62. L; 63. C; 64. J; 65. D; 66. K; 67. F; 68. B; 69. C; 70. A; 71. F; 72. D; 73. E.

29.3 Pollination, Fertilization, and Germination [pp. 714–721]

74. pollination; 75. anther; 76. stigma; 77. allele; 78. *S* allele; 79. pollen; 80. style; 81. sperm; 82. double fertilization; 83. zygote; 84. endosperm; 85. apical; 86. suspensor; 87. cotyledons; 88. cotyledon; 89. endosperm; 90. radicle; 91. plumule; 92. coat; 93. coleorhizae; 94. coleoptiles; 95. ovule; 96. ovary; 97. pollen; 98. pericarp; 99. protection; 100. dispersal; 101. dormancy; 102. germination; 103. imbibition; 104. coat; 105. enzymes; 106. mitosis; 107. radicle; 108. root; 109. plumule; 110. A – The transfer of pollen from an anther to the stigma of the carpel in a different plant, B – The fusion of male sperm cell and the female egg cell, C – The seed imbibes water to come out of dormancy and grow into a seedling; 111. A – A fruit that develops from a single ovary of a flower, B – A fruit that develops from multiple ovaries of a single flower, C – A fruit that develops from several ovaries of multiple flowers; 112. E; 113. A; 114. B; 115. F; 116. C; 117. G; 118. D; 119. Endosperm is not produced when fertilization does not occur, whereas gametophyte tissue would be produced whether or not fertilization occurred (wasted energy cost); 120. Cotyledons in an eudicot absorb and store the nutrients absorbed from the endosperm (no endosperm in mature seed), whereas in a monocot, nutrients are stored in the endosperm.

29.4 Asexual Reproduction of Flowering Plants [pp. 721–724]
29.5 Early Development of Plant Form and Function [p. 724]

121. vegetative; 122. totipotency; 123. fragmentation; 124. unfertilized; 125. apomixis; 126. callus; 127. hormones; 128. identical; 129. root-shoot; 130. apical; 131. basal; 132. transcription factors; 133. differentiation; 134. C; 135. D; 136. A; 137. G; 138. H; 139. I; 140. E; 141. F; 142. B; 143. Totipotent describes cells that can develop into a complete new organism (in plants), pluripotent describes cells that can only develop into many kinds of cells but not a new organism (in animals), and multipotent describes cells that can only develop into specific kinds of cells.

SELF-TEST

1. b [Pollinators function to transfer pollen grains from one plant to a stigma on a different plant]
2. c [The ovule of the flower transforms into a seed after fertilization]
3. b [A three-celled pollen grain is a male gametophyte because it produces the male gametes (sperm cells)]
4. b [In monoecious species, each plant contains male and female reproductive structures but not on the same flower]
5. d [A mature pollen grain is composed of one pollen tube cell and two sperm cells]
6. c [The pathway the growing pollen tube travels is through stigma, then style, then micropyle, the latter being the entrance into the ovule]
7. d [The (diploid) central cell of the embryo sac fuses with the (haploid) sperm cell to form triploid endosperm]
8. a [Self-fertilization is reduced due to the incompatibility of a pollen grain and a stigma having the same *S* gene allele. This prevents inbreeding and promotes genetic variation]
9. c [An endosperm contains three nuclei, two it received from the diploid central cell in the ovule and one it received from the sperm cell]
10. c [The type of fruit that is formed from ovaries from different flowers is a multiple fruit]
11. b [In a developing seed, the suspensor transfers nutrients from the parent plant to the embryo, ensuring that the developing embryo has the energy it needs to reach maturity]
12. c [A developing eudicot embryo becomes heart-shaped because some of the embryo cells will differentiate and form the two cotyledons]
13. d [For seeds requiring a dormancy period, dormancy ends when germination begins. During dormancy, no biological activity is occurring; however, during germination, many reactions are occurring]
14. d [A radicle forms roots since the radicle is an embryonic root]

15. a [The correct order of processes occurring during germination is imbibition (absorption of water), seed swelling (due to hydration), seed coat rupturing (due to swelling), and radicle growing (root growth)]
16. d [Different plants have different cues to promote germination and increased day length, soil moisture, and temperature are all possible cues]
17. d [Plants can reproduce asexually due to many of their cells being totipotent]
18. b [An advantage of reproducing asexually is that there is a lower energy cost for producing a new plant than for sexual reproduction. There are a number of disadvantages to reproducing asexually]
19. c [A somatic embryo can develop following differentiation of totipotent cells, which results in the formation of unspecialized cells that can then to develop to form a new embryo]
20. a [All the cells in a callus are genetically alike since they arise from one or more cells of a single plant]

INTEGRATING AND APPLYING KEY CONCEPTS

1. Totipotency is a characteristic of virtually all cells in a plant and it is the ability for a cell to be able to form an entire new organism. If a branch (or root, or leaf, etc.) was cut off a plant and provided the correct conditions (water and nutrients), the cells at the cut would dedifferentiate and be able to form root cells so that the branch became an entire new plant.
2. The S gene concept is that there are multiple alleles for the S gene so that individual plants of the same species will have different alleles. If the S gene allele in the pollen grain is different from the S gene allele in the stigma, then the pollen grain and stigma are compatible (came from different plants) and the processes for sexual reproduction will occur. However, if the S gene alleles in the pollen grain and the stigma are the same, they are incompatible (and possibly could have come from the same plant), fertilization will not occur (no seed production). This prevents inbreeding, which reduces the variation (and therefore success) in a plant population.
3. Colony Collapse Disorder (CCD) is the mysterious loss of honeybee colonies that have been noted globally. Since pollination of apples and berries require honeybee pollinators, continued loss of further colonies will have an impact on these plant species, as well as on all of the other plant species that rely on these pollinators (about 1/3 of North American plants). Since apple and berry farmers rely on bees to pollinate their orchards and crops, if the cause of CCD cannot be found and eliminated, there will be a drastic reduction in fruit production, resulting in the loss of their livelihood.

Chapter 30   Control of Plant Growth and Development

Why It Matters [pp. 727–728]

1. sessile; 2. defence; 3. germination; 4. reproductive; 5. senescence; 6. environment; 7.volatile.

30.1 Plant Hormones [pp. 728–739]

8. chemical; 9. environmental; 10. hormones; 11. small; 12. vascular; 13. meristems; 14. stimulate; 15. elongation;

16. light; 17. bend; 18. phototropism; 19. promote; 20. tips; 21. stimulate; 22. internodes; 23. bolting; 24. dormancy;

25. tips; 26. division; 27. xylem; 28. gas; 29. division; 30. fruit; 31. senescence; 32. asbscission zones; 33. steroid;

34. shoot; 35. elongation; 36. inhibits; 37. carotenoids; 38. inhibits; 39. environmental 40. germinate; 41. fatty;

42. carbohydrates; 43. regulate; 44. pathogens; 45. F; 46. A; 47. G; 48. B; 49. D; 50. C; 51. E; 52. D; 53. A; 54. B; 55. C;

56. A – Promote growth of plant primarily through cell elongation, promote fruit development, help plant in responding to light and gravity, B – Promote cell division and elongation, seed germination, and bolting, C – Promote cell division and inhibit senescence, D – Regulate many physiological processes, promote senescence, abscission, and fruit ripening, E – Promote stem cell division and elongation, inhibits root elongation, promotes vascular development and growth of pollen tube, F – Inhibits growth and promotes dormancy, G – Protect plants from pathogens, regulates growth and seed germination.

30.2 Signal Responses at the Cellular Level [pp. 739–740]
30.3 Plant Chemical Defences [pp. 740–744]

57. response; 58. chemical message; 59. growth; 60. receptor; 61. cytoplasm; 62. protein; 63. signal; 64. secondary;

65. target; 66. bacteria, viruses, fungi, and insects; 67. pathway; 68. jasmonates; 69. systemin; 70. inhibitor; 71. proteins;

72. hypersensitive; 73. oxygen-containing; 74. nutrient; 75. salicylic acid; 76. pathogenesis-related; 77. secondary;

78. herbivores; 79. volatile; 80. predators; 81. specific; 82. avirulence; 83. receptor; 84. resistance; 85. hypersensitive;

86. salicylic acid; 87. long-term; 88. A secondary messenger is produced by a primary messenger and functions as an intermediary to cause a change in a cell's activity, whereas a secondary metabolite is a molecule that is not usually a product of metabolism but is produced when needed as a defense response; 89. Pathogenesis-response proteins produce hydrolytic enzymes that break down a pathogen's cell walls. This kills pathogen cells, wounding and killing the pathogen; 90. C; 91. B; 92. A; 93. E; 94. D.

30.4 Plant Responses to the Environment: Movements [pp. 744–749]
30.5 Plant Responses to the Environment: Biological Clocks [pp. 749–753]
30.6 Plant Responses to the Environment: Responses to Temperature Extremes [p. 753]

95. tropism; 96. phototropism; 97. cryptochrome; 98. Gravitropism; 99. downward; 100. upward; 101. elongation;

102. Thigmotropism; 103. tendrils; 104. support; 105. Nastic; 106. turgor; 107. biological clock; 108. circadian;

109. photoperiodism; 110. phytochrome; 111. long-day; 112. short-day; 113. darkness; 114. vernalization;

115. dormancy; 116. long; 117. E; 118. F; 119. D; 120. G; 121. H; 122. B; 123. C; 124. A.

SELF-TEST

1. a [Auxins were the first plant hormone to be identified]
2. b [Went grew his seedlings in the dark so that he could observe the effect of the agar block on plant growth]
3. b [Some brassinosteroids function in the growth of the pollen tube]
4. a [The breaking of bonds between microfibrils, increasing the plasticity of the cell wall]
5. b [Gibberellins are involved in breaking of seed and bud dormancy]
6. d [During a hypersensitive response, an oxygen-containing compound (such as H_2O_2) is produced]
7. c [Cytokinins coordinate growth of roots and shoots in concert with the auxins]
8. c [Ethylene stimulates the ripening of fruit]
9. c [Abscisic acid promotes dormancy in plants]
10. b [Abscission is the process of dropping of flowers, fruits, and leaves]
11. d [Bolting is used for extension of the floral stem in rosette plants]
12. d [Systemin, first peptide hormone, provides a defence response when it binds to a receptor, causing jasmonate (not ethylene) to be synthesized]
13. b [Shoots grow upward, so show negative gravitropism]
14. b [Thigmomorphogenesis results in plants that remain short, putting increased biomass into girth to withstand constant or repeated mechanical stress]
15. d [Nastic movement refers to temporary, reversible response to a non-directional stimulus]
16. d [Phytochrome acts as a switch mechanism within a plant to changes in photoperiod]
17. a [Vernalization is low temperature stimulation of flowering]
18. b [Heat-shock proteins bind to other proteins and protect them in high temperatures (release them when temperatures decrease)]
19. c [SAR uses secondary metabolites for defence, but this does not involve the synthesis of Jasmonate (which is a general defence)]
20. d [Multiple genes are required to cue *Arabidopsis* to flower]

1. Fruit growers are able to pick and transport their fruit before it has completely ripened, which reduces the damage caused during transport. Once at the destination, ethylene can be applied to the fruit, which will cause it to ripen quickly for sale. Also, since fruit produces its own ethylene, fruit growers can apply a chemical to inhibit ethylene production by fruit, thereby allowing storage of fruit for a long period of time.

2. A phytochrome pigment occurs in two forms: P_r, which absorbs red light, and P_{fr}, which absorbs far-red light. As P_f absorbs the red light, it is converted to P_{fr}, and as P_{fr} absorbs far-red light, it is converted to P_r. A high concentration of P_{fr} tells a plant that there is lots of sunlight (middle of the summer), but this concentration will decrease as the plant approaches the end of the season.

3. An action potential is a reversal to the membrane charge across a plasma membrane, relative to the membrane potential at rest. Resulting from this charge reversal, potassium ion channels in the plasma membrane open and potassium ions will move out of a cell, reverting the membrane charge to its original state. The increased ion concentration outside of the cell causes water to move out of the cell by osmosis, resulting in decreased turgor pressure in the cell. When pulvinar cells become flaccid, associated leaves will move closer together (and when these cells become turgid again, associated leaves will spread apart).

Chapter 31   Introduction to Animal Organization and Physiology

Why It Matters [pp. 756–757]

1. homeostasis; 2. internal; 3. organ systems; 4. tissue; 5. function; 6. physiology; 7. anatomy.

31.1 Organization of the Animal Body [pp. 757–758]

8. multicellular; 9. interstitial fluid; 10. molecules; 11. waste; 12. cells; 13. osmosis; 14. function; 15. tissue; 16. organ; 17. different; 18. organ system; 19. organs.

31.2 Animal Tissues [pp. 758–767]

20. cytoskeleton; 21. extracellular; 22. junctions; 23. epithelial; 24. cells; 25. shape; 26. extracellular; 27. fibres; 28. gel-like; 29. three; 30. muscle; 31. smooth; 32. nervous; 33. neurons; 34. glial; 35. D; 36. A; 37. B; 38. C; 39. D; 40. A; 41. B; 42. E; 43. C; 44. C; 45. G; 46. A; 47. F; 48. B; 49. E; 50. D; 51. B; 52. D; 53. E; 54. A – Absorption, secretion, protection, diffusion, B – Lines body cavities, covers surfaces, C – Connective, D – Contraction (shorten), E – Body muscles, walls of organs and tubes, heart, F – Communication and control between body parts, conducts electrical signals; 55. Tight junctions hold epithelial cells together to line the urinary bladder. This junction is necessary since only this junction seals the spaces between cells, so waste molecules and ions cannot leak out of the bladder into other body tissues. 56. An osteoblast produces the collagen and mineral deposits of the extracellular matrix (building bone tissue), whereas osteoclasts remove the mineral deposits (break down bone tissue); 57. Fat is able to store more chemical energy per weight than carbohydrates.

31.3 Coordination of Tissues in Organs and Organ Systems [pp. 767–768]

58. cell; 59. survive; 60. organ system; 61. 11; 62. nutrients, 63. wastes; 64. responding; 65. reproducing; 66. C; 67. D; 68. F; 69. E; 70. K; 71. A; 72. I; 73. J; 74. B; 75. E; 76. G; 77. F; 78. A, I; 79. I; 80. C; 81. G; 82. H.

31.4 Homeostasis [pp. 768–772]

83. Homeostasis is a dynamic process that ensures animals maintain a relatively constant internal environment (within an acceptable range). If a body function, such as body temperature, changes due to a change in the external (or internal) environment, the body's control mechanisms are able to detect any changes and make modifications accordingly to keep (or return) the body function to within its acceptable range; 84. A positive feedback mechanism is an amplification

process, intensifying the change and therefore producing even more of the product, whereas a negative feedback mechanism will respond to this excess product by compensating for this change and reducing the amount of product being produced, returning the amount of product to within an acceptable range; 85. C; 86. F; 87. E. 88. B; 89. A; 90. D.

SELF-TEST

1.	a	11.	b
2.	b	12.	c
3.	a	13.	a
4.	d	14.	b
5.	c	15.	b
6.	d	16.	e
7.	b	17.	c
8.	c	18.	b
9.	c	19.	a
10.	b		

INTEGRATING AND APPLYING KEY CONCEPTS

1. Sweat is produced in epithelial tissue that has formed an exocrine gland and therefore the sweat secretions produced by these secreting epithelial cells are emptied onto the epithelial surface via ducts.
2. Bone, cartilage, and adipose are all connective tissues and therefore are composed of cells in extracellular matrices. Bone is composed of bone cells, called osteocytes, and a surrounding porous extracellular matrix composed of collagen fibres and glycoproteins impregnated with calcium phosphate minerals. This tissue functions to form the skeleton, supports the body, and protects softer tissues. Cartilage is composed of cells called chondrocytes that are surrounded by collagen fibres in an elastic and resilient matrix of glycoprotein. It functions in various ways including as a support for body parts such as larynx, trachea, and small air passages, a cushion between vertebrae, and a precursor to bone during embryonic development. Adipose tissue is composed of cells called adipocytes (store fat) that is surrounded by little extracellular matrix. It cushions the body and may help insulate it.
3. The three types of muscle tissue are skeletal, cardiac, and smooth muscle tissue. All three function to contract, shortening to provide movement. Skeletal tissue is composed of long muscle cells (muscle fibres) that have striations due to the orderly actin and myosin filaments with each of the cells. It is attached to bones by tendons and forms muscle organs, such as the biceps. Cardiac tissue is found in the walls of the heart and is composed of relatively short striated cells, like skeletal tissue, but unlike skeletal tissue, the cells are connected to neighbouring cells by intercalated disks in branches and form a network. This allows contractions in many directions (unlike the other tissues), allowing for the pumping action required to produce a heartbeat. Smooth tissue, like the other two tissues, contains actin and myosin filaments but they are arranged so loosely that no visible striations are apparent in their small, spindle-shaped cells. Contraction is relatively slow but can be maintained for a longer period than the other two tissues. It is found in the walls of the digestive tract organs, walls of many blood vessels, and the wall of the uterus.

Chapter 32   Transport in Animals: The Circulatory System

Why It Matters [pp. 774–775]

1. circulatory system; 2. lymphatic system; 3. defences.

32.1 Animal Circulatory Systems: An Introduction [pp. 775–780]

4. open circulatory system; 5. hemolymph; 6. sinuses; 7. closed circulatory system; 8. arteries; 9. capillaries; 10. veins; 11. atria; 12. ventricles; 13. systemic circuit; 14. pulmonocutaneous circuit; 15. pulmonary circuit; 16. Specialized fluid medium contain some cells (carries nutrients, wastes, gases), tubular vessels for the specialized fluid, and a muscular heart that pumps the fluid through the circulatory system; 17. Functions: circulation of respiratory gases, transport of nutrients, transport of products of metabolism, transport of wastes, maintaining blood pressure, immune defences, blood clotting; 18. In an open circulatory system, vessels leaving the heart release fluid, hemolymph, directly into the body

spaces or into sinuses surrounding organs. The hemolymph re-enters the heart through valves in the heart wall that close each time the heart pumps. In a closed circulatory system, the blood is confined to blood vessels and is distinct from the interstitial fluid. Substances are exchanged between the blood and the interstitial fluid, and then between the interstitial fluid and cells; 19. A; 20. A; 21. B; 22. B; 23. B; 24. A; 25. B; 26. C; 27. A; 28. B.

32.2 Blood and Its Components [pp. 780–783]

29. plasma; 30. albumins; 31. globulins; 32. fibrinogen; 33. Erythrocytes; 34. red blood cells; 35. Erythropoietin; 36. leukocytes; 37. platelets; 38. fibrin; 39. erythrocyte; 40. leukocyte; 41. hemoglobin; 42. Leukocytes; 43. Specialized to transport O_2; 44. Platelets; 45. D; 46. B; 47. C; 48. H; 49. F; 50. A; 51. G; 52. E; 53. C; 54. Hemoglobin consists of four polypeptides, each linked to a nonprotein heme group that contains an iron atom in its centre. The iron atom binds O_2 molecules as the blood circulates through the lungs and releases the O_2 as the blood flows through other body tissues; 55. When blood vessels are damaged, collagen fibres in the extracellular matrix are exposed to the leaking blood. Platelets in the blood stick to the collagen fibres and release signalling molecules that induce additional platelets to stick to them. The process continues, forming a plug that helps seal off the damaged site. As the plug forms, platelets release other factors that convert the soluble plasma protein, fibrinogen, into insoluble threads of fibrin. Crosslinks between the fibrin threads form a meshlike network that traps blood cells and platelets and further seals the damaged area.

32.3 The Heart [pp. 783–787]
32.4 Blood Vessels of the Circulatory System [pp. 787–790]
37.5 Maintaining Blood Flow and Pressure [pp. 790–791]
37.6 The Lymphatic System [pp. 791–793]

56. aorta; 57. systole; 58. diastole; 59. atrioventricular valves; 60. neurogenic heart; 61. myogenic heart; 62. sinoatrial node; 63. pacemaker cells; 64. atrioventricular node; 65. electrocardiogram; 66. arterioles; 67. precapillary sphincter; 68. venules; 69. cardiac output; 70. lymphatic system; 71. lymph; 72. Lymph nodes; 73. A; 74. B; 75. B; 76. A; 77. B; 78. A; 79. A; 80. B; 81. Extensive network of vessels that collects excess interstitial fluid; 82. Lymph node; 83. Lymph; 84. A record reflecting the electrical activity of the heart by attaching electrodes to the surface of the body; 85. a) Heart is relaxed, atria begins to fill with blood, b) Blood fills atria and pushes AV valves open, ventricles begin to fill with blood, c) Atria contract, filling ventricles completely, d) Ventricles begin to contract, forcing AV valves closed, e) Ventricles contract fully, forcing semilunar valves open and ejecting blood into arteries; 86. See figure 37.11; 87. Pacemakers generate a wave of signals (action potentials) in the SA node, which spreads into both atria. This wave of signals cause the atria to contract. The propagation of the wave reaches the AV node. The AV node cells are stimulated to produce a signal, which spreads along Purkinje fibres to the bottom of the heart. The signals then spread from the bottom of the heart upward, causing the ventricles to contract.

88.

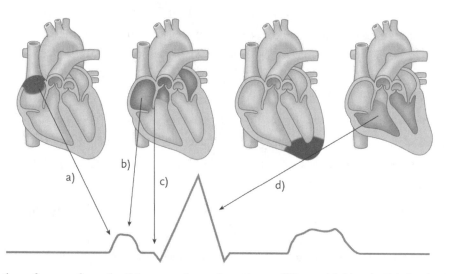

a) Prior to the generation of waves from the SA pacemakers, the atria are filling with blood. This beginning of the first wave of the ECG appears (depolarization of the pacemakers). b) Once the action potentials are produced and spread to the both atria, the atria will contract to pump the blood into the ventricle (peak of the first wave of the ECG). c) The spread of the wave reaches the AV node. The delay in the spread of the wave allows the ventricles to fill with blood (delay between depolarization of the atria and the depolarization wave of the ventricles (d)). d) Once the AV node is stimulated to produce a signal, the signal spreads to the Purkinje fibres and upwards the heart, causing the ventricles to contract and pump the blood out of the heart (depolarization wave of the ventricles on the ECG). The last wave is related to the repolarization of the ventricles. During this time the heart is filling with blood once again; 89. A; 90. G; 91. D; 92. H; 93. F; 94. B; 95. E; 96. C.

SELF-TEST

1.	c	12.	d
2.	a	13.	d
3.	d	14.	b
4.	b	15.	c
5.	a	16.	b
6.	d	17.	b
7.	d	18.	b
8.	a	19.	a
9.	e	20.	c
10.	c	21.	c
11.	a		

INTEGRATING AND APPLYING KEY CONCEPTS

1. A closed circulatory system allows for blood to circulate inside blood vessels with more pressure, thus reaching farther distances between peripheral tissues. Such a system also makes possible more oxygen supply to tissues and the removal of CO_2. Organisms with a closed circulatory system have higher metabolic rates than organisms with an open circulatory system.

2. Some arterioles vasoconstrict and others vasodilate in response to epinephrine based on the subtype of adrenergic receptors the tissue expresses (i.e., alpha- or beta- receptors) and the responses they generate in that particular tissue. The functional significance of the different responses allows for the circulatory system to control the flow of blood the organs. For example, muscles require more oxygen and metabolic fuel (e.g., glucose) during exercise and therefore the circulatory system will divert blood flow to muscles (and away from less active organs during exercise such as the digestive system) to support its metabolic needs.

Chapter 33   Reproduction in Animals

Why It Matters [pp. 797–799]

1. egg; 2. sperm; 3. full; 4. external; 5. synchronized; 6. cryptochromes; 7. blue; 8. lunar; 9. species; 10. coatings; 11. acrosome.

33.1 The Drive to Reproduce [p. 799]
33.2 Asexual and Sexual Reproduction [pp. 799–800]

12. genes; 13. asexual; 14. one; 15. three; 16. identical; 17. parthenogenesis; 18. unfertilized; 19. zygote; 20. gametes; 21. sexual; 22. genetic diversity; 23. environment; 24. survive; 25. two; 26. genetic recombination; 27. chromosomes; 28. independent assortment; 29. randomly; 30. mutation; 31. C; 32. D; 33. A; 34. B.

33.3 Mechanisms of Sexual Reproduction [pp. 800–808]

35. spermatogenesis; 36. testes; 37. spermagonia; 38. meiosis; 39. spermatids; 40. sperm; 41. ovaries; 42. meiosis; 43. cytoplasm; 44. ootid; 45. egg/ovum; 46. oogenesis; 47. external; 48. swim; 49. contact; 50. female; 51. D; 52. H; 53. A; 54. I; 55. F; 56. C; 57. B; 58. E; 59. G; 60. E, B, F, D, A, C; 61. External fertilization occurs outside of the body, typically in aquatic species; synchronization of female and male gametes is critical to success. Internal fertilization occurs within the female reproductive tract in many terrestrial species; typically synchronization of gamete release is not necessary; 62. The acrosome reaction involves release of enzymes that breakdown egg-coating material. Fast block is a wave of depolarization at the egg plasma membrane that occurs within seconds of fusion of the sperm nucleus into the cytoplasm of the egg, while the slow block involves the release of calcium ions from ER into cytosol, causing release of enzymes from cortical granules outside egg (barrier to sperm penetration). These are mechanisms to prevent multiple sperm from fusing with the egg; 63. Hermaphrodites are individuals that can produce eggs and sperm. Simultaneous hermaphroditism occurs in organisms that develop functional ovaries and testes at the same time, whereas sequential hermaphroditism is when organism changes from one sex to the other.

33.4 Sexual Reproduction in Mammals [pp. 808–817]
33.5 Controlling Reproduction [pp. 817–819]

64. two; 65. hormone; 66. follicle-stimulating (FSH); 67. luteinizing (LH); 68. gonadotropin-releasing (GnRH); 69. oocytes; 70. estrogen; 71. LH; 72. ovulation; 73. progesterone; 74. Sertoli; 75. spermatogenesis; 76. Leydig; 77. testosterone; 78. output; 79. extinct; 80. pregnant; 81. K; 82. J; 83. D; 84. N; 85. M; 86. I; 87. C; 88. B; 89. E; 90. H; 91. A; 92. L; 93. G; 94. F; 95. C; 96. E; 97. F; 98. C; 99. B; 100. A; 101. A; 102. E; 103. F; 104. B; 105. F; 106. D; 107. G; 108. E.

Self-Test

1.	a	11.	d
2.	d	12.	c
3.	d	13.	b
4.	d	14.	c
5.	c	15.	c
6.	b	16.	b
7.	c	17.	a
8.	a	18.	e
9.	a	19.	a
10.	b	20.	d

1. For external fertilization to occur, mass spawning of egg and sperm into open water must be synchronized. Furthermore, successful fertilization requires that the egg and sperm belong to the same species. Since it is likely that gametes from more than one species will be present in the water during a mating season, it is important for reproductive success that gametes can recognize whether a potential mate belongs to the same species. This is not important for species that use internal fertilization since sperm are released close to or inside a female's reproductive tract.

2. Semen is composed of a) sperm, which carry a haploid set of chromosomes to contribute to the offspring, b) secretion from seminal vesicles, viscous liquid which contains prostaglandins that trigger contractions in the female reproductive tract, c) secretion from the prostate gland, milky alkaline fluid that raises the pH of the semen to pH=6 and also provides an enzyme that changes semen into a gel at ejaculation to prevent it from draining out of the vagina, and e) secretion from bulbourethral glands, mucus-rich fluid that lubricates the tip of the penis and neutralizes any residual acidity in the urethra.

3. If, after pregnancy, progesterone levels started to drop, the arteries supplying blood to the uterine lining would contract, removing the blood supply and causing the endometrium to break down. A menstrual flow would occur, removing the degenerating endometrium and the dying embryo from the female's body. A miscarriage has occurred, so the pregnancy is terminated.

Chapter 34   Animal Development

Why It Matters [pp. 821–822]

1. parturition; 2. canal; 3. pelvic; 4. small; 5. relaxin; 6. ovaries; 7. elastic; 8. ligaments; 9. stretchability.

34.1 Housing and Fuelling developing Young [pp. 822–824]

10. greater/higher; 11. genes; 12. protection; 13. development; 14. milk; 15. growth.

34.2 Mechanisms of Embryonic Development [pp. 824–827]
34.3 Major Patterns of Cleavage and Gastrulation [pp. 827–831]

16. zygote; 17. genetic (nuclear); 18. cytoplasmic 19. egg; 20. animal; 21. vegetal; 22. polarity; 23. three; 24. three;

25. cleavage; 26. morula; 27. mitotic; 28. blastula; 29. gastrulation; 30. ectoderm; 31. endoderm; 32. mesoderm;

33. archenteron; 34. blastopore; 35. protostome; 36. deuterostome; 37. organogenesis; 38. organ; 39. adhesions;

40. differentiation; 41. C; 42. B; 43. A; 44. A, B, C; 45. C; 46. B; 47. C; 48. C; 49. C; 50. B; 51. E; 52. I; 53. G; 54. B;

55. F; 56. A; 57. D; 58. C; 59. H; 60. B; 61. B; 62. A; 63. C; 64. B; 65. C; 66. A; 67. C.

34.4 Organogenesis: Gastrulation to Adult Body Structures [pp. 831–834]

68. organogenesis; 69. organs; 70. notochord; 71. mesoderm; 72. nervous; 73. neurulation; 74. induction; 75. plate;

76. mesoderm; 77. somites; 78. apoptosis; 79. D, B, C, E, A, G, F.

34.5 Embryonic Development of Humans and Other Mammals [pp. 835–839]

80. 38; 81. trimesters; 82. cleavage; 83. gastrulation; 84. organogenesis; 85. fetus; 86. fertilization; 87. third;

88. implantation; 89. blastocyst; 90. blastocoel; 91. inner cell mass; 92. trophoblast; 93. proteases; 94. endometrium (uterine wall); 95. disc; 96. epiblast; 97. embryo; 98. hypoblast; 99. membranes; 100. eight; 101. growth; 102. birds;

103. reptiles; 104. D; 105. A; 106. G; 107. E; 108. C; 109. B; 110. F; 111. D; 112. A; 113. C; 114. B; 115. A; 116. D;

117. C; 118. A; 119. The presence of SRY gene (sex-determining region of the Y chromosome) determines that the embryo will become male (if absent, the embryo will become female). This gene encodes a protein that initiates development of fetal testes which secrete testosterone and anti-Müllerian hormone. These two hormones cause the

Wolffian ducts to become male reproductive organs and inhibit the development of Müllerian ducts; 120. The extra-embryonic membranes, the chorion, amnion, yolk sac, and allantoic membrane are primarily derived from the hypoblast cell layer of the embryonic disc and the trophoblast layer of cells.

34.6 Cellular Basis of Development [pp. 840–845]
34.7 Genetic and Molecular Control of Development [pp. 845–851]

121. orientation; 122. rate; 123. G1; 124. microtubules; 125. microfilaments; 126. induction; 127. determination; 128. adhesion; 129. genes; 130. regulatory; 131. *Hox*; 132. metamorphosis; 133. F – gap; 134. T; 135. T; 136. F – pair-rule; 137. F – and; 138. F – induction; 139. T; 140. F – anterior; 141. T; 142. F – undifferentiated; 143. F – microfilaments.

SELF-TEST

1.	c	11.	c
2.	c	12.	b
3.	b	13.	b
4.	d	14.	d
5.	b	15.	a
6.	b	16.	a
7.	b	17.	c
8.	d	18.	c
9.	a	19.	d
10.	a	20.	a

INTEGRATING AND APPLYING KEY CONCEPTS

1. Each organ or organ system arises from one of the three primary tissues: ectoderm, mesoderm, or endoderm. The organs of the nervous system and integumentary system arise from the ectoderm; the muscular, skeletal, circulatory, reproductive, and excretory systems primarily arise from the mesoderm; and the lining of many organs, including those in the digestive tract and respiratory tract, arise from the endoderm.
2. Apoptosis functions to break down tissues no longer required as newly formed adult tissues are formed. This allows developing organisms to change structures in preparation for its adult form; for example, removal of tissue between fingers and toes, changing paddle-shaped structures into freely moving fingers and toes.
3. The movement of a whole cell involves attachment, stretching, and contraction steps. If a cell is attached to a substrate, it will elongate itself (using its microtubules and microfilaments) and attach itself to the substrate at the advancing tip. The cell will then contract itself at the back end of the cell so that it eventually breaks free from its previous attachment point. These steps will be repeated until the cell reaches its destination.

35 Control of Animal Processes: Endocrine Control

Why It Matters [pp. 854–855]

1. hormones; 2. endocrine systems.

35.1 Hormones and Their Secretions [pp. 855–858]

3. neurohormone; 4. hyposecretion; 5. hypersecretion; 6. hyperglycemic; 7. endocrine; 8. The nervous system and the endocrine system regulates and coordinates bodily functions. The two systems are structurally, chemically, and functionally related, but they control different types of activities. The nervous system communicates through neurons and primarily by chemical synapses and involve rapid communication. The nervous system directs highly specific localized targets. It is a "private mode" of communication. The endocrine system typically involves the secretion of hormones in the blood circulation that act at distant target sites. The endocrine system controls activities that involve slower, longer-lasting responses. The endocrine system is more "public," often affecting several tissues or organs; 9. A

signalling molecule secreted by a cell that can alter the activities of any cell with receptors for it. Hormones are typically transported in the bloodstream to alter its physiological activity of target cells/tissues; 10. System of glands that release their secretions (hormones) directly into the circulatory system to alter the physiological activity of target tissues. 11. Hormones within an endocrine axis can interact with the cells that secreted the hormones within the axis to either inhibit or activate further secretion of hormones within that axis. In the case of negative feedback, an example includes the ability of cortisol to inhibit cortisol secretion from the adrenal cortex, inhibit the secretion of ACTH from the anterior pituitary, and inhibit CRH secretion from the hypothalamus. Overall, this inhibition controls the secretion of cortisol from the adrenal cortex. An example of positive feedback control includes the continuous secretion of prolactin as an infant suckles the breast of a lactating mother. The suckling reflex causes additional secretion of prolactin from the pituitary which promotes milk secretion. In this way, the mother continuously provides milk to her offspring. The benefits of such regulatory pathways to organisms is to regulate hormone concentrations in the blood and to regulate cell/tissue responses to the hormones; 12. At any given time, a number of hormones are secreted into the bloodstream to elicit a number of physiological responses. The hormones secreted at any given time will interact with a number of cells/tissues/organs to coordinate the integration of a number of physiological responses that will ultimately controls a given process; 13. Endocrine glands; 14. Neurosecretory cells; 15. amine; 16. peptide; 17. steroid; 18. fatty acid derivative; 19. growth factors; 20. prostaglandins; 21. target cells; 22. target proteins; 23. Neurosecretion; 24. The release of a hormone from an epithelial cell in a gland that is transported in the blood and generally effective at a distance from its site of secretion; 25. The release of a chemical signal into extracellular fluid that regulates the activity of a neighbouring cell; 26. Autocrine (or autoregulation); 27. Epinephrine; 28. Insulin; 29. Cortisol; 30. Fatty acid derivative; 31. C; 32. D; 33. B; 34. A.

35.2 Mechanisms of Hormone Action [pp. 858–862]

35. Many hormones are secreted in an inactive or less active form (a prohormone) and converted by the target cells or enzymes in the blood or other tissue to the active form; 36. Hydrophilic hormones bind cell surface receptors and activate a signal transduction cascade, involving enzymatic reactions, inside the cell that leads to a cell response. Hydrophobic hormones are usually transported bound to a protein and bind to receptors inside cells, activating or inhibiting genetic regulatory proteins. Both cases include reception of the signal (cell surface or intracellular receptor), transduction and amplification of the signal, and a cellular response; 37. Only cells that express receptors to a given hormone will respond to that hormone. Cells may express a number of different types of receptors and therefore respond to different hormones. Different cells may respond differently to the same hormone owing to the different mechanisms that are activated by the receptors in those cell types. In addition, the actions of one hormone may modify the responses to another hormone in different cell types; 38. Epinephrine is an amine and a hydrophilic compound, it interacts with cell surface receptors; 39. Insulin is a protein and is hydrophilic, it interacts with cell surface receptors; 40. Testosterone is a steroid and is hydrophobic, it interacts with intracellular receptors to regulate gene expression; 41. Oxytocin is a peptide and is hydrophilic, and interacts with cell surface receptors; 42. Estrogen is a steroid and is hydrophobic, it interacts with intracellular receptors to regulate gene expression; 43. Aldosterone is a steroid and is hydrophobic, it interacts with intracellular receptors to regulate gene expression; 44. Thyroid hormone is an amine but is hydrophobic, it interacts with intracellular receptors to regulate gene expression; 45. Prostaglandin is derived from fatty acids and is hydrophobic. Prostaglandins, however, interacts with cell surface receptors.

35.3 The Hypothalamus and Pituitary [pp. 862–865]

46. pituitary gland; 47. posterior pituitary; 48. anterior pituitary; 49. tropic hormone; 50. releasing hormones; 51. inhibiting hormones; 52. antidiuretic hormone (ADH); 53. oxytocin; 54. prolactin; 55. growth hormone; 56. thyroid stimulating hormone (TSH); 57. adrenocorticotropic hormone (ACTH); 58. follicle stimulating hormone (FSH); 59. luteinizing hormone (LH); 60. gonadotropins; 61. melanocyte stimulating hormone (MSH); 62. endorphins; 63. The anterior pituitary is a distinct lobe that produces and secretes many hormones into the general circulation (e.g., growth hormone). The posterior pituitary does not produce any hormone. It is the site where axons from the hypothalamus terminate to release tropic hormones into the portal system that regulate the anterior pituitary or to release peptides such as ADH or oxytocin directly into the general circulation; 64. Peptide; 65. Anterior pituitary; 66. Stimulates growth and regulates metabolism; 67. Prolactin; 68. Peptide; 69. Anterior pituitary; 70. TSH; 71. Peptide; 72. Anterior pituitary; 73. Stimulates adrenal cortex to produce cortisol and aldosterone; 74. Peptide; 75. Anterior pituitary; 76. Promotes gamete development; 77. Peptide; 78. Anterior pituitary; 79. Promotes sex steroid production; 80. MSH; 81. Peptide; 82. Anterior pituitary (intermediate lobe, when present); 83. Peptide; 84. Anterior pituitary (intermediate lobe, when present); 85. Inhibit perception of pain; 86. Peptide; 87. Posterior pituitary (produced in hypothalamus); 88. Stimulates water reabsorption (conservation); 89. Oxytocin; 90. Peptide; 91. Posterior pituitary (produced in hypothalamus); 92. Neurosecretory neuron (some produce releasing hormones; some produce inhibiting hormones); 93. Hypothalamus; 94. Protein vein; 95. Posterior pituitary; 96. Anterior pituitary; 97. Neurosecretory neuron (some produce ADH, some produce oxytocin); 98. Hypothalamus; 99. Anterior pituitary; 100. Posterior pituitary.

35.4 Other Major Endocrine Glands of Vertebrates [pp. 865-871]

101. thyroid gland; 102. thyroxin (T4); 103. triiodothyronine (T3); 104. metamorphosis; 105. calcitonin; 106. Parathyroid hormone; 107. parathyroid gland; 108. vitamin D; 109. adrenal medulla; 110. adrenal cortex; 111. catecholamines; 112. epinephrine; 113. norepinephrine; 114. glucocorticoids; 115. mineralocorticoids; 116. Cortisol; 117. aldosterone; 118. testes; 119. ovaries; 120. androgens; 121. estrogens; 122. progestins; 123. Testosterone; 124. 17β-estradiol; 125. progesterone; 126. Islets of Langerhans; 127. pancreas; 128. insulin; 129. Glucagon; 130. Diabetes mellitus; 131. pineal gland; 132. melatonin; 133. A; 134. C; 135. E; 136. G; 137. I; 138. J; 139. F; 140. H; 141. B; 142. D; 143. Amine; 144. Regulate basal metabolic rate, triggers metamorphosis in amphibians; 145. Calcitonin; 146. Thyroid gland; 147. Increases blood calcium; 148. Epinephrine; 149. Adrenal medulla; 150. Cortisol; 151. Steroid; 152. Steroid; 153. Adrenal cortex; 154. Increase sodium and water reabsorption; 155. Testosterone; 156. Estradiol; 157. Steroid; 158. Promotes development and maintenance of secondary sex characteristics; 159. Prepares and maintains uterus for implantation; 160. Gonadotropin releasing hormone; 161. Posterior pituitary (produced in hypothalamus); 162. Peptide; 163. Islets of Langerhans; 164. Anabolic, stimulates nutrient uptake into cells and macromolecule synthesis; 165. Glucagon; 166. Peptide; 167. Islets of Langerhans; 168. Melatonin; 169. Peptide; 170. Helps maintain daily biorhythms.

35.5 Endocrine Systems in Invertebrates [p. 871-873]

171. brain hormone; 172. ecdysone; 173. juvenile hormone; 174. moult-inhibiting hormone; 175. A; 176. D; 177. B; 178. C.

1.	a	11.	b
2.	a	12.	b
3.	c	13.	d
4.	b	14.	a
5.	c	15.	a
6.	c	16.	a
7.	b	17.	a
8.	d	18.	c
9.	c	19.	e
10.	b	20.	b

INTEGRATING AND APPLYING KEY CONCEPTS

1. Both systems are involved in secreting chemical signals involved in regulating the various functions of the cells. Whereas the endocrine system typically release hormones (e.g., chemical signals) in the bloodstream, affecting cells at a distance and having longer lasting effects and thus longer term regulation, the nervous system allows for rapid and immediate adjustments of cellular function. Together, these coordinate the function of animals.

2. The regulation of cortisol secretion from the adrenal gland is achieved by the release of CRH (corticotropic releasing hormone) from the hypothalamus and stimulation of corticotropic cells of the anterior pituitary. In response to CRH, the corticotropes release ACTH (adrenocorticotropic hormone) into the blood circulation. ACTH then stimulates the adrenal gland to release cortisol in the blood circulation.

   In the case of the regulation of catecholamine release from the adrenal medulla, nerves of the sympathetic nervous system extend from the hypothalamus to the adrenal medulla. Upon stimulation, these nerves release the neurotransmitter Ach (acetylcholine) which stimulate the secretion of catecholamines in the blood circulation.

3. Given that feedback loops play a role in controlling the concentration for circulating hormones, disruptions would cause hyposecretion or hypersecretion of hormones causing systems to be underactive or overactive.

Chapter 36 Control of Animal Processes: Neural Control

Why It Matters [pp. 876–877]

1. nervous system.

36.1 Neurons and Their Organization in Nervous System: An Overview [pp. 877–880]

2. Neural signalling; 3. neurons; 4. Reception; 5. Transmission; 6. Integration; 7. Response; 8. Afferent neurons; 9. sensory neurons; 10. interneurons; 11. Efferent neurons; 12. effectors; 13. cell body; 14. Dendrites; 15. axons; 16. axon hillock; 17. axon terminals; 18. neural circuit; 19. glial cells; 20. astrocytes; 21. oligodendrocytes; 22. Schwann cells; 23. nodes of Ranvier; 24. synapse; 25. presynaptic; 26. postsynaptic; 27. electrical synapse; 28. chemical synapse; 29. neurotransmitter; 30. synaptic cleft; 31. pre-; 32. post-; 33. interneuron; 34. B; 35. A; 36. A; 37. B; 38. B; 39. C; 40. A; 41. Efferent neurons carry impulses away from the interneuron/network to effectors in general (could be a gland or muscle). Motor neurons are specific efferent neurons that carry impulses to muscle (could be smooth muscle, skeletal muscle, or cardiac muscle); 42. B; 43. D; 44. A; 45. C; 46. Neural support cells; 47. Astrocytes; 48. Wrap around axons of neurons in the central nervous system; 49. Wrap around axons of neurons in the peripheral nervous system; 50. Neurons; 51. E; 52. C; 53. F; 54. D; 55. B; 56. G; 57. A; 58. Dendrites; 59. Axon; 60. Axon hillock; 61. Axon terminal; 62. Cell body (soma)

36.2 Signal Initiation by Neurons [pp. 881–887]
36.3 Conduction of Action Potentials along Neurons and across Chemical Synapses [pp. 887–893]
36.4 Integration of Incoming Signals by Neurons [pp. 894–895]

63. Membrane potential; 64. resting potential; 65. polarized; 66. action potential; 67. depolarized; 68. threshold potential; 69. hyperpolarized; 70. all-or-nothing principle; 71. refractory period; 72. voltage-gated ion channels; 73. Propagation;

74. salutatory conduction; 75. presynaptic membrane; 76. ligand-gated ion channels; 77. postsynaptic membrane; 78. synaptic vesicles; 79. exocytosis; 80. Direct neurotransmitters; 81. Indirect neurotransmitters; 82. excitatory postsynaptic potential (EPSP); 83. inhibitory postsynaptic potential (IPSP); 84. graded potentials; 85. Temporal summation; 86. Spatial summation; 87. neuro-; 88. de-; 89. hyper-; 90. A; 91. B; 92. B; 93. A; 94. A; 95. B; 96. B; 97. A; 98. B; 99. A; 100. All cells display a separation of positive and negative charges across their membrane, but this potential (membrane potential) remains unchanged. Some cells, such as neurons and muscles, possess membranes (excitable membranes) that are capable of changing their potential. The resting potential is the membrane potential of an unstimulated nerve or muscle cell; 101. E; 102. B; 103. A; 104. D; 105. C; 106. F; 107. Resting potential; 108. Threshold potential; 109. Depolarization; 110. Repolarization; 111. Refractory period; 112. Hyperpolarization (undershoot).

36.5 Evolutionary Trends in Neural Integration: Networks, Nerves, Ganglia, and Brains [pp. 895–901]

113. nerve nets; 114. ganglia; 115. brain; 116. nerve cords; 117. central (CNS); 118. peripheral (PNS); 119. neural tube; 120. spinal cord; 121. ventricles; 122. central canal; 123. forebrain; 124. midbrain; 125. hindbrain; 126. hypothalamus; 127. postganglionic; 128. preganglionic; 129. a; 130. b; 131. Loose meshes of neurons in certain animal groups with radial symmetry; 132. Ganglion; 133. Bundle of nerves that extend from a central ganglion. 134. Control body movement (mostly voluntary); 135. Autonomic; 136. Sympathetic; 137. Parasympathetic.

SELF-TEST

1.	a	10.	b
2.	b	11.	d
3.	b	12.	a
4.	a	13.	d
5.	c	14.	b
6.	a	15.	b
7.	d	16.	b
8.	a	17.	a
9.	b			

INTEGRATING AND APPLYING KEY CONCEPTS

1. Both the secretion of fluid and amylase secretion are dependent on two different secondary messenging pathways. In the case of amylase secretion, epinephrine interacts with beta-adrenergic receptors activating a cAMP dependent G-protein and a corresponding increase in amylase secretion. In the case of cholinergic stimulation, the release of acetylcholine causes an increase in intracellular calcium levels that triggers events that lead to the secretion of watery saliva.
2. Cephalization allowed for the local concentrations of cell bodies permitting enhanced coordination of sensory and motor functions. Those with motile life histories would be expected to have a higher degree of cephalization given the pressures associated with the coordination and sensory needs of this particular lifestyle.

Chapter 37   Control of Animal Processes: Neural Integration

Why It Matters [pp. 904–905]
37.1 Overview of Sensory Integration [pp. 906–907]
37.2 Mechanoreceptors and the Tactile and Spatial Senses [pp. 907–911]
37.3 Mechanoreceptors and Hearing [pp. 911–913]

1. sensory receptors; 2. sensory transduction; 3. mechanoreceptors; 4. photoreceptors; 5. chemoreceptors; 6. thermoreceptors; 7. nociceptors; 8. frequency of action potentials; 9. number of neurons activated; 10. Sensory adaptation; 11. Pacinian corpuscles; 12. Proprioceptors; 13. Statocysts; 14. statoliths; 15. sensory hair cells; 16. lateral

line system; 17. neuromasts; 18. stereocilia; 19. cupula; 20. vestibular apparatus; 21. semicircular canals; 22. utricle; 23. saccule; 24. otoliths; 25. stretch receptors; 26. muscle spindles; 27. Golgi tendon organ; 28. tympanum; 29. pinna; 30. outer; 31. tympanic membrane; 32. middle; 33. malleus; 34. incus; 35. stapes; 36. oval window; 37. inner; 38. semicircular canal; 39. utricle; 40. saccule; 41. cochlea; 42. organ of Corti; 43. round window; 44. echolocation; 45. chemoreceptor; 46. thermoreceptor; 47. otolith; 48. proprioceptor; 49. photoreceptor; 50. nociceptor; 51. Lateral line system; 52. Detect position and orientation, used for equilibrium in invertebrates; 53. Perceives position and motion of head; 54. Muscle spindle; 55. Organ of Corti; 56. Proprioceptors that detect stretch and compression of tendon; 57. Neuromast; 58. A; 59. H; 60. I; 61. E; 62. C; 63. G; 64. B; 65. F; 66. D; 67. Pinna; 68. Eustachian tube; 69. Stapes; 70. Incus; 71. Malleus; 72. Semicircular canals; 73. Oval window; 74. Auditory canal; 75. Tympanic membrane; 76. Round window; 77. Cochlea; 78. Outer ear; 79. Middle ear; 80. Inner ear.

37.4 Photoreceptors and Vision [pp. 914–921]
37.5 Chemoreceptors [pp. 921–925]
37.6 Thermoreceptors and Nociceptors [pp. 925–927]
37.7 Electroreceptors and Magnetoreceptors [pp. 927–928]

81. ocellus; 82. compound; 83. ommatidia; 84. cornea; 85. photopigment; 86. single-lens; 87. lens; 88. retina; 89. iris; 90. pupil; 91. Accommodation; 92. Aqueous humour; 93. vitreous humour; 94. ciliary body; 95. rods; 96. cones; 97. fovea; 98. peripheral vision; 99. Photopigments; 100. retinal; 101. opsins; 102. Rhodopsin; 103. bipolar; 104. ganglion; 105. horizontal; 106. Amacrine; 107. lateral inhibition; 108. photopsin; 109. optic chiasm; 110. lateral geniculate nuclei; 111. sensilla; 112. Taste buds; 113. olfactory hairs; 114. transient receptor potential (TRP); 115. Magnoreceptors; 116. A compound eye contain 100s to 1000s of individual visual units. A single-lens eye has one lens and operates like a camera; 117. Photopigments consist of a covalent complex of retinal and one of several different proteins know as opsins. The photopigment in rod cells is rhodopsin. Cone cells contain different types of photopsins based upon different opsin forms, humans have three photopsins; 118. Accommodation is the process of focusing and image by moving the lens back and forth relative to the retina; 119. Electroceptors detect electric fields. Electroceptors depolarize in an electric field. Magnetoceptors allow animals to detect and use Earth's magnetic field as a source of directional information; 120. Bipolar cell; 121. Extend over entire retina, and axons come together to form optic nerve; 122. Amacrine cell; 123. Connect with different photoreceptor cells and bipolar cells; 124. Photoreceptor; 125. Radiant energy; 126. Distinguish tastes of sweet, sour, salty, and umami; 127. Olfactory hair; 128. Chemicals; 129. Electroreceptor; 130. Communication, locate objects (including prey); 131. Magnetic field; 132. Nociceptor; 1 33. Tissue damage, noxious chemicals; 134. A; 135. I; 136. F; 137. C; 138. D; 139. B; 140. E; 141. G; 142. H; 143. J;144. Ciliary body; 145. Iris; 146. Lens; 147. Pupil; 148. Cornea; 149. Aqueous humour; 150. Vitreous humour; 151. Retina; 152. Fovea; 153. Optic nerve.

37.8 Overview of Central Neural Integration [pp. 928–929]
37.9 The Central Nervous System and Its Functions [pp. 929–935]

154. meninges; 155. cerebral spinal fluid; 156. grey matter; 157. white matter; 158. reflex; 159. brain stem; 160. cerebral cortex; 161. blood-brain barrier; 162. reticular formation; 163. cerebellum; 164. thalamus; 165. hypothalamus; 166. basal nuclei; 167. limbic system; 168. amygdala; 169. hippocampus; 170. olfactory bulbs; 171. corpus callosum; 172. primary somatosensory area; 173. Association areas; 174. primary motor area; 175. lateralization; 176. B; 177. A; 178. A; 179. B; 180. A; 181. B; 182. connects the two cerebral hemispheres; 183. primary somatosensory area; 184. primary motor area;

185. integrates sensory information and formulates responses; 186. a; 187. J; 188. L; 189. E; 190. G; 191. C; 192. D; 193. I; 194. K; 195. N; 196. H; 197. M; 198. B; 199. F.

37.10 Memory, Learning, and Consciousness [pp. 935–936]

200. Memory; 201. Learning; 202. Consciousness; 203. Short-term; 204. Long-term; 205. Long-term potentiation; 206. electroencephalogram; 207. rapid eye movement (REM) sleep; 208. A; 209. B; 210. A; 211. D; 212. E; 213. C; 214. B.

Self-Test

1.	c	11.	a
2.	d	12.	b
3.	b	13.	d
4.	a	14.	b
5.	a	15.	a
6.	c	16.	a
7.	d	17.	a
8.	a	18.	c
9.	d	19.	b
10.	d		

Chapter 38   Muscle, Skeletons, and Body Movements

Why It Matters [pp. 940–941]

1. skeletal; 2. cardiac; 3. smooth; 4. skeletal muscle.

38.1 Vertebrate Skeletal Muscle: Structure and Function [pp. 941–949]

5. muscle fibres; 6. myofibrils; 7. thick filaments; 8. thin filaments; 9. sarcomere; 10. T tubules; 11. sarcoplasmic reticulum; 12. neuromuscular junction; 13. acetylcholine; 14. sliding filament mechanism; 15. muscle twitch; 16. Tetanus; 17. Slow muscle fibres; 18. fast muscle fibres; 19. motor units; 20. sarcomere; 21. myofibril; 22. myoglobin; 23. A; 24. B; 25. A; 26. H; 27. G; 28. C; 29. B; 30. D; 31. I; 32. F; 33. E; 34. Neuromuscular junction; 35. T tubule; 36. Sarcoplasmic reticulum; 37. Myofibril; 38. Sarcomere; 39. When an action potential arrives at a neuromuscular junction, the axon terminal releases a neurotransmitter, acetylcholine, which triggers an action potential in the muscle fibre. The action potential travels in all directions over the muscle fibre's surface membrane and penetrates into the interior of the fibre through the T tubules. When an action potential reaches the end of a T tubule, it opens ion channels in the sarcoplasmic reticulum that allow Ca^{2+} to flow out into the cytosol. When Ca^{2+} flows out into the cytosol, the troponin molecules of the thin filament bind the calcium and undergo a conformational change that causes the tropomyosin fibres to slip into the grooves of the actin double helix. The slippage uncovers the actin's binding site for the myosin crossbridge, allows myosin to bind to actin. Bending of the myosin molecule allows the muscle to then contract; 40. During contraction, calcium is responsible to bind to troponin so that troponin can undergo a conformational change that causes the tropomyosin fibres to slip into the grooves of the actin double helix and allow myosin to bind actin and initiate a contraction. During relaxation, calcium must be pumped back into the sarcoplasmic reticulum. The decrease in cytosolic calcium will cause troponin to cover the actin's binding site for myosin (myosin can no longer bind actin) thus relaxing the muscle. ATP, on the other hand, provides the energy for the bending of the myosin molecule to cause the movement of actin filaments relative to the myosin filaments, thus causing contraction. ATP is also needed to cause the detachment of myosin from the actin molecule. In the absence of ATP, myosin remains attached to actin and cannot proceed with contraction or relaxation (an example is *rigor mortis*); 41. Following the

arrival of the action potential at the muscle fibre and the release of calcium from the sarcoplasmic reticulum, the crossbridge events include: a) calcium binding to troponin on actin filaments, causing tropomyosin to be displaced into the grooves, this uncovers the actin's binding site for the myosin crossbridge, b) ATP is hydrolyzed and the myosin crossbridge bends and binds to a binding site on an actin molecule, c) The binding triggers the crossbridge to snap back toward the tail, pulling the thin filament over the thick filament (the power stroke), and ADP is released, d) ATP binds to the crossbridge, causing myosin to detach from actin. The cycle then repeats itself. When action potentials stop, calcium is taken up by the sarcoplasmic reticulum and the contraction stops. The thin filaments slide back to their original relaxed positions.

38.2 Skeletal Systems [pp. 949–952]

42. hydrostatic skeleton; 43. exoskeleton; 44. endoskeleton; 45. axial skeleton; 46. appendicular skeleton; 47. The skeletal system provides physical support for the body and protection for the soft tissues. It also acts as a framework against which muscles work to move parts of the body or the entire organism; 48. A; 49. B.

38.3 Vertebrate Movement: The Interactions between Muscles and Bones [pp. 952–957]

50. synovial; 51. cartilaginous; 52. fibrous; 53. agonist; 54. antagonistic pairs; 55. extensor muscles; 56. flexor muscles; 57. B; 58. A; 59. A; 60. D; 61. E; 62. F; 63. B; 64. C.

SELF-TEST

1.	c	11.	a
2.	c	12.	b
3.	b	13.	d
4.	d	14.	a
5.	d	15.	c
6.	d	16.	a
7.	c	17.	a
8.	d	18.	c
9.	a	19.	c
10.	d	20.	b

Chapter 39   Animal Behaviour

Why It Matters [pp. 960–961]

1. behaviour; 2. versatile; 3. novel; 4. learned.

39.1 Genes, Environment, and Behaviour [pp. 961–962]
39.2 Instinct [pp. 962–965]
39.3 Learning [pp. 965–966]

5. instinctive; 6. learned; 7. isolation; 8. gene–environment; 9. genetically; 10. fixed action; 11. sign; 12. more; 13. imprinting; 14. critical; 15. classical conditioning; 16. operant; 17. reinforcement; 18. insight; 19. error; 20. habituation; 21. A; 22. F; 23. B; 24. C; 25. D; 26. E; 24. C; 25. D; 26. E; 27. F – unconditioned; 28. F – operant; 29. F – habituation; 30. T; 31. F – genetic; 32. F – Instinctive.

39.4 Neurophysiology and Behaviour [pp. 966–967]
39.5 Hormones and Behaviour [pp. 967–968]
39.6 Neural Anatomy and Behaviour [pp. 969–971]

33. nerve; 34. genetic; 35. experiences; 36. territory; 37. courtship; 38. brain; 39. hormones; 40. E; 41. G; 42. A; 43. C; 44. F; 45. D; 46. B.

39.7 Communication [pp. 971–975]

47. acoustic; 48. visual; 49. chemical; 50. pheromones; 51. Tactile; 52. electrical; 53. B (and possibly A or D); 54. C (and possibly A, B, D); 55. E (and possibly A); 56. B; 57. A; 58. C.

39.8 Space [pp. 975–977]

59. habitat; 60. kinesis; 61. taxis; 62. territoriality; 63. energy; 64. benefits; 65. exclusive; 66. attracting; 67. C; 68. B; 69. A; 70. B.

39.9 Migration [pp. 977–981]

71. migration; 72. piloting; 73. compass orientation; 74. navigation; 75. mental; 76. time; 77. increase; 78. decrease; 79. longer; 80. A; 81. C, D; 82. B; 83. D; 84. D; 85. A.

39.10 Mates as Resources [pp. 981–982]
39.11 Sexual Selection [pp. 982–983]

86. sexual; 87. competition; 88. choosing; 89. investment; 90. dimorphism; 91. courting (or courtship); 92. compete; 93. lek; 94. polygyny; 95. polyandry; 96. monogamous; 97. promiscuity; 98. C; 99. B; 100. D; 101. A.

39.12 Social Behaviour [pp. 983–985]
39.13 Kin Selection and Altruism [pp. 985–987]
39.14 Eusocial Animals [pp. 987–988]
39.15 Human Social Behaviour [pp. 988–990]

102. social behaviour; 103. dominance hierarchy; 104. altruism; 105. kin selection; 106. Haplodiploidy; 107. eusocial; 108. reciprocal altruism; 109. $0.25+0.25 = 0.5$; 110. 0.5; 111. $(0.5)(0.5) = 0.25$; 112. $(0.5)(0.5)(0.5) = 0.125$; 113. C; 114. D; 115. A; 116. B.

SELF-TEST

1. b [Sparrows can make singing sounds instinctively but a song must be learned]
2. a [Species that insert their eggs into another species nest are brood parasites]
3. c [Sign stimuli cue fixed action patterns]
4. b [Newborn garter snakes instinctively were interested in eating slugs, so their food preferences must have a genetic component]
5. c [The operant is the desired behavioural response from the subject; the reinforcement is the reward for performing the operant]
6. c [Habituation is the learned response involving loss of responsiveness to a repeated stimulus, such as song of a neighbouring bird species]
7. a [Only males produce estrogen, which increases the nerve cells in the higher vocal centre, allowing the bird to sing (females do not produce estrogen)]
8. b [Honeybees produce increasing concentrations of the hormone octopamine as they age]
9. b [Crickets have ears (sensory system) that 'hear' a predator and initiates an immediate motor response]
10. d [Moles live in dark places, using the tactile (or touch) sensors on their mouth tentacles]
11. c [Herrings communicate using fast repetitive transient signals (f*rts)]

12. b [Kinesis is the change in rate of movement in response to environmental stimuli, as displayed by the planaria]
13. b [Each Tit species has a different food preference but in both species, preference is innate]
14. c [The other choices all involve greater potential for low-testosterone individual having to defend territory and he would probably lose.]
15. d [Migrating animals do not use sound cues, only visual and olfactory cues]
16. c [Females usually have a greater investment in parental care than males, which explains their different reproductive strategies]
17. c [Male ornamentation or structures are used by females who choose their mates, one of the components of sexual selection]
18. b [Polyandry is rare since females rarely mate with more than one male]
19. d [Dolphins assist other group members, as well as members of other species]
20. d [Research indicated that abuse was more likely between adults and children that were not genetically related]

INTEGRATING AND APPLYING KEY CONCEPTS

1. An insectivorous bat uses echolocation calls to "hear" if and where a potential prey is located. This involves comparing the original call with the returning echo. The black field cricket is one of the bat's prey; however, this animal has ears on its legs which sense the direction of the sound (stronger stimulus on the leg closer to the call) and causes an automatic response. The response includes a jerking motion by the hindleg farthest away from the sound that blocks wing movement on that side of the body, causing the cricket to swerve away from the sound and downward toward the ground (away from the bat).
2. A wandering raven is an intruder into another raven's territory. The wandering raven will yell when it finds a carcass because, although it will have to share its food, it needs other ravens to assist in fighting off the resident raven.
3. The new head of a pride is not altruistic because when takes over the pride, he kills all of the nursing young (infanticide) so that the female lions in the pride will go into estrus. This allows the new male to produce offspring of his own relatively quickly, passing on <u>his</u> genes to the next generation.

Chapter 40   Plant and Animal Nutrition

Why It Matters [pp. 994–995]
40.1 Nutrition: Essential Materials [pp. 995–1003]
40.2 Soil [pp. 1003–1006]

1. 90; 2. dry matter; 3. hydrogen; 4. Hydroponics; 5. minerals; 6. photosynthesis; 7. passively; 8. primary; 9. secondary;

10. Essential; 11. macronutrients;12. micronutrients; 13. stunted; 14. yellowing; 15. undernutrition; 16. loss; 17. vitamins;

18. enzymes; 19. 13; 20. water-soluble; 21. fat-soluble; 22. air spaces; 23. humus; 24. water; 25. aerating; 26. decompose;

27. oxygen; 28. soil solution; 29. cations; 30. anions; 31. negatively; 32. cation exchange; 33. J; 34. D; 35. K; 36. E; 37. C;

38. I; 39. L; 40. A; 41. F; 42. H; 43. B; 44. G; 45. A, B, F; 46. A, B, C, F, often E; 47. A, B, F, sometimes D; 48. A, B, C, D,

F; 49. A – Hold water and air, B – Source of nutrients, holds water and air, C – Provide organic chemicals and aerates the

soil, D – Nutrients for the plant.

40.3 Obtaining and Absorbing Nutrients [pp. 1006–1010]

50. 20–50; 51. tips; 52. hairs; 53. ion-specific; 54. phosphorous; 55. mycorrhizae; 56. hyphal; 57. 80; 58. enzymes;

59. bacteria; 60. nitrate; 61. ammonium; 62. amino; 63. nitrogen; 64. symbiotic; 65. nodules; 66. flavinoids; 67. nod;

68. leghemoglobin; 69. bacteroids; 70. nitrogenase; 71. adaptations; 72. four; 73. fluid; 74. suspension; 75. deposit;

76. bulk; 77. B; 78. A; 79. C; 80. D; 81. E; 82. D; 83. A; 84. C; 85. B; 86. D; 87. A; 88. C; 89. B; 90. C; 91. D.

40.4 Digestive Processes in Animals [pp. 1010–1012]

92. breakdown; 93. absorbed; 94. enzymatic hydrolysis; 95. specific; 96. intracellular; 97. extracellular; 98. five;

99. mechanical processing; 100. secretion; 101. enzymatic hydrolysis; 102. absorption; 103. elimination; 104. B; 105. D;

106. A; 107. C; 108. Intracellular digestion occurs within the cell. In order for the cell not be broken down by digestive

enzymes, particles are contained within vacuoles that will fuse with lysosomes containing digestive enzymes. Food particles are taken into the cell by endocytosis. After digestion has occurred and materials absorbed from the vacuole, waste products are eliminated from the cell by exocytosis; 109. Extracellular digestion occurs in a tube or saclike structure, actually outside of the organism. The potential for different types of food sources is increased, since size is not a limiting factor. The primary limiting factor will be the available enzymes to break down the food material; 110. B; 111. E; 112. C, D; 113. A; 114. C, D; 115. B; 116. B, C.

40.5 Digestion in Mammals [pp. 1012–1021]

117. five; 118. esophagus; 119. rectum; 120. nervous; 121. longer; 122. cellulose; 123. F; 124. I; 125. H; 126. C; 127. D; 128. B; 129. E; 130. G; 131. A; 132. 6; 133. 5; 134. 16; 135. 14; 136. 13; 137. 7; 138. 4; 139. 11; 140. 3; 141. 9; 142. 15; 143. 1; 144. 8; 145. 2; 146. 17; 147. 10; 148. 12; 149. D; 150. F; 151. E; 152. G; 153. B; 154. A; 155. C.

40.6 Regulation of the Digestive Process [pp. 1021–1023]

156. C; 157. E; 158. B; 159. F; 160. D; 161. A; 162. F – autonomic; 163. T; 164. F – hypothalamus; 165. T.

40.7 Variations in Obtaining Nutrients [pp. 1023–1029]

166. nutrients; 167. parasitic; 168. epiphytic; 169. hiding; 170. lures; 171. C; 172. E; 173. F; 174. B; 175. A; 176. D.

SELF-TEST

1.	a	11.	b
2.	d	12.	d
3.	c	13.	a
4.	b	14.	c
5.	b	15.	d
6.	c	16.	c
7.	b	17.	b
8.	c	18.	c
9.	c	19.	a
10.	b	20.	d

INTEGRATING AND APPLYING KEY CONCEPTS

1. Plants grown in clay soils tend to be more limited in nutrient uptake than plants grown in sandy soils. Since clay soils are composed of small particles, usually <0.002 mm in diameter, they are closely packed together. The resulting small air spaces, which have negatively charged surfaces, bind strongly to polar water molecules, reducing the uptake of water and dissolved minerals into plant roots. Furthermore, when water fills the small air spaces, the lack of air in the spaces reduces the uptake of oxygen into plant roots. This is quite different from sandy soils, which are composed of large particles (0.02–2.0 mm diameter) and, therefore, large air spaces. When water is present in the soil, water, minerals, and oxygen can be taken up by plant roots. However, due to the large air spaces water drains down rapidly from horizon layers containing plant roots.

2. The eight essential amino acids must be acquired through diet. Vegetarians must be careful to eat the correct combination of foods to acquire all eight of the essential amino acids because, although many meats, fish, and dairy products provide all of these amino acids, many plants are deficient in one or more of the amino acids. For example, corn contains little lysine and isoleucine and lentils contain little methionine and tryptophan. If both of these food are eaten, all of the essential amino acids will be provided; separately they will not.

3. In the small intestine, carbohydrates are digested by pancreatic amylase (secreted by the pancreas) and disaccharidases (secreted by the epithelial cells of the small intestine wall), resulting in the production of monosaccharides; proteins are digested by proteases, such as trypsin and carboxypeptidases (secreted by the pancreas) and aminopeptidase and dipeptidase (secreted by the epithelial cells of the small intestine wall), resulting in the production of amino acids; lipids are digested by bile salts (secreted by the liver) and lipase (secreted by the pancreas), resulting in the production of fatty acids and glycerol; and nucleic acids are digested by nucleases

(secreted by the pancreas) and nucleotidases, nucleosidases, and phosphatases (secreted by the epithelial cells of the small intestine wall), resulting in the production of five-carbon sugars, nitrogenous bases, and phosphates.

Chapter 41   Gas Exchange: The Respiratory System

Why It Matters [pp. 1032–1033]
41.1 General Principles of Gas Exchange [pp. 1033–1035]

1. 78%; 2. 21%; 3. less than 1%; 4. 592.8 mm Hg; 5. 159.6 mm Hg; 6. 7.6 mm Hg; 7. 390 mm Hg; 8. 105 mm Hg; 9. 5 mm Hg; 10. 195 mm Hg; 11. 52.5 mm Hg; 12. 2.5 mm Hg; 13. Gases will diffuse down their partial pressure gradient (from a region of high partial pressure to a region of low partial pressure); 14. The factors that influence the rate of diffusion are the diffusion coefficient, the surface area involved in gas exchange, the partial pressure difference of the gas being exchanged, and the distance for diffusion; 15. Physiological respiration; 16. respiratory medium; 17.Breathing; 18. respiratory surface; 19. tracheal system; 20. gills; 21. lungs; 22. Ventilation and perfusion of respiratory surfaces are essential to bring oxygenated water or air to the exchange surface and to circulate blood high in O_2 and low in CO_2 (gases that were exchanged during respiration) away from the exchange surface, respectively. This allows the respiratory system to maintain partial pressure differences to allow the gases to diffuse through the exchange surface. By maintaining a partial pressure difference, the rate of diffusion of the gases are maintained. Otherwise, equilibrium between the partial pressure difference of the gases could be reached and reduce the rate of gas diffusion to zero (no gas exchange would occur under these conditions; 23. Aquatic animals have no problems keeping respiratory surfaces wet (minimizes evaporative loss of water; this occurs in air breathing organisms); 24. Diffusion coefficient is low; less oxygen is dissolved and therefore the lower partial pressure of oxygen in water makes oxygen less available and accessible; aquatic animals must pass a greater amount of medium to obtain required oxygen; water is more dense and viscous than air, therefore much energy is required to breath water; higher temperature or salinity causes decreased amount of dissolved gases in the water, therefore changing environmental conditions such as temperature and salinity will have an impact on oxygen concentration and partial pressure; 25. Diffusion coefficient higher than water; more oxygen available in air; air is less dense and viscous than water therefore energy required to ventilate is lower; allows air-breathing animals to breathe in and out, reversing the direction of flow of the respiratory medium, without a large energy penalty; 26. Constant evaporative loss of water from the respiratory surface; animals lose water through breathing that must be replaced to keep the respiratory surface from drying out.

41.2 Adaptations for Gas Exchange [pp. 1035–1040]

27. external gills; 28. internal gills; 29. countercurrent exchange; 30. tracheae; 31. spiracles; 32. positive pressure; 33. negative pressure; 34. alveoli; 35. one-way; 36. ventilation; 37. hyperventilation; 38. hypoventilation; 39. Countercurrent exchange occurs when the respiratory medium (in this case, water) flows in the direction opposite to that which the respiratory surface (in this case, lamellae) is perfused with blood. The adaptive significance is that the diffusion gradient is maintained across the entire length of the respiratory surface, increasing the O_2 extraction efficiency; 40. Air; 41. Tracheal system; 42. Water; 43. Gills; 44. Air; 45. Lungs; 46. Air; 47. Lungs; 48. A; 49. G; 50. D; 51. B; 52. H; 53. C; 54. E; 55. F.

41.3 The Mammalian Respiratory System [pp. 1040–1043]

56. pharynx; 57. larynx; 58. trachea; 59. bronchi; 60. bronchioles; 61. pleura; 62. diaphragm; 63. external intercostals muscles; 64. internal intercostals muscles; 65; tidal volume; 66. vital capacity; 67. residual volume; 68. medulla; 69. carotid bodies; 70. aortic bodies; 71. B; 72. A; 73. B; 74. A; 75. C; 76. Nasal passages; 77. Pharynx; 78. Epiglottis; 79. Larynx; 80. Trachea; 81. Lung; 82. Bronchi; 83. Mouth; 84. Pleura; 85. Intercostals muscles; 86. Diaphragm; 87. Bronchiole; 88. Alveoli.

41.4 Mechanisms of Gas Transport [pp. 1043–1047]

89. partial pressure; 90. hemoglobin; 91. oxygen dissociation curve; 92. carbonic anhydrase; 93. buffer; 94. The sigmoidal shape of the hemoglobin–oxygen saturation curve reflects the cooperate binding characteristics of the four subunits of the Hb molecule. Initially, O_2 binds to the first subunit with some difficulty (lag phase). After O_2 binds to the first subunit, it changes the shape of the Hb molecule such that the binding affinity of the second Hb subunit is increased and O_2 binds with greater ease; similarly, binding of the second O_2 changes the shape of the Hb molecule further and results in heightened affinity of the third subunit for O_2 (exponential phase). Finally, as the fourth O_2 binds, the Hb molecule becomes saturated; 95. At the lungs, oxygen partial pressure in the lung is higher than in the blood. The partial pressure difference causes oxygen in the lung to diffuse into the blood (and binds hemoglobin in the RBCs). When the oxygenated blood arrives at tissues, the oxygen partial pressure of the blood is higher than that of tissues. The partial pressure difference, once again, causes oxygen to detach from the hemoglobin and to diffuse into cells where the partial pressure of oxygen is low. Overall, the hemoglobin-saturation curve provides a representation of the amount of oxygen that is transferred across exchange surfaces.

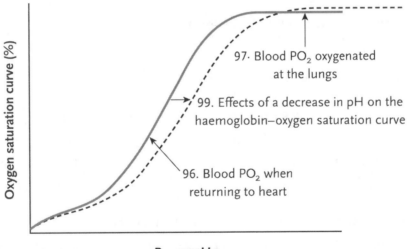

98. pH can cause a right shift or left shift in the hemoglobin–oxygen saturation curve. A decrease in pH causes the curve to right shift, whereas an increase in pH causes the curve to left shift; 100. This would occur when blood reaches tissues. A working tissue has a lower pH as a result of metabolic wastes and a region of elevated CO_2 levels. The decrease in pH promotes the delivery of oxygen to the tissues (the lower pH reduces the affinity of Hb for oxygen); 101. The significance of the steep part of the curve is related to the fact that there will be a large change in hemoglobin–oxygen saturation over small changes in oxygen partial pressure. This is the part of the curve where large changes in saturation can occur as a result of small changes in oxygen partial pressure. When one considers oxygen transfer at the lungs or at

the tissues, the oxygen partial pressure difference is such that it occurs in this part of the curve, thus underlying the large amount of oxygen that can be delivered during the transfer across the exchange surface; 102. CO_2 may be transported as CO_2 dissolved in the blood or in the red blood cell, it may be transported bound to hemoglobin, or transported as HCO_3 in the blood and red blood cells (CO_2 converted to HCO_3 by carbonic anhydrase); 103. In body tissues, some of the CO_2 released into the blood combines with water in the blood plasma to form HCO_3 and H^+. However, most of the CO_2 diffuses into erythrocytes, where some combines directly with hemoglobin and some combines with water to form HCO_3 and H^+. The H^+ formed by this reaction combines with hemoglobin; the HCO_3 is transported out of erythrocytes to add to the HCO_3 in the blood plasma. In the lungs, the reactions are reversed. Some of the HCO_3 in the blood plasma combines with H^+ to form CO_2 and water. However, most of the HCO_3 is transported into erythrocytes, where it combines with H^+ released from hemoglobin to form CO_2 and water. CO_2 is released from hemoglobin. The CO_2 diffuses from the erythrocytes and, with the CO_2 in the blood plasma, diffuses from the blood into the alveolar air; 104. B; 105. A; 106. B; 107. C; 107. A; 108. D.

SELF-TEST

1.	c	10.	c
2.	a	11.	b
3.	c	12.	a
4.	c	13.	c
5.	c	14.	b
6.	d	15.	b
7.	c	16.	e
8.	c	17.	d
9.	c	18.	d

Chapter 42   Regulating The Internal Environment

Why It Matters [pp. 1050–1051]

1. homeostasis; 2. water; 3. organ; 4. solute; 5. out of; 6. internal.

42.1 Introduction to Osmoregulation and Excretion [pp. 1051–1054]

7. Osmosis; 8. high; 9. low; 10. low; 11. high; 12. selectively permeable; 13. passive; 14. concentration; 15. osmoles; 16. isoosmotic; 17. hyperosmotic; 18. hypoosmotic; 19. osmoregulator; 20. osmoconformer; 21. ions; 22. metabolic; 23. nitrogenous; 24. excretion; 25. balance; 26. F; 27. E; 28. A; 29. B; 30. C; 31. D; 32. I; 33. G; 34. H.

42.2 Osmoregulation and Excretion in Invertebrates [pp. 1054–1057]

35. Marine; 36. osmoconformers; 37. terrestrial; 38. osmoregulators; 39. energy; 40. cells; 41. Nitrogenous/toxic metabolic; 42. ammonia; 43. energy; 44. hyperosmotic; 45. varied; 46. B; 47. C; 48. A; 49. C; 50. A; 51. B; 52. A; 53. B.

42.3 Osmoregulation and Excretion in Nonmammalian Vertebrates [pp. 1057–1059]

54. water; 55. salts; 56. hyperosmotic; 57. conserved; 58. excreted; 59. urea; 60. nitrogenous; 61. isoosmotic; 62. hyperosmotic; 63. excreting; 64. conserving; 65. conserve; 66. uric acid; 67. specializations; 68. D; 69. B; 70. B; 71. D; 72. C, E; 73. A; 74. A; 75.B,C; 76. C.

42.4 Osmoregulation and Excretion in Mammals [pp. 1059–1065]

77. kidney; 78. nephron; 79. cortex; 80. medulla; 81. juxtamedullary; 82. cortical; 83. Urine; 84. waste; 85. renal pelvis; 86. urinary bladder; 87. ureter; 88. hyperosmotic; 89. pertiubular capillaries; 90. osmolality; 91. hyperosmotic; 92. 9; 93. 7; 94. 12; 95. 1; 96. 8; 97. 5; 98. 4; 99. 3; 100. 11; 101. 10; 102. 6; 103. 2; 104. B; 105. I; 106. F; 107. H; 108. J; 109. G; 110. D; 111. C; 112. E; 113. A; 114. T; 115. F – out of; 116. F – descending; 117. T; 118. F – out of.

42.5 Introduction to Thermoregulation [pp. 1066–1068]
42.6 Ectothermy [pp. 1068–1070]
42.7 Endothermy [pp. 1070–1075]

119. negative; 120. thermoreceptors; 121. set point; 122. gain; 123. loss; 124. Endotherms; 125. ectotherms; 126. external; 127. birds; 128. mammals; 129. behavioural; 130. deep; 131. upper; 132. radiation; 133. thermal acclimatization; 134. enzymes; 135. temperature; 136. oxidative; 137. heat; 138. set point; 139. energetically; 140. broader; 141. skin; 142. increasing; 143. decreasing; 144. sweat; 145. shivering; 146. C; 147. D; 148. A; 149. B; 150. A, B; 151. B; 152. A; 153. A; 154. B; 155. B; 156. B; 157. A; 158. F – large; 159. F – summer, winter; 160. T; 161. F – conduction; 162. T.

Self-Test

1.	d	10.	b
2.	c	11.	b
3.	d	12.	a
4.	b	13.	c
5.	c	14.	b
6.	b	15.	a
7.	c	16.	b
8.	a	17.	b
9.	b	18.	c

Integrating and Applying Key Concepts

1. Most marine invertebrates are osmoconformers, so they have few, if any, structures or mechanisms for osmoregulation. The marine invertebrates that do osmoregulate are able to use behavioural mechanisms, such as closing shells or retreating into burrows to prevent dessication, often at low tide. Freshwater invertebrates must maintain their hyperosmocity, which requires using mechanisms to remove excess water and take up salt ions (in food or by active transport from environment). Osmoregulation in terrestrial invertebrates involves constantly taking up an adequate supply of water and salts from the environment, often through food. Water loss for animals on land occurs primarily through evaporation and excretion, which must continually be replaced. Some invertebrates have specialized tubule osmoregulatory systems: freshwater organisms such as flatworms and adult mollusks use protonephridian (cilia move filtrate through flame cells and tubule), terrestrial invertebrates such as annelids use metanephridia (cilia move filtrate into funnel-shaped opening and tubule), and invertebrates such as insects use Malpighian tubules (ultrafiltrate moves into tubule that empties into gut).

2. Osmolality in the filtrate of the descending segment of the loop of Henle increases as it moves downward due to the reabsorption of water from the filtrate into interstitial fluid as it travels through this segment. Increasing solute concentrations in the interstitial fluid as the tubule descends into the medulla, causes water to move by osmosis into the interstitial fluid. Furthermore, the presence of aquaporins in the wall of this segment of tubule fosters rapid movement of water molecules out of the tubule. Increasing solute concentrations in the interstitial fluid during descent in the medulla is the result of a) Na^+ and Cl^- reabsorption, primarily by active transport, to interstitial fluid surrounding the ascending segment of the loop of Henle in the medulla, and b) urea reabsorption as urine travels down the collecting duct in the medulla.

3. Ectotherms and endotherms use different mechanisms to thermoregulate. Endotherms are able to be active in a wider range of temperatures than ectotherms, but the cost of this higher metabolic rate is that they have greater energy (food) requirements and so must put themselves into danger as they forage for food. Ectotherms activities are limited by cool temperatures, when they are sluggish and therefore less likely to escape from a predator. However,

because of their lower metabolic rates, they have a relatively low energy (food) requirement and consequently spend more time in the safety of their homes and less time exposed to outside dangers while foraging for food.

Chapter 43   Defences against Disease

Why It Matters [pp. 1079–1080]
43.1 Three Lines of Defence Against Invasion [pp. 1080–1081]
43.2 Nonspecific Defences: Innate Immunity [pp. 1081–1086]

1. innate immune system; 2. adaptive immune system; 3. immune response; 4. Inflammation; 5. Macrophages; 6. cytokines; 7. Mast cells; 8. Neutophils; 9. chemokines; 10. eosinophils; 11. complement system; 12. membrane attack complexes; 13. Interferons; 14. Natural killer; 15. apoptosis; 16. lymphocyte; 17. A, B; 18. A, B; 19. A, B, C; 20. A, B, C; 21. A; 22. C; 23. B; 24. A; 25. First to recognize pathogens, engulfs pathogen and kills it, secretes signal to initiate other immune responses; 26. Mast cell; 27. Attracted to infected site by chemokines, engulfs pathogen and kills it, usually dies itself afterward; 28. Eosinophils; 29. Natural killer cells; 30. C; 31. A; 32. B; 33. F; 34. G; 35. B; 36. C; 37. E; 38. A; 39. D.

43.3 Specific Defences: Adaptive Immunity [pp. 1086–1097]

40. antigen; 41. B cells; 42. T cells; 43. thymus gland; 44. antibody-mediated; 45. antibodies; 46. cell-mediated; 47. memory; 48. antigen; 49. T cell; 50. epitopes; 51. immunoglobins; 52. heavy chains; 53. light chains; 54. Y; 55. antigen-binding; 56. bind; 57. cell division; 58. clones; 59. clear; 60. memory; 61. primary; 62. secondary; 63. Active immunity; 64. passive immunity; 65. 9; 66. 2; 67. 5; 68. 4; 69. 1; 70. 10; 71. 8; 72. 3; 73. 7; 74. 6; 75. 6; 76. 2; 77. 8; 78. 7; 79. 5; 80. 9; 81. 3; 82. 1; 83. 10; 84. 4; 85. A; 86. B. 87. A; 88. The MHC is derived from a large cluster of genes expressed in a few immune cells types (dendritic cells, macrophages, B cells). MHC proteins bind to antigen molecules inside the cell, then translocates it to the surface of the cell, making the cell an antigen-presenting cell; 89. To combat the large number of pathogens that tend to be present at an infection site, it is important that both B and T cells undergo cell division. B cells must proliferate to form plasma cells, which produce antibodies specific for the infecting pathogen that can function in various ways, including neutralizing toxins produced by the pathogens, immobilize pathogens through agglutination, and enhance phagocytosis of pathogens. Each of the cloned cytotoxic T cells function in producing perforins that form pores in the membrane of the infected cell, eventually resulting in its death.; 90. A; 91. B; 92. B; 93. A; 94. B; 95. A; 96. A; 97. B; 98. lymphocytes that arise and mature in the bone marrow; derivatives contribute to antibody-mediated immunity; 99. T cells; 100. B cell derivative that produces antibodies; 101. cell types derived from T cells and B cells and are responsible for initiating a rapid immune response upon reexposure to an antigen; 102. phagocytic cell that initiates adaptive immunity by engulfing foreign cell; 103. CD4$^+$ cell; 104. derived from activated CD4+ cells and leads to antibody-mediated immunity; 105. CD8$^+$ cell; 106. Derived from activated CD8$^+$ cells and destroys infected cells; 107. A; 108. I; 109. B; 110. F; 111. G; 112. C; 113. D; 114. E; 115. H.

43.4 Malfunctions and Failures of the Immune System [pp. 1097–1100]
43.5 Defences in Other Organisms [pp. 1101]
43.6 How Do Parasites and Pathogens Circumvent Host Responses? [pp. 1101–1103]

116. Immunological tolerance; 117. autoimmune reaction; 118. antiself; 119. Allergens; 120. anaphylactic shock; 121. epinephrine (or adrenaline); 122. low; 123. antigenic variation; 124 symbiotic; 125. reproduce; 126. new; 127. innate; 128. pathogens; 129. C; 130. E; 131. A; 132. F; 133. B; 134. D.

1. b	11. c
2. e	12. d
3. a	13. a
4. d	14. a
5. c	15. b
6. d	16. b
7. d	17. b
8. a	18. a
9. b	19. b
10. d	

INTEGRATING AND APPLYING KEY CONCEPTS

1. During an inflammation response, monocytes (one type of leukocyte) differentiate into macrophages that recognize and engulf the invading pathogens. If there are too many pathogens, the activated macrophages secrete cytokines to recruit more immune cells, as well as chemokines to attract neutrophils. As host cells die, they activate mast cells to release histamine which, with cytokines, dilate blood vessels and make them more permeable to movement of fluid, including neutrophils, from blood vessels into body tissues. Neutrophils also recognize and phagocytose pathogens. The movement of fluid into body cells results in the heat, redness, and swelling of an inflamed area. Both macrophages and neutrophils break down engulfed pathogens by various methods including enzymes, defensins, and toxic compounds.

2. During cell-mediated immunity (a type of adaptive immunity), cytotoxic T cells are produced from activated T cells and the receptors on their surfaces function to recognize antigens on antigen-presenting cells, which causes the cytotoxic T cells to destroy the pathogen. These cells have various methods to kill pathogens, including releasing the protein perforin and various proteases. Perforin causes pores to form in the pathogen's surface membrane, allowing ions and molecules to cross the membrane, which causes the infected cell to rupture. Proteases that enter the infected cell cause it to undergo apoptosis.

3. During an allergic reaction, allergen antigens cause B cells to over-secrete IgE antibodies which induce mast cells and basophil leukocytes to secrete histamine. Histamine produces inflammation in the infected area. Mast cells also release signals causing mucosal cells to secrete lots of mucus (runny nose) and smooth muscle cells to contract (constricting airways).

Chapter 44   Population Ecology

Why It Matters [pp. 1106–1107]

1. viruses; 2. epidemiology; 3. Lyssavirus; 4. saliva; 5. vaccine; 6. vector; 7. foxes; 8. estimating; 9. size; 10. behaviour.

44.1 The Science of Ecology [pp. 1107–1108]

11. Organismal; 12. population; 13. community; 14. ecosystem; 15. models; 16. field; 17. laboratory.

44.2 Population Characteristics [pp. 1108–1112]

18. range; 19. habitat; 20. density; 21. mark–release–recapture; 22. prereproductive; 23. postreproductive; 24. generation; 25. sex ratio; 26. uniform; 27. random; 28. clumped; 29. clumped; 30. random.

44.3 Demography [pp. 1112–1114]

31. immigration; 32. emigration; 33. demography; 34. cohort; 35. mortality; 36. survivorship; 37. fecundity; 38. 0.800; 39. 0.200; 40. 200; 41. 11; 42. 9; 43. 1.000; 44. 0.000; 45. Type III. This type of survivorship curve describes a population in which there is high juvenile mortality but low mortality once individuals reach approximately 4 years of age.; 46. A; 47. C; 48. B.

44.4 Evolution of Life Histories [pp. 1114–1117]

49. growth; 50. maturation; 51. reproduction; 52. energy budget; 53. tradeoffs; 54. maintenance; 55. growth;

56. reproduction; 57. passive; 58. active; 59. F, passive; 60. T; 61. F – Reproduce only once and die; 62. T; 63. T; 64. B;

65. B; 66. A; 67. B.

44.5 Models of Population Growth [pp. 1117–1122]

68. per capita growth rate; 69. exponential; 70. intrinsic rate of increase; 71. logistic; 72. carrying capacity;

73. intraspecific; 74. time lag; 75. E; 76. B; 77. A; 78. C; 79. D; 80. F – size remains constant (has zero growth rate);

81. T; 82. T; 83. F– intraspecific.

44.6 Population Regulation [pp. 1122–1127]

84. dependent; 85. independent; 86. r-selected; 87. K-selected; 88. intrinsic; 89. extrinsic; 90. cycles; 91. time lags;

92. A; 93. B; 94. A; 95. B; 96. B; 97. T; 98. F – decrease; 99. F – have no effect on; 100. F – have no effect on.

44.7 Human Population Growth [pp. 1127–1131]
44.8 Sisyphean Problems in Population Biology [p. 1133]

101. exponential; 102. geographical range; 103. habitats; 104. carrying capacity (K); 105. death; 106. demographic

transition; 107. family planning; 108. Sisyphean; 109. cycles; 110. F – high; 111. T; 112. F – decrease; 113. F – more;

114. T; 115. C; 116. B; 117. A.

Self-Test

1. a [The study of ecology involves living things, "abiotic" refers to nonliving things]
2. a [Canadian are clustered in cities, with many areas having very few people]
3. b [Demography is the study of population size, density]
4. a [High fecundity produces lots of low value offspring, which the parent generally does not provide care for]
5. c [High numbers of reproduction means the population can produce many offspring in the current generation]
6. b [Females are more limiting for producing offspring, since a single male can fertilize many females]
7. c [If there is any limit to population growth, the population will cease growing exponentially]
8. d [Carrying capacity (K) is one of the variables in the equation that defines logistic growth]
9. c [Nighttime air temperature is not related to population density]
10. b [The rabies virus concentrates in the saliva, which is then transferred through biting]
11. d [Populations inhabit suitable habitat, thus areas without suitable habitat form range boundaries]
12. a [Extrinsic cycles are controlled by external factors; predation is an external factor]
13. d [Examination of Figure 44.19 shows the human population increased from 5 to 6 billion in 12 years]
14. a [Age structure would show if there would be more schoolchildren or seniors in the next few years]
15. d [Mortality = 200/500; Survivorship = 300/500]
16. b [Lower mortality at older and bigger ages would make it more profitable to delay reproduction]
17. c [Habitat differences can lead to different survivorship curves; natural selection and predation drives life history variation]
18. b [When N is less than K, the population is below the carrying capacity, and continues to grow]
19. a [Populations that are overcrowded suffer higher death rates, a loss of condition (due to starvation), lower survivorship, and increased emigration with individuals looking for better habitat]
20. c [r-selected populations the young generally have little parental care and suffer high mortality]

Integrating and Applying Key Concepts

1. Commercial fishing pressure is more selective than the guppy predators (fishers generally target larger individuals by law). Also commercial fishing does not select based on behaviour or coloration. However, since commercial fishing does shorten the average lifespan, it will tend to drive fish toward early reproduction. Pollution is

non-selective and not density-dependent, so its effects will be quite different from either commercial fishing or natural predators. Fish may evolve natural resistance to the contaminants, but no life history changes are expected.

2. Human populations (even in developing countries) have reduced many of the density-dependent factors that may limit other species' population growth. Thus technology, medicine, civic hygiene, and very high birth rates contribute to allow very fast population growth. Secondly, more developed countries have the resources for very fast population growth, but family planning limits population growth to provide better standards of living.

3. As the population density of the rabies virus declines, the likelihood of vaccinating the few foxes still carrying the virus becomes very low indeed. Furthermore, the natural density-dependent factors that can limit the growth of the rabies population will not help the government's efforts. Furthermore, if the foxes are eliminated as a carrier species, the virus may evolve its life history to utilize a new host (e.g., skunks or bats). Finally, infected carriers may immigrate into Ontario, bring new sources for population growth.

Chapter 45   Population Interactions and Community Ecology

Why It Matters [pp.1136–1137]

1. community ecology; 2. specialized; 3. niches; 4. interactions.

45.1 Interspecific Interactions [pp. 1137–1138]

5. evolution; 6. coevolution; 7. faster; 8. prey; 9. predators.

45.2 Getting Food [pp. 1138–1139]

10. plants; 11. animals; 12. heat sensors; 13. insects; 14. generalists; 15. benefit; 16. cost; 17. optimal foraging; 18. F – specialist; 19. T; 20. F – high; 21. T.

45.3 Defence [pp. 1139–1143]

22. defence; 23. small; 24. large; 25. detecting; 26. camouflage; 27. spines; 28. chemical; 29. aposematic; 30. mimic; 31. Batesian mimicry; 32. Müllerian mimicry; 33. B; 34. D; 35. A; 36. E; 37. C; 38. B; 39. A; 40. B; 41. C; 42. D.

45.4 Competition [pp. 1143–1151]

43. interspecific; 44. interference; 45. exploitative; 46. competitive exclusion; 47. niche; 48. resource partitioning; 49. character displacement; 50. mutualism; 51. commensalism; 52. parasitism; 53. parasitoids; 54. B; 55. D; 56. A; 57. C; 58. A; 59. A.

45.5 The Nature of Ecological Communities [pp. 1151–1152]

60. antagonistic; 61. mutually beneficial; 62. differs; 63. connected; 64. weak; 65. ecotone; 66. richness; 67. F – narrow; 68. T; 69. F – individualistic; 70. F – trophic.

45.6 Community Characteristics [pp. 1152–1157]

71. richness; 72. evenness; 73. diversity; 74. trophic; 75. parasite; 76. primary; 77. heterotrophs; 78. primary; 79. third; 80. omnivores; 81. detritivores; 82. bacteria; 83. food chain; 84. food web; 85. trophic; 86. stability; 87. 0.13; 88. –0.27; 89. 0.02; 90. –0.33; 91. –1.19; 92. 1.19, more diverse since as H' increases more species diversity is present in the community; 93. D; 94. A, B, and C; 95. E; 96. E; 97. D.

45.7 Effects of Population Interactions on Community Structure [p. 1158]

98. extinct; 99. 50–75; 100. K-selected; 101. r-selected; 102. increase; 103. diversity; 104. keystone; 105. C; 106. D; 107. A; 108. B.

45.8 Effects of Disturbance on Community Characteristics [pp. 1158–1161]

109. equilibrium; 110. disturbances; 111. intermediate disturbance; 112. *r*-selected; 113. *K*-selected; 114. richness;

115. grassland; 116. F – low (large disturbances lead to loss of species, intermediate disturbances lead to high diversity);

117. T; 118. T; 119. T; 120. F – useful.

45.9 Succession [pp. 1161–1166]

121. succession; 122. primary succession; 123. climax community; 124. recovery; 125. aquatic succession;

126. facilitation; 127. inhibition; 128. tolerance; 129. disclimax; 130. D; 131. B; 132. E; 133. A; 134. E.

45.10 Variance in Species Richness among Communities [pp. 1167–1171]

135. latitudinal trends; 136. island patterns; 137. generations; 138. migration; 139. specialization; 140. equilibrium

theory; 141. species pool; 142. larger; 143. small; 144. immigration; 145. extinction; 146. D; 147. B; 148. C; 149. A.

SELF-TEST

1. b [a and c are simply adaptations that do not necessarily result from interaction with other organisms; d results from intraspecific interactions; coevolution is based on interactions between different species]
2. b [Symbioses are interactions between individuals of different species; intraspecific refers to "within" species]
3. a
4. b [a is commensalism, c is exploitative competition, and d is mutualism]
5. d
6. d [Commensalim is rarely found in nature since species interactions usually affect both species]
7. a [Parasitoids kill their "hosts," making them more like predators]
8. b
9. d [E_H is designed to reflect the variation in the relative number of each species]
10. a
11. c [A food web is used where there is more than one predator eating the same prey, and each predator may eat more than one prey type]
12. c [Complex communities are expected to be more stable since the loss of one species is unlikely to make a big difference]
13. b [Relative to exposed corals, effect of disturbances on sheltered areas was less damage, less loss of colonies, greater recruitment of new colonies]
14. a
15. d [Such a community should have a mix of *K*- and *r*-selected species, and should be no more sensitive to disturbance than any other community]
16. d [a, b, and c had established communities before the disturbance, therefore, the recovery is secondary succession]
17. a [The island equilibrium hypothesis relates to the species composition at equilibrium on isolated habitat patches]
18. d [A disturbance will allow fast-growing, high fecundity, *r*-selected species to colonize]
19. b
20. b [The assumption is that extinction rates are inversely correlated with island size; larger islands have more potential niches and competition between immigrants is less likely]

INTEGRATING AND APPLYING KEY CONCEPTS

1. i) Probably beneficial to both species. The greater the number of distasteful individuals of either species, the faster predators will learn to avoid them. ii) Probably beneficial to both species. Since the majority of individuals are models, predators are most likely to sample distasteful individuals. iii) Detrimental to both species. Predators are most likely to encounter palatable mimics and will be less apt to avoid both species.
2. *K*-selected species are generally slow-growing, high parental contribution species, usually associated with climax communities. These communities tend to have populations in which growth is limited by carrying capacity, hence there tends to be strong competitive interactions. *r*-selected species, on the other hand, are adapted to fast population growth with few resource restrictions, so there is low competition pressure between individuals in the community.
3. a) Lakes: lakes are islands of freshwater aquatic habitat surrounded by dry land. The probable source of immigrants for lakes is larger lakes or inland seas connected by rivers. b) Mountaintops: mountaintops are islands of cold, dry alpine

habitat surrounded by lowland habitat. Immigrants would be from other mountaintop habitat on mountains close by. It is unlikely that isolated mountains would follow the equilibrium theory of island biogeography. c) Coral reefs: coral reefs are islands of complex coral habitat surrounded by low productivity, deep ocean waters. Immigrants for coral reefs would be from other coral reefs or shore-line shallow coral habitat. Other possible examples exist.

Chapter 46   Ecosystems

Why It Matters [pp. 1174–1175]

1. Urban; 2. rain; 3. sun; 4. 6000; 5. biodiversity.

46.1 Energy Flow and Ecosystem Energetics [pp. 1175–1184]

6. gross; 7. net; 8. 10; 9. 50; 10. biomass; 11. standing crop; 12. synthesis; 13. limiting; 14. secondary; 15. ecological; 16. harvesting; 17. assimilation; 18. production; 19. pyramids; 20. pyramid of biomass; 21. turnover; 22. pyramid of numbers; 23. pyramid of energy; 24. cascade; 25. contaminants; 26. biological magnification; 27. A; 28. D; 29. C; 30. B; 31. F – underestimates; 32. T; 33. T; 34. F – less than 1%.

46.2 Nutrient Cycling in Ecosystems [pp. 1185–1195]

35. biogeochemical; 36. conserved; 37. generalized compartment; 38. hydrogeologic; 39. precipitation; 40. carbon dioxide; 41. available; 42. fossil fuels; 43. warming; 44. nitrogen; 45. fixation; 46. ammonification; 47. nitrification; 48. denitrification; 49. fertilizers; 50. gaseous; 51. aquatic; 52. sedimentary; 53. absorbing; 54. excreting; 55. C; 56. A; 57. C; 58. A; 59. C; 60. D; 61. B.

46.3 Ecosystem Modelling [pp. 1196–1197]
46.4 Scales, Ecosystems, Species [pp. 1197–1199]

62. simulation; 63. predict; 64. data; 65. scale; 66. abiotic; 67. nutrient; 68. empirical; 69. predict; 70. F – an ecosystem; 71. T; 72. T; 73. F – do; 74. T.

Self-Test

1. d [Urban ecosystems do have plant and animal communities, but they are very simplified]
2. b
3. d [The bigger the ecosystem, the more primary productivity possible, and the more productivity per unit ecosystem size, the greater the total productivity]
4. a
5. d
6. d [New biomass is created when existing organisms grow, reproduce, or store energy]
7. d
8. c
9. d [An ectotherm converts >50% of its assimilated energy into new biomass; an endotherm only converts <10%]
10. b [Low ecological efficiency means that there is high energy loss between steps of the pyramid]
11. a
12. c [Solar energy drives evaporation, a prime driver of the hydrogeologic cycle]
13. b
14. d [Photosynthesis is the only one the four choices that removes carbon from the atmosphere]
15. b [Denitrification is the only process that produces N_2]
16. a [Nitrogen fixation is only process to convert N_2 to ammonium and nitrate ions]
17. a
18. c
19. b [Ecosystem modelling is designed to be predictive]
20. d [All except time of day are critical ecosystem factors]

1. Ecosystem energetics rely on an external source of energy (primarily solar radiation) and energy is not conserved, but flows through the ecosystem. On the other hand, nutrients are conserved and they cycle among available and non-available forms repeatedly. Both processes limit ecosystem productivity, and hence function; both are needed for complex and dynamic ecosystems to function normally.
2. Gross primary productivity is the total proportion of the sun's energy primary producers convert into energy, for their own use (e.g., maintenance) as well as for the production of new biomass. Net primary productivity is the amount of energy available for consumers to access (gross primary productivity minus the primary producer's maintenance costs). If a particular species of primary producer has high production efficiency (i.e., it uses a low proportion of the energy it collects for its own maintenance), it will contribute to a high net primary productivity.
3. Low water and nutrient availability could limit net primary productivity—for example, desert ecosystems get plenty of sunshine, but are limited by water and nutrient availability.
4. The hydrogeologic and carbon cycles rely directly on solar radiation for evaporation and photosynthesis. The phosphorus cycle has no gaseous component, hence, it does not include the atmosphere as part of the cycle. The hydrogeologic cycle has the oceans as the main reservoir, the nitrogen cycle's main reservoir is the atmosphere, the phosphorus cycle's reservoir is the Earth's crust, and the carbon cycle's main reservoir is sedimentary rock (although the ocean is the largest reservoir of available carbon).

Chapter 47   Conservation of Biodiversity

Why It Matters [pp.1201–1202]

1. human-centric; 2. humans; 3. separation; 4. cost; 5. monocultural; 6. fertilizers; 7. Barcode of Life; 8. biodiversity.

47.1 Extinction [pp. 1202–1204]

9. background extinction; 10. turnover; 11. ancestor; 12. genes; 13. extinct; 14. outcompeted; 15. adaptive radiation; 16. five; 17. asteroid; 18. iridium; 19. crater; 20. atmosphere; 21. C; 22. E; 23. E; 24. C; 25. F; 26. C; 27. A.

47.2 The Impact of Humans [pp. 1204–1207]
47.3 Introduced and Invasive Species [pp. 1207–1210]
47.4 How We Got/Get There [pp. 1210–1213]

28. reduction; 29. extinction; 30. introducing; 31. habitat; 32. 1690; 33. predators; 34. nutrient-rich; 35. higher; 36. resource use efficiency; 37. ecosystem; 38. decrease; 39. sharks; 40. predators; 41. D; 42. C; 43. E; 44. B; 45. A; 46. B; 47. C; 48. A; 49. B; 50. C; 51. The Mauritian calvaria tree life cycle includes travel through a Dodo's digestive tract to initiate seed germination. Presently, these trees are dying of old age and cannot produce offspring since Dodo extinction has removed the possibility of seed germination; 52. The horns are not only collected as trophies but also to make bowls that some cultures believe to have magical properties, to make handles of ceremonial daggers called *jambiya,* and to break down into powder form for medicinal use as a fever suppressant.

47.5 Protecting Species [pp. 1213–1216]
47.6 Protecting What? [pp. 1216–1220]
47.7 The Downside of Being Rare [p. 1220]
47.8 Protecting Habitat [pp. 1220–1221]

53. eligible; 54. designatable; 55. data-based; 56. mortality; 57. carrying capacity; 58. COSEWIC; 59. extinct; 60. extirpated; 61. endangered; 62. threatened; 63. special concern; 64. data deficient; 65. increase; 66. protection; 67. human; 68. B; 69. C; 70. A; 71. C; 72. F; 73. C; 74. D.

47.9 Effecting Conservation [pp. 1221–1224]

47.10 Taking Action [pp. 1224–1225]

75. human population; 76. 40; 77. slowing; 78. fertility; 79. biodiversity; 80. complex; 81. decreased; 82. sustainable; 83. protecting; 84. F – more; 85. F – other birds; 86. T; 87. T.

SELF-TEST

1. c [Humans drive species to extinction for reasons ranging from survival to greed]
2. d
3. b
4. d [Life has been on Earth for ~3 billion years]
5. a [Similar to a human's survivorship curve]
6. c
7. a [Taken in at one port and released in another so potential introduction of many aquatic species]
8. c
9. d [The greater the resource use efficiency, the better a competitor the invading species will be]
10. b
11. a [Morphology alone does not determine differences between species (e.g., white moose)]
12. c
13. a [The group of organisms must be eligible for species categorization]
14. c
15. b
16. a [Populations, and even ecosystems, can be identified as "at risk"]
17. c
18. b
19. c

INTEGRATING AND APPLYING KEY CONCEPTS

1. You would find yourself among various species of dinosaurs, as well as many other organisms of that time period. After the asteroid hits the Earth, a large amount of dust would arise into the atmosphere from the collision and block out sunlight. This would reduce photosynthesis by autotrophs, resulting in the death of many species, from producers up to high-level consumers: a mass extinction.
2. American ginseng grows in areas, such as in Sugar Maple forests, that are easily accessible to humans. Since it is believed to have medicinal properties, its value has increased as its numbers have decreased. This is another species that pays a cost for being rare.
3. Birds are showing signs of stress due to loss of habitat, especially near expanding urban areas, as well as areas in which agricultural operations are expanding. Migrating birds are affected by changes occurring anywhere between tropical to temperate areas. Also, some birds, especially chickens and other domesticated birds, are raised in high densities, increasing the chance of spreading disease.

Chapter 48   Putting Selection to Work

Why It Matters [pp.1228–1229]

1. fertilizers; 2. increased; 3. green revolution; 4. Climate; 5. lower; 6. malnourished; 7. obesity; 8. diet.

48.1 Domestication [pp. 1229–1234]

9. gathering; 10. collecting; 11. cultivation; 12. domesticating; 13. plants; 14. archeology; 15. 14; 16. 55 000; 17. F – Ant farmers; 18. T; 19. T; 20. T; 21. F – terrestrial; 22. T; 23. Indehiscent wheat grains are grains that stick to the plant when they mature, so they are easy to collect for cultivation. The dehiscent wheat grains scatter when they mature, so they are very difficult to collect; 24. Fire was used by various historic settlements for "niche construction," to clear land and prepare them for cultivation of plant species.

48.2 Why Some Organisms Were Domesticated [pp. 1234–1242]

25. food; 26. A; 27. A, E; 28. A, D; 29. A; 30. A ,B, E; 31. A, C; 32. A; 33. A; 34. F; 35. D; 36. E; 37. B; 38. C.

48.3 Yields [pp. 1242–1246]
48.4 Complications [pp. 1246–1248]
48.5 Chemicals, Good and Bad [pp. 1248–1249]

39. greatest/highest; 40. highest; 41. deducting; 42; technology; 43. fertilizer; 44. B; 45. A; 46 A; 47. B; 48. B; 49. A;

50. A; 51. F – medicinal plant; 52. T; 53. F – coincided with; 54. F – insufficient.

48.6 Molecular Farming [pp. 1249–1250]
48.7 The Future [p. 1250]

55. genetically; 56. proteins; 57. molecular farming; 58. *Il-10* (or interleukin-10); 59. irritable bowel; 60. food webs; 61.

negatively; 62. nonfood; 63. exploit; 64. advantages; 65. outweigh; 66. C; 67. D; 68. B; 69. A; 70. Production of corn-

produced ethanol has an EROI of ~1:1 (1 L ethanol requires 1 L petroleum), which is a high price for petroleum fuel. Also,

the natural land cleared to grow the corn will result in much higher CO_2 generation than the original habitat produced.

SELF-TEST

1. a [Collecting grain would have been difficult to do if they were dehiscent]
2. c [With the majority of aquatic domestication occurring in the last 100 years]
3. c
4. c [Another term for niche construction is ecosystem engineering]
5. d [Climate, human behaviour, and/or human settlement could have assisted in the emergence of domestication]
6. a [Mushrooms are cultivated but they have not been domesticated]
7. c [It is believed that rice was probably domesticated in India, Myanmar, Thailand, and southern China]
8. a
9. c
10. c
11. b [Reduction in honeybees will greatly affect broccoli production, but not cotton, wheat, or rice, which do not use pollinators]
12. d [Parsley is a herb]
13. b
14. d [There were at least five founder populations of domestic cats and they were transported where needed to control the rodent population in developing agricultural areas]
15. c [GMOs may be beneficial to humans (e.g., if modified by the addition of a vitamin), but they may have a negative impact on individuals of the species found in nature]
16. d [The EROI (energy return on investment) is less than 4:1 for corn-produced ethanol]
17. b [human *IL-10* gene is inserted into plants]
18. d

INTEGRATING AND APPLYING KEY CONCEPTS

1. Domestication involves selectively breeding individuals of a plant or animal species for desireable characteristics, whereas cultivation does not require selective breeding since it involves just the systematic sowing of wild plant seeds.
2. The Abu Hureyra settlement changed between 12 000–9400 years BP from a small population of less than 200 people who lived in semi-subterranean pit dwellings and lived on the fruits and seeds of local plants and animals collected from a nearby woodlot to a large population of greater than 4000 people who lived in mud and brick dwellings and lived on cultivated plants (and relatively few wild plants). Climate change was believed to have triggered this change to cultivation, resulting in extensive development of the land.
3. Two genetic mutations occurred that made it possible to domesticate lentils: a mutation that removed dormancy as part of the lentil's life cycle and a mutation that increased the number of seeds that a lentil plant produced. The former reduced the time for seed production each generation and the latter benefitted the crop yield. Rice required a mutation that prevented the abscission layer connecting the flower to the pedicel from completely breaking down, thereby causing them to remain attached, even at maturity, allowing for easier collection of the indehiscent rice product.
4. You would need to consider many factors including (but not limited to) crop prices, technology available to increase yield, (and therefore any limitations of terrain) crop yield for different species, climate, costs associated with producing a particular crop, benefits/costs of fertilizer use, possible pests and pathogens in area, etc.